Student Solutions Manual

NANCY S. BOUDREAU
Bowling Green State University

Tenth Edition

Statistics

McCLAVE • SINCICH

PEARSON

Prentice Hall

Upper Saddle River, NJ 07458

Editor-in-Chief: Sally Yagan
Senior Acquisitions Editor: Petra Recter
Supplements Editor: Joanne Wendelken
Executive Managing Editor: Kathleen Schiaparelli
Assistant Managing Editor: Becca Richter
Production Editor: Allyson Kloss
Supplement Cover Manager: Paul Gourhan
Supplement Cover Designer: Joanne Alexandris
Manufacturing Buyer: Ilene Kahn

© 2006 Pearson Education, Inc.
Pearson Prentice Hall
Pearson Education, Inc.
Upper Saddle River, NJ 07458

The author and publisher of this book have used their best efforts in preparing this book. These efforts include the development, research, and testing of the theories and programs to determine their effectiveness. The author and publisher make no warranty of any kind, expressed or implied, with regard to these programs or the documentation contained in this book. The author and publisher shall not be liable in any event for incidental or consequential damages in connection with, or arising out of, the furnishing, performance, or use of these programs.

Printed in the United States of America

10 9 8 7 6 5 4 3 2

ISBN 0-13-149821-5

Pearson Education Ltd., *London*
Pearson Education Australia Pty. Ltd., *Sydney*
Pearson Education Singapore, Pte. Ltd.
Pearson Education North Asia Ltd., *Hong Kong*
Pearson Education Canada, Inc., *Toronto*
Pearson Educación de Mexico, S.A. de C.V.
Pearson Education—Japan, *Tokyo*
Pearson Education Malaysia, Pte. Ltd.

Contents

Preface

This solutions manual is designed to accompany the text, **_Statistics_**, Tenth Edition, by James T. McClave and Terry Sincich. It provides answers to most odd-numbered exercises for each chapter in the text. Other methods of solution may also be appropriate; however, the author has presented one that she believes to be most instructive to the beginning Statistics student. The student should first attempt to solve the assigned exercises without help from this manual. Then, if unsuccessful, the solution in the manual will clarify points necessary to the solution. The student who successfully solves an exercise should still refer to the manual's solution. Many points are clarified and expanded upon to provide maximum insight into and benefit from each exercise.

Instructors will also benefit from the use of this manual. It will save time in preparing presentations of the solutions and possibly provide another point of view regarding their meaning.

Some of the exercises are subjective in nature and thus omitted from the Answer Key at the end of **_Statistics_**, Tenth Edition. The subjective decisions regarding these exercises have been made and are explained by the author. Solutions based on these decisions are presented; the solution to this type of exercise is often most instructive. When an alternative interpretation of an exercise may occur, the author has often addressed it and given justification for the approach taken.

I would like to thank Kelly Barber for creating the art work and for typing this work.

Nancy S. Boudreau
Bowling Green State University
Bowling Green, Ohio

Statistics, Data, and Statistical Thinking

Chapter

1

1.1   Statistics is a science that deals with the collection, classification, analysis, and interpretation of information or data. It is a meaningful, useful science with a broad, almost limitless scope of applications to business, government, and the physical and social sciences.

1.3   The first element of inferential statistics is the population of interest. The population is a set of existing units. The second element is one or more variables that are to be investigated. A variable is a characteristic or property of an individual population unit. The third element is the sample. A sample is a subset of the units of a population. The fourth element is the inference about the population based on information contained in the sample. A statistical inference is an estimate, prediction, or generalization about a population based on information contained in a sample. The fifth and final element of inferential statistics is the measure of reliability for the inference. The reliability of an inference is how confident one is that the inference is correct.

1.5   Quantitative data are measurements that are recorded on a meaningful numerical scale. Qualitative data are measurements that are not numerical in nature; they can only be classified into one of a group of categories.

1.7   A population is a set of existing units such as people, objects, transactions, or events. A sample is a subset of the units of a population.

1.9   An inference without a measure of reliability is nothing more than a guess. A measure of reliability separates statistical inference from fortune telling or guessing. Reliability gives a measure of how confident one is that the inference is correct.

1.11   The data consisting of the classifications A, B, C, and D are qualitative. These data are nominal and thus are qualitative. After the data are input as 1, 2, 3, and 4, they are still nominal and thus qualitative. The only differences between the two data sets are the names of the categories. The numbers associated with the four groups are meaningless.

1.13   a.   The bacteria count is a number. Therefore, it is quantitative.

　　　 b.   Occupations take on values such as doctor, lawyer, carpenter, etc., which are not numeric. Therefore, it is qualitative.

　　　 c.   Marital status can take on values such as married, single, divorced, etc., which are not numeric. Therefore, it is qualitative.

　　　 d.   The time in months can take on values such as 1, 2, 3, etc. Therefore, it is quantitative.

1.15   a.   The population of interest is all citizens of the United States.

　　　 b.   The variable of interest is the view of each citizen as to whether the United States was justified in invading Iraq in 2003 or not. It is qualitative.

c.   The sample is the 2000 individuals selected for the poll.

d.   The inference of interest is to estimate the proportion of all citizens who believe the United States was justified in invading Iraq in 2003.

e.   The method of data collection is a survey.

f.   It is not very likely that the sample will be representative of the population of all citizens of the United States. By selecting phone numbers at random, the sample will be limited to only those people who have telephones. Also, many people share the same phone number, so each person would not have an equal chance of being contacted. Another possible problem is the time of day the calls are made. If the calls are made in the evening, those people who work in the evening would not be represented.

1.17   a.   The population of interest is the collection of the CEOs of all U. S. companies.

b.   1.   The industry type of the CEO's company is a qualitative variable. The industry type is a name.

   2.   The CEO's total compensation is a meaningful number. Thus, it is a quantitative variable.

   3.   The CEO's total compensation for the 3-year period is quantitative.

   4.   The return on a $100 investment in the CEO's company made in 2000 is quantitative.

c.   Since the only CEOs surveyed were only from the top-ranked companies, the sample is not representative of the entire population of CEOs. The total compensation and return on investment for the top-ranked companies are probably higher than that for the population of all companies.

1.19   a.   For question 1, the variable of interest is the e-commerce strategy status. Since the responses to this variable are "yes" or "no", the variable is Qualitative.

   For question 2, the variable of interest is the time of implementation of an e-commerce plan. Depending on exactly how the question was asked, the variable could be either Qualitative or Quantitative. If the question was written such that the respondent had to pick from possible answers like "within the next year", "from one to 3 years", and "over 3 years", the variable would be Qualitative. On the other hand, if the respondent was requested to give a time to the closest month, then the variable could be considered Quantitative.

   For question 3, the variable of interest is the status of delivering products over the internet. Since the responses to this variable are "yes" or "no", the variable is Qualitative.

   For question 4, the variable of interest is company's total revenue in the last fiscal year. Since the responses to this variable are numbers such as $1 million, $700,000, etc., the variable is Quantitative.

b.   The data collected from the 154 companies represent a sample. The Cutter Consortium surveyed only 154 out of many more U.S. companies. The Consortium did not survey all possible companies.

1.21   a.   Length of maximum span can take on values such as 15 feet, 50 feet, 75 feet, etc. Therefore, it is quantitative.

       b.   The number of vehicle lanes can take on values such as 2, 4, etc. Therefore, it is quantitative.

       c.   The answer to this item is "yes" or "no," which are not numeric. Therefore, it is qualitative.

       d.   Average daily traffic could take on values such as 150 vehicles, 3,579 vehicles, 53,295 vehicles, etc. Therefore, it is quantitative.

       e.   Condition can take on values "good," "fair," or "poor," which are not numeric. Therefore, it is qualitative.

       f.   The length of the bypass or detour could take on values such as 1 mile, 4 miles, etc. Therefore, it is quantitative.

       g.   Route type can take on values "interstate," U.S.," "state," "county," or "city," which are not numeric. Therefore, it is qualitative.

1.23   a.   The data collection method used by the cancer researchers is a designed experiment. Those participating in the study were randomly assigned to one of the two screening methods.

       b.   The experimental units in this study are the 50,000 smokers.

       c.   The variable measured in this study is the age at which the scanning method first detects a tumor. Since age is represented by a meaningful number, it is quantitative.

       d.   The population of interest is all smokers in the U.S. The sample of interest is the set of 50,000 smokers participating in the study.

       e.   The inference of interest is the difference in mean age at which each of the scanning methods first detects a tumor.

1.25   a.   The data collection method used by the researchers was a designed experiment. Half of the boxers received the massage and half did not.

       b.   The experimental units are the amateur boxers.

       c.   There are two variables measured on the boxers – heart rate and blood lactate level. Both of these variables are measured on a numeric scale and thus, are quantitative.

       d.   The inferences drawn from the analysis are: there is no difference in the mean heart rates between the two groups of boxers (those receiving massage and those not receiving massage) and there is no difference in the mean blood lactate levels between the two groups of boxers. Thus, massage did not affect the recovery rate of the boxers.

e. No. Only amateur boxers were used in the experiment. Thus, all inferences relate only to boxers.

1.27   a. The data for this study were collected from a designed experiment. The subjects in the study were randomly divided into two groups - one group received the drug and the other group received a placebo.

b. This study involves interential statistics. The goal of the research was to see if the drug was effective in reducing blood loss of burn patients who undergo skin replacement surgery. The researchers are not particularly interested in the outcomes for the patients in the study, but rather the outcomes for all possible burn patients.

c. The population of interest to the researchers is all possible burn patients. The sample is the 14 burn patients who participated in the study.

1.29   a. The population of interest to the psychologist is the set of all male soccer players between the ages of 14 and 29 who played up to five times per week.

b. The variables of interest are the frequency of "headers" and the IQ of each soccer player.

c. The average number of headers per game per player can take on values such as 0, 1, 2, etc. Therefore, it is quantitative. IQ can take on values such as 85, 100, 103, etc. Therefore, it is quantitative.

d. The sample is the set of 60 male soccer players between the ages of 14 and 29 who played up to five times per week.

e. The inference made by the psychologist is that "heading" the ball in soccer lowers players' IQs.

f. There could be several reasons why the inference could be misleading. First, "heading" the ball is a skill. It is possible that those players who are more athletically inclined are not as intellectually gifted as those players who are not as athletically inclined. Also, it appears that the data were collected only once per player. The only way one could conclude that "heading" the ball lowers players' IQs is by collecting data on each player over a period of time and seeing if each player's IQ decreases.

1.31   a. The population of interest to the pollsters is the set of all Americans.

b. The variable of interest is whether or not the person believes the Nazi extermination of the Jews happened. Since the views are not numeric, the variable is qualitative.

c. The sample is the set of 1000 adults and high school students who were asked the question.

d. The method of data collection is by survey.

e.   The pollsters inferred that one in five Americans believe that it is possible that the Holocaust never happened.

f.   The reliability of this inference is very suspect. The question presented to the sample is not a "yes," "no" question. It asks one to decide if it seems possible or if it seems impossible. Therefore, an answer of "yes" to this question is totally meaningless

Methods for Describing
Set of Data

2.1   The class frequency is the number of observations in the data set falling in a particular class. The class relative frequency is the class frequency divided by the total number ofobservations in the data set. The class percentage is the class relative frequency multiplied by 100.

2.3   In a bar graph, a bar or rectangle is drawn above each class of the qualitative variable corresponding to the class frequency or class relative frequency. In a Pareto diagram, the bars of the bar graph are arranged in order from the largest to the smallest from left to right.

2.5   a.   To find the frequency for each class, count the number of times each letter occurs. The frequencies for the three classes are:

Class	Frequency
X	8
Y	9
Z	3
Total	20

        b.   The relative frequency for each class is found by dividing the frequency by the total sample size. The relative frequency for the class X is $8/20 = .40$. The relative frequency for the class Y is $9/20 = .45$. The relative frequency for the class Z is $3/20 = .15$.

Class	Frequency	Relative Frequency
X	8	.40
Y	9	.45
Z	3	.15
Total	20	1.00

        c.   The frequency bar chart is:

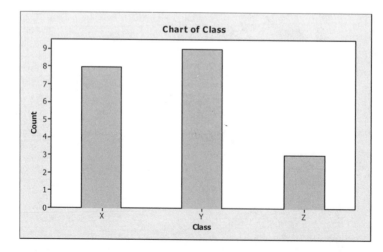

d.   The pie chart for the relative frequency distribution is:

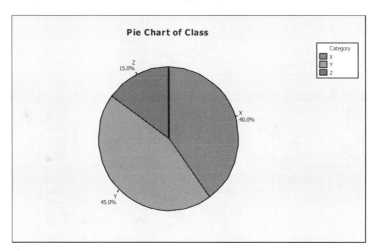

2.7   a.   The proportion of books at reading level 1 is found by dividing the number of books at level 1 by the total number of books, or $39/266 = .147$.

b.   For reading level 2, the proportion of books is $76/266 = .286$. For reading level 3, the proportion of books is $50/266 = .188$. For reading level 4, the proportion of books is $87/266 = .327$. For reading level 5, the proportion of books is $11/266 = .041$. For reading level 6, the proportion of books is $3/266 = .011$.

c.   The sum of the proportions is $.147 + .286 + .188 + .327 + .041 + .011 = 1.000$.

d.   Using MINITAB, a bar graph of the data is:

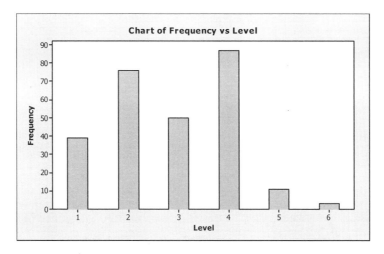

e. Using MINITAB, the Pareto diagram is:

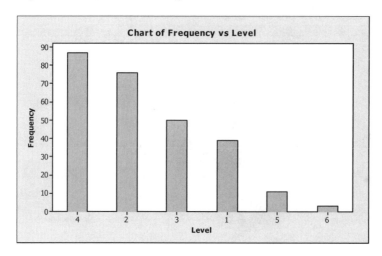

From this diagram, the reading level that occurs the most frequently is level 4.

2.9 a. To construct a relative frequency table for data, we must find the relative frequency for each species of rhinos. To find the relative frequency, divide the frequency by the total population size, 17,470. The relative frequency for African Black rhinos is $3{,}610/17{,}470 = .207$. The rest of the relative frequencies are found in a similar manner and are reported in the table.

Rhino species	Population Estimate	Relative Frequency
African Black	3,610	3610/17470 = .207
African White	11,100	11100/17470 = .635
(Asian) Sumatran	300	300/17470 = .017
(Asian) Javan	60	60/17470 = .003
(Asian) Indian	2,400	2400/17470 = .137
Total	17,470	.999

b. The relative frequency bar chart is:

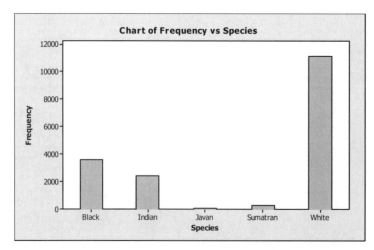

c.   The proportion of rhinos that are African is (.207 + .635) = .842.

      The proportion of rhinos that are Asian is (.017 + .003 + .137) = .157.

2.11 a.   The variable "reason" is qualitative because the responses are categories. There are 7
            values for the variable – Infant, Child, Medical, Infant & Medical, Child & Medical,
            Infant & Child, and Infant, Child & Medical.

      b.   To compute the relative frequencies, divide the frequencies (or number of requests) by
            the total sample size of 30,337. The relative frequency for Infant is 1,852 / 30,337 =
            .061. The rest of the relative frequencies are computed in the table.

Reason	Number of Requests	Computation	Relative Frequency
Infant	1,852	1,852 / 30,337	.061
Child	17,148	17,148 / 30,337	.565
Medical	8,377	8,377 / 30,337	.276
Infant & Medical	44	44 / 30,337	.001
Child & Medical	903	903 / 30,337	.030
Infant & Child	1,878	1,878 / 30,337	.062
Infant & Child & Medical	135	135 / 30,337	.004
Total	30,337		.999

      c.   A bar chart for the data is:

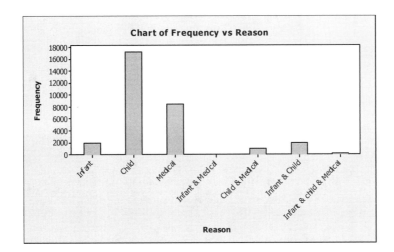

      d.   The proportion of car owners who requested on-off bag switches who gave Medical as
            one of the reasons is (8,377 + 44 + 903 + 135) / 30,337 = 9,459 / 30,337 = .312.

2.13   a.   The data collection method was a survey.

       b.   Since the data were numbers (percentage of US labor and materials), the variable is quantitative. Once the data were collected, they were grouped into 4 categories.

       c.   Using MINITAB, a pie chart of the data is:

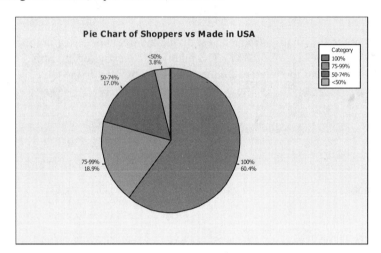

       About 60% of those surveyed believe that "Made in USA" means 100% US labor and materials.

2.15   First, construct a frequency table. There are 5 categories of highest degree obtained. The relative frequencies are found by dividing the frequencies by the total number of CEO's in the sample, which is 25. The table is:

Highest Degree Obtained	Frequency	Computation	Relative Frequency
None	4	4 / 25	.16
Bachelors	6	6 / 25	.24
Masters	9	9 / 25	.36
PhD	3	3 / 25	.12
Law	3	3 / 25	.12
Total	25		1.00

Using MINITAB, a pie chart of the data is:

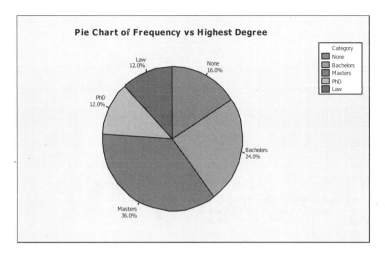

It appears that most CEO's have some type of advanced degree. Of the 25 CEO's studied, 15 or 60% had some type of advanced degree.

2.17   Using MINITAB, the side-by-side bar charts are:

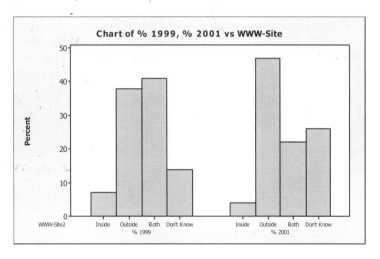

Almost twice as many companies reported that they did not know where the attacks came from in 2001 than in 1999.

2.19   A relative frequency bar graph is used to depict the data:

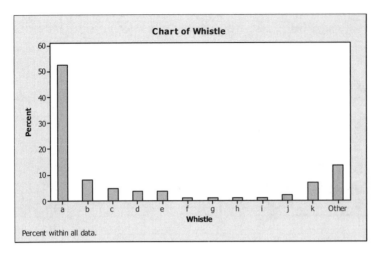

From the bar graph, over half of the whistle types were "Type a." The next most frequent category was the "Other types" with a relative frequency of about .14. Whistle types b and k were the next most frequent. None of the other whistle types had relative frequencies higher than .05.

2.21   In a dot plot, the values are placed on the horizontal axis. The numerical value of each measurement is located on the horizontal axis by a dot above the respective value. When values repeat, the dots are placed one above the other. In a stem-and-leaf display, the stems are the left-most digits of the measurements in the data set. They are arranged vertically from the smallest to the largest. The leaves are the right-most digit of the measurements in the data set. Each leaf is placed beside the appropriate stem. For each stem, the leaves are arranged in order from the smallest to the largest..

2.23   In a histogram, a class interval is a range of numbers above which the frequency of the measurements or relative frequency of the measurements is plotted.

2.25   a.   The original data set has $1 + 3 + 5 + 7 + 4 + 3 = 23$ observations.

        b.   For the bottom row of the stem-and-leaf display:

                The stem is 0.
                The leaves are 0, 1, 2.
                The numbers in the original data set are 0, 1, and 2.

        c.   The dot plot corresponding to all the data points is:

2.27   To find the number of measurements for each measurement class, multiply the relative
        frequency by the total number of observations, $n = 500$. The frequency table is:

Measurement Class	Relative Frequency	Frequency
.5 – 2.5	.10	500(.10) = 50
2.5 – 4.5	.15	500(.15) = 75
4.5 – 6.5	.25	500(.25) = 125
6.5 – 8.5	.20	500(.20) = 100
8.5 – 10.5	.05	500(.05) = 25
10.5 – 12.5	.10	500(.10) = 50
12.5 – 14.5	.10	500(.10) = 50
14.5 – 16.5	.05	500(.05) = 25
		500

The frequency histogram is:

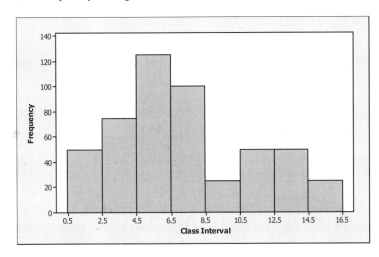

2.29   Using MINITAB, a bar chart of the data is:

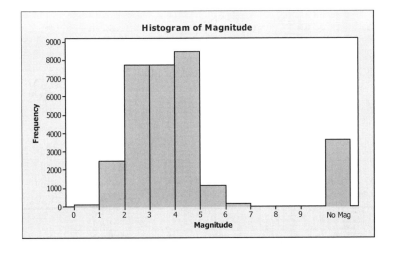

2.31   a.   Using MINITAB, the stem-and-leaf display is as follows.

Character Stem-and-Leaf Display

```
Stem-and-leaf of No. Book   N  = 14
Leaf Unit = 1.0

     1     1 6
     5     2 0124
     6     2 8
    (3)    3 044
     5     3 9
     4     4 002
     1     4
     1     5 3
```

b.   The leaves that correspond to students who earned an "A" grade are underlined in the graph above. Those students who earned A's tended to read the most books.

2.33   a.   Using MINITAB, the frequency histogram of the fish lengths is:

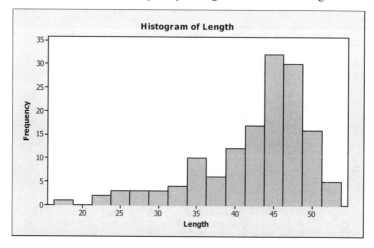

b.   Using MINITAB, the frequency histogram of the fish weights is:

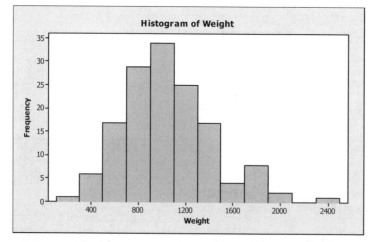

c. Using MINITAB, the frequency histogram of the DDT measurements is:

2.35   a.   Using MINITAB, the stem-and-leaf display for the duration is:

Character Stem-and-Leaf Display

```
Stem-and-leaf of Duration   N   = 18
Leaf Unit = 0.10

      7      1  0000000
      8      2  0
    (2)      3  00
      8      4  000
      5      5
      5      6
      5      7
      5      8
      5      9  0
      4     10  0
      3     11  0
      2     12  00
```

b. The leaves that correspond to sit-ins where at least one arrest was made are underlined in the graph above. The pattern revealed does not support the theory that sit-ins of longer duration are more likely to lead to arrests.

2.37   The dot plot for these data is:

From the dot plot, most of the PMI's range from 3 to 7.5 (16 of the 22). The rest of the PMI's range from 10 to 15.

2.39   a.   Using Minitab, the stem-and-leaf display for the data is:

```
Stem-and-Leaf of LOSS      N = 19
Leaf Unit = 1.0

   8       0  11234559
  (3)      1  123
   8       2  00
   6       3  9
   5       4  ⑥
   4       5  ⑥
   3       6  ① ⑤
   1       7
   1       8
   1       9
   1      10  ⓪
```

        b.   The numbers circled on the display in part **a** are associated with the eclipses of Saturnian satellites.

        c.   Since the five largest numbers are associated with eclipses of Saturnian satellites, it is much more likely that the greater light loss is associated with eclipses rather than occults.

2.41   a.   Using MINITAB, dot plots for the responses for the 3 groups are:

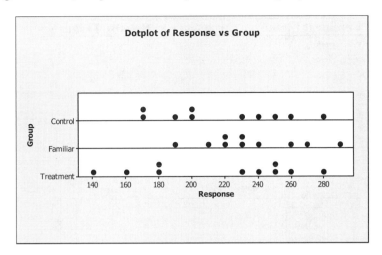

From the three dot plots, it appears that there is not much difference in the response rate between the Control group and the Treatment group. Both range from approximately 165 to 275. (The Treatment group did have a response of 139.) The response rate of the Familiarity group appears to be higher than for the other two groups. The response rate ranges from approximately 190 to 290.

b.   First, we will construct frequency tables for each of the groups. We will use the following classes: 20.5–25.05, 25.05–30.05, 30.05–35.05, 35.05–40.05, 40.0545.05, 45.05–50.05, and 50.05–55.05. The frequencies and relative frequencies (found by dividing the frequencies by the sample size) are listed in the following tables:

Control Group:

Measurement Class	Frequency	Relative Frequency
20.05–25.05	1	.1
25.05–30.05	6	.6
30.05–35.05	2	.2
35.05–40.05	1	.1
Totals	10	1.0

Treatment Group:

Measurement Class	Frequency	Relative Frequency
25.05–30.05	1	.1
30.05–35.05	4	.4
35.05–40.05	3	.3
40.05–45.05	2	.2
Totals	10	1.0

Familiarity Group:

Measurement Class	Frequency	Relative Frequency
35.05–40.05	1	.1
40.05–45.05	4	.4
45.05–50.05	4	.4
50.05–55.05	1	.1
Totals	10	1.0

The relative frequency histograms for the three groups are as follows:

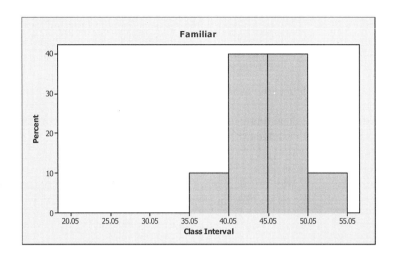

The three relative frequency histograms of the accuracy scores for the three groups indicate that the Familiarity group had the highest accuracy rate, the Treatment group had the second highest accuracy rate, and the Control group had the lowest accuracy rate.

2.43   a. $\sum x = 3 + 8 + 4 + 5 + 3 + 4 + 6 = 33$

      b. $\sum x^2 = 3^2 + 8^2 + 4^2 + 5^2 + 3^2 + 4^2 + 6^2 = 175$

      c. $\sum (x-5)^2 = (3-5)^2 + (8-5)^2 + (4-5)^2 + (5-5)^2 + (3-5)^2 + (4-5)^2$
$$+ (6-5)^2 = 20$$

      d. $\sum (x-2)^2 = (3-2)^2 + (8-2)^2 + (4-2)^2 + (5-2)^2 + (3-2)^2 + (4-2)^2$
$$+ (6-2)^2 = 71$$

      e. $\left(\sum x\right)^2 = (3 + 8 + 4 + 5 + 3 + 4 + 6)^2 = 33^2 = 1089$

2.45   a. $\sum x = 6 + 0 + (-2) + (-1) + 3 = 6$

      b. $\sum x^2 = 6^2 + 0^2 + (-2)^2 + (-1)^2 + 3^2 = 50$

      c. $\sum x^2 - \dfrac{\left(\sum x\right)^2}{5} = 50 - \dfrac{6^2}{5} = 50 - 7.2 = 42.8$

2.47   Three measures of central tendency are the mean, the median, and the mode.

2.49   The two factors that impact the accuracy of the sample mean as an estimate of the population mean are sample size and variability or spread of the data. For the sample size, the larger the sample size, the more accurate the estimate. For variability, all other factors remaining constant, the more variable the data the less accurate the estimate of the mean.

2.51   a.   For a distribution that is skewed to the left, the mean is less than the median.

       b.   For a distribution that is skewed to the right, the mean is greater than the median.

       c.   For a symmetric distribution, the mean and median are equal.

2.53   Assume the data are a sample. The mode is the observation that occurs most frequently. For this sample, the mode is 15, which occurs 3 times.

       The sample mean is:

$$\bar{x} - \frac{\sum x}{n} = \frac{18+10+15+13+17+15+12+15+18+16+11}{11} = \frac{160}{11} = 14.545$$

       The median is the middle number when the data are arranged in order. The data arranged in order are: 10, 11, 12, 13, 15, 15, 15, 16, 17, 18, 18. The middle number is the 6th number, which is 15.

2.55   a. $\bar{x} = \frac{\sum x}{n} = \frac{85}{10} = 8.5$

       b. $\bar{x} = \frac{400}{16} = 25$

       c. $\bar{x} = \frac{35}{45} = .78$

       d. $\bar{x} = \frac{242}{18} = 13.44$

2.57   a.   The mean is $\bar{x} = \frac{\sum x}{n} = \frac{443}{14} = 31.643$.

             To find the median, the data must be arranged in order. In the problem, the data are already arranged in order. The are a total of 14 observations, which is an even number. The median is the average of the middle 2 numbers which are 30 and 34. The median is $\frac{30+34}{2} = 32$. The mode is the observation appearing the most. In this data set, the mode is 34 and 40 because each appears 2 times in the data set.

       b.   Since the mean and the median are almost the same, the distribution of the data set is approximately symmetric. This can be verified by the stem-and-leaf display of Exercise 2.31.

2.59 a. The mean of the data is $\bar{x} = \dfrac{\sum x}{n} = \dfrac{11.77}{8} = 1.4713$.

b. The median is the average of the middle two numbers once the data are arranged in order. The data arranged in order are:

   1.37, 1.41, 1.42, 1.48, 1.50, 1.51, 1.53, 1.55

The middle two numbers are 1.48 and 1.50. The median is $\dfrac{1.48 + 1.50}{2} = 1.49$

c. Since the mean is less than the median, the data are somewhat skewed to the left.

2.61 a. The sample mean radioactivity level is:

$$\bar{x} = \frac{\sum x}{n} = \frac{-43.75}{9} = -4.861$$

The median is the middle observation once they have been ordered. The 5th observation is -4.85. Thus the median is -4.85.

The mode is -5.00.

b. The average radioactivity level is -4.861. Half of the radioactivity levels are less than -4.85 and half are greater. The modal observation occurred 2 times.

2.63 a. The mean response was 5.87. The average rating (across the 15 respondents) of the statement "The Training Game is a great way for students to understand the animal's perspective during training" was 5.87. Since the highest rating the statement could receive was 7, this indicated that on the average, the students rather strongly agreed with this statement.

The mode response was 6. More students rated the statement with a 6 than any other rating. A rating of 6 indicated a rather strong agreement to the statement.

b. Since the mode is only slightly larger than the mean, there probably is no skewness present. If any skewness exists, the data would probably be skewed to the left since the mode is larger than the mean and because the mode is very close to the largest value possible.

2.65 a. The first variable is gender. It has only two values which are not numerical, so it is qualitative. The next variable is group. There are three groups which are not numerical, so group is qualitative. The next variable is DIQ. This variable is measured on a numerical scale, so it is quantitative. The last variable is percent of pronoun errors. This variable is measured on the numerical scale, so it is quantitative.

b. In order to compute numerical descriptive measures, the data must have numbers associated with them. Qualitative variables do not have meaningful numbers associated with them, so one cannot compute numerical measures.

c.   The mean of the DIQ scores for the SLI children is:

$$\bar{x} = \frac{\sum x}{n} = \frac{86 + 86 + 94 + \cdots + 95}{10} = \frac{936}{10} = 93.6$$

The median is the average of the middle two numbers after they have been arranged in order: 84, 86, 86, 87, 89, 94, 95, 98, 107, 110.

The median is $\dfrac{89 + 94}{2} = \dfrac{183}{2} = 91.5$

The mode is the value with the highest frequency. Since 86 occurred twice and no other value occurred more than once, the mode is 86.

d.   The mean of the DIQ scores for the YND children is:

$$\bar{x} = \frac{\sum x}{n} = \frac{110 + 92 + 92 + \cdots + 92}{10} = \frac{953}{10} = 95.3$$

The median is the average of the middle two numbers after they have been arranged in order: 86, 90, 90, 92, 92, 92, 96, 100, 105, 110.

The median is $\dfrac{92 + 92}{2} = \dfrac{184}{2} = 92$

The mode is the value with the highest frequency. Since 92 occurred three times and no other value occurred more than twice, the mode is 92.

e.   The mean of the DIQ scores for the OND children is:

$$\bar{x} = \frac{\sum x}{n} = \frac{110 + 113 + 113 + \cdots + 98}{10} = \frac{1019}{10} = 101.9$$

The median is the average of the middle two numbers after they have been arranged in order: 87, 92, 94, 95, 98, 108, 109, 110, 113, 113.

The median is $\dfrac{98 + 108}{2} = \dfrac{206}{2} = 103$

The mode is the value with the highest frequency. Since 113 occurred twice and no other value occurred more than once, the mode is 113.

f.   Of the three groups, the SLI group had the lowest mean DIQ score (93.6), the YND group had a slightly higher mean DIQ score (95.3), while the OND group had the highest mean DIQ score (101.9). Thus, the SLI and the YND groups appear to be fairly similar with regard to DIQ, while the OND group appears to be much higher.

Of the three groups, the SLI group had the lowest median DIQ score (91.5), the YND group had a slightly higher median DIQ score (92), while the OND group had the highest median DIQ score (103). Thus, again, the SLI and the YND groups appear to be fairly similar with regard to DIQ, while the OND group appears to be much higher.

Of the three groups, the SLI group had the lowest mode DIQ score (86), the YND group had a slightly higher mode DIQ score (92), while the OND group had the highest mode IDQ score (113). Thus, again, the SLI and the YND groups appear to be fairly similar with regard to DIQ, while the OND group appears to be much higher.

For the SLI group, the mean is larger than the median and the median is larger than the mode. For the YND group, the mean is greater than the median, but the mode is equal to the median. For the OND group, the mean is smaller than the median and the median is smaller than the mode. If only the means were used, the three groups would appear to have similar distributions – the means range from 93.6 to 101.9. If the medians were used, the range gets larger – the observations range from 91.5 to 103. If the modes were used, the range is quite different – the modes range from 86 to 113. Thus, it appears that all three "centers" should be computed fro each group.

g. **YND children**: The mean percentage of pronoun errors is:

$$\bar{x} = \frac{\sum x}{n} = \frac{94.40 + 19.05 + ... + 0}{10} = \frac{468.8}{10} = 46.88$$

The median is the average of the middle 2 numbers once the data have been arranged in order: 0, 0, 18.75, 19.05, 32.43, 55.00, 62.50, 86.67, 94.40, 100.00.

The median is $\frac{32.43 + 55.00}{2} = \frac{87.43}{2} = 43.715$

The mode is the value with the highest frequency. Since 0 occurs 2 times, 0 is the mode.

SLI children: The mean percentage of pronoun errors is:

$$\bar{x} = \frac{\sum x}{n} = \frac{60.00 + 40.00 + ... + 0}{10} = \frac{301.71}{10} = 30.171$$

The median is the average of the middle 2 numbers once the data have been arranged in order: 0, 0, 0, 27.27, 31.58, 33.33, 40.00, 42.86, 60.00, 66.67.

The median is $\frac{31.58 + 33.33}{2} = \frac{64.91}{2} = 32.455$

The mode is the value with the highest frequency. Since 0 occurs 3 times, 0 is the mode.

OND children: The mean percentage of pronoun errors is:

$$\bar{x} = \frac{\sum x}{n} = \frac{0 + 0 + ... + 0}{10} = \frac{0}{10} = 0$$

The median is the average of the middle 2 numbers once the data have been arranged in order: 0, 0, 0, 0, 0, 0, 0, 0, 0, 0,.

The median is $\dfrac{0+0}{2} = \dfrac{0}{2} = 0$

The mode is the value with the highest frequency. Since 0 occurs 10 times, 0 is the mode.

2.67   a.   The mean cylinder power measurements for student #11 is:

$$\bar{x} = \frac{\sum x}{n} = \frac{-.08 + (-.06) + ... + (-.16)}{25} = \frac{-3.86}{25} = -.1544$$

The median is the middle number once the data have been arranged in order:
$-1.07, -.21, -.20, -.17, -.17, -.17, -.16, -.16, -.16, -.15, -.12, -.12, -.11, -.10,$
$-.09, -.09, -.09, -.08, -.08, -.07, -.07, -.06, -.06, -.06, -.04$

The median is $-.11$.

The mode is the value with the highest frequency. Since $-.17, -.16, -.09, -.06$ each occur 3 times, all are modes.

From the printout, the mean is -0.1544 and the median is -0.11. (All the numbers in the table are negative numbers.) Since these two values are very close together, both are good representatives of the middle of the data set.

   b.   The outlier is -1.07.

   c.   After deleting -1.07, the mean is:

$$\bar{x} = \frac{\sum x}{n} = \frac{(-.08) + (-.06) + (-.15) + \cdots + (-.16)}{24} = \frac{-2.79}{24} = -.11625$$

The median is the average of the middle two numbers once the data are arranged in order.

The middle two numbers are 10 and 11. The median is $\dfrac{(-.10) + (-.11)}{2} = -.105$

The mean changes from $-.1544$ to $-.11625$ while the median changes from $-.11$ to $-.105$. The mean changes much more than the median when the outlier is removed.

2.69   The range of a data set is the difference between the largest and smallest measurements.

2.71   The sample variance is the sum of the squared deviations from the sample mean divided by the sample size minus 1. The population variance is the sum of the squared deviations from the population mean divided by the population size.

2.73   If the standard deviation increases, this implies that the data are more variable.

2.75   a.   Range $= 42 - 37 = 5$

$$s^2 = \frac{\sum x^2 - \frac{\left(\sum x\right)^2}{n}}{n-1} = \frac{7935 - \frac{199^2}{5}}{5-1} = 3.7 \qquad s = \sqrt{3.7} = 1.92$$

b.   Range $= 100 - 1 = 99$

$$s^2 = \frac{\sum x^2 - \frac{\left(\sum x\right)^2}{n}}{n-1} = \frac{25,795 - \frac{303^2}{9}}{9-1} = 1,949.25 \qquad s = \sqrt{1,949.25} = 44.15$$

c.   Range $= 100 - 2 = 98$

$$s^2 = \frac{\sum x^2 - \frac{\left(\sum x\right)^2}{n}}{n-1} = \frac{20,033 - \frac{295^2}{8}}{8-1} = 1,307.84 \qquad s = \sqrt{1,307.84} = 36.16$$

2.77   This is one possibility for the two data sets.

Data Set 1: 1, 1, 2, 2, 3, 3, 4, 4, 5, 5
Data Set 2: 1, 1, 1, 1, 1, 5, 5, 5, 5, 5

$$\bar{x}_1 = \frac{\sum x}{n} = \frac{1+1+2+2+3+3+4+4+5+5+}{10} = \frac{30}{10} = 3$$

$$\bar{x}_2 = \frac{\sum x}{n} = \frac{1+1+1+1+1+5+5+5+5+5}{10} = \frac{30}{10} = 3$$

Therefore, the two data sets have the same mean. The variances for the two data sets are:

$$s_1^2 = \frac{\sum x^2 - \frac{\left(\sum x\right)^2}{n}}{n-1} = \frac{110 - \frac{30^2}{10}}{9} = \frac{20}{9} = 2.2222$$

$$s_2^2 = \frac{\sum x^2 - \frac{\left(\sum x\right)^2}{n}}{n-1} = \frac{130 - \frac{30^2}{10}}{9} = \frac{40}{9} = 4.4444$$

The dot diagram for the two data sets are shown below.

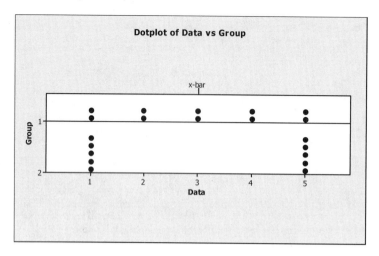

2.79   a.   Range $= 3 - 0 = 3$

$$s^2 = \frac{\sum x^2 - \dfrac{\left(\sum x\right)^2}{n}}{n-1} = \frac{15 - \dfrac{7^2}{5}}{5-1} = 1.3 \qquad s = \sqrt{1.3} = 1.1402$$

b.   After adding 3 to each of the data points,

Range $= 6 - 3 = 3$

$$s^2 = \frac{\sum x^2 - \dfrac{\left(\sum x\right)^2}{n}}{n-1} = \frac{102 - \dfrac{22^2}{5}}{5-1} = 1.3 \qquad s = \sqrt{1.3} = 1.1402$$

c.   After subtracting 4 from each of the data points,

Range $= -1 - (-4) = 3$

$$s^2 = \frac{\sum x^2 - \dfrac{\left(\sum x\right)^2}{n}}{n-1} = \frac{39 - \dfrac{(-13)^2}{5}}{5-1} = 1.3 \qquad s = \sqrt{1.3} = 1.1402$$

d.   The range, variance, and standard deviation remain the same when any number is added to or subtracted from each measurement in the data set.

2.81   a.   For those students who earned A, the range is $53 - 24 = 29$.

The variance is $s^2 = \dfrac{\sum x^2 - \dfrac{\left(\sum x\right)^2}{n}}{n-1} = \dfrac{11,482 - \dfrac{296^2}{8}}{7} = \dfrac{530}{7} = 75.7143$

The standard deviation is $s = \sqrt{s^2} = \sqrt{75.7143} = 8.701$.

b. For those students who earned a B or C, the range is $40 - 16 = 24$.

The variance is $s^2 = \dfrac{\sum x^2 - \dfrac{\left(\sum x\right)^2}{n}}{n-1} = \dfrac{3{,}965 - \dfrac{147^2}{6}}{5} = \dfrac{363.5}{5} = 72.7$

The standard deviation is $s = \sqrt{s^2} = \sqrt{72.7} = 8.526$.

c. The students who received A's have a more variable distribution of the number of books read. The range, variance, and standard deviation for this group are greater than the corresponding values for the B-C group.

2.83 a. Range $= 1.55 - 1.37 = .18$

b. $s^2 = \dfrac{\sum x^2 - \dfrac{\left(\sum x\right)^2}{n}}{n-1} = \dfrac{17.3453 - \dfrac{11.77^2}{8}}{8-1} = .0041$

c. $s = \sqrt{.0041} = .064$

d. If the standard deviation of the daily ammonia levels during the morning drive-time is 1.45 ppm (compared to .064 ppm in the afternoon drive-time), then the morning drive-time has more variable ammonia levels.

2.85 a. Range $= 13 - 1 = 12$

$s^2 = \dfrac{\sum x^2 - \dfrac{\left(\sum x\right)^2}{n}}{n-1} = \dfrac{498 - \dfrac{80^2}{20}}{20-1} = \dfrac{178}{19} = 9.3684$

$s = \sqrt{s^2} = \sqrt{9.3584} = 3.061$

b. Dropping the largest measurement:

Range $= 9 - 1 = 8$

$s^2 = \dfrac{\sum x^2 - \dfrac{\left(\sum x\right)^2}{n}}{n-1} = \dfrac{329 - \dfrac{67^2}{19}}{19-1} = \dfrac{92.7368421}{18} = 5.1520$

$s = \sqrt{s^2} = \sqrt{5.1520} = 2.270$

By dropping the largest observation from the data set, the range decreased from 12 to 8, the variance decreased from 9.3684 to 5.1520 and the standard deviation decreased from 3.061 to 2.270.

c. Dropping the largest and smallest measurements:

Range $= 9 - 1 = 8$

$$s^2 = \frac{\sum x^2 - \frac{\left(\sum x\right)^2}{n}}{n-1} = \frac{328 - \frac{66^2}{18}}{18-1} = \frac{86}{17} = 5.0588$$

$$s = \sqrt{s^2} = \sqrt{5.0588} = 2.249$$

By dropping the largest and smallest observations from the data set, the range decreased from 12 to 8, the variance decreased from 9.3684 to 5.0588 and the standard deviation decreased from 3.061 to 2.249.

2.87 a. The unit of measurement of the variable of interest is dollars (the same as the mean and standard deviation). Based on this, the data are quantitative.

b. Since no information is given about the shape of the data set, we can only use Chebyshev's rule.

$900 is 2 standard deviations below the mean, and $2100 is 2 standard deviations above the mean. Using Chebyshev's rule, at least 3/4 of the measurements (or $3/4 \times 200 = 150$ measurements) will fall between $900 and $2100.

$600 is 3 standard deviations below the mean and $2400 is 3 standard deviations above the mean. Using Chebyshev's rule, at least 8/9 of the measurements (or $8/9 \times 200 \times 178$ measurements) will fall between $600 and $2400.

$1200 is 1 standard deviation below the mean and $1800 is 1 standard deviation above the mean. Using Chebyshev's rule, nothing can be said about the number of measurements that will fall between $1200 and $1800.

$1500 is equal to the mean and $2100 is 2 standard deviations above the mean. Using Chebyshev's rule, at least 3/4 of the measurements (or $3/4 \times 200 = 150$ measurements) will fall between $900 and $2100. It is possible that all of the 150 measurements will be between $900 and $1500. Thus, nothing can be said about the number of measurements between $1500 and $2100.

2.89 According to the Empirical Rule:

a. Approximately 68% of the measurements will be contained in the interval $\bar{x} - s$ to $\bar{x} + s$.

b. Approximately 95% of the measurements will be contained in the interval $\bar{x} - 2s$ to $\bar{x} + 2s$.

c. Essentially all the measurements will be contained in the interval $\bar{x} - 3s$ to $\bar{x} + 3s$.

2.91   Using Chebyshev's rule, at least 8/9 of the measurements will fall within 3 standard deviations of the mean. Thus, the range of the data would be around 6 standard deviations. Using the Empirical Rule, approximately 95% of the observations are within 2 standard deviations of the mean. Thus, the range of the data would be around 4 standard deviations. We would expect the standard deviation to be somewhere between Range/6 and Range/4.

For our data, the range = $760 - 135 = 625$.

The Range/6 = $625/6 = 104.17$ and Range/4 = $625/4 = 156.25$.

Therefore, I would estimate that the standard deviation of the data set is between 104.17 and 156.25.

It would not be feasible to have a standard deviation of 25. If the standard deviation were 25, the data would span $625/25 = 25$ standard deviations. This would be extremely unlikely.

2.93   a. $\bar{x} = \dfrac{\sum x}{n} = \dfrac{16,429}{174} = 94.42$

$$s^2 = \frac{\sum x^2 - \dfrac{\left(\sum x\right)^2}{n}}{n-1} = \frac{1,554,537 - \dfrac{(16,429)^2}{174}}{174-1} = \frac{3,318.374}{173} = 19.18135$$

$s = \sqrt{s^2} = \sqrt{19.18135} = 4.380$

b. $\bar{x} \pm s \Rightarrow 94.42 \pm 4.38 \Rightarrow (90.04,\ \ 98.80)$

$\bar{x} \pm 2s \Rightarrow 94.42 \pm 2(4.38) \Rightarrow 94.42 \pm 8.76 \Rightarrow (85.66,\ \ 103.18)$

$\bar{x} \pm 3s \Rightarrow 94.42 \pm 3(4.38) \Rightarrow 94.42 \pm 13.14 \Rightarrow (81.28,\ \ 107.56)$

c.   There are 119 observations between 90.04 and 98.80. The percentage is $(119/174) \times 100\% = 68.4\%$.

There are 168 observations between 85.66 and 103.18. The percentage is $(168/174) \times 100\% = 96.6\%$.

There are 169 observations between 81.28 and 107.56. The percentage is $(169/174) \times 100\% = 97.1\%$.

The first 2 percentages are close to the percentages for the Empirical Rule ($\approx 68\%$ and $\approx 95\%$). The final percentage is smaller than the percentage from the Empirical Rule ($\approx 100\%$). However, all of these percentages correspond to Chebyshev's Rule (at least 4/3 or 75% within 2 standard deviations and at least 8/9 or 88.9%).

2.95   a.   The mean is 79 and the standard deviation is 23. Thus, a measurement of 102 is 1 standard deviation above the mean. If nothing is known about the shape of the distribution, we must use Chebyshev's Rule to describe the distribution. Using this, we know nothing about the number of observations within 1 standard deviation of the mean, and thus, know nothing about the percentage of observations less than 102.

b. If we assume that the distribution is mound-shaped, we can use the Empirical Rule to describe the distribution. If the distribution is mound-shaped, then it is symmetric. Thus, we know that half of the observations will be below 79. We know that about 68% of the observations are within 1 standard deviation of the mean. Therefore, about 34% of the observations will be between the mean and 1 standard deviation above the mean, or between 79 and 102. Thus, the percentage of observations less than 102 is about $50\% + 34\% = 84\%$.

2.97 For parts a and b, we must use Chebyshev's Rule to describe the data sets. For both the handrubbers and the handwashers, the standard deviation is greater than the mean. Since no observations can be less than 0, we know that the smallest observation in the data sets is less than 1 standard deviation from the mean. Thus, the distributions cannot be symmetric, but rather skewed to the right. We cannot use the Empirical Rule.

a. Using Chebyshev's Rule, we know that at least $1 - \dfrac{1}{k^2}$ of the observations fall within k standard deviations of the mean. To find k, we use:

$$.95 = 1 - \frac{1}{k^2} \Rightarrow \frac{1}{k^2} = 1 - .95 \Rightarrow \frac{1}{k^2} = .05 \Rightarrow k^2 = 20 \Rightarrow k = 4.5$$

Thus, the interval $\bar{x} \pm 4.5s$ will contain at least $1 - \dfrac{1}{4.5^2} = .95$ of the observations.

For handrubbers: $\bar{x} \pm 4.5s \Rightarrow 35 \pm 4.5(59) \Rightarrow 35 \pm 265.5 \Rightarrow (0, \; 300.5)$

b. For handwashers: $\bar{x} \pm 4.5s \Rightarrow 69 \pm 4.5(106) \Rightarrow 69 \pm 477 \Rightarrow (0, \; 546)$

2.99 a. Since no information is given about the distribution of the velocities of the Winchester bullets, we can only use Chebyshev's rule to describe the data. We know that at least 3/4 of the velocities will fall within the interval:

$$\bar{x} \pm 2s \Rightarrow 936 \pm 2(10) \Rightarrow 936 \pm 20 \Rightarrow (916, 956)$$

Also, at least 8/9 of the velocities will fall within the interval:

$$\bar{x} \pm 3s \Rightarrow 936 \pm 3(10) \Rightarrow 936 \pm 30 \Rightarrow (906, 966)$$

b. Since a velocity of 1,000 is much larger than the largest value in the second interval in part **a**, it is very unlikely that the bullet was manufactured by Winchester.

2.101 a. Regardless of the shape of the distribution, most of the observations will fall within 3 standard deviations of the mean. Thus, for the SAT-Math scores, an interval likely to contain a student's change in score is:

$$\bar{x} \pm 3s \Rightarrow 19 \pm 3(65) \Rightarrow 19 \pm 195 \Rightarrow (-176, 214)$$

b. Regardless of the shape of the distribution, most of the observations will fall within 3 standard deviations of the mean. Thus, for the SAT-Verbal scores, an interval likely to contain a student's change in score is:

$$\bar{x} \pm 3s \Rightarrow 7 \pm 3(49) \Rightarrow 7 \pm 147 \Rightarrow (-140,\ 154)$$

c. For the SAT-Verbal, the maximum increase in scores is about 154 points. For the SAT-Math, the maximum increase in scores is approximately 214. Thus, a student is more likely to get a 140-point increase on the SAT-Math test.

2.103   Using the definition of a percentile:

	Percentile	Percentage Above	Percentage Below
a.	75th	25%	75%
b.	50th	50%	50%
c.	20th	80%	20%
d.	84th	16%	84%

2.105   For mound-shaped distributions, we can use the Empirical Rule. About 95% of the observations will fall within 2 standard deviations of the mean. Thus, about 95% of the measurements will have z-scores between -2 and 2.

2.107   We first compute z-scores for each x value.

a. $z = \dfrac{x - \mu}{\sigma} = \dfrac{100 - 50}{25} = 2$

b. $z = \dfrac{x - \mu}{\sigma} = \dfrac{1 - 4}{1} = -3$

c. $z = \dfrac{x - \mu}{\sigma} = \dfrac{0 - 200}{100} = -2$

d. $z = \dfrac{x - \mu}{\sigma} = \dfrac{10 - 5}{3} = 1.67$

The above z-scores indicate that the x value in part **a** lies the greatest distance above the mean and the x value of part **b** lies the greatest distance below the mean.

2.109   The percentile ranking for the age of 25 years in the distribution of all ages of licensed drivers stopped by police is $100 - 73.5 = 26.5$ percentile.

2.111   From Exercise 2.93, $\bar{x} = 94.42$ and $s = 4.380$.

a.   The z-score for the Nautilus Explorer is: $z = \dfrac{x - \bar{x}}{s} = \dfrac{74 - 94.42}{4.380} = -4.66$

The score for the Nautilus Explorer is 4.66 standard deviations below the mean for all the cruise ships.

b.   The z-score for the Rotterdam is: $z = \dfrac{x - \bar{x}}{s} = \dfrac{93 - 94.42}{4.380} = -0.32$

The score for the Rotterdam is 0.32 standard deviations below the mean for all the cruise ships.

2.113   a.   Using SAS, the output is:

```
                              EGG LENGTH                               1

                        The UNIVARIATE Procedure
                           Variable:  length

                              Moments

N                          130      Sum Weights              130
Mean                60.6538462      Sum Observations        7885
Std Deviation       43.9861168      Variance          1934.77847
Skewness             2.1091362      Kurtosis          4.70026314
Uncorrected SS          727842      Corrected SS      249586.423
Coeff Variation     72.5199136      Std Error Mean    3.85783765

                      Basic Statistical Measures

           Location                        Variability

     Mean      60.65385      Std Deviation        43.98612
     Median    49.50000      Variance                 1935
     Mode      35.00000      Range            220.00000
                             Interquartile Range   32.00000


               Tests for Location: Mu0=0

      Test              -Statistic-      -----p Value------

      Student's t    t  15.72224      Pr > |t|      <.0001
      Sign           M        65      Pr >= |M|     <.0001
      Signed Rank    S    4257.5      Pr >= |S|     <.0001


              Quantiles (Definition 5)

                  Quantile      Estimate

                  100% Max         236.0
                  99%              218.0
                  95%              160.0
                  90%              122.0
                  75% Q3            67.0
                  50% Median        49.5
                  25% Q1            35.0
                  10%              23.0
                  5%               19.0
                  1%               16.0
                  0% Min           16.0
```

```
                    The UNIVARIATE Procedure
                        Variable:  length

                      Extreme Observations

       ----Lowest----            ----Highest---

       Value      Obs            Value      Obs

        16.0      102             195       128
        16.0       90             205       123
        17.0      101             216       122
        18.0      103             218       129
        18.5      100             236       130


                       Missing Values

                          -----Percent Of-----
         Missing                          Missing
          Value       Count    All Obs       Obs

            .           2        1.52      100.00
```

The 10th percentile egg length is 23.

b. From the printout, $\bar{x} = 60.65$ and $s = 43.99$. The z-score corresponding to the Moas, P. australis bird species' egg length is:

$$z = \frac{x - \bar{x}}{s} = \frac{205 - 60.65}{43.99} = 3.28$$

The z-score for Moas, P. australis is 3.28 standard deviations above the mean. This is a fairly large value for a z-score. This indicates that the egg length for Moas, P. australis could be very unusual.

2.115   We will use SAS to compute the percentiles. The output is:

```
                    The UNIVARIATE Procedure
                       Variable:  LEFTEYE

                             Moments

   N                         25    Sum Weights               25
   Mean                 -0.1544    Sum Observations       -3.86
   Std Deviation     0.19676721    Variance          0.03871733
   Skewness          -4.5220839    Kurtosis          21.7019614
   Uncorrected SS        1.5252    Corrected SS        0.929216
   Coeff Variation    -127.4399    Std Error Mean    0.03935344

                  Basic Statistical Measures

         Location                        Variability

     Mean     -0.15440      Std Deviation          0.19677
     Median   -0.11000      Variance               0.03872
     Mode     -0.17000      Range                  1.03000
                            Interquartile Range    0.08000

   NOTE: The mode displayed is the smallest of 4 modes with a count of 3.
```

Methods for Describing Sets of Data   **33**

```
                Tests for Location: Mu0=0

     Test              -Statistic-      -----p Value------

     Student's t    t  -3.92342      Pr > |t|    0.0006
     Sign           M     -12.5      Pr >= |M|    <.0001
     Signed Rank    S    -162.5      Pr >= |S|    <.0001

                 Quantiles (Definition 5)

                 Quantile       Estimate

                 100% Max        -0.04
                 99%             -0.04
                 95%             -0.06
                 90%             -0.06
                 75% Q3          -0.08
                 50% Median      -0.11
                 25% Q1          -0.16
                 10%             -0.20
                 5%              -0.21
                 1%              -1.07
                 0% Min          -1.07

                 Extreme Observations

        ----Lowest----            ----Highest---

        Value      Obs          Value       Obs

        -1.07       7           -0.07        23
        -0.21      18           -0.06         2
        -0.20      11           -0.06        12
        -0.17      22           -0.06        21
        -0.17      17           -0.04        16
```

a. From the printout above, the 10th percentile is −0.20. Thus, 10% of the cylinder power measurements are below −0.20 and 90% are above −0.20.

b. From the printout above, the 95th percentile is −0.06. Thus, 95% of the cylinder power measurements are below −0.06 and 5% are above −0.06.

c. $z = \dfrac{x - \bar{x}}{s} = \dfrac{-1.07 - (-.1544)}{.19677} = -4.65$. A power measurement of −1.07 is 4.65 standard deviations below the mean. Since this z-score is so small, it is an extremely unlikely value to observe. The cylinder value of −1.07 is an extreme value.

2.117   a.   From the problem, $\mu = 2.7$ and $\sigma = .5$

$$z = \frac{x - \mu}{\sigma} \Rightarrow z\sigma = x - \mu \Rightarrow x = \mu + z\sigma$$

For $z = 2.0$, $x = 2.7 + 2.0(.5) = 3.7$

For $z = -1.0$, $x = 2.7 - 1.0(.5) = 2.2$

For $z = .5$, $x = 2.7 + .5(.5) = 2.95$

For $z = -2.5$, $x = 2.7 - 2.5(.5) = 1.45$

   b.   For $z = -1.6$, $x = 2.7 - 1.6(.5) = 1.9$

   c.   If we assume the distribution of GPAs is approximately mound-shaped, we can use the Empirical Rule.

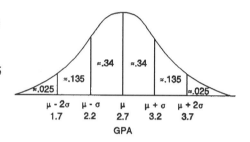

From the Empirical Rule, we know that $-.025$ or -2.5% of the students will have GPAs above 3.7 (with $z = 2$). Thus, the GPA corresponding to summa cum laude (top 2.5%) will be greater than 3.7 ($z > 2$).

We know that $-.16$ or 16% of the students will have GPAs above 3.2 ($z = 1$). Thus, the limit on GPAs for cum laude (top 16%) will be greater than 3.2 ($z > 1$).

We must assume the distribution is mound-shaped.

2.119   The 25th percentile is the observation with 25% of the observations below it and 75% of the observations above it. Another name for the 25th percentile is the lower quartile.

The 50th percentile is the observation with 50% of the observations below it and 50% of the observations above it. Another name for the 50th percentile is the median.

The 75th percentile is the observation with 75% of the observations below it and 25% of the observations above it. Another name for the 75th percentile is the upper quartile.

2.121   The hinges of a box plot are the upper quartile and the lower quartile (top and bottom of the rectangle).

2.123   To determine if the measurements are outliers, compute the *z*-score.

a. $z = \dfrac{x - \bar{x}}{s} = \dfrac{65 - 57}{11} = .727$

Since this *z*-score is less than 3 in magnitude, 65 is not an outlier.

b. $z = \dfrac{x - \bar{x}}{s} = \dfrac{21 - 57}{11} = -3.273$

Since this *z*-score is more than 3 in magnitude, 21 is an outlier.

c. $z = \dfrac{x - \bar{x}}{s} = \dfrac{72 - 57}{11} = 1.364$

Since this *z*-score is less than 3 in magnitude, 72 is not an outlier.

d. $z = \dfrac{x - \bar{x}}{s} = \dfrac{98 - 57}{11} = 3.727$

Since this *z*-score is more than 3 in magnitude, 98 is an outlier.

2.125   a.   The median is approximately 4.

c. Q_L (Lower quartile) is approximately 3 and Q_U (Upper quartile) is approximately 6.

d.   The interquartile range is $IQR = Q_U - Q_L \approx 6 - 3 = 3$.

e.   The data set is skewed to the right since the right whisker is longer than the left and there are outlying observations to the right.

f.   50% of the observations lie to the right of the median. 75% of the observations lie to the left of the upper quartile.

g.   The outliers in the data set are 12, 13, and 16.

2.127   a.   The z-score is $z = \dfrac{x - \bar{x}}{s} = \dfrac{3.3 - 7.3}{3.18} = -1.26$.

b.   A PMI score of 3.3 would not be considered an outlier. The z-score is -1.26. A z-score this small is not considered unusual.

2.129   a.   Using MINITAB, the side-by-side box plots are:

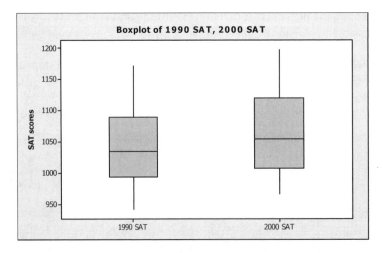

b.   Using MINITAB, the descriptive statistics are:

Descriptive Statistics

Variable	N	Mean	Median	TrMean	StDev	SE Mean
1990 SAT	51	1043.7	1034.0	1042.4	59.5	8.3
2000 SAT	51	1066.1	1054.0	1064.1	65.9	9.2

Variable	Minimum	Maximum	Q1	Q3
1990 SAT	942.0	1172.0	993.0	1089.0
2000 SAT	966.0	1197.0	1007.0	1120.0

The standard deviation for 1990 is 59.5 and the standard deviation for 2000 is 65.9. Also, the IQR for 1990 is $Q_U - Q_L = 1089 - 993 = 96$ while the IQR for 2000 is $Q_U - Q_L = 1120 - 1007 = 113$. Thus, the variability for 2000 is slightly greater than that for 1990.

c.   Since there are no observations outside the inner fences for either year, there are no outliers.

2.131 a.   Using MINITAB, the side-by-side box plots are:

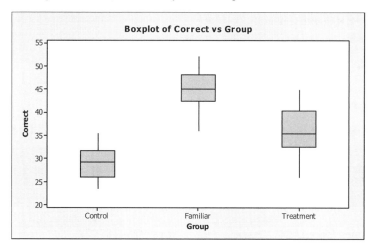

b.   The median for the Control group is approximately 29, the median for the Familiar group is approximately 45, and the median for the Treatment group is approximately 35. It appears that the learned breathing pattern strategy helped make the speech more understandable.

c.   The interquartile range for the Control group is from about 26 to 31 or 5 units, the interquartile range for the Familiar group is from about 42.5 to 47.5 or 5 units, and the interquartile range for the Treatment group is from about 32.5 to 40 or 7.5 units. The spread for the Treatment group is larger than the spreads for the other two groups.

d.   The standard deviations for the three groups agree fairly well with the corresponding interquartile ranges. The standard deviation for the Treatment group is the largest as is the interquartile range. The standard deviation for the Control group is the smallest, while the interquartile range for the Control group is tied with the Familiar group.

e.   Since there are no asterisks or observations outside the inner fences, there is no evidence that there are any outliers.

2.133 a.   Using MINITAB, the box plot of the data is:

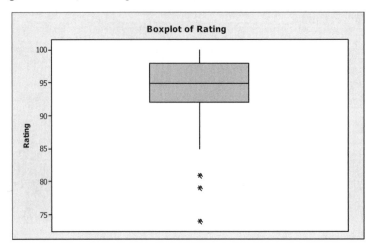

The descriptive statistics are:

Descriptive Statistics: Rating

```
Variable          N        Mean      Median      TrMean       StDev      SE Mean
Rating          174      94.420      95.000      94.814       4.380        0.332

Variable   Minimum     Maximum          Q1          Q3
Rating      74.000     100.000      92.000      98.000
```

The median is 95, the upper quartile is $Q_U = 98$ and the lower quartile is $Q_L = 92$. The interquartile range is $IQR = Q_U - Q_L = 98 - 92 = 6$.

The lower inner fence is $Q_L - 1.5(IQR) = 92 - 1.5(6) = 92 - 9 = 83$.

The upper inner fence is $Q_U + 1.5(IQR) = 98 + 1.5(6) = 98 + 9 = 107$.

The lower outer fence is $Q_L - 3(IQR) = 92 - 3(6) = 92 - 18 = 74$.

The upper outer fence is $Q_U + 3(IQR) = 98 + 3(6) = 98 + 18 = 116$.

There are 5 observations below the lower inner fence. These are suspect outliers. The observations have values 74, 79, 79, 81, and 81.There are no observations below the lower outer fence.

b.   The z-scores corresponding to these points are:

74: $z = \dfrac{x - \bar{x}}{s} = \dfrac{74 - 94.42}{4.38} = -4.66$ $\qquad$ 79: $z = \dfrac{x - \bar{x}}{s} = \dfrac{79 - 94.42}{4.38} = -3.52$

81: $z = \dfrac{x - \bar{x}}{s} = \dfrac{81 - 94.42}{4.38} = -3.06$

c.   According to the box plot, there are 5 suspect outliers. According to the z-score method, all of the suspect outliers have z-scores more than 3 standard deviations from the mean. They would all be considered outliers.

2.135   First, compute the z-score for 1.80: $z = \dfrac{x - \mu}{\sigma} = \dfrac{1.80 - 2.00}{.08} = -2.5$

If the data are actually mound-shaped, it would be very unusual (less than 2.5%) to observe a batch with 1.80% zinc phosphide if the true mean is 2.0%. Thus, if we did observe 1.8%, we would conclude that the mean percent of zinc phosphide in today's production is probably less than 2.0%.

2.137   A bivariate relationship is a relationship between 2 quantitative variables.

2.139   Using MINITAB, the scatterplot is:

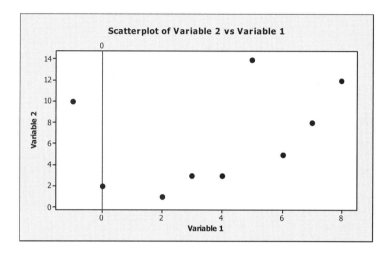

From the scatterplot, there does not appear to be much of a trend between variable 1 and variable 2. There is a slight positive linear trend - as variable 1 increases, variable 2 tends to increase. However, this relationship appears to be very weak.

2.141   Using MINITAB, a scatterplot of the data is:

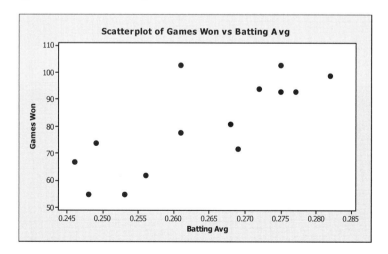

There appears to be a positive relationship between the number of games won and the team batting average. As the team batting average increases, the teams tend to win more games.

2.143   a.   Using MINITAB, the scatterplot is:

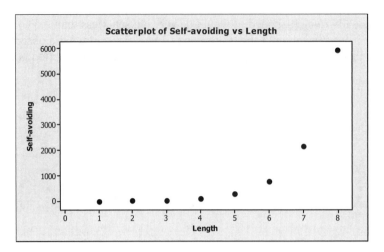

It appears that as length increases, the self-avoiding walks increase, but at an increasing rate.

b.   Using MINITAB, the scatterplot of the data is:

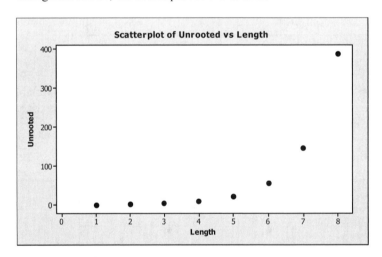

It appears that as the length increases, the unrooted walks also increase, but at an increasing rate.

2.145   a.   Using MINITAB, a scatterplot of the data is:

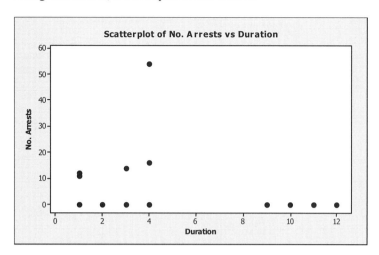

There does not appear to be much of a trend between the number of arrests and the duration of the sit-in.

b.   Using MINITAB, a scatterplot of the data using only those observations where there was at least one arrest is:

There appears to be a positive relationship between the number of arrests and the duration of the sit-in. As the duration increases, the number of arrests tend to increase.

c.   Since there are only 5 observations used in the scatterplot in part **b**, the reliability is suspect.

2.147 a.   Using MINITAB, a scatterplot of the data is:

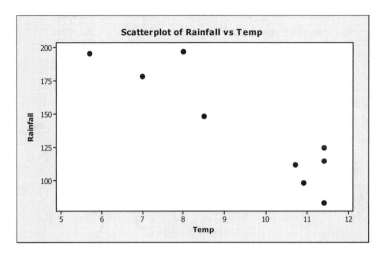

There appears to be a negative relationship between the annual rainfall and the maximum daily temperature. As the maximum daily temperature increases, the amount of annual rainfall tends to decrease.

b.   Using MINITAB, a scatterplot of the relationship between annual rainfall and total plant cover is:

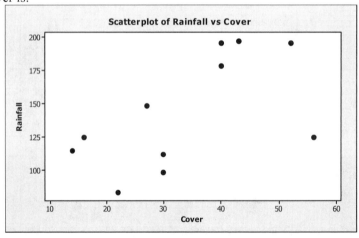

There appears to be a positive relationship between annual rainfall and total plant cover. As the total plant cover increases, the annual rainfall tends to increase.

c.   Using MINITAB, a scatterplot of the relationship between annual rainfall and number of ant species is:

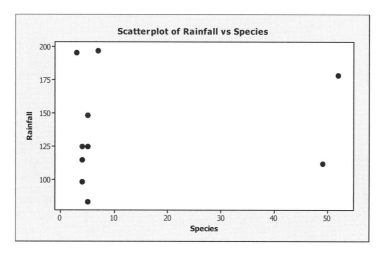

There does not appear to be a relationship between annual rainfall and number of ant species.

d.   Using MINITAB, a scatterplot of the relationship between annual rainfall and species diversity index is:

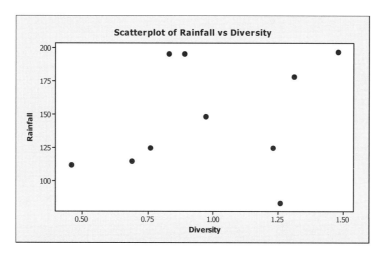

There appears to be a positive relationship between annual rainfall and species diversity index.   As the species diversity index increases, the annual rainfall tends to increase.

2.149   The median is preferred to the mean as a measure of central tendency when the data set is skewed either right or left.   If the data set has some extreme observations, the median better measure of central tendency than the mean.

2.151   A stem-and-leaf display is generally preferred over a histogram when the data set is relatively small.

2.153 One technique for distorting information on a graph is by stretching the vertical axis by starting the vertical axis somewhere above 0.

2.155 a. $z = \dfrac{x - \mu}{\sigma} = \dfrac{50 - 60}{10} = -1$

$z = \dfrac{70 - 60}{10} = 1$

$z = \dfrac{80 - 60}{10} = 2$

b. $z = \dfrac{x - \mu}{\sigma} = \dfrac{50 - 60}{5} = -2$

$z = \dfrac{70 - 60}{5} = 2$

$z = \dfrac{80 - 60}{5} = 4$

c. $z = \dfrac{x - \mu}{\sigma} = \dfrac{50 - 40}{10} = 1$

$z = \dfrac{70 - 40}{10} = 3$

$z = \dfrac{80 - 40}{10} = 4$

d. $z = \dfrac{x - \mu}{\sigma} = \dfrac{50 - 40}{100} = .1$

$z = \dfrac{70 - 40}{100} = .3$

$z = \dfrac{80 - 40}{100} = 4$

2.157 a. $s^2 = \dfrac{\sum x^2 - \dfrac{\left(\sum x\right)^2}{n}}{n - 1} = \dfrac{246 - \dfrac{63^2}{22}}{22 - 1} = 3.1234$

b. $s^2 = \dfrac{\sum x^2 - \dfrac{\left(\sum x\right)^2}{n}}{n - 1} = \dfrac{666 - \dfrac{106^2}{25}}{25 - 1} = 9.0233$

c. $s^2 = \dfrac{\sum x^2 - \dfrac{\left(\sum x\right)^2}{n}}{n - 1} = \dfrac{76 - \dfrac{11^2}{7}}{7 - 1} = 9.7857$

2.159 a. $\sum x = 4 + 6 + 6 + 5 + 6 + 7 = 34$

$\sum x^2 = 4^2 + 6^2 + 6^2 + 5^2 + 6^2 + 7^2 = 198$

$$\bar{x} = \frac{\sum x}{n} = \frac{34}{6} = 5.67$$

$$s^2 = \frac{\sum x^2 - \dfrac{\left(\sum x\right)^2}{n}}{n-1} = \frac{198 - \dfrac{34^2}{6}}{6-1} = \frac{5.3333}{5} = 1.0667$$

$s = \sqrt{1.0667} = 1.03$

b. $\sum x = -1 + 4 + (-3) + 0 + (-3) + (-6) = -9$

$\sum x^2 = (-1)^2 + 4^2 + (-3)^2 + 0^2 + (-3)^2 + (-6)^2 = 71$

$$\bar{x} = \frac{\sum x}{n} = \frac{-9}{6} = -\$1.5$$

$$s^2 = \frac{\sum x^2 - \dfrac{\left(\sum x\right)^2}{n}}{n-1} = \frac{71 - \dfrac{(-9)^2}{6}}{6-1} = \frac{57.5}{5} = 11.5 \text{ dollars squared}$$

$s = \sqrt{11.5} = \$3.39$

c. $\sum x = \dfrac{3}{5} + \dfrac{4}{5} + \dfrac{2}{5} + \dfrac{1}{5} + \dfrac{1}{16} = 2.0625$

$\sum x^2 = \left(\dfrac{3}{5}\right)^2 + \left(\dfrac{4}{5}\right)^2 + \left(\dfrac{2}{5}\right)^2 + \left(\dfrac{1}{5}\right)^2 + \left(\dfrac{1}{16}\right)^2 = 1.2039$

$$\bar{x} = \frac{\sum x}{n} = \frac{2.0625}{5} = .4125\%$$

$$s^2 = \frac{\sum x^2 - \dfrac{\left(\sum x\right)^2}{n}}{n-1} = \frac{1.2039 - \dfrac{2.0625^2}{5}}{5-1} = \frac{.3531}{4} = .0883\% \text{ squared}$$

$s = \sqrt{.0883} = .30\%$

d.   (a)   Range $= 7 - 4 = 3$

(b)   Range $= \$4 - (\$-6) = \$10$

(c)   Range $= \dfrac{4}{5}\% - \dfrac{1}{16}\% = \dfrac{64}{80}\% - \dfrac{5}{80}\% = \dfrac{59}{80\%} = .7375\%$

2.161   Using MINITAB, the scatterplot is:

From the scatterplot, it appears that there is a trend. As variable 1 increases, variable 2 also tends to increase.

2.163   a.   The pie chart for the 1954 data is:

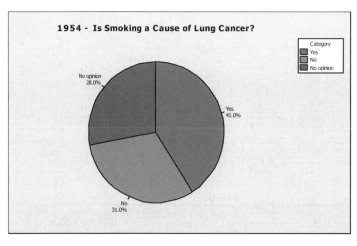

b.   The pie chart for the 1999 data is:

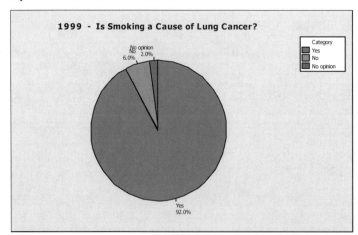

c.   There is a big change in the graphs. The percent of those responding with "Yes" in 1999 (92%) is more than twice the percent responding with "Yes" in 1954 (41%).

2.165   The z-score is: $z = \dfrac{x - \bar{x}}{s} = \dfrac{408 - 603.7}{185.4} = -1.06$

A head-injury rating of 408 is less than the mean head-injury rating. It is a little more than one standard deviation below the mean.

2.167   a.   To display the status, we use a pie chart. From the pie chart, we see that 58% of the Beanie babies are retired and 42% are current.

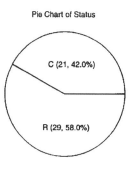

Pie Chart of Status

C (21, 42.0%)

R (29, 58.0%)

b.   Using Minitab, a histogram of the values is:

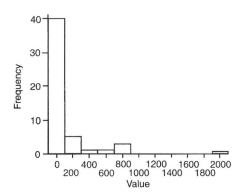

Most (40 of 50) Beanie babies have values less than $100. Of the remaining 10, 5 have values between $100 and $300, 1 has a value between $300 and $500, 1 has a value between $500 and $700, 2 have values between $700 and $900, and 1 has a value between $1900 and $2100.

c.   A plot of the value versus the age of the Beanie Baby is as follows:

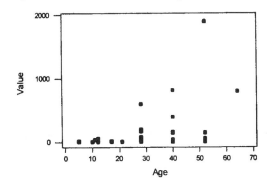

From the plot, it appears that as the age increases, the value tends to increase.

d. Using MINITAB, the descriptive statistics are:

Descriptive Statistics: Age, Value

Variable	N	N*	Mean	SE Mean	StDev	Minimum	Q1	Median	Q3	Maximum
Age	50	0	26.52	2.25	15.92	5.00	12.00	28.00	40.00	64.00
Value	50	0	128.9	44.3	313.2	10.0	15.0	26.5	65.0	1900.0

According to Chebyshev's Rule, at least $1-\dfrac{1}{k^2}$ of the measurements will fall within k standard deviations of the mean (for k > 1). Thus, we can say nothing about the percentage of measurements that will fall within .75 standard deviations of the mean.

At least $1-\dfrac{1}{2.5^2}=1-.16=.84$ or 84% of the measurements will fall within 2.5 standard deviations of the mean. At least $1-\dfrac{1}{4^2}=1-.0625=.9375$ or 93.75% of the measurements will fall within 4 standard deviations of the mean.

e. For the interval $\bar{x}\pm.75s \Rightarrow 26.52\pm.75(15.92) \Rightarrow 26.52\pm11.94 \Rightarrow (14.58,\ 38.46)$, there are 22 measurements or (22 / 50)*100% = 44% of the measurements.

For the interval $\bar{x}\pm2.5s \Rightarrow 26.52\pm2.5(15.92) \Rightarrow 26.52\pm39.8 \Rightarrow (-13.28,\ 66.32)$, there are 50 measurements or (50 / 50)*100% = 100% of the measurements. This is at least 84%.

For the interval $\bar{x}\pm4s \Rightarrow 26.52\pm4(15.92) \Rightarrow 26.52\pm63.68 \Rightarrow (-37.16,\ 90.20)$, there are 50 measurements or (50 / 50)*100% = 100% of the measurements. This is at least 93.75%.

f. For the interval $\bar{x}\pm.75s \Rightarrow 128.90\pm.75(313.20) \Rightarrow 26.52\pm234.90 \Rightarrow (-106.00,\ 363.80)$, there are 45 measurements or (45 / 50)*100% = 90% of the measurements.

For the interval $\bar{x}\pm2.5s \Rightarrow 128.90\pm2.5(313.20) \Rightarrow 26.52\pm783.00 \Rightarrow (-654.10,\ 911.90)$, there are 49 measurements or (49 / 50)*100% = 98% of the measurements. This is at least 84%.

For the interval $\bar{x}\pm4s \Rightarrow 128.90\pm4(313.20) \Rightarrow 26.52\pm1,252.80 \Rightarrow (-1,123.90,\ 1,381.70)$, there are 49 measurements or (49 / 50)*100% = 98% of the measurements. This is at least 93.75%.

2.169 a. The mean COMPAS score for the male teachers is 26.4. This is just about in the middle of the possible range of from 0 to 50. This is the average score for the 68 male teachers.

b. The mean COMPAS score for the female teachers is 24.5. This is just about in the middle of the possible range of from 0 to 50. This is the average score for the 48 female teachers.

c. By the Empirical Rule, approximately 95% of the measurements will fall within 2 standard deviations of the mean. This interval for the male teachers would be:

$$\bar{x} \pm 2s \Rightarrow 26.4 \pm 2(10.6) \Rightarrow 26.4 \pm 21.2 \Rightarrow (5.2, 47.6)$$

d. By the Empirical Rule, approximately 95% of the measurements will fall within 2 standard deviations of the mean. This interval for the female teachers would be:

$$\bar{x} \pm 2s \Rightarrow 24.5 \pm 2(11.2) \Rightarrow 24.5 \pm 22.4 \Rightarrow (2.1, 46.9)$$

2.171 a. Using MINITAB, the Pareto diagram is:

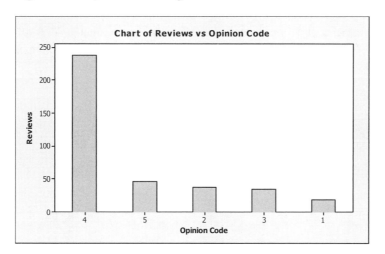

The opinion that occurred most often was "favorable/recommended" with 238 responses. The total number of responses was $19 + 37 + 35 + 238 + 46 = 375$. The proportion of books receiving a "favorable/recommended" opinion is $238/375 = .635$.

b. Books receiving either a 4 (favorable/recommended or a 5 (outstanding/significant) were reviewed as favorable and recommended for purchase. The total number of books receiving a rating of 4 or 5 is $238 + 46 = 284$. The proportion of books receiving these ratings is $284/375 = .757$. This proportion is more than .75 of 75%. Thus, the statement made is correct.

2.173 a. Summing the percents in the bars above 20, the percentage of male USGA golfers with a handicap greater than 20 is approximately 28.5%.

b. Summing the percents in the bars above 20, the percentage of female USGA golfers with a handicap greater than 20 is approximately 71%.

c. Female golfers tend to have higher handicaps.

2.175   a.   From the information given, we have $\bar{x} = 375$ and $s = 25$. From Chebyshev's rule, we know that at least three-fourths of the measurements are within the interval:

$$\bar{x} \pm 2s, \text{ or } (325, 425)$$

Thus, at most one-fourth of the measurements exceed 425. In other words, more than 425 vehicles used the intersection on at most 25% of the days.

b.   According to the Empirical Rule, approximately 95% of the measurements are within the interval:

$$\bar{x} \pm 2s, \text{ or } (325, 425)$$

This leaves approximately 5% of the measurements to lie outside the interval. Because of the symmetry of a mound-shaped distribution, approximately 2.5% of these will lie below 325, and the remaining 2.5% will lie above 425. Thus, on approximately 2.5% of the days, more than 425 vehicles used the intersection.

2.177   a.   Using Minitab, the box plot is:

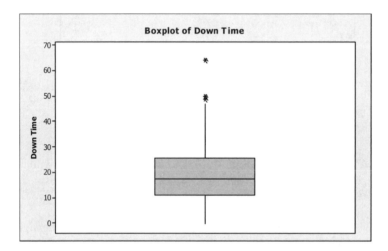

The median is about 18. The data appear to be skewed to the right since there are 4 suspect outliers to the right and none to the left. The variability of the data is fairly small because the IQR is fairly small, approximately $26 - 10 = 16$.

b.   The customers associated with the suspected outliers are customers 238, 268, 269, and 264.

c.   In order to find the z-scores, we must first find the mean and standard deviation.

$$\bar{x} = \frac{\sum x}{n} = \frac{815}{40} = 20.375$$

$$s^2 = \frac{\sum x^2 - \frac{\left(\sum x\right)^2}{n}}{n-1} = \frac{24129 - \frac{815^2}{40}}{40-1} = 192.90705$$

$$s = \sqrt{192.90705} = 13.89$$

The z-scores associated with the suspected outliers are:

$$\text{Customer 238} \quad z = \frac{x - \bar{x}}{s} = \frac{47 - 20.375}{13.89} = 1.92$$

$$\text{Customer 268} \quad z = \frac{49 - 20.375}{13.89} = 2.06$$

$$\text{Customer 269} \quad z = \frac{50 - 20.375}{13.89} = 2.13$$

$$\text{Customer 264} \quad z = \frac{64 - 20.375}{13.89} = 3.14$$

All but one of the z-scores is greater than 2. These are very unusual values.

2.179   a.   For each transect, three variables were measured. The number of seabirds found is quantitative. The length of the transect is also quantitative. Whether or not the transect was in an oiled area is qualitative.

        b.   The experimental unit is the transect.

        c.   A pie chart of the oiled and unoiled areas is:

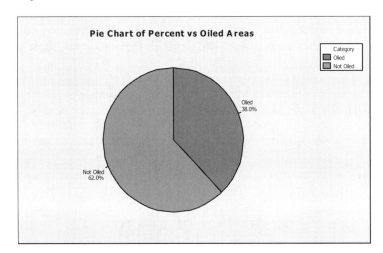

d.   Using MINITAB, a scattergram of the data is:

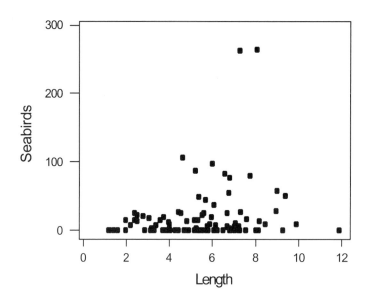

e.   The mean density for the unoiled area is 3.27, while the mean for the oiled area is 3.495. The median for the unoiled area is .89 and is .70 for the oiled area. These are both fairly similar.

f.   Using Chebyshev's Theorem, at least 75% of the observations will fall within 2 standard deviations of the mean. This interval for unoiled areas would be:

$$\bar{x} \pm 2s \Rightarrow 3.27 \pm 2(6.7) \Rightarrow 3.27 \pm 13.4 \Rightarrow (-10.13,\ 16.67)$$

g.   Using Chebyshev's Theorem, at least 75% of the observations will fall within 2 standard deviations of the mean. This interval for oiled areas would be:

$$\bar{x} \pm 2s \Rightarrow 3.495 \pm 2(5.968) \Rightarrow 3.495 \pm 11.936 \Rightarrow (-8.441,\ 15.431)$$

h.   From the above two intervals, we know that at least 75% of the observations for the unoiled area will fall between –10.31 and 16.67 and at most 25% of the observations will fall above 15.431 for the oiled areas. Thus, the unoiled areas would be more likely to have a seabird density of 16.

2.181   a.   Using Minitab, a stem-and-leaf display of the data is:

```
Stem-and-leaf of VELOCITY      N = 51
Leaf Unit = 100

   1    18 4
   3    18 79
  12    19 001112444
  18    19 566788
  20    20 12
  21    20 7
  21    21
  23    21 99
  (5)   22 11344
  23    22 5666777777889
  10    23 001222344
   1    23
   1    24
   1    24 9
```

b.   From this stem-and-leaf display, it is fairly obvious that there are two different distributions since there are two groups of data.

c.   Since there appears to be two distributions, we will compute two sets of numerical descriptive measures. We will call the group with the smaller velocities A1775A and the group with the larger velocities A1775B.

For A1775A:

$$\bar{x} = \frac{\sum x}{n} = \frac{408{,}707}{21} = 19{,}462.2$$

$$s^2 = \frac{\sum x^2 - \dfrac{\left(\sum x\right)^2}{n}}{n-1} = \frac{7{,}960{,}019{,}531 - \dfrac{408{,}707^2}{21}}{21-1} = 283{,}329.3$$

$$s = \sqrt{283{,}329.3} = 532.29$$

For A1775B:

$$\bar{x} = \frac{\sum x}{n} = \frac{685{,}154}{30} = 22{,}838.5$$

$$s^2 = \frac{\sum x^2 - \dfrac{\left(\sum x\right)^2}{n}}{n-1} = \frac{15{,}656{,}992{,}942 - \dfrac{685{,}154^2}{30}}{30-1} = 314{,}694.83$$

$$s = \sqrt{314{,}694.83} = 560.98$$

d. To determine which of the two clusters this observation probably belongs to, we will compute z-scores for this observation for each of the two clusters.

For A1775A:
$$z = \frac{20{,}000 - 19{,}462.2}{532.29} = 1.01$$

Since this z-score is so small, it would not be unlikely that this observation came from this cluster.

For A1775B:

$$z = \frac{20{,}000 - 22{,}838.5}{560.98} = -5.06$$

Since this z-score is so large (in magnitude), it would be very unlikely that this observation came from this cluster.

Thus, this observation probably came from the cluster A1775A.

2.183   a. The variable "Days in Jail Before Suicide" is measured on a numerical scale, so it is quantitative. The variables "Marital Status", "Race", "Murder/Manslaughter Charge", and "Time of Suicide" are not measured on a numerical scale, so they are all qualitative. The variable "Year" is measured on a numerical scale, so it is quantitative.

b. Using MINITAB, the pie chart for the data is:

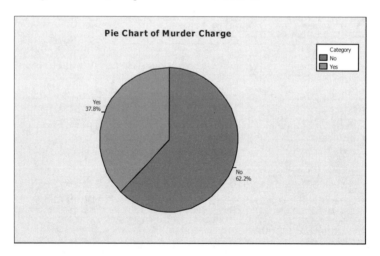

Suicides are more likely to be committed by inmates charged with lesser crimes than by inmates charged with murder/manslaughter. Of the suicides reported, 62.2% are committed by those convicted of a lesser charge.

c. Using MINITAB, the pie chart for the data is:

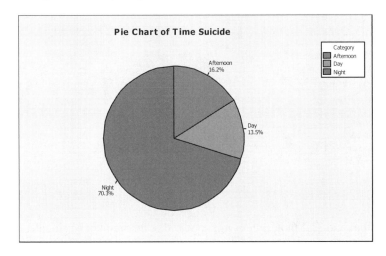

Suicides are much more likely to be committed at night than any other time. Of the suicides reported, 70.3% were committed at night.

d. Using MINITAB, the descriptive statistics are:

Variable	N	Mean	Median	TrMean	StDev	SE Mean
Jail	37	41.4	15.0	30.3	66.7	11.0

Variable	Minimum	Maximum	Q1	Q3
Jail	1.0	309.0	4.0	41.5

The mean length of time an inmate spent in jail before committing suicide is 41.4 days. The median length of time an inmate spent in jail before committing suicide is 15 days. Since the mean is much larger than the median, the data are skewed to the right. Most of those committing suicide, commit it within 15 days of arriving in jail. However, there are a few inmates who spend many more days in jail before committing suicide.

e. First, compute the z-score associated with 200 days:

$$z = \frac{x - \bar{x}}{s} = \frac{200 - 41.4}{66.7} = 2.38$$

Using Chebyshev's rule, we know that at most $1/2^2 = 1/4$ of the observations will fall more than 2 standard deviations from the mean. Also, we know at most $1/3^2 = 1/9$ of the observations will fall more than 3 standard deviations from the mean. The score 200 is 2.38 standard deviations from the mean. Since we know that at most 1/4 of the observations will fall in this range, it looks like it would not be that unusual to see someone commit suicide after 200 days. However, if we look at the data, of the 37 observations, there are only 2 observations of 200 or larger. This proportion is 2/37 = .054. Using this information, it would be rather unusual for an inmate to commit suicide after 200 days.

f. Using MINITAB, the stem-and-leaf plot of the data is:

```
Stem-and-leaf of Year      N = 37
Leaf Unit = 1.0

  1    196  7
  5    196  8889
 11    197  000001
 13    197  23
 16    197  455
 18    197  66
 (2)   197  99
 17    198  000111
 11    198  233
  8    198  55555
  3    198  77
  1    198  9
```

From the stem-and-leaf plot, it does not appear that the number of suicides have decreased over time.

2.185 a. Due to the "elite" superstars, the salary distribution is skewed to the right. Since this implies that the median is less than the mean, the players' association would want to use the median.

b. The owners, by the logic of part **a**, would want to use the mean.

Probability

3.1 An experiment is an act or process of observation that leads to a single outcome that cannot be predicted with certainty.

3.3 A sample space of an experiment is a collection of all its sample points.

3.5 Two probability rules for sample points are:

1. All sample point probabilities **must** lie between 0 and 1, i.e. $0 \le p_i \le 1$.

2. The probabilities of all sample points within a sample space **must** sum to 1, i.e., $\sum p_i = 1$.

3.7 The probability of an event A is calculated by summing the probabilities of the sample points in the sample space for A.

3.9 a. Since the probabilities must sum to 1,

$$P(E_3) = 1 - P(E_1) - P(E_2) - P(E_4) - P(E_5) = 1 - .1 - .2 - .1 - .1 = .5$$

b. $P(E_3) = 1 - P(E_3) - P(E_2) - P(E_4) - P(E_5)$
$$\Rightarrow 2P(E_3) = 1 - .1 - .2 - .1 \Rightarrow 2P(E_3) = .6 \Rightarrow P(E_3) = .3$$

c. $P(E_3) = 1 - P(E_1) - P(E_2) - P(E_4) - P(E_5) = 1 - .1 - .1 - .1 - .1 = .6$

3.11 $P(A) = P(1) + P(2) + P(3) = .05 + .20 + .30 = .55$

$P(B) = P(1) + P(3) + P(5) = .05 + .30 + .15 = .50$

$P(C) = P(1) + P(2) + P(3) + P(5) = .05 + .20 + .30 + .15 = .70$

3.13 a. $\binom{5}{2} = \dfrac{5!}{2!(5-2)!} = \dfrac{5!}{2!3!} = \dfrac{5 \cdot 4 \cdot 3 \cdot 2 \cdot 1}{2 \cdot 1 \cdot 3 \cdot 2 \cdot 1} = 10$

b. $\binom{6}{3} = \dfrac{6!}{3!(6-3)!} = \dfrac{6!}{3!3!} = \dfrac{6 \cdot 5 \cdot 4 \cdot 3 \cdot 2 \cdot 1}{3 \cdot 2 \cdot 1 \cdot 3 \cdot 2 \cdot 1} = 20$

c. $\binom{20}{5} = \dfrac{20!}{5!(20-5)!} = \dfrac{20!}{5!15!} = \dfrac{20 \cdot 19 \cdot 18 \cdots 2 \cdot 1}{5 \cdot 4 \cdot 3 \cdot 2 \cdot 1 \cdot 15 \cdot 14 \cdot 13 \cdots 2 \cdot 1} = 15,504$

3.15   a.   If we denote the marbles as B_1, B_2, R_1, R_2, R_3, then the ten equally likely sample points in the sample space would be:

$$S: \begin{bmatrix} (B_1, B_2), (B_1, R_1), (B_1, R_2), (B_1, R_3), (B_2, R_1) \\ (B_2, R_2), (B_2, R_3), (R_1, R_2), (R_1, R_3), (R_2, R_3) \end{bmatrix}$$

Notice that order is ignored, as the only concern is whether or not a marble is selected.

b.   Each of these ten would be equally likely, implying that each occurs with a probability 1/10.

c. $P(A) = \dfrac{1}{10}$ $P(B) = 6\left(\dfrac{1}{10}\right) = \dfrac{6}{10} = \dfrac{3}{5}$ $P(C) = 3\left(\dfrac{1}{10}\right) = \dfrac{3}{10}$

3.17   Use the relative frequency as an estimate for the probability. Thus,
$P(\text{physically assaulted}) = 600/12{,}000 = .05$.

3.19   a.   Let A = {chicken passes inspection with fecal contamination}. $P(A) = 1 / 100 = .01$.

b.   Yes. The relative frequency of passing inspection with fecal contamination is $306/32{,}075 = .0095 \approx .01$.

3.21   a.   Define the following event:

A: {Beech tree is damaged by fungi}

$$P(A) = \frac{49}{188} = .261$$

b.   There would be 3 sample points for this experiment: trunk, leaves, and branch. We can convert the percentages to proportions and use these to estimate the probabilities.

Sample Points	Probabilities
Trunk	.85
Leaves	.10
Branch	.05
Total	**1.00**

3.23   a.   The sample points would correspond to the possible outcomes: 1, 2, 3, 4, 5, 6, 7, 8, and 9.

b.   From the sample, the number of times each of these sample points occurred was different. We would expect the probability of each sample point to the close to the relative frequency of that outcome.

c. Reasonable probabilities would be the relative frequencies of the sample points:

First Digit	Frequency	Relative Frequency
1	109	109/743 = .147
2	75	75/743 = .101
3	77	77/743 = .104
4	99	99/743 = .133
5	72	72/743 = .097
6	117	117/743 = .157
7	89	89/743 = .120
8	62	62/743 = .083
9	43	43/743 = .058
Total	743	1.000

d. P(first digit is 1 or 2) = P(first digit is 1) + P(first digit is 2) = .147 + .101 = .248

e. P(first digit > 5) = P(first digit is 6) + P(first digit is 7) + P(first digit is 8)
     + P(first digit is 9) = .157 + .120 + .083 + .058 = .418

3.25 a. There are a total of $\binom{5}{3} = \frac{5!}{3!(5-3)!} = \frac{5!}{3!2!} = \frac{5\cdot4\cdot3\cdot2\cdot1}{3\cdot2\cdot1\cdot2\cdot1} = 10$ ways to get 3-grill displays.

These 10 display combinations are:

1, 2, 3   1, 3, 4   2, 3, 4   3, 4, 5
1, 2, 4   1, 3, 5   2, 3, 5
1, 2, 5   1, 4, 5   2, 4, 5

However, since grill #2 must be selected, there are only 6 possibilities:

1, 2, 3   2, 3, 4
1, 2, 4   2, 3, 5
1, 2, 5   2, 4, 5

b. We can estimate the probabilities by using the relative frequency for each sample point. The relative frequency is found by dividing the frequency by the total sample size of 124. These estimates are contained in the following table:

Grill Display Combination	Number of Students	Probability
1-2-3	35	.282
1-2-4	8	.065
1-2-5	42	.339
2-3-4	4	.032
2-3-5	1	.008
2-4-5	34	.274
TOTAL	124	1.0000

c. Of the 6 sample points, only 3 of them contain Grill #1.

P(Grill #1 chosen) = P(1-2-3 or 1-2-4 or 1-2-5) = .282 + .065 + .339 = .686.

3.27 a. There are a total of $\binom{8}{2} = \frac{8!}{2!(8-2)!} = \frac{8!}{2!6!} = \frac{8 \cdot 7 \cdot 6 \cdot 5 \cdot 4 \cdot 3 \cdot 2 \cdot 1}{2 \cdot 1 \cdot 6 \cdot 5 \cdot 4 \cdot 3 \cdot 2 \cdot 1} = 28$ possible

Quinella bets.

b. If all the players are of equal ability, then the probability of getting any combination is 1/28.

3.29 If each of 3 players uses a fair coin, the sample space is:

HHH *HTT*
HHT *THT*
HTH *TTH*
THH *TTT*

Since each event is equally likely, each event will have probability 1/8.

The probability of odd man out on the first roll is:

$P(HHT) + P(HTH) + P(THH) + P(HTT) + P(THT) + P(TTH)$
$= 1/8 + 1/8 + 1/8 + 1/8 + 1/8 + 1/8 = 6/8 = 3/4$

If one player uses a two-headed coin, the sample space will be (assume 3rd player has the two-headed coin):

HHH *THH*
HTH *TTH*

Since each event is equally likely, each will have probability 1/4.

The probability the 3rd player is odd man out is $P(TTH) = 1/4$.

From the first part, the probability the 3rd player is odd man out is $P(HHT) + P(TTH) = 1/8 + 1/8 = 1/4$. Thus, the two probabilities are the same.

3.31 a. $\binom{6}{2} = \frac{6!}{2!(6-2)!} = \frac{6!}{2!4!} = \frac{6 \cdot 5 \cdot 4 \cdot 3 \cdot 2 \cdot 1}{2 \cdot 1 \cdot 4 \cdot 3 \cdot 2 \cdot 1} = 15$

b. $\binom{6}{3} = \frac{6!}{3!(6-3)!} = \frac{6!}{3!3!} = \frac{6 \cdot 5 \cdot 4 \cdot 3 \cdot 2 \cdot 1}{3 \cdot 2 \cdot 1 \cdot 3 \cdot 2 \cdot 1} = 20$

c. $\binom{6}{4} = \frac{6!}{4!(6-4)!} = \frac{6!}{4!2!} = \frac{6 \cdot 5 \cdot 4 \cdot 3 \cdot 2 \cdot 1}{4 \cdot 3 \cdot 2 \cdot 1 \cdot 2 \cdot 1} = 15$

d. $\dbinom{6}{5} = \dfrac{6!}{5!(6-5)!} = \dfrac{6!}{5!1!} = \dfrac{6 \cdot 5 \cdot 4 \cdot 3 \cdot 2 \cdot 1}{5 \cdot 4 \cdot 3 \cdot 2 \cdot 1 \cdot 1} = 6$

e. In addition to the combinations computed in parts a – d, we need to find the number of 0-drug combinations, 1-drug combination, and 6-drug combinations.

$$\dbinom{6}{0} = \dfrac{6!}{0!(6-0)!} = \dfrac{6!}{0!6!} = \dfrac{6 \cdot 5 \cdot 4 \cdot 3 \cdot 2 \cdot 1}{1 \cdot 6 \cdot 5 \cdot 4 \cdot 3 \cdot 2 \cdot 1} = 1$$

$$\dbinom{6}{1} = \dfrac{6!}{1!(6-1)!} = \dfrac{6!}{1!5!!} = \dfrac{6 \cdot 5 \cdot 4 \cdot 3 \cdot 2 \cdot 1}{1 \cdot 5 \cdot 4 \cdot 3 \cdot 2 \cdot 1} = 6$$

$$\dbinom{6}{6} = \dfrac{6!}{6!(6-6)!} = \dfrac{6!}{6!0!} = \dfrac{6 \cdot 5 \cdot 4 \cdot 3 \cdot 2 \cdot 1}{6 \cdot 5 \cdot 4 \cdot 3 \cdot 2 \cdot 1 \cdot 1} = 1$$

The total number of ways the 6 drugs can be combined is $15 + 20 + 15 + 6 + 1 + 6 + 1 = 64$.

3.33 The union of 2 events A and B is the event that occurs if either A or B or both occur on a single performance of the experiment.

3.35 The complement of an event A is the event that A does not occur – that is, the event consisting of all sample points that are not in event A.

3.37 The Additive Rule of Probability is: The probability of the union of events A and B is the sum of the probability of events A and B minus the probability of the intersection of events A and B, that is $P(A \cup B) = P(A) + P(B) – P(A \cap B)$.

3.39 The Additive Rule of Probability for mutually exclusive events is: If 2 events A and B are mutually exclusive, the probability of the union of A and B equals the sum of the probabilities of A and B; that is, $P(A \cup B) = P(A) + P(B)$.

3.41 a.
A: {$HHH, HHT, HTH, THH, TTH, THT, HTT$}
B: {HHH, TTH, THT, HTT}
$A \cup B$: {$HHH, HHT, HTH, THH, TTH, THT, HTT$}
A^c: {TTT}
$A \cap B$: {HHH, TTH, THT, HTT}

b. If the coin is fair, then each of the 8 possible outcomes are equally likely, with probability 1/8.

$$P(A) = \dfrac{7}{8} \qquad P(B) = \dfrac{4}{8} = \dfrac{1}{2} \qquad P(A \cup B) = \dfrac{7}{8}$$

$$P(A^c) = \dfrac{1}{8} \qquad P(A \cap B) = \dfrac{4}{8} = \dfrac{1}{2}$$

c. $P(A \cup B) = P(A) + P(B) - P(A \cap B) = \dfrac{7}{8} + \dfrac{1}{2} - \dfrac{1}{2} = \dfrac{7}{8}$

d. No. $P(A \cap B) = \dfrac{1}{2}$ which is not 0.

3.43 a. $P(A) = P(E_1) + P(E_2) + P(E_3) + P(E_5) + P(E_6) = \dfrac{1}{5} + \dfrac{1}{5} + \dfrac{1}{5} + \dfrac{1}{20} + \dfrac{1}{10} = \dfrac{15}{20} = \dfrac{3}{4}$

b. $P(B) = P(E_2) + P(E_3) + P(E_4) + P(E_7) = \dfrac{1}{5} + \dfrac{1}{5} + \dfrac{1}{20} + \dfrac{1}{5} = \dfrac{13}{20}$

c. $P(A \cup B) = P(E_1) + P(E_2) + P(E_3) + P(E_4) + P(E_5) + P(E_6) + P(E_7)$
$$= \dfrac{1}{5} + \dfrac{1}{5} + \dfrac{1}{5} + \dfrac{1}{20} + \dfrac{1}{20} + \dfrac{1}{10} + \dfrac{1}{5} = 1$$

d. $P(A \cap B) = P(E_2) + P(E_3) = \dfrac{1}{5} + \dfrac{1}{5} = \dfrac{2}{5}$

e. $P(A^c) = 1 - P(A) = 1 - \dfrac{3}{4} = \dfrac{1}{4}$

f. $P(B^c) = 1 - P(B) = 1 - \dfrac{13}{20} = \dfrac{7}{20}$

g. $P(A \cup A^c) = P(E_1) + P(E_2) + P(E_3) + P(E_4) + P(E_5) + P(E_6) + P(E_7)$
$$= \dfrac{1}{5} + \dfrac{1}{5} + \dfrac{1}{5} + \dfrac{1}{20} + \dfrac{1}{20} + \dfrac{1}{10} + \dfrac{1}{5} = 1$$

h. $P(A^c \cap B) = P(E_4) + P(E_7) = \dfrac{1}{20} + \dfrac{1}{5} = \dfrac{5}{20} = \dfrac{1}{4}$

3.45 a. $P(A) = .50 + .10 + .05 = .65$

b. $P(B) = .10 + .07 + .50 + .05 = .72$

c. $P(C) = .25$

d. $P(D) = .05 + .03 = .08.$

e. $P(A^c) = .25 + .07 + .03 = .35$ (Note: $P(A^c) = 1 - P(A) = 1 - .65 = .35$)

f. $P(A \cup B) = P(B) = .10 + .07 + .50 + .05 = .72$

g. $P(A \cap B) = P(A) = .50 + .10 + .05 = .65$

h. Two events are mutually exclusive if they have no sample points in common or if the probability of their intersection is 0.

$P(A \cap B) = .50 + .10 + .05 = .65.$ Since this is not 0, A and B are not mutually exclusive.

$P(A \cap C) = 0$. Since this is 0, A and C are mutually exclusive.

$P(A \cap D) = .05$. Since this is not 0, A and D are not mutually exclusive.

$P(B \cap C) = 0$. Since this is 0, B and C are mutually exclusive.

$P(B \cap D) = .05$. Since this is not 0, B and D are not mutually exclusive.

$P(C \cap D) = 0$. Since this is 0, C and D are mutually exclusive.

3.47   Suppose we define the following event:

$A = \{$eighth-grader scores above 655 on mathematics assessment test$\}$

Then the probability that a randomly selected eighth-grader has a score of 655 or below on the mathematics assessment test is:

$P(A^c) = 1 - P(A) = 1 - .05 = .95.$

3.49   a.   The event $A \cap B$ is the event the outcome is black and odd. The event is $A \cap B$: $\{11, 13, 15, 17, 29, 31, 33, 35\}$

       b.   The event $A \cup B$ is the event the outcome is black or odd or both. The event $A \cup B$ is $\{2, 4, 6, 8, 10, 11, 13, 15, 17, 20, 22, 24, 26, 28, 29, 31, 33, 35, 1, 3, 5, 7, 9, 19, 21, 23, 25, 27\}$

       c.   Assuming all events are equally likely, each has a probability of 1/38.

$$P(A) = 18\left(\frac{1}{38}\right) = \frac{18}{38} = \frac{9}{19}$$

$$P(B) = 18\left(\frac{1}{38}\right) = \frac{18}{38} = \frac{9}{19}$$

$$P(A \cap B) = 8\left(\frac{1}{38}\right) = \frac{8}{38} = \frac{4}{19}$$

$$P(A \cup B) = 28\left(\frac{1}{38}\right) = \frac{28}{38} = \frac{14}{19}$$

$$P(C) = 18\left(\frac{1}{38}\right) = \frac{18}{38} = \frac{9}{19}$$

       d.   The event $A \cap B \cap C$ is the event the outcome is odd and black and low. The event $A \cap B \cap C$ is $\{11, 13, 15, 17\}$.

       e. $P(A \cup B) = P(A) + P(B) - P(A \cap B) = \dfrac{9}{19} + \dfrac{9}{19} - \dfrac{4}{19} = \dfrac{14}{19}$

       f. $P(A \cap B \cap C) = 4\left(\dfrac{1}{38}\right) = \dfrac{4}{38} = \dfrac{2}{19}$

g. The event $A \cup B \cup C$ is the event the outcome is odd or black or low. The event $A \cup B \cup C$ is:

$$\{1, 2, 3, \dots , 29, 31, 33, 35\}$$

or

$$\{\text{All simple events except } 00, 0, 30, 32, 34, 36\}$$

h. $P(A \cup B \cup C) = 32\left(\dfrac{1}{38}\right) = \dfrac{32}{38} = \dfrac{16}{19}$

3.51 a. The sample points for this experiment are:

(PTW-R, Jury), (PTW-R, Judge), (PTW-A/D, Jury), (PTW-A/D, Judge), (DTW-R, Jury), (DTW-R, Judge), (DTW-A/D, Jury), (DTW-A/D, Judge)

b. $P(A) = \dfrac{1,465}{2,143} = .684$

c. $P(B) = \dfrac{265}{2,143} = .124$

d. No. $P(A \cap B) = \dfrac{194}{2,143} = .091$. Since this is not 0, events A and B are not mutually exclusive.

e. $P(A^c) = 1 - P(A) = 1 - .684 = .316.$

f. $P(A \cup B) = P(A) + P(B) - P(A \cap B) = .684 + .124 - .091 = .717$

g. $P(A \cap B) = \dfrac{194}{2,143} = .091$

3.53 Define the following events:

A: {Wheelchair user had an injurious fall}
B: {Wheelchair user had all 5 features}
C: {Wheelchair user had at least 1 feature but not all 5 features}
D: {Wheelchair user had no features}

a. $P(A) = \dfrac{48}{306} = .157$

b. $P(B) = \dfrac{9}{306} = .029$

c. $P(A^c \cap D) = \dfrac{89}{306} = .291$

3.55　a.　First, we will set up the sample space. The possible ways to select 2 firms from the 4 are:

$(G_1, G_2)\ (G_1, P_1)\ (G_1, P_2)\ (G_2, P_1)\ (G_2, P_2)\ (P_1, P_2)$

We will assume that all firms have an equal chance of being selected. Thus, the probability of any sample point being chosen is 1/6.

$P(P_1 \text{ is selected}) = P[(G_1, P_1)] + P[(G_2, P_1)] + P[(P_1, P_2)]$
$= 1/6 + 1/6 + 1/6 = 3/6 = 1/2.$

　　　b.　P(at least one firm is in good financial condition)

$= P[(G_1, G_2)] + P[(G_1, P_1)] + P[(G_1, P_2)] + P[(G_2, P_1)] + P[(G_2, P_2)]$
$= 1/6 + 1/6 + 1/6 + 1/6 + 1/6 = 5/6$

3.57　A conditional probability is the probability of an event based on another event, while an unconditional probability is not based on another event.

3.59　The Multiplicative Rule of Probability is:

$$P(A \cap B) = P(A)P(B\,|\,A), \text{ or equivalently } P(A \cap B) = P(B)P(A\,|\,B)$$

3.61　The Multiplicative Rule of Probability for two independent events is:

$$P(A \cap B) = P(A)P(B)$$

3.63　a.　$P(A\,|\,B) = \dfrac{P(A \cap B)}{P(B)} = \dfrac{.1}{.2} = .5$

　　　b.　$P(B\,|\,A) = \dfrac{P(A \cap B)}{P(A)} = \dfrac{.1}{.4} = .25$

　　　c.　No, events A and B are not independent. If A and B were independent, then $P(A\,|\,B) = P(A)$. For this problem, $P(A\,|\,B) = .5$ and $P(A) = .4$.

3.65　a.　$P(A \cap B) = P(A)\,P(B) = .4(.2) = .08$

　　　b.　$P(A\,|\,B) = \dfrac{P(A \cap B)}{P(B)} = \dfrac{.08}{.2} = .4$

　　　c.　$P(A \cup B) = P(A) + P(B) - P(A \cap B) = .4 + .2 - .08 = .52$

3.67　a.　$P(A) = P(E_1) + P(E_2) + P(E_3) = .1 + .1 + .2 = .4$
$P(B) = P(E_2) + P(E_3) + P(E_5) = .1 + .2 + .1 = .4$
$P(A \cap B) = P(E_2) + P(E_3) = .1 + .2 = .3$

b. $P(E_1|A) = \dfrac{P(E_1 \cap A)}{P(A)} = \dfrac{.1}{.4} = .25$

$P(E_2|A) = \dfrac{P(E_2 \cap A)}{P(A)} = \dfrac{.1}{.4} = .25$

$P(E_3|A) = \dfrac{P(E_3 \cap A)}{P(A)} = \dfrac{.2}{.4} = .5$

We are given that $P(E_1) = .1$, $P(E_2) = .1$, and $P(E_3) = .2$

Thus, $P(E_1) = P(E_2)$ and $P(E_3) = 2P(E_1)$

From above, $P(E_1 \mid A) = P(E_2 \mid A)$ and $P(E_3|A) = 2P(E_1 \mid A)$

$P(E_1 \mid A) + P(E_2 \mid A) + P(E_3 \mid A) = .25 + .25 + .50 = 1.00$

c. Using the sum of the conditional probabilities,

$P(B|A) = P(E_2|A) + P(E_3|A) = .25 + .5 = .75$

Using the formula,

$P(B|A) = \dfrac{P(A \cap B)}{P(A)} = \dfrac{.3}{.4} = .75$

3.69   The 36 possible outcomes obtained when tossing two dice are listed below:

(1, 1) (1, 2) (1, 3) (1, 4) (1, 5) (1, 6)
(2, 1) (2, 2) (2, 3) (2, 4) (2, 5) (2, 6)
(3, 1) (3, 2) (3, 3) (3, 4) (3, 5) (3, 6)
(4, 1) (4, 2) (4, 3) (4, 4) (4, 5) (4, 6)
(5, 1) (5, 2) (5, 3) (5, 4) (5, 5) (5, 6)
(6, 1) (6, 2) (6, 3) (6, 4) (6, 5) (6, 6)

A: {(1, 2), (1, 4), (1, 6), (2, 1), (2, 3), (2, 5), (3, 2), (3, 4), (3, 6), (4, 1), (4, 3), (4, 5), (5, 2), (5, 4), (5, 6), (6, 1), (6, 3), (6, 5)}

B: {(3, 6), (4, 5), (5, 4), (5, 6), (6, 3), (6, 5), (6, 6)}

$A \cap B$: {(3, 6), (4, 5), (5, 4), (5, 6), (6, 3), (6, 5)}

If A and B are independent, then $P(A)P(B) = P(A \cap B)$.

$P(A) = \dfrac{18}{36} = \dfrac{1}{2}$ $P(B) = \dfrac{7}{36}$ $P(A \cap B) = \dfrac{6}{36} = \dfrac{1}{6}$

$P(A)P(B) = \dfrac{1}{2} \cdot \dfrac{7}{36} = \dfrac{7}{72} \neq \dfrac{1}{6} = P(A \cap B)$. Thus, A and B are not independent.

3.71   Let W_1 and W_2 represent the two white chips, R_1 and R_2 represent the two red chips, and B_1 and B_2 represent the two blue chips. The sample space is:

W_1W_2	W_2R_1	R_1B_1
W_1R_1	W_2R_2	R_1B_2
W_1R_2	W_2B_1	R_2B_1
W_1B_1	W_2B_2	R_2B_2
W_1B_2	R_1R_2	B_1B_2

Assuming each event is equally likely, each event will have a probability of 1/15.

Then, $P(A) = P(W_1W_2) + P(R_1R_2) + P(B_1B_2) = 3\left(\dfrac{1}{15}\right) = \dfrac{3}{15} = \dfrac{1}{5}$

$P(B) = P(R_1R_2) = \dfrac{1}{15}$

$P(C) = P(W_1W_2) + P(W_1R_1) + P(W_1R_2) + P(W_1B_1) + P(W_1B_2) + P(W_2R_1)$
$\qquad\quad + P(W_2R_2) + P(W_2B_1) + P(W_2B_2) + P(R_1R_2) + P(R_1B_1) + P(R_1B_2)$
$\qquad\quad + P(R_2B_1) + P(R_2B_2)$

$\qquad = 14\left(\dfrac{1}{15}\right) = \dfrac{14}{15}$

$P(A \cap B) = P(R_1R_2) = \dfrac{1}{15}$

$P(A^c) = 1 - P(A) = 1 - \dfrac{1}{5} = \dfrac{4}{5}$

$P(A^c \cap B) = 0$

$P(B \cap C) = P(R_1R_2) = \dfrac{1}{15}$

$P(A \cap C) = P(W_1W_2) + P(R_1R_2) = 2\left(\dfrac{1}{15}\right) = \dfrac{2}{15}$

$P(A^c \cap C) = P(W_1R_1) + P(W_1R_2) + P(W_1B_1) + P(W_1B_2) + P(W_2R_1)$
$\qquad\qquad\quad + P(W_2R_2) + P(W_2B_1) + P(W_2B_2) + P(R_1B_1) + P(R_1B_2)$
$\qquad\qquad\quad + P(R_2B_1) + P(R_2B_2)$

$\qquad\quad = 12\left(\dfrac{1}{15}\right) = \dfrac{12}{15} = \dfrac{4}{5}$

$P(B\,|\,A) = \dfrac{P(A \cap B)}{P(A)} = \dfrac{\dfrac{1}{15}}{\dfrac{1}{5}} = \dfrac{1}{3}$

$P(B\,|\,A^c) = \dfrac{P(A^c \cap B)}{P(A^c)} = \dfrac{0}{\dfrac{4}{5}} = 0$

$$P(B \mid C) = \frac{P(B \cap C)}{P(C)} = \frac{\frac{1}{15}}{\frac{14}{15}} = \frac{1}{14}$$

$$P(A \mid C) = \frac{P(A \cap C)}{P(C)} = \frac{\frac{2}{15}}{\frac{14}{15}} = \frac{1}{7}$$

$$P(C \mid A^c) = \frac{P(A^c \cap C)}{P(A^c)} = \frac{\frac{4}{5}}{\frac{4}{5}} = 1$$

3.73   Let A = {Executive cheated at golf} and B = {Executive lied in business}. From the problem, $P(A)$ = .55 and $P(A \cap B)$ = .20.

$P(B \mid A) = P(A \cap B) / P(A) = .20 / .55 = .364$

3.75   a.   Define the following event:

   A: {Psychic picks box with crystal}
   If psychic is just guessing, $P(A)$ = 1/10 = .1

   b. P(Psychic guesses correct at least once in 7 trials)
   = 1 − P(Psychic does not guess correct in 7 trials)

   = 1 − $P(A^c \cap A^c \cap A^c \cap A^c \cap A^c \cap A^c \cap A^c)$ = 1 − .9(.9)(.9)(.9)(.9)(.9)(.9)
   = 1 − .478 = .522 (This assumes that the trials are independent)

   c.   If the psychic is just guessing, then P(Psychic does not guess correct in 7 trials) = .478.

   Thus, if the person was not a psychic (and was merely guessing) we would expect the person to guess wrong in all seven trials about half the time. This would not be a rare event. Thus, this outcome would support the notion that the person is guessing.

3.77   Define the following events:

   A: {Winner is from National League}

   B: {Winner is from American League}

   C: {Winner is from Eastern Division}

   D: {Winner is from Central Division}

   E: {Winner is from Western Division}

a. $P(C|B) = \dfrac{P(C \cap B)}{P(B)} = \dfrac{6/13}{8/13} = \dfrac{6}{8} = .75$

b. $P(A|D) = \dfrac{P(A \cap D)}{P(D)} = \dfrac{1/13}{2/13} = \dfrac{1}{2} = .5$

c. $P(C^c|A) = \dfrac{P(C^c \cap A)}{P(A)} = \dfrac{2/13}{5/13} = \dfrac{2}{5} = .4$

3.79   a. $P(\text{Species extinct}) = 38/132 = .2879$

   b.   If 9 species are chosen and all are extinct, then for the 10th pick, there are only $132 - 9 = 123$ species to pick from, of which $38 - 9 = 29$ are extinct. $P(\text{Species extinct on } 10^{th} \text{ selection} \mid \text{first 9 species are extinct}) = 29/123 = .236$.

3.81   Define the following events:

I: {Intruder}
N: {No intruder}
A: {System A sounds alarm}
B: {System B sounds alarm}

   a.   From the problem:

   $P(A|I) = .9$.

   $P(B|I) = .95$

   $P(A|N) = .2$

   $P(B|N) = .1$

   b.   We know that events A and B are independent. Thus,

   $P(A \cap B|I) = P(A|I)\,P(B|I) = .9(.95) = .855$

   c. $P(A \cap B|N) = P(A|N)\,P(B|N) = .2(.1) = .02$

   d. $P(A \cup B|I) = P(A|I) + P(B|I) - P(A \cap B|I) = .9 + .95 - .855 = .995$

3.83   Define the following events:

   A: {Player is white}

   B: {Player is black}

   C: {Player is a guard}

   D: {Player is a forward}

   E: {Player is a center}

a. $P(E \mid A) = \dfrac{P(E \cap A)}{P(A)} = \dfrac{28/368}{84/368} = \dfrac{28}{84} = .333$

b. $P(E \mid B) = \dfrac{P(E \cap B)}{P(B)} = \dfrac{34/368}{284/368} = \dfrac{34}{284} = .120$

c.   Events A and E are independent if $P(E \mid A) = P(E)$. From part a, $P(E \mid A) = .333$.

     $P(E) = 62 / 368 = .168$

     Since $P(E \mid A) \ne P(E)$, the events are not independent.

d.   Since the events {White player} and {Center} are not independent, this supports the theory of "stacking". Also, from part a, we found that $P(\text{Center} \mid \text{White}) = .333$ and from part b, $P(\text{Center} \mid \text{Black}) = .120$. Thus, the probability of playing Center depends on race. Again, this supports the theory of "stacking".

3.85   First, define the following events:

     A: {Driver was African American}
     B: {Driver exceeded the speed limit by at least 5 mph}
     C: {Driver was stopped for speeding}

a. $P(A) = .14$
      $P(B) = .98$
      $P(A \mid B) = .15$
      $P(A \mid C) = .35$

b. $P(A \cap B) = P(A \mid B)\, P(B) = .15(.98) = .147$

c. $P(A^c \mid B) = 1 - P(A \mid B) = 1 - .15 = .85$

d. $P(A^c \mid C) = 1 - P(A \mid C) = 1 - .35 = .65$

e.   If events A and B are independent, then $P(A \mid B) = P(A)$. $P(A \mid B) = .15$ and $P(A) = .14$. For this example, $P(A \mid B) \ne P(A)$, but they are very close to each other. To a close approximation, A and B are independent.

f.   If African Americans are not stopped more often for speeding than expected, then events A and C should be independent. We already know from part e that events A and B are essentially independent - i.e. the proportion of the speeders who are African American is equal to the proportion of African Americans.

     Are events A and C independent? If they are, then $P(A \mid C) = P(A)$. From the above, $P(A \mid C) = .35$ and $P(A) = .14$. Thus, events A and C are not independent. This means that the proportion of those stopped for speeding who are African American is not equal to the proportion of African Americans in the population. Since the $P(A \mid C) > P(A)$, this implies that on this stretch of highway, African Americans are stopped for speeding at a higher rate than would be expected.

3.87   Define the following events:

        A: {Seed carries single spikelets}
        B: {Seed carries paired spikelets}
        C: {Seed produces ears with single spikelets}
        D: {Seed produces ears with paired spikelets}

From the problem, $P(A) = .4$, $P(B) = .6$, $P(C|A) = .29$, $P(D|A) = .71$, $P(C|B) = .26$, and $P(D|B) = .74$.

a. $P(A \cap C) = P(C|A)P(A) = .29(.4) = .116$

b. $P(D) = P(A \cap D) + P(B \cap D) = P(D|A)P(A) + P(D|B)P(B) = .71(.4) + .74(.6)$
        $= .284 + .444 = .728$

3.89   a.   Define the following events:

        W: {Player wins the game Go}
        F: {Player plays first (black stones)}

        $P(W \cap F) = 319/577 = .553$

b. $P(W \cap F | CA) = 34/34 = 1$
       $P(W \cap F | CB) = 69/79 = .873$
       $P(W \cap F | CC) = 66/118 = .559$
       $P(W \cap F | BA) = 40/54 = .741$
       $P(W \cap F | BB) = 52/95 = .547$
       $P(W \cap F | BC) = 27/79 = .342$
       $P(W \cap F | AA) = 15/28 = .536$
       $P(W \cap F | AB) = 11/51 = .216$
       $P(W \cap F | AC) = 3/39 = .077$

c.   There are three combinations where the player with the black stones (first) is ranked higher than the player with the white stones: *CA*, *CB*, and *BA*.

       $P(W \cap F | CA \cup CB \cup BA) = (34 + 69 + 40)/(34 + 79 + 54) = 143/167 = .856$

d.   There are three combinations where the players are of the same level: *CC*, *BB*, and *AA*.

       $P(W \cap F | CC \cup BB \cup AA) = (66 + 52 + 15)/(118 + 95 + 28) = 133/241 = .552$

3.91   a.   The total number of outcomes is a combination of 14 numbers taken 4 at a time.

$$\binom{14}{4} = \frac{14!}{4!(14-4)!} = \frac{14!}{4!10!} = \frac{14 \cdot 13 \cdot 12 \cdots 2 \cdot 1}{4 \cdot 3 \cdot 2 \cdot 1 \cdot 10 \cdot 9 \cdots 2 \cdot 1} = 1,001$$

b. The probability that any team obtains the first pick in the draft is that team's number of combinations divided by 1000. The probabilities are:

NBA Lottery Team	Number of Combinations	Probability
Worst Record	250	.250
2nd worst record	200	.200
3rd worst record	157	.157
4th worst record	120	.120
5th worst record	89	.089
6th worst record	64	.064
7th worst record	44	.044
8th worst record	29	.029
9th worst record	18	.018
10th worst record	11	.011
11th worst record	7	.007
12th worst record	6	.006
13th worst record	5	.005
Total	1000	1.000

c. Define the following events:

W_{i1}: {i^{th} worst team gets 1st pick}
W_{12}: {Worst team gets 2nd pick}

If the 2nd worst team obtains the number 1 pick, then that team is removed from the group that could obtain the number 2 pick. Thus, the 200 combinations assigned to the team with the 2nd worst record are removed from the available combinations. Now, there are only 800 possible combinations. The probability that the team with the worst record will get the 2nd pick in the draft given that the team with the 2nd worst record gets the first pick would be $P(W_{12} \mid W_{21}) = 250 / 800 = .313$.

d. If the 3rd worst team obtains the number 1 pick, then that team is removed from the group that could obtain the number 2 pick. Thus, the 157 combinations assigned to the team with the 3rd worst record are removed from the available combinations. Now, there are only $1000 - 157 = 843$ possible combinations. The probability that the team with the worst record will get the 2nd pick in the draft given that the team with the 3rd worst record gets the first pick would be $P(W_{12} \mid W_{31}) = 250 / 843 = .297$.

Similarly, $P(W_{12} \mid W_{41}) = 250 / (1000 - 120) = 250 / 880 = .284$

$$P(W_{12} \mid W_{51}) = 250 / (1000 - 89) = 250 / 911 = .274$$
$$P(W_{12} \mid W_{61}) = 250 / (1000 - 64) = 250 / 936 = .267$$
$$P(W_{12} \mid W_{71}) = 250 / (1000 - 44) = 250 / 956 = .262$$
$$P(W_{12} \mid W_{81}) = 250 / (1000 - 29) = 250 / 971 = .257$$
$$P(W_{12} \mid W_{91}) = 250 / (1000 - 18) = 250 / 982 = .255$$
$$P(W_{12} \mid W_{10\,1}) = 250 / (1000 - 11) = 250 / 989 = .253$$

$$P(W_{12} \mid W_{11\,1}) = 250 / (1000 - 7) = 250 / 993 = .252$$
$$P(W_{12} \mid W_{12\,1}) = 250 / (1000 - 6) = 250 / 994 = .252$$
$$P(W_{12} \mid W_{13\,1}) = 250 / (1000 - 5) = 250 / 995 = .251$$

e. We need to find $P(W_{12} \mid W_{11}^c) = \dfrac{P(W_{12} \cap W_{11}^c)}{P(W_{11}^c)} = \dfrac{P(W_{12})}{1 - P(W_{11})}$

Now, $P(W_{11}^c) = 1 - P(W_{11}) = 1 - .250 = .750$

$$P(W_{12}) = P(W_{12} \mid W_{21})P(W_{21}) + P(W_{12} \mid W_{31})P(W_{31})$$
$$+ P(W_{12} \mid W_{41})P(W_{41}) + \cdots + + P(W_{12} \mid W_{13\,1})P(W_{13\,1})$$

To aid in the computation, we will use the following table:

NBA Lottery Team	Number of Combinations	Probability $P(W_{i1})$	$P(W_{12} \mid W_{i1})$	$P(W_{12} \mid W_{i1})P(W_{i1})$
Worst Record	250	.250		
2nd worst record	200	.200	.313	.0626
3rd worst record	157	.157	.297	.0466
4th worst record	120	.120	.284	.0341
5th worst record	89	.089	.274	.0244
6th worst record	64	.064	.267	.0171
7th worst record	44	.044	.262	.0115
8th worst record	29	.029	.257	.0075
9th worst record	18	.018	.255	.0046
10th worst record	11	.011	.253	.0028
11th worst record	7	.007	.252	.0018
12th worst record	6	.006	.252	.0015
13th worst record	5	.005	.251	.0013
Total	1000	1.000		.2158

Thus,
$$P(W_{12}) = P(W_{12} \mid W_{21})P(W_{21}) + P(W_{12} \mid W_{31})P(W_{31})$$
$$+ P(W_{12} \mid W_{41})P(W_{41}) + \cdots + + P(W_{12} \mid W_{13\,1})P(W_{13\,1}) = .2158$$

Finally, $P(W_{12} \mid W_{11}^c) = \dfrac{P(W_{12} \cap W_{11}^c)}{P(W_{11}^c)} = \dfrac{P(W_{12})}{1 - P(W_{11})} = \dfrac{.2158}{.750} = .288$

3.93 A representative sample exhibits characteristics typical of those possessed by the population of interest. The most common way to obtain a representative sample is to use a random sample.

3.95 A blind study is one where the participants in the study do not know what treatment they are receiving.

3.97 a. $\dbinom{600}{3} = \dfrac{600!}{(3!)(597!)} = \dfrac{(600)(599)(598)}{(1)(2)(3)} = 35{,}820{,}200$

b. All sets are equally likely in random sampling, so that the probability of any particular sample is:

$$\frac{1}{35,820,200}$$

c. Repeated samples would be highly unlikely.

3.99 a. Decide on a starting point on the random number table. Then take the first n numbers reading down, and this would be the sample. Group the digits on the random number table into groups of 7 (for part **b**) or groups of 4 (for part **c**). Eliminate any duplicates and numbers that begin with zero since they are not valid telephone numbers.

b. Starting in Row 6, column 5, take the first 10 seven-digit numbers reading down. The telephone numbers are:

277-5653
988-7231
188-7620
174-5318
530-6059
709-9779
496-2669
889-7433
482-3752
772-3313

c. Starting in Row 10, column 7, take the first 5 four-digit numbers reading down. The 5 telephone numbers are:

373-3886
373-5686
373-1866
373-3632
373-6768

3.103 First, number the intersections from 1 to 5000. Using the random number table, select a starting point that contains 4 digits. Following either the row or column, select successive 4 digit numbers until 50 different 4 digit numbers between 0001 and 5000 are selected. The intersections corresponding to these 50 four digit numbers are selected for sampling.

The second method requires the rows to be numbered from 00 to 99 and the columns to be numbered from 1 to 50. Using the random number table, select a starting point that contains 2 digits. Following either the row or column, select successive 2 digit numbers in sets of 2. The first 2 digit number will correspond to the row number. The second 2 digit number must be between 1 and 50 and corresponds to the column number. This procedure is followed until 50 pairs of 2 digit numbers are selected that correspond to 50 different intersections.

3.105 Suppose a basketball team has a total of 10 players. There are 5 distinct positions on the team – center, forward 1, forward 2, shooting guard, and point guard. How many different ways could a coach arrange the starting lineup, assuming that all players could play all positions?

We can apply the Permutations Rule to find the number of combinations.

$$P_n^N = N(N-1)(N-2)\cdots(N-n+1) = \frac{N!}{(N-n)!} = \frac{10!}{(10-5)!}$$

$$= \frac{10!}{5!} = \frac{10 \cdot 9 \cdots 1}{5 \cdot 4 \cdot 3 \cdot 2 \cdot 1} = 10 \cdot 9 \cdot 8 \cdot 7 \cdot 6 = 30,240.$$

3.107   The Combinations Rule does not take order into account, while the Permutations Rule does take order into account.

3.109   Since the number of possible outcomes from tossing a coin is always two on each flip, the multiplicative rule would yield a product of a series of 2's.

    a. $(2)(2) = 2^2 = 4$

    b. $(2)(2)(2) = 2^3 = 8$

    c. $(2)(2)(2)(2)(2) = 2^5 = 32$

    d. 2^n

3.111   a. $\binom{7}{3} = \frac{7!}{(3!)(4!)} = \frac{7 \cdot 6 \cdot 5}{3 \cdot 2 \cdot 1} = 35$

    b. $\binom{6}{2} = \frac{6!}{(2!)(4!)} = \frac{6 \cdot 5}{2 \cdot 1} = 15$

    c. $\binom{30}{2} = \frac{30!}{(2!)(28!)} = \frac{30 \cdot 29}{2 \cdot 1} = 435$

    d. $\binom{10}{8} = \frac{10!}{(8!)(2!)} = \frac{10 \cdot 9}{2 \cdot 1} = 45$

    e. $\binom{q}{r} = \frac{q!}{r!(q-r!)}$

3.113   a.   Since order is not important, the number of choices is:

$$\binom{8}{5} = \frac{8!}{5!3!} = 56$$

    b.   Order is important because it is necessary to distinguish between the positions (guard, forward, and center). However, the two players chosen as guards and the two forwards are indistinguishable once they are chosen. That is, choosing player #1 as the first guard and player #3 as the second guard results in the same team as choosing player #3 for the first guard and player #1 for the second guard. Denote the five positions to be filled as $G_1, G_2, F_1, F_2,$ and C. The number of distinct teams, assuming each position was distinct is:

$$P_5^8 = \frac{8!}{3!} = 8(7)(6)(5)(4) = 6720$$

However, since G_1 and G_2 are indistinguishable, this number must be divided by 2, or $6720/2 = 3360$ possible teams. Similarly, F_1 and F_2 are indistinguishable, so that there are in fact only $3360/2 = 1680$ possible teams.

c. In this situation, all five positions are distinct. Thus, there are $P_5^8 = 6720$ possible teams.

3.115 a. To visit all 4 cities and then return home, the order of the visits is important. The number of different orders is a permutation of 4 things taken 4 at a time or

$$P_4^4 = \frac{4!}{(4-4)!} = \frac{4 \cdot 3 \cdot 2 \cdot 1}{1} = 24$$

b. If the salesperson visits B first, then he only has 2 choices for the next city (D or E), since B and C are not connected. Once in D or E, he has 2 choices for the next city (if in D, can choose C or E; if in E, can choose D or C). Once in the third city, there is only one choice for the fourth city. The possible trips with B first are $2 \times 2 \times 1 = 4$: BDEC, BDCE, BEDC, BECD.

Similarly, if city C is the first city, there are 2 choices for the second city (D or E), 2 choices for the third, and one for the fourth. Thus, there are $2 \times 2 \times 1 = 4$ choices: CDEB, CDBE, CEDB, CEBD.

If city D is the first chosen, then to visit all four cities exactly once, city B or C must be chosen next. The third city must be E, and the fourth city the only one left. Thus, there are $2 \times 1 \times 1 = 2$ choices: DBEC, DCEB.

Similarly, if city E is the first chosen, then B or C must be the second city, D must be the third, and the fourth city must be the one remaining. Thus, there are $2 \times 1 \times 1 = 2$ choices: EBDC, ECDB.

The total number of routes are $4 + 4 + 2 + 2 = 12$.

3.117 a. The total number of distributors that make up Elaine's group is $6(5) = 30$.

b. The total number of distributors that make up Elaine's group now is $6(5)(7)(5) = 1,050$.

3.119 a. From the problem, we have three students and three hospitals. Suppose we consider the three hospitals as three positions. Using the permutations rule, there are

$$P = P_3^3 = \frac{3!}{(3-3)!} = \frac{3 \cdot 2 \cdot 1}{1} = 6 \text{ different assignments possible.}$$

These assignments are:

$[S_1H_A \ \ S_2H_B \ \ S_3H_C] \ [S_1H_A \ \ S_3H_B \ \ S_2H_C]$
$[S_2H_A \ \ S_1H_B \ \ S_3H_C] \ [S_2H_A \ \ S_3H_B \ \ S_1H_C]$
$[S_3H_A \ \ S_1H_B \ \ S_2H_C] \ [S_3H_A \ \ S_2H_B \ \ S_1H_C]$

b.   Assuming that all of the above assignments are equally likely, the probability of any one of them is 1/6. The probability that student #1 is assigned to hospital B is 2/6 = 1/3.

3.121   a.   The number of ways to select 5 members from 15 is a combination of 15 things taken 5 at a time, or

$$\binom{15}{5} = \frac{15!}{5!(15-5)!} = \frac{15 \cdot 14 \cdot 13 \cdots 1}{5 \cdot 4 \cdot 3 \cdot 2 \cdot 1 \cdot 10 \cdot 9 \cdots 1} = 3003$$

b.   To get no democrats, all 5 members chosen must be Republicans. The number of ways to select 5 members from 8 is a combination of 8 things taken 5 at a time or

$$\binom{8}{5} = \frac{8!}{5!(8-5)!} = \frac{8 \cdot 7 \cdot 6 \cdot 5 \cdots 1}{5 \cdot 4 \cdot 3 \cdot 2 \cdot 1 \cdot 3 \cdot 2 \cdot 1} = 56$$

The probability that no Democrat is appointed is the number of ways to select no Democrats divided by the total number of ways to select 5 members, or

$$P(\text{no Democrats}) = \frac{56}{3003} = .0186$$

Since this probability is so small, we have either seen a rare event or the appointments were not made at random.

c.   To get a majority of Republicans, 3, 4, or 5 members must be Republicans. We computed the number of ways to get 5 Republicans in part **b**. The number of ways to select 4 Republicans from 8 and 1 Democrat from 7 is:

$$\binom{8}{4}\binom{7}{1} = \frac{8!}{4!(8-4)!} \cdot \frac{7!}{1!(7-1)!}$$

$$= \frac{8 \cdot 7 \cdots 1}{4 \cdot 3 \cdot 2 \cdot 1 \cdot 4 \cdot 3 \cdot 2 \cdot 1} \cdot \frac{7 \cdot 6 \cdots 1}{1 \cdot 6 \cdot 5 \cdots 1} = 490$$

The number of ways to select 3 Republicans from 8 and 2 Democrats from 7 is:

$$\binom{8}{3}\binom{7}{2} = \frac{8!}{3!(8-3)!} \cdot \frac{7!}{2!(7-2)!}$$

$$= \frac{8 \cdot 7 \cdots 1}{3 \cdot 2 \cdot 1 \cdot 5 \cdot 4 \cdot 3 \cdot 2 \cdot 1} \cdot \frac{7 \cdot 6 \cdots 1}{2 \cdot 1 \cdot 5 \cdot 4 \cdot 3 \cdot 2 \cdot 1}$$

The probability that the majority of committee members are Republican is the number of ways to get 3, 4, or 5 Republicans divided by the total number of ways to get 5 members, or

$$P(\text{Majority Republican}) = \frac{56 + 490 + 1176}{3003} = \frac{1722}{3003} = .5734$$

This is not an unusual event because the probability is so high. There would be no reason to doubt the governor made the selections randomly.

3.123   The professor will choose 5 of 10 questions. Of these 10 questions, the student has prepared answers for 7, and has not prepared the other three. The 5 questions on the exam can be chosen in

$$\binom{10}{5} = \frac{10!}{5!5!} = 252 \text{ ways}$$

a.   If the student has prepared all 5 exam questions, the professor has chosen 5 from the 7 prepared questions. This can be done in

$$\binom{7}{5} = 21 \text{ ways}$$

Hence, the desired probability is 21/252.

b.   Define the following events.

   A: {The student is prepared for no questions}
   B: {The student is prepared for 1 question}
   C: {The student is prepared for 2 questions}

A will occur if the professor picks 0 questions from the 7 prepared and 5 from the 3 unprepared. This is impossible, as is B. C will occur if the professor picks 2 questions from the 7 prepared and 3 questions from the 3 unprepared. This can happen in

$$\binom{7}{2}\binom{3}{3} = 21(1) = 21 \text{ ways}$$

Hence, $P(\text{prepared for less than 3}) = P(A) + P(B) + P(C) = 0 + 0 + 21/252 = 21/252$

c.   The professor must pick 4 from the 7 prepared questions and 1 from the remaining 3 questions. This can happen in

$$\binom{7}{4}\binom{3}{1} = 35(3) = 105 \text{ ways}$$

Hence, $P(\text{prepared for exactly 4}) = 105/252$

3.125   a.   The number of hands possible is:

$$\binom{52}{5} = \frac{52!}{5!47!} = \frac{52 \cdot 51 \cdot 50 \cdot 49 \cdot 48}{5 \cdot 4 \cdot 3 \cdot 2 \cdot 1} = 2{,}598{,}960$$

b.   Every set of five cards would be equally likely. Therefore, the probability of any one type of hand can be calculated by finding the number of ways of obtaining that particular type of hand and dividing by the total number of hands possible. For example,

$$P(A) = \frac{\text{Number of ways of obtaining a flush}}{\text{Number of hands possible}}$$

To determine the number of flushes possible, it is necessary to recognize that there would be the same number of flushes in spades as hearts, diamond, or clubs. If we can determine the number of ways of obtaining a flush in any particular suit, then four times that amount would be the number of flushes possible. However, since there are 13 cards of each suit, it follows that the number of flushes for any particular suit is:

$$\binom{13}{5} = \frac{13!}{5!8!} = 1,287$$

Then the total number of flushes possible would be:

$$4 \cdot 1,287 = 5,148$$

Then $P(A) = \dfrac{5,148}{2,598,960} \approx .002$

c.   To compute $P(B)$, it is necessary to recognize that there are 10 different sets of cards' values which result in straights:

$$\{A, 2, 3, 4, 5\}$$
$$\{2, 3, 4, 5, 6\}$$
$$\{3, 4, 5, 6, 7\}$$
$$\{4, 5, 6, 7, 8\}$$
$$\{5, 6, 7, 8, 9\}$$
$$\{6, 7, 8, 9, 10\}$$
$$\{7, 8, 9, 10, J\}$$
$$\{8, 9, 10, J, Q\}$$
$$\{9, 10, J, Q, K\}$$
$$\{10, J, Q, K, A\}$$

We can determine the total number of possible straights by determining the number of ways that any one particular type of straight could occur and then multiply this amount by 10. But the number of ways of obtaining any one straight, say $\{10, J, Q, K, A\}$, is done easily by the multiplicative rule. Since there would be one 10 from four to be selected, and one jack from four to be selected, etc., the number of ways of obtaining a straight of the form $\{10, J, Q, K, A\}$ is:

$$4 \cdot 4 \cdot 4 \cdot 4 \cdot 4 = 1024$$

There would then be $10 \cdot 1024 = 10,240$ possible straights, so that $P(B) = \dfrac{10,240}{2,598,960}$

$$\approx .00394$$

d.   There are only four straight flushes of each type. For example, a straight flush of the type $\{10, J, Q, K, A\}$ can occur in spades, hearts, diamonds, and clubs. Since there are 10 types of straights, there are $4 \cdot 10 = 40$ possible straight flushes.

Thus, $P(A \cap B) = \dfrac{40}{2,598,960} = .0000154$

3.127   If events A and B are independent, then the probability that event B occurs does not depend on whether event A has occurred or not. If events A and B are independent, then $P(B \mid A) = P(B)$.

3.129 a. $P(B_1 \cap A) = P(A \mid B_1)P(B_1) = .3(.75) = .225$

b. $P(B_2 \cap A) = P(A \mid B_2)P(B_2) = .5(.25) = .125$

c. $P(A) = P(B_1 \cap A) + P(B_2 \cap A) = .225 + .125 = .35$

d. $P(B_1 \mid A) = \dfrac{P(B_1 \cap A)}{P(A)} = \dfrac{.225}{.35} = .643$

e. $P(B_2 \mid A) = \dfrac{P(B_2 \cap A)}{P(A)} = \dfrac{.125}{.35} = .357$

3.131 If A is independent of B_1, B_2, and B_3, then $P(A \mid B_1) = P(A) = .4$.

Then $P(B_1 \mid A) = \dfrac{P(A \mid B_1)P(B_1)}{P(A)} = \dfrac{.4(.2)}{.4} = .2$

3.133 Define the following events:

T: {Athlete illegally uses testosterone}
P: {Test for testosterone is positive}
N: {Athlete does not illegally use testosterone}

a. $P(P \mid T) = \dfrac{50}{100} = .50$

b. $P(P^c \mid N) = 1 - P(P \mid N) = 1 - \dfrac{9}{900} = 1 - .01 = .99$

c. $P(T \mid P) = \dfrac{P(P \mid T)P(T)}{P(P)}$.

Now, $P(P) = P(P \mid N)P(N) + P(P \mid T)P(T) = .01(.9) + .5(.1) = .009 + .05 = .059$

$P(T \mid P) = \dfrac{P(P \mid T)P(T)}{P(P)} = \dfrac{.5(.1)}{.059} = \dfrac{.05}{.059} = .847$

3.135 From Exercise 3.81, we defined the following events:

I: {Intruder}
N: {No intruder}
A: {System A sounds alarm}
B: {System B sounds alarm}
Also, from Exercise 3.81, $P(A \cap B \mid I) = .855$ and $P(A \cap B \mid N) = .02$.

Thus, $P(A \cap B) = P(A \cap B \mid I)P(I) + P(A \cap B \mid N)P(N) = .855(.4) + .02(.6)$
$$= .342 + .012 = .354$$

$P(I \cap A \cap B) = P(A \cap B \mid I)P(I) = .855(.4) = .342$

$$P(I \mid A \cap B) = \frac{P(I \cap A \cap B)}{P(A \cap B)} = \frac{.342}{.354} = .966$$

3.137   Define the following event:

D: {Chip is defective}

From the Exercise, $P(S_1) = .15$, $P(S_2) = .05$, $P(S_3) = .10$, $P(S_4) = .20$, $P(S_5) = .12$, $P(S_6) = .20$, and $P(S_7) = .18$. Also, $P(D|S_1) = .001$, $P(D|S_2) = .0003$, $P(D|S_3) = .0007$, $P(D|S_4) = .006$, $P(D|S_5) = .0002$, $P(D|S_6) = .0002$, and $P(D|S_7) = .001$.

a.   We must find the probability of each supplier given a defective chip.

$$P(S_1 \mid D) = \frac{P(S_1 \cap D)}{P(D)} =$$

$$\frac{P(D \mid S_1)P(S_1)}{P(D \mid S_1)P(S_1) + P(D \mid S_2)P(S_2) + P(D \mid S_3)P(S_3) + P(D \mid S_4)P(S_4) + P(D \mid S_5)P(S_5) + P(D \mid S_6)P(S_6) + P(D \mid S_7)P(S_7)}$$

$$= \frac{.001(.15)}{.001(.15) + .0003(.05) + .0007(.10) + .006(.20) + .0002(.12) + .0002(.02) + .001(.18)}$$

$$= \frac{.00015}{.00015 + .000015 + .00007 + .0012 + .000024 + .00004 + .00018} = \frac{.00015}{.001679} = .0893$$

$$P(S_2 \mid D) = \frac{P(S_2 \cap D)}{P(D)} = \frac{P(D \mid S_2)P(S_2)}{P(D)} = \frac{.0003(.05)}{.001679} = \frac{.000015}{.001679} = .0089$$

$$P(S_3 \mid D) = \frac{P(S_3 \cap D)}{P(D)} = \frac{P(D \mid S_3)P(S_3)}{P(D)} = \frac{.0007(.10)}{.001679} = \frac{.00007}{.001679} = .0417$$

$$P(S_4 \mid D) = \frac{P(S_4 \cap D)}{P(D)} = \frac{P(D \mid S_4)P(S_4)}{P(D)} = \frac{.006(.20)}{.001679} = \frac{.0012}{.001679} = .7147$$

$$P(S_5 \mid D) = \frac{P(S_5 \cap D)}{P(D)} = \frac{P(D \mid S_5)P(S_5)}{P(D)} = \frac{.0002(.12)}{.001679} = \frac{.000024}{.001679} = .0143$$

$$P(S_6 \mid D) = \frac{P(S_6 \cap D)}{P(D)} = \frac{P(D \mid S_6)P(S_6)}{P(D)} = \frac{.0002(.20)}{.001679} = \frac{.00004}{.001679} = .0238$$

$$P(S_7 \mid D) = \frac{P(S_7 \cap D)}{P(D)} = \frac{P(D \mid S_7)P(S_7)}{P(D)} = \frac{.001(.18)}{.001679} = \frac{.00018}{.001679} = .1072$$

Of these probabilities, .7147 is the largest. This implies that if a failure is observed, supplier number 4 was most likely responsible.

b. If the seven suppliers all produce defective chips at the same rate of .0005, then $P(D|S_i)$ =.0005 for all $i = 1, 2, 3, \ldots 7$ and $P(D) = .0005$.

For any supplier i, $P(S_i \cap D) = P(D \mid S_i)P(S_i) = .0005P(S_i)$ and

$$P(S_i \mid D) = \frac{P(S_i \cap D)}{P(D)} = \frac{P(D \mid S_i)P(S_i)}{.0005} = \frac{.0005P(S_i)}{.0005} = P(S_i)$$

Thus, if a defective is observed, then it most likely came from the supplier with the largest proportion of sales (probability). In this case, the most likely supplier would be either supplier 4 or supplier 6. Both of these have probabilities of .20.

3.139   a. $A \cup B$

b. B^c

c. $A \cap B$

d. $A^c \mid B$

3.141   a.   Since events A and B are mutually exclusive, $P(A \cap B) = 0$.

$$P(A \mid B) = \frac{P(A \cap B)}{P(B)} = \frac{0}{.3} = 0$$

b. If Events A and B are independent, then $P(A \mid B) = P(A)$. From part **a**, we know $P(A \mid B) = 0$. However, we also know $P(A) = .2$. Thus, events A and B are not independent.

3.143   We know $P(A \mid B) = \dfrac{P(A \cap B)}{P(B)}$. Thus, $P(B) = \dfrac{P(A \cap B)}{P(A \mid B)} = \dfrac{.4}{.8} = .5$.

3.145   a.

(1, *H*)	(2, 1)	(3, *H*)	(4, 1)	(5, *H*)	(6, 1)
(1, *T*)	(2, 2)	(3, *T*)	(4, 2)	(5, *T*)	(6, 2)
	(2, 3)		(4, 3)		(6, 3)
	(2, 4)		(4, 4)		(6, 4)
	(2, 5)		(4, 5)		(6, 5)
	(2, 6)		(4, 6)		(6, 6)

b. Each simple event is an intersection of two independent events. Each simple event whose first element is 1, 3, or 5 has probability

$$\left(\frac{1}{6}\right)\left(\frac{1}{2}\right) = \frac{1}{12}$$

while each simple event whose first element is 2, 4, or 6 has probability

$$\left(\frac{1}{6}\right)\left(\frac{1}{6}\right) = \frac{1}{36}$$

c. $P(A) = P\{(1, H), (3, H), (5, H)\} = \dfrac{1}{12} + \dfrac{1}{12} + \dfrac{1}{12} = \dfrac{3}{12} = \dfrac{1}{4}$

$P(B) = P\{(1, H), (1, T), (3, H), (3, T), (5, H), (5, T)\} = \dfrac{6}{12} = \dfrac{1}{2}$

d. A^c: {all except $(1, H)$, $(3, H)$, and $(5, H)$}
B^c: $\{(2, 1), (2, 2), (2, 3), (2, 4), (2, 5), (2, 6), (4, 1), (4, 2), (4, 3), (4, 4), (4, 5), (4, 6),$
$\quad\ (6, 1), (6, 2), (6, 3), (6, 4), (6, 5), (6, 6)\}$
$A \cap B$: $\{(1, H), (3, H), (5, H)\}$
$A \cup B$: $\{(1, H), (1, T), (3, H), (3, T), (5, H), (5, T)\}$

e. $P(A^c) = 1 - P(A) = 1 - \dfrac{1}{4} = \dfrac{3}{4}$

$P(B^c) = 1 - P(B) = 1 - \dfrac{1}{2} = \dfrac{1}{2}$

$P(A \cap B) = P(A) = \dfrac{1}{4}$

$P(A \cup B) = P(A) + P(B) - P(A \cap B) = \dfrac{1}{4} + \dfrac{1}{2} - \dfrac{1}{4} = \dfrac{1}{2}$

$P(A \mid B) = \dfrac{P(A \cap B)}{P(B)} = \dfrac{1/4}{1/2} = \dfrac{1}{2}$

$P(B \mid A) = \dfrac{P(A \cap B)}{P(A)} = \dfrac{1/4}{1/4} = 1$

f. $P(A \cap B) \neq 0$, so that A and B are not mutually exclusive.
$P(A \mid B) \neq P(A)$, so that A and B are not independent.

3.147 a. Because events A and B are independent, we have:

$$P(A \cap B) = P(A)P(B) = (.3)(.1) = .03$$

Thus, $P(A \cap B) \neq 0$, and the two events cannot be mutually exclusive.

b. $P(A \mid B) = \dfrac{P(A \cap B)}{P(B)} = \dfrac{.03}{.1} = .3 \qquad P(B \mid A) = \dfrac{P(A \cap B)}{P(A)} = \dfrac{.03}{.1} = .1$

c. $P(A \cup B) = P(A) + P(B) - P(A \cap B) = .3 + .1 - .03 = .37$

3.149 From the problem, to find probabilities, we must convert the percents to proportions by dividing by 100. Thus, $P(1 \text{ star}) = 0$, $P(2 \text{ stars}) = .0408$, $P(3 \text{ stars}) = .1735$, $P(4 \text{ stars}) = .6020$, and $P(5 \text{ stars}) = .1837$.

    a.   False. The probability of an event cannot be 4. The probability of an event must be between 0 and 1.

    b.   True. $P(4 \text{ or } 5 \text{ stars}) = P(4 \text{ stars}) + P(5 \text{ stars}) = .6020 + .1837 = .7857$.

    c.   True. No cars have a rating of 1 star, thus $P(1 \text{ star}) = 0$.

    d.   False. $P(2 \text{ stars}) = .0408$ and $P(5 \text{ stars}) = .1837$. Since .0408 us smaller than .1837, the car has a better chance of having a 5-star rating than a 2-star rating.

3.151 Let A = {Company is trading company} and B = {Company based in Japan}. From the problem, $P(B) = 11 / 20 = .55$ and $P(A \cap B) = 6 / 20 = .3$.

    $P(A \mid B) = P(A \cap B) / P(B) = .3 / .55 = .545$.

3.153 Let us define the following events:

    S: {School is a subscriber}
    N: {School never uses the CCN broadcast}
    F: {School uses the CCN broadcast more than 5 times per week}

From the problem, $P(S) = .40$, $P(N \mid S) = .05$, and $P(F \mid S) = .20$.

    a. $P(S \cap N) = P(N \mid S) P(S) = .05(.40) = .02$

    b. $P(S \cap F) = P(F \mid S) P(S) = .20(.40) = .08$

3.155   a.   The sample points would correspond to the possible outcomes: Violence to others, sympathetic, Harm to self, Comic images, and Criticism of definitions.

    b.   From the sample, the number of times each of these sample points occurred was different. We would expect the probability of each sample point to be close to the relative frequency of that outcome.

    c.   Reasonable probabilities would be the relative frequencies of the sample points:

Media Coverage	Frequency	Relative Frequency
Violence to others	373	373/562 = .6637
Sympathetic	102	102/562 = .1815
Harm to self	71	71/562 = .1263
Comic images	12	12/562 = .0214
Criticism of definitions	4	4/562 = .0071
Total	562	1.0000

    d.   This probability would be $.1815 + .0214 = .2029$.

3.157 a. The sample points would be the possible answers to the question. Thus, the sample points would be: Total population, Agricultural change, Presence of industry, Growth, and Population concentration.

b. Reasonable probabilities would correspond to the proportions given in the pie chart. These would be:

P(Total population) = .18, P(Agricultural change) = .05, P(Presence of industry) = .27, P(growth) = .05, and P(Population concentration) = .45.

c. Sample points related to population are Total population and Population concentration. P(population-related) = P(Total population) + P(Population concentration) = .18 + .45 = .63.

3.159 a. P(Most salient role is spouse) = 424 / 1,102 = .385

b. P(Most salient role is parent or grandparent)
= 269 / 1,102 + 148 / 1,102 = .244 + .134 = .378

c. P(Most salient role does not involve a spouse or relative)
= 73 / 1,102 + 59 / 1,102 + 34 / 1,102 + 36 / 1,102 = .066 + .054 + .031 + .033 = .184

3.161 a. Define the following event:

F_i: {Player makes a foul shot on ith attempt} $P(F_i) = .8$
$P(F_i') = 1 - P(F_i) = 1 - .8 = .2$

The event "the player scores on both shots" is $F_1 \cap F_2$. If the throws are independent, then:

$P(F_1 \cap F_2) = P(F_1)P(F_2) = .8(.8) = .64$

The event "the player scores on exactly one shot" is:

$(F_1 \cap F_2^c) \cup (F_1^c \cap F_2) = P(F_1 \cap F_2^c) + P(F_1^c \cap F_2)$
$= P(F_1)P(F_2^c) + P(F_1^c)P(F_2)$
$= .8(.2) + .2(.8) = .16 + .16 = .32$

The event "the player scores on neither shot" is $F_1^c \cap F_2^c$.

$P(F_1^c \cap F_2^c) = P(F_1^c)P(F_2^c) = .2(.2) = .04$

b. We know $P(F_1) = .8$, $P(F_2 | F_1) = .9$, and $P(F_2 | F_1^c) = .7$

The probability the player scores on both shots is:

$P(F_1 \cap F_2) = P(F_2 | F_1)P(F_1) = .9(.8) = .72$

The probability the player scores on exactly one shot is:

$P(F_1 \cap F_2^c) + P(F_1^c \cap F_2) = P(F_2^c | F_1)P(F_1) + P(F_2 | F_1^c)P(F_1^c)$
$= [1 - P(F_2 | F_1)]P(F_1) + P(F_2 | F_1^c)P(F_1^c)$
$= (1 - .9)(.8) + .7(.2) = .08 + .14 = .22$

The probability the player scores on neither shot is:

$$P(F_1^c \cap F_2^c) = P(F_2^c \mid F_1^c)P(F_1^c) = [1 - P(F_2 \mid F_1^c)]P(F_1^c) = (1 - .7)(.2) = .06$$

c. Two consecutive foul shots are probably dependent. The outcome of the second shot probably depends on the outcome of the first.

3.163   Define the following events:

> S: {Patient receiving cyclosporine survives through the first year}
> F: {Patient receiving cyclosporine does not survive through the first year}

From the problem, $P(S) = .80$. Since $F = S^c$, $P(F) = P(S^c) = 1 - .80 = .20$

If four patients receive the transplant and cyclosporine, the possible outcomes are:

> *SSSS, SSSF, SSFS, SFSS, FSSS, SSFF, SFSF, SFFS, FSSF, FSFS, FFSS, SFFF, FSFF, FFSF, FFFS, FFFF*

a. $P(SSSS) = P(S \cap S \cap S \cap S) = P(S)P(S)P(S)P(S) = .8(.8)(.8)(.8) = .4096$ (assuming the events are independent)

b. $P(FFFF) = P(F \cap F \cap F \cap F) = P(F)P(F)P(F)P(F) = .2(.2)(.2)(.2) = .0016$

c. $P(\text{at least one patient is alive}) = 1 - P(FFFF) = 1 - .0016 = .9984$

3.165   Define the following events:

> A_1: {Component 1 in System A works properly}
> A_2: {Component 2 in System A works properly}
> A_3: {Component 3 in System A works properly}
> B_1: {Component 1 in System B works properly}
> B_2: {Component 2 in System B works properly}
> B_3: {Component 3 in System B works properly}
> B_4: {Component 4 in System B works properly}
> A: {System A works properly}
> B: {System B works properly}
> C: {Subsystem C works properly}
> D: {Subsystem D works properly}

$$P(A_1) = 1 - P(A_1^c) = 1 - .12 = .88 \qquad P(B_1) = 1 - P(B_1^c) = 1 - .1 = .9$$
$$P(A_2) = 1 - P(A_2^c) = 1 - .09 = .91 \qquad P(B_2) = 1 - P(B_2^c) = 1 - .1 = .9$$
$$P(A_3) = 1 - P(A_3^c) = 1 - .11 = .89 \qquad P(B_3) = 1 - P(B_3^c) = 1 - .1 = .9$$
$$ \qquad P(B_4) = 1 - P(B_4^c) = 1 - .1 = .9$$

a. $P(A) = P(A_1 \cap A_2 \cap A_3) = P(A_1)P(A_2)P(A_3) = .88(.91)(.89) = .7127$
    (since the three components operate independently)

b. $P(A^c) = 1 - P(A) = 1 - .7127 - .2873$

c. Subsystem C works properly if both components B_1 and B_2 work properly.

$$P(C) = P(B_1 \cap B_2) = P(B_1)P(B_2) = .9(.9) = .81$$
$$\text{(since the 2 components operate independently)}$$

Similarly, subsystem D works properly if both components B_3 and B_4 work properly.

$$P(D) = P(B_3 \cap B_4) = P(B_3)P(B_4) = .9(.9) = .81$$

System B operates properly if either subsystem C or subsystem D operates properly.

$$P(B) = P(C \cup D) = P(C) + P(D) - P(C \cap D) = P(C) + P(D) - P(C)P(D)$$
$$= .81 + .81 - .81(.81) = .9639$$

d. The probability that at least one subsystem in System B fails is:

$$P(C \cap D^c) + P(C^c \cap D) = P(C)P(D^c) + P(C^c)P(D)$$
$$= .81(1 - .81) + (1 - .81)(.81) = .1539 + .1539 = .3078$$

e. System B fails to operate only if both subsystems C and D fail.

$$P(B^c) = P(C^c \cap D^c) = P(C^c)P(D^c) = (1 - .81)(1 - .81) = .0361$$

f. If System B operates correctly 99% of the time, then it fails 1% of the time. The probability that one of the subsystems fails is 1 - .81 = .19. The probability that n subsystems fail is $.19^n$. Thus, we must find n such that

$$.19^n \le .01 \implies n \ge 3$$

3.167   a. To solve this part, we think of the televisions as being sent to the three dealers in sequence. First we determine in how many ways 10 televisions can be sent to dealer A. Then, from the remaining 10 televisions, in how many ways can 6 of these be sent to dealer B. Then dealer C would receive the remaining televisions. The multiplicative rule would then be used to determine the total number of ways these televisions can be divided among the three dealers. This results in the following:

$$\binom{20}{10}\binom{10}{6}\binom{4}{4} = \left(\frac{20!}{10!10!}\right)\left(\frac{10!}{6!4!}\right)\left(\frac{4!}{4!0!}\right)$$
$$= \left(\frac{20 \cdot 19 \cdot 18 \cdot 17 \cdot 16 \cdot 15 \cdot 14 \cdot 13 \cdot 12 \cdot 11}{10 \cdot 9 \cdot 8 \cdot 7 \cdot 6 \cdot 5 \cdot 4 \cdot 3 \cdot 2 \cdot 1}\right)\left(\frac{10 \cdot 9 \cdot 8 \cdot 7}{4 \cdot 3 \cdot 2 \cdot 1}\right)$$
$$= \left(\frac{20 \cdot 19 \cdot 18 \cdot 17 \cdot 16 \cdot 15 \cdot 14 \cdot 13 \cdot 12 \cdot 11}{(6 \cdot 5 \cdot 4 \cdot 3 \cdot 1) \cdot (4 \cdot 3 \cdot 2 \cdot 1)}\right) = 38,798,760$$

b. To determine the probability that dealer A receives all the defective sets, we count the number of ways this could occur and divide by the total number of possibilities, calculated above. This can be done by subdividing the sets into defective and non-defective and counting the number of ways that all three defectives could be sent to dealer A, as well as seven non-defectives. The rest of the counting for the other dealers is done in a fashion similar to the above. This results in:

$$\binom{3}{3}\binom{17}{7}\binom{10}{6}\binom{4}{4} = \left(\frac{3!}{3!0!}\right)\left(\frac{17!}{7!10!}\right)\left(\frac{10!}{6!4!}\right)\left(\frac{4!}{4!0!}\right)$$

$$= 1\left(\frac{17\cdot16\cdot15\cdot14\cdot13\cdot12\cdot11}{7\cdot6\cdot5\cdot4\cdot3\cdot2\cdot1}\right)\left(\frac{10\cdot9\cdot8\cdot7}{4\cdot3\cdot2\cdot1}\right)1 = 4,084,080$$

Thus, the probability is:

$$\frac{4,084,080}{38,798,760} \approx .105$$

c. To determine the probability that dealer A receives two of the defective sets and dealer B the other defective, we again count the number of ways this could occur and divide by the total number of possibilities. Again, this can be done by subdividing the sets into defective and non-defective. First we would count the number of ways that two of the three defectives could be sent to dealer A, as well as seven non-defectives. Then we would count the number of ways the remaining defective and five non-defectives could be sent to dealer B. Dealer C is sent the remainder. The result is:

$$\binom{3}{2}\binom{17}{8}\binom{1}{1}\binom{9}{5}\binom{4}{4} = \left(\frac{3!}{2!1!}\right)\left(\frac{17!}{8!9!}\right)\left(\frac{1!}{1!0!}\right)\left(\frac{9!}{5!4!}\right)\left(\frac{4!}{4!0!}\right)$$

$$= \binom{3}{1}\left(\frac{17\cdot16\cdot15\cdot14\cdot13\cdot12\cdot11\cdot10}{8\cdot7\cdot6\cdot5\cdot4\cdot3\cdot2\cdot1}\right)1\left(\frac{9\cdot8\cdot7\cdot6}{4\cdot3\cdot2\cdot1}\right)1$$

$$= 9,189,18$$

Thus, the probability is:

$$\frac{9,189,180}{38,798,760} \approx .237$$

3.169   a. The odds in favor of Smarty Jones are $\frac{1}{3}$ to $\left(1-\frac{1}{3}\right)$ or $\frac{1}{3}$ to $\frac{2}{3}$ or 1 to 2

b. If the odds are 1 to 1, P(Smarty Jones will win) $= \frac{1}{1+1} = \frac{1}{2} = .5$

c. If the odds against Smarty Jones winning are 3 to 2, the odds for Smarty Jones winning are 2 to 3. The probability Smarty Jones will win is $\frac{2}{2+3} = \frac{2}{5} = .4$

3.171 Define the following event:

A: {Antigens match}

From the problem, $P(A) = .25$ and $P(A') = 1 - P(A) = 1 - .25 = .75$

a. The probability that one sibling has a match is $P(A) = .25$

b. The probability that all three will match is:

$$P(AAA) = P(A \cap A \cap A) = P(A)P(A)P(A) = .25^3 = .0156$$

c. The probability that none of the three match is:

$$P(A^c A^c A^c) = P(A^c \cap A^c \cap A^c) = P(A^c)P(A^c)P(A^c) = .75^3 = .4219$$

d. For this part, $P(A) = .001$ and $P(A^c) = 1 - P(A) = 1 - .001 = .999$

$P(A) = .001$

$$P(AAA) = P(A \cap A \cap A) = P(A)P(A)P(A) = .001^3 = .000000001$$

$$P(A^c A^c A^c) = P(A^c \cap A^c \cap A^c) = P(A^c)P(A^c)P(A^c) = .999^3 = .9970$$

3.173 We will work with the following events:

A: {Woman is pregnant}
B: {Pregnancy test is positive}

The given probabilities can be written as:

$$P(A) = .75, \quad P(B \mid A) = .99, \quad P(B \mid A^c) = .02$$

Then, $P(A \mid B) = \dfrac{P(A \cap B)}{P(B)} = \dfrac{P(B \mid A) \cdot P(A)}{P(A \cap B) + P(A^c \cap B)}$

$$= \dfrac{P(B \mid A) \cdot P(A)}{P(B \mid A) \cdot P(A) + P(B \mid A^c) \cdot P(A^c)}$$

$$= \dfrac{(.99)(.75)}{(.99)(.75) + (.02)(.25)} = \dfrac{.7425}{.7475} \approx .993$$

3.175 We first determine the number of simple events for this experiment. According to the partitions rule, the number of ways of dealing 52 cards so that each of the four players receives 13 cards is:

$$\frac{52!}{13!13!13!13!} = 5.3644738 \times 10^{28}$$

If the cards are well shuffled, then the probability of each simple event is:

$$\frac{1}{5.3644738} \text{ times } 10^{-28}$$

We now need to count the number of simple events that result in one player receiving all the diamonds, another all the hearts, another all the spades, and another all the clubs. To do this, first consider a particular *ordering* that yields the desired result:

Player #1 receives 13 diamonds
Player #2 receives 13 hearts
Player #3 receives 13 spades
Player #4 receives 13 clubs

This particular *ordered* event can happen in

$$\binom{13}{13}\binom{13}{13}\binom{13}{13}\binom{13}{13} = 1$$

way. However, the *ordering* of the players is not relevant to us.

Since there are $P_4^4 = \dfrac{4!}{(4-4)!} = 24$ possible orderings of the players, we conclude that the

probability of the rare event observed in Dubuque is:

$$\frac{24}{5.3644738 \times 10^{28}} \approx 4.4739 \times 10^{-28}$$

3.177   If a coin is balanced, then $P(H) = P(T) = .5$. To find the probability of any sequence, you find the probability of the intersection of the simple events. Thus,

$P(HHHHHHHHHH) = P(H \cap H \cap H \cap H \cap H \cap H \cap H \cap H \cap H \cap H)$

$= P(H)P(H)P(H)P(H)P(H)P(H)P(H)P(H)P(H)P(H) = .5(.5)(.5)(.5)(.5)(.5)(.5)(.5)(.5)$

$= .00098$

Similarly, $P(HHTTHTTHHH) = P(H \cap H \cap T \cap T \cap H \cap T \cap T \cap H \cap H \cap H)$

$= P(H)P(H)P(T)P(T)P(H)P(T)P(T)P(H)P(H)P(H) = .5(.5)(.5)(.5)(.5)(.5)(.5)(.5)(.5)$

$= .00098$

Similarly, $P(TTTTTTTTTT) = P(T \cap T \cap T \cap T \cap T \cap T \cap T \cap T \cap T \cap T)$

$= P(T)P(T)P(T)P(T)P(T)P(T)P(T)P(T)P(T)P(T) = .5(.5)(.5)(.5)(.5)(.5)(.5)(.5)(.5)$

$= .00098$

Thus, any of these 3 sequences are equally likely. In fact, any specific sequence has the same probability.

Now, suppose we compute the probability of getting all heads or all tails:

$P(\text{All heads or all tails}) = P(\text{All heads} \cup \text{All tails})$

$$= P(\text{All heads}) + P(\text{All tails}) - P(\text{All heads} \cap \text{All tails}) = .00098 + .00098 - 0 = .00196$$

Consequently, the probability of getting a mix of heads and tails is:

$$P(10 \text{ coin tosses result in a mix of heads and tails}) = 1 - P(\text{All heads or all tails})$$

$$= 1 - .00196 = .99804$$

So, even though any particular sequence has a probability of .00098, we just found out the probability of getting all heads or all tails is only .00196 and the probability of getting a mix of heads and tails is .99804. If we know that one of these sequences actually occurred, then we would conclude that it was probably the one with the mix of heads and tails because the probability of a mix is close to 1.

3.179   First, we will list all possible sample points for placing a car (C) and 2 goats (G) behind doors #1, #2, and #3. If the first position corresponds to door #1, the second position corresponds to door #2, and the third position corresponds to door #3, the sample space is:

(C G G) (G C G) (G G C)

Now, suppose you pick door #1. Initially, the probability that you will win the car is 1/3 – only one of the sample points has a car behind door #1.

The host will now open a door behind which is a goat. If you pick door #1 in the first sample point (C G G), the host will open either door #2 or door #3. Suppose he opens door #3 (it really does not matter). If you pick door #1 in the second sample point (G C G), the host will open door #3. If you pick door #1 in the third sample point (G G C), the host will open door #2. Now, the new sample space will be:

(C G) (G C) (G C)

where the first position corresponds to door #1 (the one you chose) and the second position corresponds to the door that was not opened by the host.

Now, if you keep door #1, the probability that you win the car is 1/3. However, if you switch to the remaining door, the probability that you win the car is now 2/3. Based on these probabilities, it is to your advantage to switch doors.

The above could be repeated by selecting door #2 initially or door #3 initially. In either of these cases, again, the probability of winning the car is 1/3 if you do not switch and 2/3 if you switch. Thus, Marilyn was correct.

Discrete Random Variables

Chapter

4

4.1   A random variable is a rule that assigns one and only one value to each simple event of an experiment.

4.3   a.   Since we can count the number of words spelled correctly, the random variable is discrete.

        b.   Since we can assume values in an interval, the amount of water flowing through the Hoover Dam in a day is continuous.

        c.   Since time is measured on an interval, the random variable is continuous.

        d.   Since we can count the number of bacteria per cubic centimeter in drinking water, this random variable is discrete.

        e.   Since we cannot count the amount of carbon monoxide produced per gallon of unleaded gas, this random variable is continuous.

        f.   Since weight is measured on an interval, weight is a continuous random variable.

4.5   a.   The reaction time difference is continuous because it lies within an interval.

        b.   Since we can count the number of violent crimes, this random variable is discrete.

        c.   Since we can count the number of near misses in a month, this variable is discrete.

        d.   Since we can count the number of winners each week, this variable is discrete.

        e.   Since we can count the number of free throws made per game by a basketball team, this variable is discrete.

        f.   Since distance traveled by a school bus lies in some interval, this is a continuous random variable.

4.7   The values x can assume are 0, 1, 2, 3, 4, …. Thus, x is a discrete random variable.

4.9   The probability distribution of a discrete random variable can be represented by a table, graph, or formula that specifies the probability associated with each possible value the random variable can assume.

4.11   a.   We know $\sum p(x) = 1$. Thus, $p(2) + p(3) + p(5) + p(8) + p(10) = 1$

$$\Rightarrow p(5) = 1 - p(2) - p(3) - p(8) - p(10) = 1 - .15 - .10 - .25 - .25 = .25$$

        b. $P(x = 2 \text{ or } x = 10) = P(x = 2) + P(x = 10) = .15 + .25 = .40$

c. $P(x \le 8) = P(x = 2) + P(x = 3) + P(x = 5) + P(x = 8) = .15 + .10 + .25 + .25 = .75$

4.13   a. $P(x \le 12) = P(x = 10) + P(x = 11) + P(x = 12) = .2 + .3 + .2 = .7$

        b. $P(x > 12) = 1 - P(x \le 12) = 1 - .7 = .3$

        c. $P(x \le 14) = P(x = 10) + P(x = 11) + P(x = 12) + P(x = 13) + P(x = 14)$
                       $= .2 + .3 + .2 + .1 + .2 = 1$

        d. $P(x = 14) = .2$

        e. $P(x \le 11 \text{ or } x > 12) = P(x \le 11) + P(x > 12)$
                                 $= P(x = 10) + P(x = 11) + P(x = 13) + P(x = 14)$
                                 $= .2 + .3 + .1 + .2 = .8$

4.15   a.   The simple events are (where H = head, T = tail):

                          HHH HHT HTH THH HTT THT TTH TTT
             $x = \text{\# heads}$ 3   2   2   2   1   1   1   0

        b.   If each event is equally likely, then $P(\text{simple event}) = \dfrac{1}{n} = \dfrac{1}{8}$

$$p(3) = \frac{1}{8}, p(2) = \frac{1}{8} + \frac{1}{8} + \frac{1}{8} = \frac{3}{8}, \ p(1) = \frac{1}{8} + \frac{1}{8} + \frac{1}{8} = \frac{3}{8}, \text{ and } p(0) = \frac{1}{8}$$

        c.

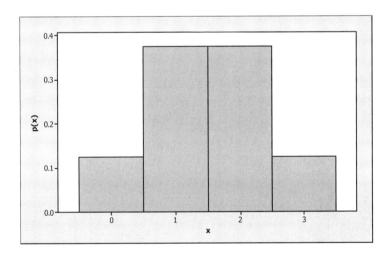

        d. $P(x = 2 \text{ or } x = 3) = p(2) + p(3) = \dfrac{3}{8} + \dfrac{1}{8} = \dfrac{4}{8} = \dfrac{1}{2}$

4.17   a. $p(0) + p(1) + p(2) + p(3) + p(4) = .09 + .30 + .37 + .20 + .04 = 1.00$

        b. $P(x = 3 \text{ or } 4) = p(3) + p(4) = .20 + .04 = .24$

        c. $P(x < 2) = p(0) + p(1) = .09 + .30 = .39$

4.19   Suppose we define the following events:

P: {Student scores perfect 1600}
N: {Student does not score perfect 1600}

From the text, $P(P) = 5/10,000 = .0005$. Thus, $P(N) = 1 - P(P) = 1 - .0005 = .9995$

a.   If three students are randomly selected, the possible outcomes for the 3 students are as follows:
PPP   PPN   PNP   NPP   PNN   NPN   NNP   NNN

Each of the sample points listed is really the intersection of independent events.

Thus, $P(PPP) = P(P \cap P \cap P) = P(P)P(P)P(P) = .0005(.0005)(.0005) = .0000$

$P(PPN) = P(P \cap P \cap N) = P(P)P(P)P(N) = .0005(.0005)(.9995) = .0000$
$\qquad = P(PNP) = P(NPP)$

$P(PNN) = P(P \cap N \cap N) = P(P)P(N)P(N) = .0005(.9995)(.9995) = .0005$
$\qquad = P(NPN) = P(NNP)$

$P(NNN) = P(N \cap N \cap N) = P(N)P(N)P(N) = .9995(.9995)(.9995) = .9985$

Thus, $P(x = 0) = P(NNN) = .9985$
$\qquad P(x = 1) = P(PNN) + P(NPN) + P(NNP) = .0005(3) = .0015$
$\qquad P(x = 2) = P(PPN) + P(PNP) + P(NPP) = .0000(3) = .0000$
$\qquad P(x = 3) = P(PPP) = .0000$

b.   The graph of $p(x)$ is:

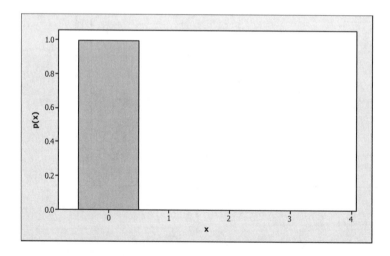

c. $P(x \le 1) = P(x = 0) + P(x = 1) = .9985 + .0015 = 1.0000$

4.21   Assigning points according to the directions is:

OUTCOME OF APPEAL	Number of cases	Points awarded, x
Plaintiff trial win – reversed	71	−1
Plaintiff trial win – affirmed/dismissed	240	5
Defendant trial win – reversed	68	−3
Defendant trial win – affirmed/dismissed	299	5
TOTAL	678	

To find the probabilities for x, we divide the frequencies by the total sample size. The probability distribution for x is:

x	p(x)
−3	68 / 678 = .100
−1	71 / 678 = .105
5	(240+299)/678 = .795
TOTAL	1.000

Using MINITAB, the graph of the probability distribution is:

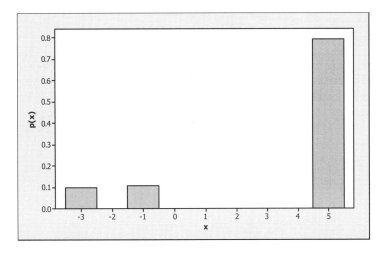

4.23   a.   The properties of valid probability distributions are:

$$\sum p(x) = 1 \text{ and } 0 \le p(x) \le 1 \text{ for all } x.$$

For ARC a_1: $0 \le p(x) \le 1$ for all x and $\sum p(x) = .6 + .25 + .1 + .05 = 1.00$
Thus, this is a valid probability distribution.

For ARC a_2: $0 \le p(x) \le 1$ for all x and $\sum p(x) = .6 + .3 + .1 = 1.00$
Thus, this is a valid probability distribution.

For ARC a_3: $0 \leq p(x) \leq 1$ for all x and $\sum p(x) = .9 + .1 = 1.00$
Thus, this is a valid probability distribution.

For ARC a_4: $0 \leq p(x) \leq 1$ for all x and $\sum p(x) = .9 + .1 = 1.00$
Thus, this is a valid probability distribution.

For ARC a_5: $0 \leq p(x) \leq 1$ for all x and $\sum p(x) = .9 + .1 = 1.00$
Thus, this is a valid probability distribution.

For ARC a_6: $0 \leq p(x) \leq 1$ for all x and $\sum p(x) = .7 + .25 + .05 = 1.00$
Thus, this is a valid probability distribution.

b.   For Arc a_1, $P(x > 1) = P(x = 2) + P(x = 3) = .25 + .6 = .85$

c.   For Arc a_2, $P(x > 1) = P(x = 2) = .6$
For Arc a_3, $P(x > 1) = 0$
For Arc a_4, $P(x > 1) = 0$
For Arc a_5, $P(x > 1) = 0$
For Arc a_6, $P(x > 1) = P(x = 2) = .7$

4.25   The sample space of the experiment would be:

S: {BBB, BBG, BGB, GBB, GGB, GBG, BGG, GGG}

where B and G represent a boy and girl respectively. Since the female parent always donates an X chromosome, the gender of any child is determined by the chromosome donated by the father; an X chromosome donated by the father will produce a girl, a Y, a boy. Each child therefore has a .5 probability of being either gender (as might be expected). From this, it follows that each of the above simple events has a probability of 1/8. If we let z represent the number of male offspring, the probability distribution of z is:

z	0	1	2	3
$p(z)$	1/8	3/8	3/8	1/8

Then,

$P(\text{At least one boy}) = P(z \geq 1) = 1 - P(z = 0) = 1 - 1/8 = 7/8$

4.27   The expected value of a random variable represents the mean of the probability distribution. You can think of the expected value as the mean value of x in a *very large* (actually, *infinite*) number of repetitions of the experiment.

4.29   For a mound-shaped, symmetric distribution, the probability that x falls in the interval $\mu \pm 2\sigma$ is approximately .95. This follows the probabilities associated with the Empirical Rule.

4.31   a. $\mu = E(x) = \sum xp(x) = 1(.2) + 2(.4) + 4(.2) + 10(.2) = .2 + .8 + .8 + 2 = 3.8$

b. $\sigma^2 = E[(x - \mu)^2] = \sum(x - \mu)^2 p(x)$

$$= (1 - 3.8)^2(.2) + (2 - 3.8)^2(.4) + (4 - 3.8)^2(.2) + (10 - 3.8)^2(.2)$$
$$= 1.568 + 1.296 + .008 + 7.688 = 10.56$$

c. $\sigma = \sqrt{10.59} = 3.2496$

d. The average value of x over many trials is 3.8.

e. No. The random variable can only take on values 1, 2, 4, or 10.

f. Yes. It is possible that μ can be equal to an actual value of x.

4.33 a. It would seem that the mean of both would be 1 since they both are symmetric distributions centered at 1.

b. $P(x)$ seems more variable since there appears to be greater probability for the two extreme values of 0 and 2 than there is in the distribution of y.

c. For x: $\mu = E(x) = \sum xp(x) = 0(.3) + 1(.4) + 2(.3) = 0 + .4 + .6 = 1$

$\sigma^2 = E[(x - \mu)^2] = \sum(x - \mu)^2 p(x)$

$$= (0 - 1)^2(.3) + (1 - 1)^2(.4) + (2 - 1)^2(.3) = .3 + 0 + .3 = .6$$

For y: $\mu = E(y) = \sum yp(y) = 0(.1) + 1(.8) + 2(.1) = 0 + .8 + .2 = 1$

$\sigma^2 = E[(y - \mu)^2] = \sum(y - \mu)^2 p(y)$

$$= (0 - 1)^2(.1) + (1 - 1)^2(.8) + (2 - 1)^2(.1) = .1 + 0 + .1 = .2$$

The variance for x is larger than that for y.

4.35 a. To find the probabilities associated with each value of x, we divide the frequency associated with each value by the total sample size, 743. The probabilities appear in the table:

First Digit	Frequency of Occurrence	Probability
1	109	109 / 743 = .1467
2	75	75 / 743 = .1009
3	77	77 / 743 = .1036
4	99	99 / 743 = .1332
5	72	72 / 743 = .0969
6	117	117 / 743 = .1575
7	89	89 / 743 = .1198
8	62	62 / 743 = .0834
9	43	43 / 743 = 0579
Total	743	1.0000

b. $\mu = E(x) = \sum xp(x) = 1(.1467) + 2(.1009) + 3(.1036) + 4(.1332) + 5(.0969)$

$+ 6(.1575) + 7(.1198) + 8(.0834) + 9(.0579) = 4.6485$

c. Over a very large number of trials, the average first significant digit is 4.6485.

4.37 a. **For ARC a_1:** $\mu = E(x) = \sum xp(x) = 0(.05) + 1(.10) + 2(.25) + 3(.60) = 2.4$

The mean capacity for ARC a_1 is 2.4

For ARC a_2: $\mu = E(x) = \sum xp(x) = 0(.10) + 1(.30) + 2(.60) = 1.5$

The mean capacity for ARC a_2 is 1.5

For ARC a_3: $\mu = E(x) = \sum xp(x) = 0(.10) + 1(.90) = .90$

The mean capacity for ARC a_3 is .90

For ARC a_4: $\mu = E(x) = \sum xp(x) = 0(.10) + 1(.90) = .90$

The mean capacity for ARC a_4 is .90

For ARC a_5: $\mu = E(x) = \sum xp(x) = 0(.10) + 1(.90) = .90$

The mean capacity for ARC a_5 is .90

For ARC a_6: $\mu = E(x) = \sum xp(x) = 0(.05) + 1(.25) + 2(.70) = 1.65$

The mean capacity for ARC a_6 is 1.65

b. **For ARC a_1:** $\sigma^2 = E(x - \mu)^2 = \sum (x - \mu)^2 p(x)$

$= (3 - 2.4)^2(.60) + (2 - 2.4)^2(.25) + (1 - 2.4)^2(.10) + (0 - 2.4)^2(.05)$

$= .216 + .040 + .196 + .288 = .74$

$\sigma = \sqrt{\sigma^2} = \sqrt{.74} = .8602$

For ARC a_2: $\sigma^2 = E(x - \mu)^2 = \sum (x - \mu)^2 p(x)$

$= (2 - 1.5)^2(.60) + (1 - 1.5)^2(.30) + (0 - 1.5)^2(.10)$

$= .15 + .075 + .225 = .45$

$\sigma = \sqrt{\sigma^2} = \sqrt{.45} = .6708$

For ARC a_3: $\sigma^2 = E(x - \mu)^2 = \sum (x - \mu)^2 p(x)$

$= (1 - .9)^2(.90) + (0 - .9)^2(.10)$

$= .009 + .081 = .09$

$\sigma = \sqrt{\sigma^2} = \sqrt{.09} = .3$

For ARC a_4: $\sigma^2 = E(x - \mu)^2 = \sum (x - \mu)^2 p(x)$

$= (1 - .9)^2(.90) + (0 - .9)^2(.10)$

$= .009 + .081 = .09$

$\sigma = \sqrt{\sigma^2} = \sqrt{.09} = .3$

For ARC a_5: $\sigma^2 = E(x - \mu)^2 = \sum(x - \mu)^2 p(x)$

$$= (1 - .9)^2(.90) + (0 - .9)^2(.10)$$
$$= .009 + .081 = .09$$
$$\sigma = \sqrt{\sigma^2} = \sqrt{.09} = .3$$

For ARC a_6: $\sigma^2 = E(x - \mu)^2 = \sum(x - \mu)^2 p(x)$

$$= (2 - 1.65)^2(.70) + (1 - 1.65)^2(.25) + (0 - 1.65)^2(.05)$$
$$= .08575 + .105625 + .136125 = .3275$$
$$\sigma = \sqrt{\sigma^2} = \sqrt{.09} = .5723$$

4.39   For a \$5 bet, you will either win \$5 or lose \$5 (−\$5). The probability distribution for the net winnings is:

x	$p(x)$
−5	20/38
5	18/38

$$\mu = E(x) = \sum xp(x) = -5\left(\frac{20}{38}\right) + 5\left(\frac{18}{38}\right) = -.263$$

Over a large number of trials, the average winning for a \$5 bet on red is -\$0.263.

4.41   a.   Since there are 20 possible outcomes that are all equally likely, the probability of any of the 20 numbers is 1/20. The probability distribution of x is:

$$P(x = 5) = 1/20 = .05; \quad P(x = 10) = 1/20 = .05; \text{ etc.}$$

x	5	10	15	20	25	30	35	40	45	50	55	60	65	70	75	80	85	90	95	100
$p(x)$	.05	.05	.05	.05	.05	.05	.05	.05	.05	.05	.05	.05	.05	.05	.05	.05	.05	.05	.05	.05

b. $E(x) = \sum xp(x) = 5(.05) + 10(.05) + 15(.05) + 20(.05) + 25(.05) + 30(.05) + 35(.05)$
$+ 40(.05) + 45(.05) + 50(.05) + 55(.05) + 60(.05) + 65(.05) + 70(.05) + 75(.05)$
$+ 80(.05) + 85(.05) + 90(.05) + 95(.05) + 100(.05) = 52.5$

c. $\sigma^2 = E(x - \mu)^2 = \sum(x - \mu)^2 p(x) = (5 - 52.5)^2(.05) + (10 - 52.5)^2(.05)$
$+ (15 - 52.5)^2(.05) + (20 - 52.5)^2(.05) + (25 - 52.5)^2(.05) + (30 - 52.5)^2(.05)$
$+ (35 - 52.5)^2(.05) + (40 - 52.5)^2(.05) + (45 - 52.5)^2(.05) + (50 - 52.5)^2(.05)$
$+ (55 - 52.5)^2(.05) + (60 - 52.5)^2(.05) + (65 - 52.5)^2(.05) + (70 - 52.5)^2(.05)$
$+ (75 - 52.5)^2(.05) + (80 - 52.5)^2(.05) + (85 - 52.5)^2(.05) + (90 - 52.5)^2(.05)$
$+ (95 - 52.5)^2(.05) + (100 - 52.5)^2(.05)$
$= 831.25$

$$\sigma = \sqrt{\sigma^2} = \sqrt{831.25} = 28.83$$

Since the uniform distribution is not mound-shaped, we will use Chebyshev's theorem to describe the data. We know that at least 8/9 of the observations will fall with 3 standard deviations of the mean and at least 3/4 of the observations will fall within 2 standard deviations of the mean. For this problem,

$\mu \pm 2\sigma \Rightarrow 52.5 \pm 2(28.83) \Rightarrow 52.5 \pm 57.66 \Rightarrow (-5.16, 110.16)$. Thus, at least 3/4 of the data will fall between -5.16 and 110.16. For our problem, all of the observations will fall within 2 standard deviations of the mean. Thus, x is just as likely to fall within any interval of equal length.

d. If a player spins the wheel twice, the total number of outcomes will be $20(20) = 400$. The sample space is:

5, 5	10, 5	15, 5	20, 5	25, 5...	100, 5
5,10	10,10	15,10	20,10	25,10...	100,10
5,15	10,15	15,15	20,15	25,15...	100,15
⋮	⋮	⋮	⋮	⋮	⋮
5,100	10,100	15,100	20,100	25,100...	100,100

Each of these outcomes are equally likely, so each has a probability of $1/400 = .0025$.

Now, let x equal the sum of the two numbers in each sample. There is one sample with a sum of 10, two samples with a sum of 15, three samples with a sum of 20, etc. If the sum of the two numbers exceeds 100, then x is zero. The probability distribution of x is:

x	$p(x)$
0	.5250
10	.0025
15	.0050
20	.0075
25	.0100
30	.0125
35	.0150
40	.0175
45	.0200
50	.0225
55	.0250
60	.0275
65	.0300
70	.0325
75	.0350
80	.0375
85	.0400
90	.0425
95	.0450
100	.0475

e. We assumed that the wheel is fair, or that all outcomes are equally likely.

f. $\mu = E(x) = \sum xp(x) = 0(.5250) + 10(.0025) + 15(.0050) + 20(.0075) + ...+ 100(.0475)$
$= 33.25$

$\sigma^2 = E(x - \mu)^2 = \sum (x - \mu)^2 p(x) = (0 - 33.25)^2(.525) + (10 - 33.25)^2(.0025)$
$+ (15 - 33.25)^2(.0050) + (20 - 33.25)^2(.0075) + ...+ (100 - 33.25)^2(.0475)$
$= 1471.3125$

$\sigma = \sqrt{\sigma^2} = \sqrt{1471.3125} = 38.3577$

g. $P(x = 0) = .525$

h. Given that the player obtains a 20 on the first spin, the possible values for x (sum of the two spins) are 0 (player spins 85, 90, 95, or 100 on the second spin), 25, 30, ..., 100. In order to get an x of 25, the player would spin a 5 on the second spin. Similarly, the player would have to spin a 10 on the second spin order to get an x of 30, etc. Since all of the outcomes are equally likely on the second spin, the distribution of x is:

x	$p(x)$
0	.20
25	.05
30	.05
35	.05
40	.05
45	.05
50	.05
55	.05
60	.05
65	.05
70	.05
75	.05
80	.05
85	.05
90	.05
95	.05
100	.05

i. The probability that the players total score will exceed one dollar is the probability that x is zero. $P(x = 0) = .20$

j. Given that the player obtains a 65 on the first spin, the possible values for x (sum of the two spins) are 0 (player spins 40, 45, 50, up to 100 on second spin), 70, 75, 80,..., 100. In order to get an x of 70, the player would spin a 5 on the second spin. Similarly, the player would have to spin a 10 on the second spin in order to get an x of 75, etc. Since all of the outcomes are equally likely on the second spin, the distribution of x is:

x	$p(x)$
0	.65
70	.05
75	.05
80	.05
85	.05
90	.05
95	.05
100	.05

The probability that the players total score will exceed one dollar is the probability that x is zero. $P(x = 0) = .65$.

4.43   a. Let x = number of training units necessary to master the complex computer software program.

$$\mu = E(x) = \sum xp(x) = 1(.1) + 2(.25) + 3(.4) + 4(.15) + 5(.1)$$
$$= .1 + .5 + 1.2 + .6 + .5 = 2.9$$

This is the average number of units necessary to master the complex software program.

Median = 3 (first observation where the cumulative probability is $\geq .5$)

At least half of the observations are less than or equal to 3 and at least half of the observations are greater than or equal to 3.

b. $P(x \leq k) \geq .75 \Rightarrow k = 3$
$P(x \leq k) \geq .90 \Rightarrow k = 4$

c. $\mu = E(x) = \sum xp(x) = 1(.25) + 2(.35) + 3(.40) = .25 + .70 + 1.2 = 2.15$

This is smaller than the answer in part **a**. Again, this is the average number of units necessary to master the complex software program.

Median = 2 (first observation where the cumulative probability is $\geq .5$)

$P(x \leq k) \geq .75 \Rightarrow k = 3$
$P(x \leq k) \geq .90 \Rightarrow k = 3$

4.45   The formula for p(x) for a binomial random variable with n = 7 and p = .2 is:

$$p(x) = \binom{n}{x} p^x q^{n-x} = \binom{7}{x} .2^x .8^{7-x} \quad (x = 0, 1, 2, ..., 7)$$

4.47 a. $\dfrac{6!}{2!(6-2)!} = \dfrac{6!}{2!4!} = \dfrac{6\cdot5\cdot4\cdot3\cdot2\cdot1}{(2\cdot1)(4\cdot3\cdot2\cdot1)} = 15$

b. $\dbinom{5}{2} = \dfrac{5!}{2!(5-2)!} = \dfrac{5!}{2!3!} = \dfrac{5\cdot4\cdot3\cdot2\cdot1}{(2\cdot1)(3\cdot2\cdot1)} = 10$

c. $\dbinom{7}{0} = \dfrac{7!}{0!(7-0)!} = \dfrac{7!}{0!7!} = \dfrac{7\cdot6\cdot5\cdot4\cdot3\cdot2\cdot1}{(1)(7\cdot6\cdot5\cdot4\cdot3\cdot2\cdot1)} = 1$

(Note: $0! = 1$)

d. $\dbinom{6}{6} = \dfrac{6!}{6!(6-6)!} = \dfrac{6!}{6!0!} = \dfrac{6\cdot5\cdot4\cdot3\cdot2\cdot1}{(6\cdot5\cdot4\cdot3\cdot2\cdot1)(1)} = 1$

e. $\dbinom{4}{3} = \dfrac{4!}{3!(4-3)!} = \dfrac{4!}{3!1!} = \dfrac{4\cdot3\cdot2\cdot1}{(3\cdot2\cdot1)(1)} = 4$

4.49 a. $P(x=1) = \dfrac{5!}{1!4!}(.2)^1(.8)^4 = \dfrac{5\cdot4\cdot3\cdot2\cdot1}{(1)(4\cdot3\cdot2\cdot1)}(.2)^1(.8)^4 = 5(.2)^1(.8)^4 = .4096$

b. $P(x=2) = \dfrac{4!}{2!2!}(.6)^2(.4)^2 = \dfrac{4\cdot3\cdot2\cdot1}{(2\cdot1)(2\cdot1)}(.6)^2(.4)^2 = 6(.6)^2(.4)^2 = .3456$

c. $P(x=0) = \dfrac{3!}{0!3!}(.7)^0(.3)^3 = \dfrac{3\cdot2\cdot1}{(1)(3\cdot2\cdot1)}(.7)^0(.3)^3 = 1(.7)^0(.3)^3 = .027$

d. $P(x=3) = \dfrac{5!}{3!2!}(.1)^3(.9)^2 = \dfrac{5\cdot4\cdot3\cdot2\cdot1}{(3\cdot2\cdot1)(2\cdot1)}(.1)^3(.9)^2 = 10(.1)^3(.9)^2 = .0081$

e. $P(x=2) = \dfrac{4!}{2!2!}(.4)^2(.6)^2 = \dfrac{4\cdot3\cdot2\cdot1}{(2\cdot1)(2\cdot1)}(.4)^2(.6)^2 = 6(.4)^2(.6)^2 = .3456$

f. $P(x=1) = \dfrac{3!}{1!2!}(.9)^1(.1)^2 = \dfrac{3\cdot2\cdot1}{(1)(2\cdot1)}(.9)^1(.1)^2 = 3(.9)^1(.1)^2 = .027$

4.51 a. $\mu = np = 25(.5) = 12.5$

$\sigma^2 = np(1-p) = 25(.5)(.5) = 6.25$
$\sigma = \sqrt{\sigma^2} = \sqrt{6.25} = 2.5$

b. $\mu = np = 80(.2) = 16$

$\sigma^2 = np(1-p) = 80(.2)(.8) = 12.8$
$\sigma = \sqrt{\sigma^2} = \sqrt{12.8} = 3.578$

c. $\mu = np = 100(.6) = 60$

$\sigma^2 = np(1-p) = 100(.6)(.4) = 24$
$\sigma = \sqrt{\sigma^2} = \sqrt{24} = 4.899$

d. $\mu = np = 70(.9) = 63$

$\sigma^2 = np(1-p) = 70(.9)(.1) = 6.3$
$\sigma = \sqrt{\sigma^2} = \sqrt{6.3} = 2.510$

e. $\mu = np = 60(.8) = 48$

$\sigma^2 = np(1-p) = 60(.8)(.2) = 9.6$
$\sigma = \sqrt{\sigma^2} = \sqrt{9.6} = 3.098$

f. $\mu = np = 1,000(.04) = 40$

$\sigma^2 = np(1-p) = 1,000(.04)(.96) = 38.4$
$\sigma = \sqrt{\sigma^2} = \sqrt{38.4} = 6.197$

4.53   a. $P(x < 10) = P(x \le 9) = 0$

      b. $P(x \ge 10) = 1 - P(x \le 9) = 1 - .002 = .998$

      c. $P(x = 2) = P(x \le 2) - P(x \le 1) = .206 \ .069 = .137$

4.55 x is a binomial random variable with $n = 4$.

      a.   If the probability distribution of x is symmetric, $p(0) = p(4)$ and $p(1) = p(3)$.

Since $p(x) = \binom{n}{x} p^x q^{n-x}$ $x = 0, 1, \ldots, n,$

When $n = 4$,

$$\binom{4}{0} p^0 q^4 = \binom{4}{4} p^4 q^0$$

$$\Rightarrow \frac{4!}{0!4!} p^0 q^4 = \frac{4!}{4!0!} p^4 q^0$$
$$\Rightarrow q^4 = p^4$$
$$\Rightarrow p = q$$

Since $p + q = 1, p = .5$

Therefore, the probability distribution of x is symmetric when $p = .5$.

      b.   If the probability distribution of x is skewed to the right, then the mean is greater than the median. Therefore, there are more small values in the distribution (0, 1) than large values (3, 4). Therefore, p must be smaller than .5. Let $p = .2$ and the probability distribution of x will be skewed to the right.

c.   If the probability distribution of x is skewed to the left, then the mean is smaller than the median. Therefore, there are more large values in the distribution (3, 4) than small values (0, 1). Therefore, p must be larger than .5. Let $p = .8$ and the probability distribution of x will be skewed to the left.

d.   In part **a**, x is a binomial random variable with $n = 4$ and $p = .5$.

$$p(x) = \binom{4}{x}.5^x.5^{4-x} \qquad x = 0, 1, 2, 3, 4$$

$$p(0) = \binom{4}{0}.5^0.5^4 = \frac{4!}{0!4!}.5^4 = 1(.5)^4 = .0625$$

$$p(1) = \binom{4}{1}.5^1.5^3 = \frac{4!}{1!3!}.5^4 = 4(.5)^4 = .25$$

$$p(2) = \binom{4}{2}.5^2.5^2 = \frac{4!}{2!2!}.5^4 = 6(.5)^4 = .375$$

$$p(3) = p(1) = .25 \text{ (since the distribution is symmetric)}$$
$$p(4) = p(0) = .0625$$

The probability distribution of x in tabular form is:

x	0	1	2	3	4
$p(x)$	.0625	.25	.375	.25	.0625

$$\mu = np = 4(.5) = 2$$

The graph of the probability distribution of x when $n = 4$ and $p = .5$ is as follows.

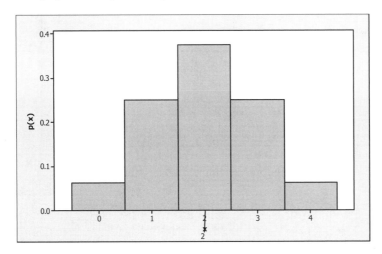

In part **b**, x is a binomial random variable with $n = 4$ and $p = .2$.

$$p(x) = \binom{4}{x}.2^x.8^{4-x} \quad x = 0, 1, 2, 3, 4$$

$$p(0) = \binom{4}{0}.2^0.8^4 = 1(1).8^4 = .4096$$

$$p(1) = \binom{4}{1}.2^1.8^3 = 4(.2)(.8)^3 = .4096$$

$$p(2) = \binom{4}{2}.2^2.8^2 = 6(.2)^2(.8)^2 = .1536$$

$$p(3) = \binom{4}{3}.2^3.8^1 = 4(.2)^3(.8) = .0256$$

$$p(4) = \binom{4}{0}.2^4.8^0 = 1(.2)^4(1) = .0016$$

The probability distribution of x in tabular form is:

x	0	1	2	3	4
$p(x)$	.4096	.4096	.1536	.0256	.0016

$\mu = np = 4(.2) = .8$

The graph of the probability distribution of x when $n = 4$ and $p = .2$ is as follows:

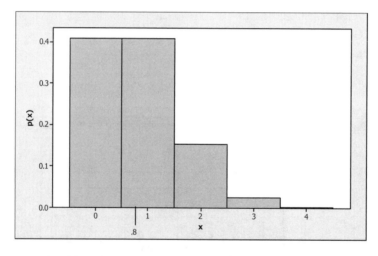

In part **c**, x is a binomial random variable with $n = 4$ and $p = .8$.

$$p(x) = \binom{4}{x}.8^x.2^{4-x} \quad x = 0, 1, 2, 3, 4$$

$$p(0) = \binom{4}{0}.8^0.2^4 = 1(1).2^4 = .0016$$

$$p(1) = \binom{4}{1}.8^1.2^3 = 4(.8)(.2)^3 = .0256$$

$$p(2) = \binom{4}{2}.8^2.2^2 = 6(.8)^2(.2)^2 = .1536$$

$$p(3) = \binom{4}{3}.8^3.2^1 = 4(.8)^3(.2) = .4096$$

$$p(4) = \binom{4}{4}.8^4.2^0 = 1(.8)^4(1) = .4096$$

The probability distribution of x in tabular form is:

x	0	1	2	3	4
$p(x)$	.0016	.0256	.1536	.4096	.4096

Note: The distribution of x when $n = 4$ and $p = .2$ is the reverse of the distribution of x when $n = 4$ and $p = .8$.

$\mu = np = 4(.8) = 3.2$

The graph of the probability distribution of x when $n = 4$ and $p = .8$ is as follows:

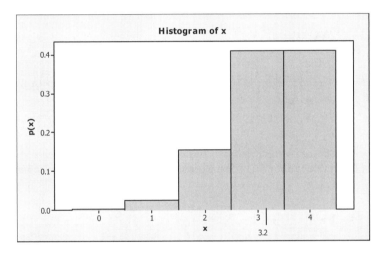

e. In general, when $p = .5$, a binomial distribution will be symmetric regardless of the value of n. When p is less than .5, the binomial distribution will be skewed to the right; and when p is greater than .5, it will be skewed to the left. (Refer to parts **a**, **b**, and **c**.)

4.57 a. For this experiment, there are $n = 200$ smokers (n identical trials). For each smoker, there are 2 possible outcomes: S = smoker enters treatment program and F = smoker does not enter treatment program. The probability of S (smoker enters treatment program) is the same from trial to trial. This probability is $P(S) = p = .05$. $P(F) = 1 - P(S) = 1 - .05 = .95$. The trials are independent and x = number of smokers entering treatment program in 200 trials. Thus, x is a binomial random variable.

b. $p = P(S) = .05$. Of all the smokers, only .05 or 5% enter treatment programs.

c. $E(x) = np = 200(.05) = 10$. For all samples of 200 smokers, the average number of smokers who enter a treatment program will be 10.

4.59 a. From the problem, x is a binomial random variable with $n = 10$ and $p = .8$.

$P(x = 3) = P(x \le 3) - P(x \le 2) = .001 - .000 = .001$ (from Table II, Appendix A)

b. $P(x \le 7) = .322$

c. $P(x > 4) = 1 - P(x \le 4) = 1 - .006 = .994$

4.61 a. Let x = number of beach trees damaged by fungi in 20 trials. Then x is a binomial random variable with $n = 20$ and $p = .25$.

$P(x < 10) = P(x = 0) + P(x = 1) + \cdots + P(x = 9)$

$$= \binom{20}{0}.25^0.75^{20} + \binom{20}{1}.25^1.75^{19} + \binom{20}{2}.25^2.75^{18} + \cdots + \binom{20}{9}.25^9.75^{11}$$

$$= .0032 + .0211 + .0669 + .1339 + .1897 + .2023 + .1686 + .1124 + .0609 + .0271$$

$$= .9861$$

b. $P(x > 15) = P(x = 16) + P(x = 17) + \cdots + P(x = 20)$

$$= \binom{20}{16}.25^{16}.75^4 + \binom{20}{17}.25^{17}.75^3 + \binom{20}{18}.25^{18}.75^2 + \cdots + \binom{20}{20}.25^{20}.75^0$$

$$= .000000356 + .000000027 + .000000001 + 0 + 0 = .000000384$$

4.63 a. Let x = number of women out of 15 that have been abused. Then x is a binomial random variable with $n = 15$, S = woman has been abused, F = woman has not been abused, $P(S) = p = 1/3$ and $q = 1 - p = 1 - 1/3 = 2/3$.

$P(x \ge 4) = 1 - P(x < 4) = 1 - P(x = 0) - P(x = 1) - P(x = 2) - P(x = 3)$

$$= 1 - \frac{15!}{0!\,15!}\left(\frac{1}{3}\right)^0\left(\frac{2}{3}\right)^{15} - \frac{15!}{1!\,14!}\left(\frac{1}{3}\right)^1\left(\frac{2}{3}\right)^{14} - \frac{15!}{2!\,13!}\left(\frac{1}{3}\right)^2\left(\frac{2}{3}\right)^{13}$$

$$- \frac{15!}{3!\,12!}\left(\frac{1}{3}\right)^3\left(\frac{2}{3}\right)^{12}$$

$$= 1 - .0023 - .0171 - .0599 - .1299 = .7908$$

b. For $p = .1$,

$P(x \ge 4) = 1 - P(x < 4) = 1 - P(x = 0) - P(x = 1) - P(x = 2) - P(x = 3)$

$$= 1 - \frac{15!}{0!\,15!}.1^0.9^{15} - \frac{15!}{1!\,14!}.1^1.9^{14} - \frac{15!}{2!\,13!}.1^2.9^{13} - \frac{15!}{3!\,12!}.1^3.9^{12}$$

$$= 1 - .2059 - .3432 - .2669 - .1285 = .0555$$

c. We sampled 15 women and actually found that 4 had been abused. If $p = 1/3$, the probability of observing 4 or more abused women is .7908. If $p = .1$, the probability of observing 4 or more abused women is only .0555. If $p = .1$, we would have seen a very unusual event because the probability is so small (.0555). If $p = 1/3$, we would have seen an event that was very common because the probability was very large (.7908). Since we normally do not see rare events, the true probability of abuse is probably close to 1/3.

4.65 a. If the psychic is just guessing, she has 1 chance out of 10 of guessing the correct decision. Thus, $p = 1/10 = .1$.

b. Let x = number of correct decisions in 7 trials. Then x is a binomial random variable with $n = 7$ and $p = .1$. The expected number of correct decisions in 7 trials is

$$E(x) = np = 7(.1) = .7.$$

Thus, if the psychic is just guessing, we would expect her to make less than 1 correct decision in 7 trials.

c. $P(x = 0) = \binom{7}{0}.1^0.9^7 = .4783$

d. Now, let $p = .5$. $P(x = 0) = \binom{7}{0}.5^0.5^7 = .0078$

e. Yes. If the psychic is just guessing, the probability that she makes no correct decisions is .4783. Thus, if the psychic, in fact, made no correct decisions, this would not be an unusual event if she is guessing. However, on the other hand, if she does have ESP ($p = .5$) and made no correct decisions, this would be a very unusual event ($P(x = 0) = .0078$). The evidence indicates the psychic probably is just guessing and does not have ESP.

4.67 a. We must assume that the probability that a specific type of ball meets the requirements is always the same from trial to trial and the trials are independent. To use the binomial probability distribution, we need to know the probability that a specific type of golf ball meets the requirements.

b. For a binomial distribution,

$$\mu = np$$
$$\sigma = \sqrt{npq}$$

In this example, n = two dozen = $2 \cdot 12 = 24$.

$p = .10$ (Success here means the golf ball *does not* meet standards.)
$q = .90$
$\mu = np = 24(.10) = 2.4$
$\sigma = \sqrt{npq} = \sqrt{24(.10)(.90)} = 1.47$

c.   In this situation,

p = Probability of success
     = Probability golf ball *does* meet standards
     = .90
$q = 1 - .90 = .10$
$n = 24$
$E(x) = \mu = np = 24(.90) = 21.60$
$\sigma = \sqrt{npq} = \sqrt{24(.10)(.90)} = 1.47$ (Note that this is the same as in part **b**.)

4.69   The four characteristics of a Poisson random variable are:

a.   The experiment consists of counting the number of times a certain event occurs during a given unit of time or in a given area or volume (or weight, distance, or any other unit of measurement).
b.   The probability that an event occurs in a given unit of time, area, or volume is the same for all the units.
c.   The number of events that occur in one unit of time, area, or volume is independent of the number that occur in other units.
d.   The mean (or expected) number of events in each unit is denoted by the Greek letter lambda, λ.

4.71   For the Poisson probability distribution

$$p(x) = \frac{3^x e^{-3}}{x!} \qquad (x = 0, 1, 2, ...)$$

the value of λ is 3.

4.73   a.   In order to graph the probability distribution, we need to know the probabilities for the possible values of x. Using Table III of Appendix A with $\lambda = 3$:

$p(0) = .050$
$p(1) = P(x \le 1) - P(x = 0) = .199 - .050 = .149$
$p(2) = P(x \le 2) - P(x \le 1) = .423 - .199 = .224$
$p(3) = P(x \le 3) - P(x \le 2) = .647 - .423 = .224$
$p(4) = P(x \le 4) - P(x \le 3) = .815 - .647 = .168$
$p(5) = P(x \le 5) - P(x \le 4) = .916 - .815 = .101$
$p(6) = P(x \le 6) - P(x \le 5) = .966 - .916 = .050$
$p(7) = P(x \le 7) - P(x \le 6) = .988 - .966 = .022$
$p(8) = P(x \le 8) - P(x \le 7) = .996 - .988 = .008$
$p(9) = P(x \le 9) - P(x \le 8) = .999 - .996 = .003$
$p(10) \approx .001$

The probability distribution of x in graphical form is:

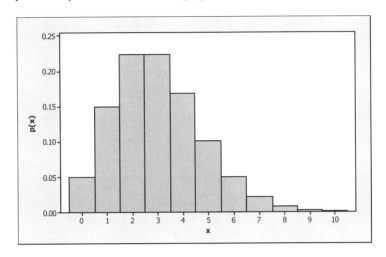

b. $\mu = \lambda = 3$
$\sigma^2 = \lambda = 3$
$\sigma = \sqrt{3} = 1.7321$

4.75 $\mu = \lambda = 1.5$

Using Table III of Appendix A:

a. $P(x \le 3) = .934$

b. $P(x \ge 3) = 1 - P(x \le 2) = 1 - .809 = .191$

c. $P(x = 3) = P(x \le 3) - P(x \le 2) = .934 - .809 = .125$

d. $P(x = 0) = .223$

e. $P(x > 0) = 1 - P(x = 0) = 1 - .223 = .777$

f. $P(x > 6) = 1 - P(x \le 6) = 1 - .999 = .001$

4.77   a. To graph the Poisson probability distribution with $\lambda = 3$, we need to calculate $p(x)$ for $x = 0$ to 10. Using Table III, Appendix A,

$p(0) = .050$
$p(1) = P(x \le 1) - P(x = 0) = .199 - .050 = .149$
$p(2) = P(x \le 2) - P(x \le 1) = .423 - .199 = .224$
$p(3) = P(x \le 3) - P(x \le 2) = .647 - .423 = .224$
$p(4) = P(x \le 4) - P(x \le 3) = .815 - .647 = .168$
$p(5) = P(x \le 5) - P(x \le 4) = .916 - .815 = .101$
$p(6) = P(x \le 6) - P(x \le 5) = .966 - .916 = .050$
$p(7) = P(x \le 7) - P(x \le 6) = .988 - .966 = .022$
$p(8) = P(x \le 8) - P(x \le 7) = .996 - .988 = .008$
$p(9) = P(x \le 9) - P(x \le 8) = .999 - .996 = .003$
$p(10) = P(x \le 10) - P(x \le 9) \approx 1 - .999 = .001$

The graph is shown here.

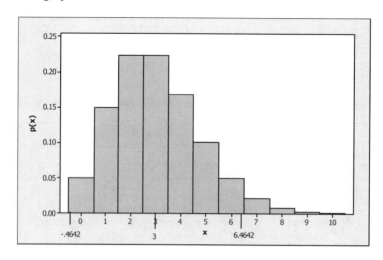

b. $\mu = \lambda = 3$

$\sigma = \sqrt{\lambda} = \sqrt{3} = 1.7321$

$\mu \pm 2\sigma \Rightarrow 3 \pm 2(1.7321) \Rightarrow (-.4642, 6.4642)$

c. $P(\mu - 2\sigma < x < \mu + 2\sigma) = P(-.4642 < x < 6.4642) = P(0 \le x \le 6)$
$= P(x \le 6) = .966$

4.79 a. Using Table III, Appendix A, with $\lambda = 1$, $P(x = 0) = .368$.

b. Using Table III, Appendix A, with $\lambda = 1$, $P(x > 1) = 1 - P(x \le 1) = 1 - .736 = .264$.

c. Using Table III, Appendix A, with $\lambda = 1$, $P(x \le 2) = .920$.

4.81 a. $P(x = 0) = \dfrac{\lambda^0 e^{-\lambda}}{0!} = \dfrac{3.8^0 e^{-3.8}}{0!} \quad .0224$

b. $P(x = 1) = \dfrac{\lambda^1 e^{-\lambda}}{1!} = \dfrac{3.8^1 e^{-3.8}}{1!} = .0850$

c. $E(x) = \mu = \lambda = 3.8$

$\sigma^2 = \lambda = 3.8$
$\sigma = \sqrt{3.8} = 1.9494$

4.83 a. $\sigma = \sqrt{\lambda} = \sqrt{4} = 2$

b. $P(x > 10) = 1 - P(x \le 10) = 1 - .997 = .003$ from Table III, Appendix A, with $\lambda = 4$. Since the probability is so small (.003), it would be very unlikely that the plant would yield a value that would exceed the EPA limit.

4.85 a. Using Table III and $\lambda = 6.2$, $P(x = 2) = P(x \le 2) - P(x \le 1) = .054 - .015 = .039$
$P(x = 6) = P(x \le 6) - P(x \le 5) = .574 - .414 = .160$
$P(x = 10) = P(x \le 10) - P(x \le 9) = .949 - .902 = .047$

b. The plot of the distribution is:

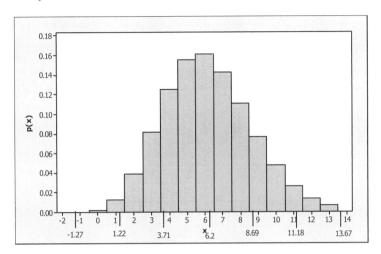

c. $\mu = \lambda = 6.2$, $\sigma = \sqrt{\lambda} = \sqrt{6.2} = 2.490$
$\mu \pm \sigma \Rightarrow 6.2 \pm 2.49 \Rightarrow (3.71, 8.69)$
$\mu \pm 2\sigma \Rightarrow 6.2 \pm 2(2.49) \Rightarrow 6.2 \pm 4.98 \Rightarrow (1.22, 11.18)$
$\mu \pm 3\sigma \Rightarrow 6.2 \pm 3(2.49) \Rightarrow 6.2 \pm 7.47 \Rightarrow (-1.27, 13.67)$

See the plot in part **b**.

d. First, we need to find the mean number of customers per hour. If the mean number of customers per 10 minutes is 6.2, then the mean number of customers per hour is $6.2(6) = 37.2 = \lambda$.

$\mu = \lambda = 37.2$ and $\sigma = \sqrt{\lambda} = \sqrt{37.2} = 6.099$
$\mu \pm 3\sigma \Rightarrow 37.2 \pm 3(6.099) \Rightarrow 37.2 \pm 18.297 \Rightarrow (18.903, 55.498)$

Using Chebyshev's Rule, we know at least 8/9 or 88.9% of the observations will fall within 3 standard deviations of the mean. The number 75 is way beyond the 3 standard deviation limit. Thus, it would be very unlikely that more than 75 customers entered the store per hour on Saturdays.

4.87 Let x = number of cars that will arrive within the next 30 minutes. If the average number of cars that arrive in 60 minutes is 10, the average number of cars that arrive in 30 minutes is $\lambda = 5$.

In order for no cars to be in line at closing time, no more than 1 car can arrive in the next 30 minutes.

$P(x \le 1) = .040$ from Table III, Appendix A, with $\lambda = 5$.

Since this probability is so small, it is very likely that at least one car will be in line at closing time. The probability that at least one car will be in line at closing is $1 - .040 = .960$.

Discrete Random Variables

4.89   A binomial random variable is characterized by n trials where the trials are identical. In order for the trials to be identical, we have to sample from an infinite population or sample from a finite population with replacement. The probability of success on any trial remains constant from trial to trial and the trials are independent. A hypergeometric random variable is characterized by n trials where the elements are selected from a finite population without replacement. The probability of success on any trial depends on what happened on previous trials, and thus the trials are not independent.

Both a binomial random variable and a hypergeometric random variable are characterized by n trials, 2 possible outcomes on each trial (S or F), and the random variable represents the number of successes in n trials.

4.91   a. $$P(x=1) = \frac{\binom{r}{x}\binom{N-r}{n-x}}{\binom{N}{n}} = \frac{\binom{3}{1}\binom{5-3}{3-1}}{\binom{5}{3}} = \frac{\frac{3!}{1!2!}\frac{2!}{2!0!}}{\frac{5!}{3!2!}} = \frac{3(1)}{10} = .3$$

   b. $$P(x=3) = \frac{\binom{r}{x}\binom{N-r}{n-x}}{\binom{N}{n}} = \frac{\binom{3}{3}\binom{9-3}{5-3}}{\binom{9}{5}} = \frac{\frac{3!}{3!0!}\frac{6!}{2!4!}}{\frac{9!}{5!4!}} = \frac{1(15)}{126} = .119$$

   c. $$P(x=2) = \frac{\binom{r}{x}\binom{N-r}{n-x}}{\binom{N}{n}} = \frac{\binom{2}{2}\binom{4-2}{2-2}}{\binom{4}{2}} = \frac{\frac{2!}{2!0!}\frac{2!}{0!2!}}{\frac{4!}{2!2!}} = \frac{1(1)}{6} = .167$$

   d. $$P(x=0) = \frac{\binom{r}{x}\binom{N-r}{n-x}}{\binom{N}{n}} = \frac{\binom{2}{0}\binom{4-2}{2-0}}{\binom{4}{2}} = \frac{\frac{2!}{0!2!}\frac{2!}{2!0!}}{\frac{4!}{2!2!}} = \frac{1(1)}{6} = .167$$

4.93   With $N = 12$, $n = 8$ and $r = 6$, x can take on values 2, 3, 4, 5, or 6.

   a. $$P(x=2) = \frac{\binom{r}{x}\binom{N-r}{n-x}}{\binom{N}{n}} = \frac{\binom{6}{2}\binom{12-6}{8-2}}{\binom{12}{8}} = \frac{\frac{6!}{2!4!}\frac{6!}{6!0!}}{\frac{12!}{8!4!}} = \frac{15(1)}{495} = .030$$

   $$P(x=3) = \frac{\binom{r}{x}\binom{N-r}{n-x}}{\binom{N}{n}} = \frac{\binom{6}{3}\binom{12-6}{8-3}}{\binom{12}{8}} = \frac{\frac{6!}{3!3!}\frac{6!}{5!1!}}{\frac{12!}{8!4!}} = \frac{20(6)}{495} = .242$$

$$P(x=4) = \frac{\binom{r}{x}\binom{N-r}{n-x}}{\binom{N}{n}} = \frac{\binom{6}{4}\binom{12-6}{8-4}}{\binom{12}{8}} = \frac{\frac{6!}{4!2!}\frac{6!}{4!2!}}{\frac{12!}{8!4!}} = \frac{15(15)}{495} = .455$$

$$P(x=5) = \frac{\binom{r}{x}\binom{N-r}{n-x}}{\binom{N}{n}} = \frac{\binom{6}{5}\binom{12-6}{8-5}}{\binom{12}{8}} = \frac{\frac{6!}{5!1!}\frac{6!}{3!3!}}{\frac{12!}{8!4!}} = \frac{6(20)}{495} = .242$$

$$P(x=6) = \frac{\binom{r}{x}\binom{N-r}{n-x}}{\binom{N}{n}} = \frac{\binom{6}{6}\binom{12-6}{8-6}}{\binom{12}{8}} = \frac{\frac{6!}{6!0!}\frac{6!}{2!4!}}{\frac{12!}{8!4!}} = \frac{1(15)}{495} = .030$$

The probability distribution of x in tabular form is:

x	$p(x)$
2	.030
3	.242
4	.455
5	.242
6	.030

b. $\mu = \dfrac{nr}{N} = \dfrac{8(6)}{12} = 4$

$\sigma^2 = \dfrac{r(N-r)n(N-n)}{N^2(N-1)} = \dfrac{6(12-6)8(12-8)}{12^2(12-1)} = \dfrac{1{,}152}{1{,}584} = .7273$

$\sigma = \sqrt{.7273} = .853$

c. $\mu \pm 2\sigma \Rightarrow 4 \pm 2(.853) \Rightarrow 4 \pm 1.706 \Rightarrow (2.294, 5.706)$

The graph of the distribution is:

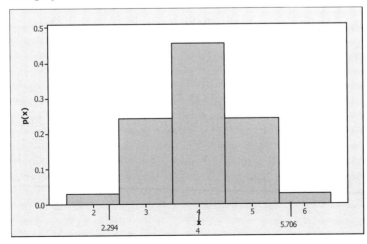

d. $P(2.294 < x < 5.706) = P(3 \leq x \leq 5) = .242 + .455 + .242 = .939$

4.95   For this problem, $N = 100$, $n = 10$, and $x = 4$.

a.   If the sample is drawn without replacement, the hypergeometric distribution should be used. The hypergeometric distribution requires that sampling be done without replacement.

b.   If the sample is drawn with replacement, the binomial distribution should be used. The binomial distribution requires that sampling be done with replacement.

4.97   Let x = number of men chosen in a sample of 4. For this problem, $N = 650$, $r = 3$, and $n = 4$.

$$P(x \geq 1) = 1 - P(x = 0) = 1 - \frac{\binom{3}{0}\binom{650-3}{4-0}}{\binom{650}{4}}$$

$$= 1 - \frac{\frac{3!}{0!3!}\frac{647!}{4!643!}}{\frac{650!}{4!646!}} = 1 - \frac{1(7,233,877,315)}{7,369,297,650} = 1 - .9816 = .0184$$

4.99   Let x = number of "clean" cartridges selected in 5 trials. For this problem, $N = 158$, $r = 122$, and $n = 5$.

$$P(x = 5) = \frac{\binom{r}{x}\binom{N-r}{n-x}}{\binom{N}{n}} = \frac{\binom{122}{5}\binom{36}{0}}{\binom{158}{5}} = \frac{\frac{122!}{5!117!}\frac{36!}{0!36!}}{\frac{158!}{5!153!}} = .2693$$

4.101   Let x = number of extinct bird species in $n = 10$ trials. Then x is a hypergeometric random variable with $N = 132$, $r = 38$, and $n = 10$.

a. $$P(x = 5) = \frac{\binom{38}{5}\binom{132-38}{10-5}}{\binom{132}{10}} = \frac{\frac{38!}{5!(33)!} \cdot \frac{94!}{5!(89)!}}{\frac{132!}{10!(122)!}} = \frac{501,942(54,891,018)}{3.12058705x10^{14}} = .0883$$

b. $$P(x \leq 1) = P(x = 0) + P(x = 1) = \frac{\binom{38}{0}\binom{132-38}{10-0}}{\binom{132}{10}} = \frac{\frac{38!}{0!(38)!} \cdot \frac{94!}{10!(84)!}}{\frac{132!}{10!(122)!}} + \frac{\frac{38!}{1!(37)!} \cdot \frac{94!}{9!(85)!}}{\frac{132!}{10!(122)!}}$$

$$= \frac{9.041256842x10^{12}}{3.12058705x10^{14}} + \frac{4.041973645x10^{13}}{3.12058705x10^{14}} = .0290 + .1295 = .1585$$

4.103 Let x = number of spoiled bottles in the sample of 3. Since the sampling will be done without replacement, x is a hypergeometric random variable with $N = 12$, $n = 3$, and $r = 1$.

$$P(x = 1) = \frac{\binom{r}{x}\binom{N-r}{n-x}}{\binom{N}{n}} = \frac{\binom{1}{1}\binom{12-1}{3-1}}{\binom{12}{3}} = \frac{\frac{1!}{1!0!}\frac{11!}{2!9!}}{\frac{12!}{3!9!}} = \frac{55}{220} = .25$$

4.105 Let x = number of grants awarded to the north side in 140 trials. The random variable x has a hypergeometric distribution with $N = 743$, $n = 140$, and $r = 601$.

a. $\mu = E(x) = \dfrac{nr}{N} = \dfrac{140(601)}{743} = 113.24$

$\sigma^2 = \dfrac{r(N-r)n(N-n)}{N^2(N-1)} = \dfrac{601(743-601)140(743-140)}{743^2(743-1)} = 17.5884$

$\sigma = \sqrt{17.5884} = 4.194$

b. If the grants were awarded at random, we would expect approximately 113 to be awarded to the north side. We observed 140. The z-score associated with 140 is:

$$z = \frac{x - \mu}{\sigma} = \frac{140 - 113.24}{4.194} = 6.38$$

Because this z-score is so large, it would be extremely unlikely to observe all 140 grants to the north side if they are randomly selected. Thus, we would conclude that the grants were not randomly selected.

4.107 a. Poisson

b. Binomial

c. Binomial

4.109 From Table II, Appendix A:

a. $P(x = 14) = P(x \le 14) - P(x \le 13) = .584 - .392 = .192$

b. $P(x \le 12) = .228$

c. $P(x > 12) = 1 - P(x \le 12) = 1 - .228 = .772$

d. $P(9 \le x \le 18) = P(x \le 18) - P(x \le 8) = .992 - .005 = .987$

e. $P(8 < x < 18) = P(x \le 17) - P(x \le 8) = .965 - .005 = .960$

f. $\mu = np = 20(.7) = 14$

$\sigma^2 = npq = 20(.7)(.3) = 4.2$, $\sigma = \sqrt{4.2} = 2.049$

g. $\mu \pm 2\sigma \Rightarrow 14 \pm 2(2.049) \Rightarrow 14 \pm 4.098 \Rightarrow (9.902, 18.098)$

$$P(9.902 < x < 18.098) = P(10 \leq x \leq 18) = P(x \leq 18) - P(x \leq 9)$$
$$= .992 - .017 = .975$$

4.111 a. $P(x = 1) = \binom{3}{1}(.1)^1(.9)^{3-1} = \dfrac{3!}{1!2!}(.1)^1(.9)^2 = 3(.1)(.81) = .243$

b. $P(x = 4) = P(x \leq 4) - P(x \leq 3) = .238 - .107 = .131$ from Table II, Appendix A.

c. $P(x = 0) = \binom{2}{0}(.4)^0(.6)^{2-0} = \dfrac{2!}{0!2!}(1)(.6)^2 = .36$

d. $P(x = 4) = P(x \leq 4) - P(x \leq 3) = .969 - .812 = .157$ from Table II, Appendix A.

e. $P(x = 12) = P(x \leq 12) - P(x \leq 11) = .184 - .056 = .128$ from Table II, Appendix A.

f. $P(x = 8) = P(x \leq 8) - P(x \leq 7) = .954 - .833 = .121$ from Table II, Appendix A.

4.113   Using Table III, Appendix A,

a. When $\lambda = 2$, $p(3) = P(x \leq 3) - P(x \leq 2) = .857 - .677 = .180$

b. When $\lambda = 1$, $p(4) = P(x \leq 4) - P(x \leq 3) = .996 - .981 = .015$

c. When $\lambda = .5$, $p(2) = P(x \leq 2) - P(x \leq 1) = .986 - .910 = .076$

4.115 a. In order to be a binomial random variable, the five characteristics must hold.

1. For this problem, there are 5 items scanned. We will assume that these 5 trials are identical.

2. For each item scanned, there are 2 possible outcomes: priced incorrectly (S) or priced correctly (F).

3. The probability of being priced incorrectly remains constant from trial to trial. For this problem, we will assume that the probability of being priced incorrectly is $P(S) = 1/30$ for each trial.

4. We will assume that whether one item is priced incorrectly is independent of any other.

5. The random variable x is the number of items priced incorrectly in 5 trials.

Thus, x is a binomial random variable.

b. The estimate of p, the probability of an item being priced incorrectly is 1/30.

c. $P(x = 1) = \binom{5}{1}(1/30)^1(29/30)^4 = .1455$

d. $P(x \geq 1) = 1 - P(x = 0) = 1 - \binom{5}{0}(1/30)^0(29/30)^5 = 1 - .8441 = .1559$

4.117   The random variable x would have a binomial distribution:

     1. n identical trials. A sample of married women was taken and would be considered small compared to the entire population of married women, so the trials would be very close to identical.

     2.   There are only two possible outcomes for each trial. In this experiment, there are only two possible outcomes: the woman would marry the same man (S) or she would not (F).

     3.   The probability of Success stays the same from trial to trial. Here, $P(S) = .80$ and $P(F) = .20$. In reality, these probabilities would not be exactly the same from trial to trial, but rounded off to 4 decimal places, they would be the same.

     4.   The trials are independent. In this experiment, the trials would not be exactly independent because we would be sampling without replacement from a finite population. However, if the sample size is fairly small compared to the population size, the trials will be essentially independent.

     5.   The binomial random variable x would be the number of successes in n trials. For this experiment, $x =$ the number of women out of those sampled who would marry the same man again.

     Thus, x would possess (approximately) a binomial distribution.

4.119   a.   In order for this to be a valid probability distribution, $\sum p(x) = 1$ and $0 \leq p(x) \leq 1$ for all values of x.

       In this distribution, $0 \leq p(x) \leq 1$ for all values of x and $\sum p(x) = .051 + .099 + .093 + .635 + .122 = 1.000$. Thus, this is a valid probability distribution.

    b. $P(x = 1) = .051$

    c. $P(x \geq 4) = P(x = 4) + P(x = 5) = .635 + .122 = .757$

    d. $P(x = 2 \text{ or } x = 3) = P(x = 2) + P(x = 3) = .099 + .093 = .192$

    e. $E(x) = \mu = \sum xp(x) = 1(.051) + 2(.099) + 3(.093) + 4(.635) + 4(.122) = 3.678$

    f.   The average rating of all books rated is 3.678.

4.121   a. $\mu = E(x) = np = 800(.65) = 520$
         $\sigma = \sqrt{npq} = \sqrt{800(.65)(.35)} = 13.491$

b.   Half of the 800 food items is 400. A value of $x = 400$ would have a z-score of:

$$z = \frac{x - \mu}{\sigma} = \frac{400 - 520}{13.491} = -8.895$$

Since the z-score associated with 400 items is so small (-8.895), it would be virtually impossible to observe less than half without any traces of pesticides if the 65% value was correct.

4.123   Let x = number of parents who yell at their child before, during, or after a meet in 20 trials. Then x has a binomial distribution with $n = 20$ and $p = .05$.

$P(x \geq 1) = 1 - P(x = 0) = 1 - .358 = .642$ (Using Table II, Appendix A)

4.125   a.   For this problem, let x = the number of students who have nasal allergies in 25 trials. The variable x is a binomial random variable with $n = 25$ and $p = .8$.

$P(x < 20) = P(x \leq 19) = .383$ (Using Table II, Appendix A)

b. $P(x > 15) = 1 - P(x \leq 15) = 1 - .017 = .983$

c. $E(x) = np = 25(.8) = 20$. On the average, out of 25 students, we would expect to find 20 with nasal allergies.

4.127   Using Table II with $n = 25$ and $p = .8$:

a. $P(x < 15) = P(x \leq 14) = .006$

b.   Since the probability of such an event is so small when $p = .8$, if less than 15 insects die we would conclude that the insecticide is not as effective as claimed.

4.129   a.   For company A,

$$E(x) = \sum_{\text{All } x} xp(x) = 2(.05) + 3(.15) + 4(.20) + 5(.35) + 6(.25)$$

$$= .10 + .45 + .80 + 1.75 + 1.50 = 4.60$$

For company B,

$$E(x) = \sum_{\text{All } x} xp(x) = 2(.15) + 3(.30) + 4(.30) + 5(.20) + 6(.05)$$

$$= .30 + .90 + 1.20 + 1.00 + .30 = 3.70$$

b.   The expected profit equals the expected value of x times the profit for each job.

For company A, $4.6(\$10,000) = \$46,000$

For company B, $3.7(\$15,000) = \$55,500$

c. For company A,

$$\sigma^2 = \sum_{All\,x} (x-\mu)^2 p(x) = (2-4.6)^2.05 + (3-4.6)^2.15 + (4-4.6)^2.20$$

$$+ (5-4.6)^2.35 + (6-4.6)^2.25$$
$$= .338 + .384 + .072 + .056 + .49 = 1.34$$

$$\sigma = \sqrt{\sigma^2} = \sqrt{1.34} = 1.16$$

For company B,

$$\sigma^2 = \sum_{All\,x} (x-\mu)^2 p(x) = (2-3.7)^2.15 + (3-3.7)^2.30 + (4-3.7)^2.30$$

$$+ (5-3.7)^2.20 + (6-3.7)^2.05$$
$$= .4335 + .147 + .027 + .338 + .2645 = 1.21$$

$$\sigma = \sqrt{\sigma^2} = \sqrt{1.21} = 1.10$$

d. For company A, the graph of $p(x)$ is given here.

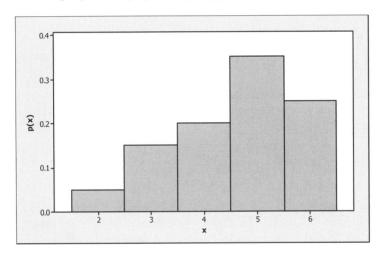

For company A,

$$\mu \pm 2\sigma \Rightarrow 4.6 \pm 2(1.16) \Rightarrow 4.6 \pm 2.32 \Rightarrow (2.28, 6.92)$$

$$P(2.28 < x < 6.92) = p(3) + p(4) + p(5) + p(6) = .15 + .20 + .35 + .25 = .95$$

For company B, the graph of $p(x)$ is given here.

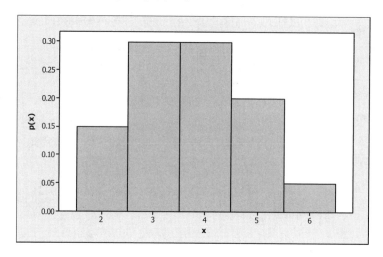

For company B,

$$\mu \pm 2\sigma \Rightarrow 3.70 \pm 2(1.10) \Rightarrow 3.67 \pm 2.2 \Rightarrow (1.5, 5.9)$$

$$P(1.5 < x < 5.9) = p(2) + p(3) + p(4) + p(5) = .15 + .30 + .30 + .20 = .95$$

4.131   Define x as the number of components that operate successfully. The random variable x is a binomial random variable (the components operate independently and there are only two possible outcomes) with $n = 4$ and $p = .85$.

$$P(\text{system fails}) = P(x = 0) = \binom{4}{0}.85^0(.15)^{4-0} = \frac{4!}{0!4!}.85^0(.15)^4 = .15^4 = .0005$$

4.133   Let x = number of disasters in 25 trials. If NASA's assessment is correct, then x is a binomial random variable with $n = 25$ and $p = 1 / 60,000 = .00001667$. If the Air Force's assessment is correct, then x is a binomial random variable with $n = 25$ and $p = 1 / 35 = .02857$.

If NASA's assessment is correct, then the probability of no disasters in 25 missions would be:

$$P(x = 0) = \binom{25}{0}(1/60,000)^0(59,999/60,000)^{25} = .9996$$

Thus, the probability of at least one disaster would be

$$P(x \geq 1) = 1 - P(x = 0) = 1 - .9996 = .0004$$

If the Air Force's assessment is correct, then the probability of no disasters in 25 missions would be:

$$P(x = 0) = \binom{25}{0}(1/35)^0(34/35)^{25} = .4845$$

Thus, the probability of at least one disaster would be

$$P(x \geq 1) = 1 - P(x = 0) = 1 - .4845 = .5155$$

One disaster actually did occur. If NASA's assessment were correct, it would be almost impossible for at least one disaster to occur in 25 trials. If the Air Force's assessment were correct, one disaster in 25 trials would not be an unusual event. Thus, the Air Force's assessment appears to be appropriate.

Continuous Random Variables

5.1   A uniform random variable is a continuous random variable that appears to have equally likely outcomes over its range of possible values.

5.3   a.   For a uniform random variable,

$$f(x) = \begin{cases} \dfrac{1}{d-c} = \dfrac{1}{30-10} = \dfrac{1}{20} & 10 \le x \le 30 \\ 0 & \text{otherwise} \end{cases}$$

b. $\mu = \dfrac{c+d}{2} = \dfrac{10+30}{2} = 20$

$\sigma = \dfrac{d-c}{\sqrt{12}} = \dfrac{30-10}{\sqrt{12}} = 5.774$

c.

$\mu \pm 2\sigma \Rightarrow 20 \pm 2(5.774) \Rightarrow 20 \pm 11.584 \Rightarrow (8.452, 31.548)$

5.5   a.   For a uniform random variable,

$$f(x) = \begin{cases} \dfrac{1}{d-c} = \dfrac{1}{4-2} = \dfrac{1}{2} & 2 \le x \le 4 \\ 0 & \text{otherwise} \end{cases}$$

b. $\mu = \dfrac{c+d}{2} = \dfrac{2+4}{2} = 3$

$\sigma = \dfrac{d-c}{\sqrt{12}} = \dfrac{4-2}{\sqrt{12}} = .577$

c. $\mu \pm \sigma \Rightarrow 3 \pm .577 \Rightarrow (2.423, 3.577)$

$$P(2.423 \le x \le 3.577) = (3.577 - 2.423)\frac{1}{2} = .577$$

d. $P(x > 2.78) = (4 - 2.78)\frac{1}{2} = .61$

e. $P(2.4 \le x \le 3.7) = (3.7 - 2.4)\frac{1}{2} = .65$

f. $P(x < 2) = 0$

5.7   For the uniform random variable,

$$f(x) = \begin{cases} \dfrac{1}{d-c} = \dfrac{1}{200-100} = \dfrac{1}{100} & 100 \le x \le 200 \\ 0 & \text{otherwise} \end{cases}$$

a. $\mu = \dfrac{c+d}{2} = \dfrac{100+200}{2} = 150 \qquad\qquad \sigma = \dfrac{d-c}{\sqrt{12}} = \dfrac{200-100}{\sqrt{12}} = 28.87$

$\mu \pm 2\sigma \Rightarrow 150 \pm 2(28.87) \Rightarrow 150 \pm 57.74 \Rightarrow (92.26, 207.74)$

$P(x < 92.26) + P(x > 207.74) = 0 + 0 = 0$

b. $\mu \pm 3\sigma \Rightarrow 150 \pm 3(28.87) \Rightarrow 150 \pm 86.61 \Rightarrow (63.39, 236.61)$

$P(63.39 < x < 236.61) = P(100 \le x \le 200) = 1$

c. $P(92.26 < x < 207.74) = P(100 \le x \le 200) = 1$

5.9 a. Suppose no bolt-on trace elements are used. Let x be a uniform random variable on the interval 260 to 290. From this, c = 260 and d = 290.

$$f(x) = \begin{cases} \dfrac{1}{d-c} = \dfrac{1}{290-260} = \dfrac{1}{30} & 260 \le x \le 290 \\ 0 & \text{otherwise} \end{cases}$$

$$P(280 \le x \le 284) = (284 - 280)\left(\frac{1}{30}\right) = 4\left(\frac{1}{30}\right) = .1333$$

Suppose bolt-on trace elements are used. Let y be a uniform random variable on the interval 278 to 285. From this, c = 278 and d = 285.

$$f(y) = \begin{cases} \dfrac{1}{d-c} = \dfrac{1}{285-278} = \dfrac{1}{7} & 278 \le y \le 285 \\ 0 & \text{otherwise} \end{cases}$$

Continuous Random Variables   **125**

$$P(280 \le y \le 284) = (284-280)\left(\frac{1}{7}\right) = 4\left(\frac{1}{7}\right) = .5714$$

b. Suppose no bolt-on trace elements are used.

$$P(x \le 268) = (268-260)\left(\frac{1}{30}\right) = 8\left(\frac{1}{30}\right) = .2667$$

Suppose bolt-on trace elements are used.

$$P(x \le 268) = (0)\left(\frac{1}{7}\right) = 0$$

5.11   Using MINITAB, the histogram of the data is:

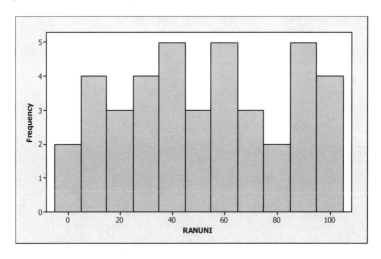

The histogram looks like the data could come from a uniform distribution. There is some variation in the height of the bars, but we cannot expect a perfect graph from a sample of only 40 observations.

5.13   a.   The amount dispensed by the beverage machine is a continuous random variable since it can take on any value between 6.5 and 7.5 ounces.

b.   Since the amount dispensed is random between 6.5 and 7.5 ounces, x is a uniform random variable.

$$f(x) = \frac{1}{d-c} \quad (c \le x \le d)$$

$$\frac{1}{d-c} = \frac{1}{7.5-6.5} = \frac{1}{1} = 1$$

Therefore, $f(x) = \begin{cases} 1 & (6.5 \le x \le 7.5) \\ 0 & \text{otherwise} \end{cases}$

The graph is as follows:

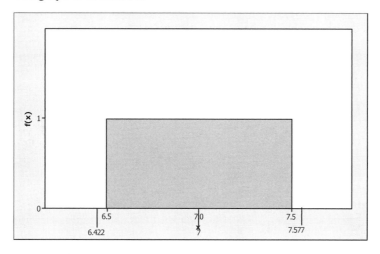

c. $\mu = \dfrac{c+d}{2} = \dfrac{6.5+7.5}{2} = \dfrac{14}{2} = 7$

$\sigma = \dfrac{d-c}{\sqrt{12}} = \dfrac{7.5-6.5}{\sqrt{12}} = .2887$

$\mu \pm 2\sigma \Rightarrow 7 \pm 2(.2887) \Rightarrow 7 \pm .5774 \Rightarrow (6.422, 7.577)$

d. $P(x \geq 7) = (7.5 - 7)(1) = .5$

e. $P(x < 6) = 0$

f. $P(6.5 \leq x \leq 7.25) = (7.25 - 6.5)(1) = .75$

g. The probability that the next bottle filled will contain more than 7.25 ounces is:

$$P(x > 7.25) = (7.5 - 7.25)(1) = .25$$

The probability that the next 6 bottles filled will contain more than 7.25 ounces is:

$$P[(x > 7.25) \cap (x > 7.25) \cap (x > 7.25) \cap (x > 7.25) \cap (x > 7.25) \cap (x > 7.25)]$$
$$= [P(x > 7.25)]^6 = .25^6 = .0002$$

5.15 Let x = number of inches a gouge is from one end of the spindle. Then x has a uniform distribution with $f(x)$ as follows:

$$f(x) = \begin{cases} \dfrac{1}{d-c} = \dfrac{1}{18-0} = \dfrac{1}{18} & 0 \leq x \leq 18 \\ 0 & \text{otherwise} \end{cases}$$

In order to get at least 14 consecutive inches without a gouge, the gouge must be within 4 inches of either end. Thus, we must find:

$$P(x < 4) + P(x > 14) = (4 - 0)(1/18) + (18 - 14)(1/18)$$
$$= 4/18 + 4/18 = 8/18 = .4444$$

5.17   A normal distribution is a bell-shaped curve with the center of the distribution at μ.

5.19   If x has a normal distribution with mean μ and standard deviation σ, then the distribution of $z = \dfrac{x - \mu}{\sigma}$ is a normal with a mean of $\mu = 0$ and a standard deviation of $\sigma = 1$.

5.21   a. $P(-2.00 < z < 0) = .4772$
            (from Table IV, Appendix A)

       b. $P(-1.00 < z < 0) = .3413$
            (from Table IV, Appendix A)

       c. $P(-1.69 < z < 0) = .4545$
            (from Table IV, Appendix A)

       d. $P(-.58 < z < 0) = .2190$
            (from Table IV, Appendix A)

5.23   a. $P(z = 1) = 0$, since a single point does not have an area.

       b. $P(z \le 1) = P(z \le 0) + P(0 < z \le 1)$
            $= A_1 + A_2$
            $= .5 + .3413$
            $= .8413$
            (Table IV, Appendix A)

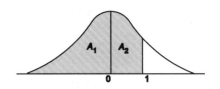

       c. $P(z < 1) = P(z \le 1) = .8413$ (Refer to part **b**.)

       d. $P(z > 1) = 1 - P(z \le 1) = 1 - .8413 = .1587$ (Refer to part **b**.)

       e. $P(-1 \le z \le 1) = A_1 + A_2$
                              $= .3413 + .3413$
                              $= .6826$

f. $P(-2 \leq z \leq 2) = A_1 + A_2$
$$= .4772 + .4772$$
$$= .9544$$

g. $P(-2.16 < z \leq 0.55) = A_1 + A_2$
$$= .4846 + .2088$$
$$= .6934$$

h. $P(-.42 < z < 1.96)$
$$= P(-.42 \leq z \leq 0) + P(0 \leq z \leq 1.96)$$
$$= A_1 + A_2$$
$$= .1628 + .4750$$
$$= .6378$$

5.25   Using Table IV, Appendix A:

a. $P(z \geq z_0) = .05$
$A_1 = .5 - .05 = .4500$
Looking up the area .4500 in Table IV gives
$z_0 = 1.645$.

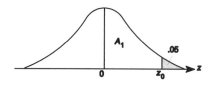

b. $P(z \geq z_0) = .025$
$A_1 = .5 - .025 = .4750$
Looking up the area .4750 in Table IV
gives $z_0 = 1.96$.

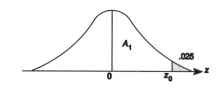

c. $P(z \leq z_0) = .025$
$A_1 = .5 - .025 = .4750$
Looking up the area .4750 in Table IV gives
$z = 1.96$. Since z_0 is to the left of 0, $z_0 = 1.96$.

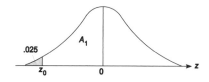

d. $P(z \geq z_0) = .10$
$A_1 = .5 - .1 = .4$
Looking up the area .4000 in Table IV
gives $z_0 = 1.28$.

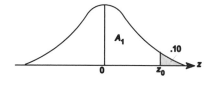

e. $P(z > z_0) = .10$
$A_1 = .5 - .1 = .4$
$z_0 = 1.28$ (same as in **d**)

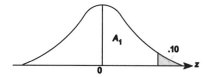

5.27   Using the formula $z = \dfrac{x - \mu}{\sigma}$ with $\mu = 25$ and $\sigma = 5$:

a. $z = \dfrac{25 - 25}{5} = 0$

b. $z = \dfrac{30 - 25}{5} = 1$

c. $z = \dfrac{37.5 - 25}{5} = 2.5$

d. $z = \dfrac{10 - 25}{5} = -3$

e. $z = \dfrac{50 - 25}{5} = 5$

f. $z = \dfrac{32 - 25}{5} = 1.4$

5.29   a. $P(x < \mu - 2\sigma) + P(x > \mu + 2\sigma) = P(z < -2) + P(z > 2)$
$= (.5 - .4772) + (.5 - .4772)$
$= 2(.5 - .4772) = .0456$
(from Table IV, Appendix A)

$P(x < \mu - 3\sigma) + P(x > \mu + 3\sigma) = P(z < -3) + P(z > 3)$
$= (.5 - .4987) + (.5 - .4987)$
$= 2(.5 - .4987) = .0026$
(from Table IV, Appendix A)

b. $P(\mu - \sigma < x < \mu + \sigma) = P(-1 < z < 1)$
$= P(-1 < z < 0) + P(0 < z < 1)$
$= .3413 + .3413$
$= 2(.3413) = .6826$
(from Table IV, Appendix A)

$P(\mu - 2\sigma < z < \mu + 2\sigma) = P(-2 < z < 2)$
$= P(-2 < z < 0) + P(0 < z < 2)$
$= .4772 + .4772$
$= 2(.4772) = .9544$
(from Table IV, Appendix A)

c. $P(x \leq x_0) = .80$. Find x_0.

$$P(x \leq x_0) = P\left(z \leq \frac{x_0 - 300}{30}\right) = P(z \leq z_0) = .80$$

$A_1 = .80 - .5 = .3000$

Looking up area .3000 in Table IV, $z_0 = .84$.

$$z_0 = \frac{x_0 - 300}{30} \Rightarrow .84 = \frac{x_0 - 300}{30} \Rightarrow x_0 = 325.2$$

$P(x \leq x_0) = .10$. Find x_0.

$$P(x \leq x_0) = P\left(z \leq \frac{x_0 - 300}{30}\right) = P(z \leq z_0) = .10$$

$A_1 = .50 - .10 = .4000$

Looking up area .4000 in Table IV, $z_0 = -1.28$.

$$z_0 = \frac{x_0 - 300}{30} \Rightarrow -1.28 = \frac{x_0 - 300}{30} \Rightarrow x_0 = 261.6$$

5.31   a. $P(x < x_0) = .10 \Rightarrow P\left(z < \dfrac{x_0 - 30}{8}\right)$

$\qquad = P(z < z_0) = .10$

$A_1 = .5 - .10 = .4000$

Looking up the area .4000 in Table IV gives $z_0 = 1.28$. Since z_0 is to the left of 0, $z_0 = -1.28$.

$$z_0 = -1.28 = \frac{x_0 - 30}{8} \Rightarrow x_0 = 8(-1.28) + 30 = 19.76$$

b. $P(x < x_0) = .80 \Rightarrow P\left(z < \dfrac{x_0 - 30}{8}\right)$

$\qquad = P(z < z_0) = .80$

$A_1 = .80 - .5 = .3000$

Looking up the area .3000 in Table IV gives $z_0 = 0.84$.

$$z_0 = 0.84 = \frac{x_0 - 30}{8} \Rightarrow x_0 = 8(0.84) + 30 = 36.72$$

c. $P(x > x_0) = .01 \Rightarrow P\left(z > \dfrac{x_0 - 30}{8}\right)$

$\qquad = P(z > z_0) = .01$

$A_1 = .5 - .01 = .4900$

Looking up the area .4900 in Table IV gives $z_0 = 2.33$.

$$z_0 = 2.33 = \frac{x_0 - 30}{8} \Rightarrow x_0 = 8(2.33) + 30 = 48.64$$

5.33   The random variable x has a normal distribution with $\sigma = 25$.

We know $P(x > 150) = .90$. So, $A_1 + A_2 = .90$. Since $A_2 = .50$, $A_1 = .90 - .50 = .40$. Look up the area .40 in the body of Table IV; (take the closest value) $z_0 = -1.28$.

To find μ, substitute all the values into the z-score formula:

$$z = \frac{x - \mu}{\sigma}$$

$$\Rightarrow -1.28 = \frac{150 - \mu}{25}$$

$$\Rightarrow \quad \mu = 150 + 25(1.28) = 182$$

5.35   a.   Let x = alkalinity level of water specimens collected from the Han River.

Using Table IV, Appendix A,

$$P(x > 45) = P\left(z > \frac{45 - 50}{3.2}\right) = P(z > -1.56) = .5 + .4406 = .9406.$$

b.   Using Table IV, Appendix A,

$$P(x < 55) = P\left(z < \frac{55 - 50}{3.2}\right) = P(z < 1.56) = .5 + .4406 = .9406.$$

c.   Using Table IV, Appendix A,

$$P(51 < x < 52) = P\left(\frac{51 - 50}{3.2} < z < \frac{52 - 50}{3.2}\right) = P(.31 < z < .63) = .2357 - .1217 = .1140.$$

5.37   a.   Let x = age of powerful woman. Using Table IV, Appendix A,

$$P(55 < x < 60) = P\left(\frac{55 - 50}{6} < z < \frac{60 - 50}{6}\right) = P(.83 < z < 1.67) = .4525 - .2967 = .1558$$

b. $$P(48 < x < 52) = P\left(\frac{48 - 50}{6} < z < \frac{52 - 50}{6}\right) = P(-.33 < z < .33) = .1293 + .1293 = .2586$$

c. $$P(x < 35) = P\left(z < \frac{35 - 50}{6}\right) = P(z < -2.50) = .5 - .4938 = .0062$$

d. $$P(x > 40) = P\left(z > \frac{40 - 50}{6}\right) = P(z > -1.67) = .5 + .4525 = .9525$$

5.39   a.   Let x = driver's head injury rating. Using Table IV, Appendix A,

$$P(500 < x < 700) = P\left(\frac{500 - 605}{185} < z < \frac{700 - 605}{185}\right) = P(-.57 < z < .51)$$
$$= .2157 + .1950 = .4107$$

b. $$P(400 < x < 500) = P\left(\frac{400 - 605}{185} < z < \frac{500 - 605}{185}\right) = P(-1.11 < z < -.57)$$
$$= .3665 - .2157 = .1508$$

c. $$P(x < 850) = P\left(z < \frac{850 - 605}{185}\right) = P(z < 1.32)\ = .5 + .4066 = .9066$$

d. $$P(x > 1,000) = P\left(z > \frac{1,000 - 605}{185}\right) = P(z > 2.14)\ = .5 - .4838 = .0162$$

e. $$P(x > x_o) = .10 \Rightarrow P\left(z > \frac{x_o - 605}{185}\right) = .10 \Rightarrow z = 1.28 = \frac{x_o - 605}{185}$$
$$\Rightarrow 236.8 = x_o - 605 \Rightarrow x_o = 841.8$$

5.41   a.   Using Table IV, Appendix A, with $\mu = 9.06$ and $\sigma = 2.11$,

$$P(x < 6) = \left(z < \frac{6 - 9.06}{2.11}\right) = P(z < -1.45) = .5 - P(-1.45 \le z \le 0)$$
$$= .5 - .4265 = .0735$$

b. $$P(8 < x < 10) = P\left(\frac{8 - 9.06}{2.11} < z < \frac{10 - 9.06}{2.11}\right) = P(-.50 < z < .45)$$

$$= P(-.50 < z < 0) + P(0 < z < .45) = .1915 + .1736 = .3651$$

c. $P(x < x_0) = .2000$.

If $P(x < x_0) = .2000$, then $P\left(z < \dfrac{x_0 - 9.06}{2.11}\right) = P(z < z_0) = .2000$

If $P(z < z_0)$, then $P(z_0 < z < 0) = .3000$. Looking up .3000 in Table IV, the z-score is .84. Since $z_0 < 0$, $z_0 = -.84$. Now, we must convert z_0 back to an x score.

$$z_0 = \frac{x_0 - 9.06}{2.11} \Rightarrow -.84 = \frac{x_0 - 9.06}{2.11} \Rightarrow x_0 = 2.11(-.84) + 9.06 = 7.29$$

5.43   Using Table IV, Appendix A, with $\mu = 50$ and $\sigma = 12$,

$$P(x > d) = .30 \Rightarrow P\left(z > \frac{d - 50}{12}\right) = P(z > z_0) = .30$$

$A_1 = .5 - .30 = .2000$
Looking up the area .2000 in Table IV gives $z_0 = .52$.

$$z_0 = .52 = \frac{d - 50}{12} \Rightarrow d = 12(.52) + 50 = 56.24 \text{ cm}$$

5.45   a.   Using Table IV, Appendix A, with $\mu = 208$ and $\sigma = 25$,

$$P(x < 200) = P\left(z < \frac{200 - 208}{25}\right) = P(z < -.32) = .5 - .1255 = .3745$$

      b.   Let y = number of patients out of three who have cholesterol levels below 200. Assuming that the patients are independent, then y is a binomial random variable with $n = 3$ and $p = .3745$.

$$P(y \geq 1) = 1 - P(y = 0) = 1 - \binom{3}{0}.3745^0.6255^3 = 1 - .2447 = .7553$$

5.47   a.   If z is a standard normal random variable,

       $Q_L = z_L$ is the value of the standard normal distribution which has 25% of the data to the left and 75% to the right.

       Find z_L such that $P(z < z_L) = .25$

       $A_1 = .50 - .25 = .25$.

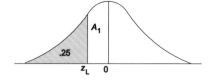

       Look up the area $A_1 = .25$ in the body of Table IV of Appendix A; $z_L = -.67$ (taking the closest value). If interpolation is used, $-.675$ would be obtained.

       $Q_U = z_U$ is the value of the standard normal distribution which has 75% of the data to the left and 25% to the right.

       Find z_U such that $P(z < z_U) = .75$

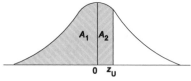

$$A_1 + A_2 = P(z \leq 0) + P(0 \leq z \leq z_U)$$
$$= .5 + P(0 \leq z \leq z_U)$$
$$= .75$$

       Therefore, $P(0 \leq z \leq z_U) = .25$.

       Look up the area .25 in the body of Table IV of Appendix A; $z_U = .67$ (taking the closest value).

b. Recall that the inner fences of a box plot are located $1.5(Q_U - Q_L)$ outside the hinges (Q_L and Q_U).

To find the lower inner fence,

$$Q_L - 1.5(Q_U - Q_L) = -.67 - 1.5(.67 - (-.67))$$
$$= -.67 - 1.5(1.34)$$
$$= -2.68 \ (-2.70 \text{ if } z_L = -.675 \text{ and } z_U = +.675)$$

The upper inner fence is:

$$Q_U + 1.5(Q_U - Q_L) = .67 + 1.5(.67 - (-.67))$$
$$= .67 + 1.5(1.34)$$
$$= 2.68 \ (+2.70 \text{ if } z_L = -.675 \text{ and } z_U = +.675)$$

c. Recall that the outer fences of a box plot are located $3(Q_U - Q_L)$ outside the hinges (Q_L and Q_U).

To find the lower outer fence,

$$Q_L - 3(Q_U - Q_L) = -.67 - 3(.67 - (.67))$$
$$= -.67 - 3(1.34)$$
$$= -4.69 \ (-4.725 \text{ if } z_L = -.675 \text{ and } z_U = +.675)$$

The upper outer fence is:

$$Q_U + 3(Q_U - Q_L) = .67 + 3(.67 - (-.67))$$
$$= .67 + 3(1.34)$$
$$= 4.69 \ (4.725 \text{ if } z_L = -,675 \text{ and } z_U = +.675)$$

d. $P(z < -2.68) + P(z > 2.68)$
   $= 2P(z > 2.68)$
   $= 2(.5000 - .4963)$
       (Table IV, Appendix A)
   $= 2(.0037) = .0074$

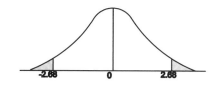

(or $2(.5000 - .4965) = .0070$ if -2.70 and 2.70 are used)

$P(z < -4.69) + P(z > 4.69)$
   $= 2P(z > 4.69)$
   $\approx 2(.5000 - .5000) \approx 0$

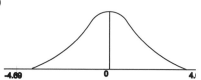

e. In a normal probability distribution, the probability of an observation being beyond the inner fences is only .0074 and the probability of an observation being beyond the outer fences is approximately zero. Since the probability is so small, there should not be any observations beyond the inner and outer fences. Therefore, they are probably outliers.

5.49 Several statistical techniques are based on the assumption that the population is approximately normally distributed. Thus, it is important to determine whether the sample data come from a normal population so that the techniques can be properly applied.

5.51 a. The proportion of measurements that one would expect to fall in the interval $\mu \pm \sigma$ is about .68.

b. The proportion of measurements that one would expect to fall in the interval $\mu \pm 2\sigma$ is about .95.

c. The proportion of measurements that one would expect to fall in the interval $\mu \pm 3\sigma$ is about 1.00.

5.53 If the data are normally distributed, then the normal probability plot should be an approximate straight line. Of the three plots, only plot c implies that the data are normally distributed. The data points in plot c form an approximately straight line. In both plots a and b, the plots of the data points do not form a straight line.

5.55 a. Using MINITAB, the stem-and-leaf display is:

Stem-and-Leaf Display: Data

```
Stem-and-leaf of Data  N  = 40
Leaf Unit = 10

   14    0   00012223333344
  (10)   0   5556666889
   16    1   001334
   10    1   5689
    6    2   01
    4    2
    4    3   000
    1    3
    1    4   0
```

The distribution from the stem-and-leaf display looks like it is skewed to the right. Thus, it does not appear that the data are normally distributed.

b. Using MINITAB, the descriptive statistics are:

Descriptive Statistics: Data

Variable	N	N*	Mean	SE Mean	StDev	Minimum	Q1	Median	Q3	Maximum
Data	40	0	105.1	15.1	95.8	1.00	37.5	65.0	152.8	401.0

The lower quartile is $Q_L = 37.5$ and the upper quartile is $Q_U = 152.8$.

c. The interquartile range is IQR $= Q_U - Q_L = 152.8 - 37.5 = 115.3$. From the printout, $s = 95.8$. IQR $/ s = 115.3 / 95.8 = 1.204$. If the data are approximately normal, then this ratio should be 1.3. Since the actual ratio is 1.204 which is close to 1.3, it appears that the data could be approximately normal.

d. Using MINITAB, the normal probability plot is:

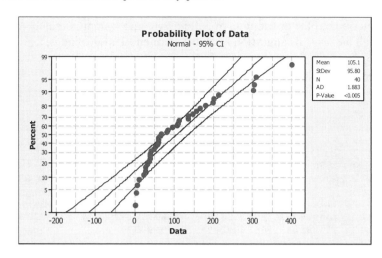

Probability Plot of Data
Normal - 95% CI

Mean	105.1
StDev	95.80
N	40
AD	1.883
P-Value	<0.005

Since the data points do not fall along the straight line, the data do not appear to be normally distributed.

5.57   a.   IQR $= Q_U - Q_L = 53 - 46 = 7$.

b.   From the printout, $s = 6.124$.

c.   If the data are approximately normal, then IQR $/ s \approx 1.3$. For this data, IQR $/ s = 7 / 6.124 = 1.14$. This is somewhat close to 1.3, so the data may be normal.

d.   Using MINITAB, a relative frequency histogram of the data is:

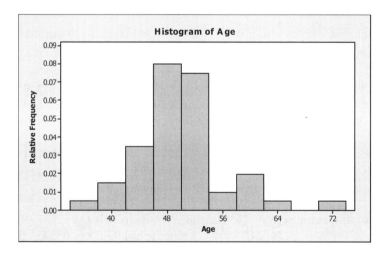

Histogram of Age

From the histogram, the data appear to be close to mound-shaped, so the data may be normally distributed.

5.59   From the graph, the data appear to be very mound-shaped. It appears that the data are approximately normally distributed.

5.61   American League

To determine if the distribution of batting averages is approximately normal, we will run through the tests. Using MINITAB, the stem-and-leaf display is:

Stem-and-Leaf Display: AVE

```
Stem-and-leaf of AVE   N  = 207
Leaf Unit = 0.010

   1    1  4
   4    1  777
   9    1  88999
  23    2  00000011111111
  46    2  2222222222233333333333333
  97    2  44444444444444444444455555555555555555555555555555555
 (48)   2  6666666666666666666666666777777777777777777777
  62    2  888888888888888899999999999999999999
  27    3  00000000000000011111111
   5    3  22222
```

From the stem-and-leaf display, the data look to be mound-shaped. The data may be normal.

Using MINITAB, the descriptive statistics are:

Descriptive Statistics: AVE

Variable	N	N*	Mean	SE Mean	StDev	Minimum	Q1	Median
AVE	207	0	0.26111	0.00232	0.03343	0.14200	0.24300	0.26200

Variable	Q3	Maximum
AVE	0.28700	0.32600

The interval $\bar{x} \pm s \Rightarrow .261 \pm .033 \Rightarrow (.228, \ .294)$ contains 142 of the 207 observations. The proportion is $142 / 207 = .686$. This is very close to the .68 from the Empirical Rule.

The interval $\bar{x} \pm 2s \Rightarrow .261 \pm 2(.033) \Rightarrow .261 \pm .066 \Rightarrow (.195, \ .327)$ contains 200 of the 207 observations. The proportion is $200 / 207 = .966$. This is somewhat larger than the .95 from the Empirical Rule.

The interval $\bar{x} \pm 3s \Rightarrow .261 \pm 3(.033) \Rightarrow .261 \pm .099 \Rightarrow (.162, \ .360)$ contains 206 of the 207 observations. The proportion is $206 / 207 = .995$. This is very close to the .997 from the Empirical Rule. Thus, it appears that the data may be normal.

The lower quartile is $Q_L = .243$ and the upper quartile is $Q_U = .287$. The interquartile range is $IQR = Q_U - Q_L = .287 - .243 = .044$. From the printout, $s = .03343$. $IQR / s = .044 / .03343 = 1.32$. This is very close to the 1.3 that we would expect if the data were normal. Thus, there is evidence that the data are normal.

Using MINITAB, the normal probability plot is:

Probability Plot of AVE
Normal - 95% CI

Mean	0.2611
StDev	0.03343
N	207
AD	0.669
P-Value	0.079

The data are very close to a straight line. Thus, it appears that the data may be normal.

From all 4 indicators, it appears that the batting averages from the American League come from an approximate normal distribution.

National League

To determine if the distribution of batting averages is approximately normal, we will run through the tests. Using MINITAB, the stem-and-leaf display is:

Stem-and-Leaf Display: AVE

```
Stem-and-leaf of AVE   N  = 228
Leaf Unit = 0.0010

    2    18  13
    9    19  3344459
   14    20  00789
   24    21  3556678888
   35    22  01456788999
   53    23  000012344557889999
   77    24  00000111222345667778 9999
  103    25  000111122334555666677 77899
 (25)    26  0011122233334456677788899
  100    27  001111222233333556667 7777888999
   69    28  00222223455556666778 99
   47    29  0011224667778899
   31    30  00122345579
   20    31  03444467
   12    32  58
   10    33  000007
    4    34  13
    2    35  89
```

From the stem-and-leaf display, the data look to be mound-shaped. The data may be normal.

Using MINITAB, the descriptive statistics are:

Descriptive Statistics: AVE

```
Variable    N   N*     Mean  SE Mean     StDev  Minimum        Q1    Median
AVE       228   0  0.26351  0.00225   0.03401  0.18100   0.24000   0.26300

Variable       Q3  Maximum
AVE       0.28500  0.35900
```

The interval $\bar{x} \pm s \Rightarrow .264 \pm .034 \Rightarrow (.230, .298)$ contains 160 of the 228 observations. The proportion is $160 / 228 = .701$. This is fairly close to the .68 from the Empirical Rule.

The interval $\bar{x} \pm 2s \Rightarrow .264 \pm 2(.034) \Rightarrow .264 \pm .068 \Rightarrow (.196, .332)$ contains 215 of the 228 observations. The proportion is $215 / 228 = .943$. This is somewhat smaller than the .95 from the Empirical Rule.

The interval $\bar{x} \pm 3s \Rightarrow .264 \pm 3(.034) \Rightarrow .264 \pm .102 \Rightarrow (.162, .366)$ contains 228 of the 228 observations. The proportion is $228 / 228 = 1.000$. This is very close to the .997 from the Empirical Rule. Thus, it appears that the data may be normal.

The lower quartile is $Q_L = .240$ and the upper quartile is $Q_U = .285$. The interquartile range is $IQR = Q_U - Q_L = .285 - .240 = .045$. From the printout, $s = .03401$. $IQR / s = .045 / .03401 = 1.32$. This is very close to the 1.3 that we would expect if the data were normal. Thus, there is evidence that the data are normal.

Using MINITAB, the normal probability plot is:

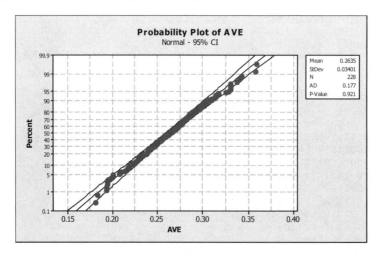

The data are very close to a straight line. Thus, it appears that the data may be normal.

From all 4 indicators, it appears that the batting averages from the National League come from an approximate normal distribution.

5.63   We will look at the 4 methods for determining if the data are normal. First, we will look at a histogram of the data. Using MINITAB, the histogram of the driver's head injury ratings is:

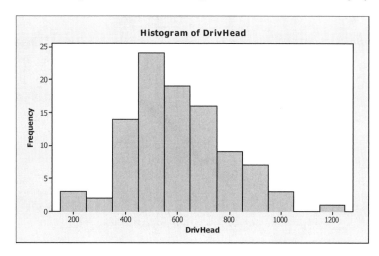

From the histogram, the data appear to be somewhat mound-shaped, but also somewhat skewed to the right. This indicates that the data may be normal.

Next, we look at the intervals $\bar{x} \pm s$, $\bar{x} \pm 2s$, $\bar{x} \pm 3s$. If the proportions of observations falling in each interval are approximately .68, .95, and 1.00, then the data are approximately normal.

Using MINITAB, the summary statistics are:

Descriptive Statistics: DrivHead

```
Variable    N  N*   Mean  SE Mean  StDev  Minimum     Q1  Median     Q3  Maximum
DrivHead   98  0   603.7     18.7  185.4    216.0  475.0   605.0  724.3   1240.0
```

$\bar{x} \pm s \Rightarrow 603.7 \pm 185.4 \Rightarrow (418.3, \ 789.1)$ 68 of the 98 values fall in this interval. The proportion is .69. This is very close to the .68 we would expect if the data were normal.

$\bar{x} \pm 2s \Rightarrow 603.7 \pm 2(185.4) \Rightarrow 603.7 \pm 370.8 \Rightarrow (232.9, \ 974.5)$ 96 of the 98 values fall in this interval. The proportion is .98. This is a fair amount larger than the .95 we would expect if the data were normal.

$\bar{x} \pm 3s \Rightarrow 603.7 \pm 3(185.4) \Rightarrow 603.7 \pm 556.2 \Rightarrow (47.5, \ 1,159.9)$ 97 of the 98 values fall in this interval. The proportion is .99. This is fairly close to the 1.00 we would expect if the data were normal.

From this method, it appears that the data may be normal.

Next, we look at the ratio of the IQR to s. IQR = $Q_U - Q_L = 724.3 - 475 = 249.3$.

$\dfrac{\text{IQR}}{s} = \dfrac{249.3}{185.4} = 1.3$ This is equal to the 1.3 we would expect if the data were normal. This method indicates the data may be normal.

Finally, using MINITAB, the normal probability plot is:

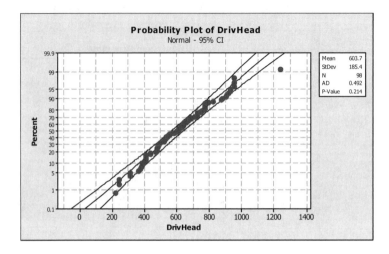

Probability Plot of DrivHead
Normal - 95% CI

Mean	603.7
StDev	185.4
N	98
AD	0.492
P-Value	0.214

Since the data form a fairly straight line, the data may be normal.

From the 4 different methods, all indications are that the driver's head injury rating data are normal.

5.65   The lowest score possible is 0. The sample mean is 7.62 and the standard deviation is 8.91. Since the lower limit of 0 is less than one standard deviation below the mean, this implies that the data are not normal, but skewed to the right.

5.67   The binomial probability distribution is a discrete distribution. The random variable can take on only a limited number of values. The normal distribution is a continuous distribution. The random variable can take on an infinite number of values. To get a better estimate of probabilities for the binomial probability distribution using the normal distribution, we use the continuity correction factor.

5.69   a.   In order to approximate the binomial distribution with the normal distribution, the interval $\mu \pm 3\sigma \Rightarrow np \pm 3\sqrt{npq}$ should lie in the range 0 to n.

When $n = 25$ and $p = .4$,
$$np \pm 3\sqrt{npq} \Rightarrow 25(.4) \pm 3\sqrt{25(.4)(1-.4)}$$
$$\Rightarrow 10 \pm 3\sqrt{6} \Rightarrow 10 \pm 7.3485 \Rightarrow (2.6515, 17.3485)$$

Since the interval calculated does lie in the range 0 to 25, we can use the normal approximation.

b. $\mu = np = 25(.4) = 10$
$\sigma^2 = npq = 25(.4)(.6) = 6$

c. $P(x \geq 9) = 1 - P(x \leq 8) = 1 - .274 = .726$ (Table II, Appendix A)

d. $P(x \geq 9) \approx P\left(z \geq \dfrac{(9-.5)-10}{\sqrt{6}}\right)$

$= P(z \geq -.61)$

$= .5000 + .2291 = .7291$

(Using Table IV in Appendix A.)

5.71 x is a binomial random variable with $n = 100$ and $p = .4$.

$$\mu \pm 3\sigma \Rightarrow np \pm 3\sqrt{npq} \Rightarrow 100(.4) \pm 3\sqrt{100(.4)(1-.4)}$$

$$\Rightarrow 40 \pm 3(4.8990) \Rightarrow (25.303, 54.697)$$

Since the interval lies in the range 0 to 100, we can use the normal approximation to approximate the probabilities.

a. $P(x \leq 35) \approx P\left(z \leq \dfrac{(35+.5)-40}{4.899}\right)$

$= P(z \leq -.92)$

$= .5000 - .3212 = .1788$

(Using Table IV in Appendix A.)

b. $P(40 \leq x \leq 50)$

$$\approx P\left(\dfrac{(40-.5)-40}{4.899} \leq z \leq \dfrac{(50+.5)-40}{4.899}\right)$$

$= P(-.10 \leq z \leq 2.14)$

$= P(-.10 \leq z \leq 0) + P(0 \leq z \leq 2.14)$

$= .0398 + .4838 = .5236$

(Using Table IV in Appendix A.)

c. $P(x \geq 38) \approx P\left(z \geq \dfrac{(38-.5)-40}{4.899}\right)$

$= P(z \geq -.51)$

$= .5000 + .1950 = .6950$

(Using Table IV in Appendix A.)

5.73   a. $\mu = np = 200(.2) = 40$

b. $\sigma = \sqrt{npq} = \sqrt{200(.2)(.8)} = \sqrt{32} = 5.657$

c. $z = \dfrac{x-\mu}{\sigma} = \dfrac{50.5-40}{5.657} = 1.86$

d. $P(x \leq 50) \approx P\left(z \leq \dfrac{(50+.5)-40}{5.657}\right) = P(z \leq 1.86) = .5 + .4686 = .9686$

(Using Table IV, Appendix A)

5.75   a. $\mu = E(x) = np = 200(.05) = 10$. This is the same value that was found in Exercise 4.57 c.

        b. $\sigma = \sqrt{npq} = \sqrt{200(.05)(1-.05)} = \sqrt{9.5} = 3.082$

        c. $z = \dfrac{x - \mu}{\sigma} = \dfrac{10.5 - 10}{3.082} = .16$

        d. $P(x \geq 11) \approx P\left(z \geq \dfrac{10.5 - 10}{3.082}\right) = P(z \geq .16) = .5 - .0636 = .4364$

        (Using Table IV, Appendix A)

5.77   a.   For $n = 100$ and $p = .01$:

            $$\mu \pm 3\sigma \Rightarrow np \pm 3\sqrt{npq} \Rightarrow 100(.01) \pm 3\sqrt{100(.01)(.99)}$$
            $$\Rightarrow 1 \pm 3(.995) \Rightarrow 1 \pm 2.985 \Rightarrow (-1.985, 3.985)$$
            Since the interval does not lie in the range 0 to 100, we cannot use the normal approximation to approximate the probabilities.

        b.   For $n = 100$ and $p = .5$:

            $$\mu \pm 3\sigma \Rightarrow np \pm 3\sqrt{npq} \Rightarrow 100(.5) \pm 3\sqrt{100(.5)(.5)}$$
            $$\Rightarrow 50 \pm 3(5) \Rightarrow 50 \pm 15 \Rightarrow (35, 65)$$

            Since the interval lies in the range 0 to 100, we can use the normal approximation to approximate the probabilities.

        c.   For $n = 100$ and $p = .9$:

            $$\mu \pm 3\sigma \Rightarrow np \pm 3\sqrt{npq} \Rightarrow 100(.9) \pm 3\sqrt{100(.9)(.1)}$$
            $$\Rightarrow 90 \pm 3(3) \Rightarrow 90 \pm 9 \Rightarrow (81, 99)$$

            Since the interval lies in the range 0 to 100, we can use the normal approximation to approximate the probabilities.

5.79   Let x = number of beech trees damaged by fungi in 200 trees. Then x is a binomial random variable with $n = 200$ and $p = .25$.

    $\mu = np = 200(.25) = 50$

    $\sigma = \sqrt{npq} = \sqrt{200(.25)(.75)} = \sqrt{37.5} = 6.124$

    $P(x > 100) \approx P\left(z > \dfrac{(100 + .5) - 50}{6.124}\right) = P(z > 8.25) \approx 0$

    Since this probability is so small, it is almost impossible for more than half of the trees to have fungi damage.

5.81   a.   Let x = number of abused women in a sample of 150. The random variable x is a binomial random variable with $n = 150$ and $p = 1/3$. Thus, for the normal approximation,

$$\mu = np = 150(1/3) = 50 \text{ and } \sigma = \sqrt{npq} = \sqrt{150(1/3)(2/3)} = 5.7735$$

$$\mu \pm 3\sigma \Rightarrow 50 \pm 3(5.7735) \Rightarrow 50 \pm 17.3205 \Rightarrow (32.6795, 67.3205)$$

Since this interval lies in the range from 0 to $n = 150$, the normal approximation is appropriate.

$$P(x > 75) \approx P\left(z > \frac{(75 + .5) - 50}{5.7735}\right) = P(z > 4.42) \approx .5 - .5 = 0$$

(Using Table IV, Appendix A.)

b. $P(x < 50) \approx P\left(z < \dfrac{(50 - .5) - 50}{5.7735}\right) = P(z < -.09) \approx .5 - .0359 = .4641$

c. $P(x < 30) \approx P\left(z < \dfrac{(30 - .5) - 50}{5.7735}\right) = P(z < -3.55) \approx .5 - .5 = 0$

Since the probability of seeing fewer than 30 abused women in a sample of 150 is so small ($p \approx 0$), it would be very unlikely to see this event.

5.83   a.   If 80% of the passengers pass through without their luggage being inspected, then 20% will be detained for luggage inspection. The expected number of passengers detained will be:

$$E(x) = np = 1,500(.2) = 300$$

b.   For $n = 4,000$, $E(x) = np = 4,000(.2) = 800$

c. $P(x > 600) \approx P\left(z > \dfrac{(600 + .5) - 800}{\sqrt{4000(.2)(.8)}}\right) = P(z > -7.89) = .5 + .5 = 1.0$

5.85   The amount of time or distance between occurrences of random events can be described by the exponential probability distribution. This distribution has the property that the mean is equal to the standard deviation.

5.87   For $\theta = 3$, $f(x) = \dfrac{1}{3}e^{-x/3}$. Using Table V, Appendix A:

x	$f(x)$
0	.333
1	.239
2	.171
3	.123
4	.088
5	.063
6	.045

For $\theta = 1$, $f(y) = e^{-y}$. Using Table V, Appendix A:

x	$f(x)$
0	1.000
1	.368
2	.135
3	.050
4	.018
5	.007
6	.002

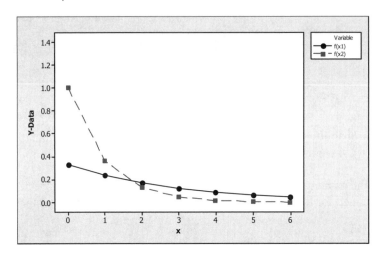

5.89 $P(x \geq a) = e^{-a/\theta} = e^{-a/1}$. Using Table V, Appendix A:

a. $P(x > 1) = e^{-1/1} = e^{-1} = .367879$

b. $P(x \leq 3) = 1 - P(x > 3) = 1 - e^{-3/1} = 1 - e^{-3} = 1 - .049787 = .950213$

c. $P(x > 1.5) = e^{-1.5/1} = e^{-1.5} = .223130$

d. $P(x \leq 5) = 1 - P(x > 5) = 1 - e^{-5/1} = 1 - e^{-5} = 1 - .006738 = .993262$

5.91 $\mu = \theta = 1$, $\sigma = \theta = 1$

$\mu \pm 2\sigma \Rightarrow 1 \pm 2(1) \Rightarrow 1 \pm 2 \Rightarrow (-1, 3)$

$P(-1 < x < 3) = P(0 < x < 3) = 1 - P(x \geq 3) = 1 - e^{-3/1}$
$= 1 - e^{-3} = 1 - .049787 = .950213$
(from Table V, Appendix A)

5.93   a. $P(x > 2) = e^{-2/2.5} = e^{-.8} = .449329$ (using Table V, Appendix A)

b. $P(x < 5) = 1 - P(x \geq 5) = 1 - e^{-5/2.5} = 1 - e^{-2} = 1 - .135335 = .864665$
(Using Table V, Appendix A)

5.95   Let x = breast height diameter of the western hemlock. Then x has an exponential distribution with a mean of 30 cm.

$$P(x > 25) + e^{-25/30} = e^{-.833333} = .434598$$

5.97   a.   Let x_1 = repair time for machine 1. Then x_1 has an exponential distribution with $\mu_1 = 1$ hour.

$$P(x_1 > 1) = e^{-1/1} = e^{-1} = .367879 \text{ (using Table V, Appendix A)}$$

b.   Let x_2 = repair time for machine 2. Then x_2 has an exponential distribution with $\mu_2 = 2$ hours.

$$P(x_2 > 1) = e^{-1/2} = e^{-.5} = .606531 \text{ (using Table V, Appendix A)}$$

c.   Let x_3 = repair time for machine 3. Then x_3 has an exponential distribution with $\mu_3 = .5$ hours.

$$P(x_3 > 1) = e^{-1/.5} = e^{-2} = .135335 \text{ (using Table V, Appendix A)}$$

Since the mean repair time for machine 4 is the same as for machine 3, $P(x_4 > 1)$ $= P(x_3 > 1) = .135335$.

d.   The only way that the repair time for the entire system will not exceed 1 hour is if all four machines are repaired in less than 1 hour. Thus, the probability that the repair time for the entire system exceeds 1 hour is:

P(Repair time entire system exceeds 1 hour)
$$= 1 - P((x_1 \leq 1) \cap (x_2 \leq 1) \cap (x_3 \leq 1) \cap (x_4 \leq 1))$$
$$= 1 - P(x_1 \leq 1)P(x_2 \leq 1)P(x_3 \leq 1)P(x_4 \leq 1)$$
$$= 1 - (1 - .367879)(1 - .606531)(1 - .135335)(1 - .135335)$$
$$= 1 - (.632121)(.393469)(.864665)(.864665) = 1 - .185954 = .814046$$

5.99   a.   For $\mu = 17 = \theta$. To graph the distribution, we will pick several values of x and find the value of $f(x)$, where x = time between arrivals of the smaller craft at the pier.

$$f(x) = \frac{1}{\theta}e^{-x/\theta} = \frac{1}{17}e^{-x/17}$$

$$f(1) = \frac{1}{17}e^{-1/17} = .0555$$

$$f(3) = \frac{1}{17}e^{-3/17} = .0493$$

$$f(5) = \frac{1}{17}e^{-5/17} = .0438$$

$$f(7) = \frac{1}{17}e^{-7/17} = .0390$$

$$f(10) = \frac{1}{17}e^{-10/17} = .0327$$

$$f(15) = \frac{1}{17}e^{-15/17} = .0243$$

$$f(20) = \frac{1}{17} e^{-20/17} = .0181$$

$$f(25) = \frac{1}{17} e^{-25/17} = .0135$$

The graph is:

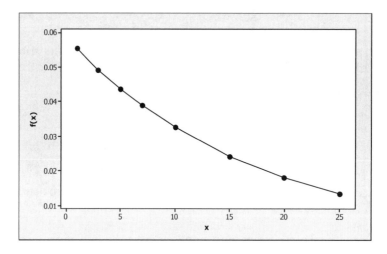

b. We want to find the probability that the time between arrivals is less than 15 minutes.

$$P(x < 15) = 1 - P(x \geq 15) = 1 - e^{-15/17} = 1 - .4138 = .5862$$

5.101   a.   For $\theta = 250$, $P(x > a) = e^{-a/250}$

For $a = 300$ and $b = 200$, show $P(x > a + b) \geq P(x > a)P(x > b)$

$$P(x > 300 + 200) = P(x > 500) = e^{-500/250} = e^{-2} = .1353$$

$$P(x > 300) \, P(x > 200) = e^{-300/250} \, e^{-200/250} = e^{-1.2} \, e^{-.8} = .3012(.4493) = .1353$$

Since $P(x > 300 + 200) = P(x > 300) \, P(x > 200)$, then
$P(x > 300 + 200) \geq P(x > 300) \, P(x > 200)$

Also, show $P(x > 300 + 200) \leq P(x > 300) \, P(x > 200)$. Since we already showed that
$P(x > 300 + 200) = P(x > 300) \, P(x > 200)$,
then $P(x > 300 + 200) \leq P(x > 300) \, P(x > 200)$.

b.   Let $a = 50$ and $b = 100$. Show $P(x > a + b) \geq P(x > a) \, P(x > b)$

$$P(x > 50 + 100) = P(x > 150) = e^{-150/250} = e^{-.6} = .5488$$

$$P(x > 50) \, P(x > 100) = e^{-50/250} \, e^{-100/250} = e^{-.2} e^{-.4} = .8187(.6703) = .5488$$

Since $P(x > 50 + 100) = P(x > 50) \, P(x > 100)$, then
$P(x > 50 + 100) \geq P(x > 50) \, P(x > 100)$

Also, show $P(x > 50 + 100) \leq P(x > 50) \, P(x > 100)$. Since we already showed that $P(x > 50 + 100) = P(x > 50) \, P(x > 100)$,
then $P(x > 50 + 100) \leq P(x > 50) \, P(x > 100)$.

c. Show $P(x > a + b) \geq P(x > a) \, P(x > b)$
$P(x > a + b) = e^{-(a+b)/250} = e^{-a/250} \, e^{-b/250} = P(x > a) \, P(x > b)$

5.103   a. For the probability density function, $f(x) = \dfrac{e^{-x/7}}{7}$, $x > 0$, x is an exponential random variable.

b. For the probability density function, $f(x) = \dfrac{1}{20}$, $5 < x < 25$, x is a uniform random variable.

c. For the probability function, $f(x) = \dfrac{e^{-.5[(x-10)/5]^2}}{5\sqrt{2\pi}}$, x is a normal random variable.

5.105   a. $P(z \leq -2.1) = A_1 + A_2$
$ = .5 + .4821$
$ = .9821$

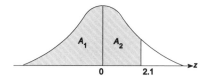

b. $P(z \geq 2.1) = A_2 = .5 - A_1$
$ = .5 - .4821$
$ = .0179$

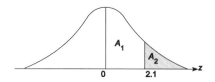

c. $P(z \geq -1.65) = A_1 + A_2$
$ = .4505 + .5000$
$ = .9505$

d. $P(-2.13 \leq z \leq -.41)$
$ = P(-2.13 \leq z \leq 0) - P(-.41 \leq z \leq 0)$
$ = .4834 - .1591$
$ = .3243$

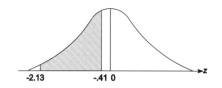

e. $P(-1.45 \le z \le 2.15) = A_1 + A_2$
$$= .4265 + .4842$$
$$= .9107$$

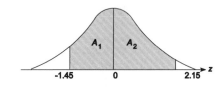

f. $P(z \le -1.43) = A_1 = .5 - A_2$
$$= .5000 - .4236$$
$$= .0764$$

5.107 a. $P(x \le 75) = P\left(z \le \dfrac{75 - 70}{10}\right)$

$$= P(z \le .50)$$
$$= .5 + .1915 = .6915$$

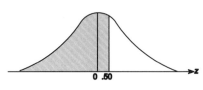

b. $P(x \ge 90) = P\left(z \ge \dfrac{90 - 70}{10}\right)$

$$= P(z \ge 2.00)$$
$$= .5000 - .4772 = .0228$$

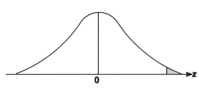

c. $P(60 \le x \le 75) = P\left(\dfrac{60 - 70}{10} \le z \le \dfrac{75 - 70}{10}\right)$

$$= P(-1.00 \le z \le .50)$$
$$= .3413 + .1915 = .5328$$

d. This is the probability of the complement of the event in part **a**. Therefore:

$$P(x > 75) = 1 - P(x \le 75) = 1 - .6915 = .3085$$

e. $P(x = 75) = 0$ (True for any continuous random variable.)

f. $P(x \le 95) = P\left(z \le \dfrac{95 - 70}{10}\right)$

$$= P(z \le 2.50)$$
$$= .5000 + .4938 = .9938$$

5.109 $\mu = np = 100(.5) = 50$, $\sigma = \sqrt{npq} = \sqrt{100(.5)(.5)} = 5$

a. $P(x \le 48) = P\left(z \le \dfrac{(48 + .5) - 50}{5}\right)$

$$= P(z \le -.30)$$
$$= .5 - .1179 = .3821$$

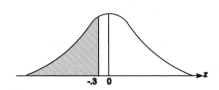

b. $P(50 \leq x \leq 65)$

$$= P\left(\frac{(50-.5)-50}{5} \leq z \leq \frac{(65+.5)-50}{5}\right)$$

$$= P(-.10 \leq z \leq 3.10)$$
$$= .0398 + .5000 = .5398$$

c. $P(x \geq 70) = P\left(z \geq \frac{(70-.5)-50}{5}\right)$

$$= (z \geq 3.90)$$
$$= .5 - .5 = 0$$

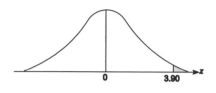

d. $P(55 \leq x \leq 58)$

$$= P\left(\frac{(55-.5)-50}{5} \leq z \leq \frac{(58+.5)-50}{5}\right)$$

$$= P(.90 \leq z \leq 1.70)$$
$$= P(0 \leq z \leq 1.70) - P(0 \leq z \leq .90)$$
$$= .4554 - .3159 = .1395$$

e. $P(x = 62)$

$$= P\left(\frac{(62-.5)-50}{5} \leq z \leq \frac{(62+.5)-50}{5}\right)$$

$$= P(2.30 \leq z \leq 2.50)$$
$$= P(0 \leq z \leq 2.50) - (0 \leq z \leq 2.30)$$
$$= .4938 - .4893 = .0045$$

f. $P(x \leq 49 \text{ or } x \geq 72)$

$$= P\left(z \leq \frac{(49+.5)-50}{5}\right) + P\left(z \geq \frac{(72-.5)-50}{5}\right)$$

$$= P(z \leq -.10) + P(z \geq 4.30)$$
$$= (.5 - .0398) + (.5 - .5) = .4602$$

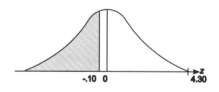

5.111 Let x = score for first time students on mathematics achievement test. Then x is a normal random variable with $\mu = 77$ and $\sigma = 7.3$.

$$P(x \geq 70) = P\left(z \geq \frac{70-77}{7.3}\right)$$

$$= P(z \geq -.96)$$
$$= .3315 + .5000 = .8315$$

Thus, 83.15% of students will pass the test the first time.

5.113 Let x = number of African-Americans with sickle-cell anemia. Then x is a binomial random variable with $n = 1,000$ and $p = .08$.

$$\mu = np = 1,000(.08) = 80 \quad \text{and} \quad \sigma = \sqrt{npq} = \sqrt{1,000(.08)(.92)} = 8.579$$

a. $P(x > 175) = P\left(z > \dfrac{(175 + .5) - 80}{8.579}\right) = P(z > 11.13) \approx .5 - .5 = 0$

b. $P(x < 140) = P\left(z < \dfrac{(140 - .5) - 80}{8.579}\right) = P(z < 6.94) = .5 + .5 = 1.0$

5.115 a. Using Table IV, Appendix A, with $\mu = 20.2$ and $\sigma = .65$,

$$P(20 < x < 21) = P\left(\dfrac{20 - 20.2}{.65} < z < \dfrac{21 - 20.2}{.65}\right) = P(-.31 < z < 1.23)$$
$$= P(-.31 < z < 0) + P(0 \le z < 1.23) = .1217 + .3907 = .5124$$

b. $P(x < 19.84) = P\left(z < \dfrac{1984 - 20.2}{.65}\right) = P(z < -.55) = .5 - .2088 = .2912$

c. $P(x > 22.01) = P\left(z > \dfrac{22.01 - 20.2}{.65}\right) = P(z > 2.78) = .5 - .4973 = .0027$

5.117 For the uniform distribution,

$$f(x) = \begin{cases} \dfrac{1}{d-c} = \dfrac{1}{90-75} = \dfrac{1}{15} & 75 \le x \le 90 \\ 0 & \text{otherwise} \end{cases}$$

a. $P(x > 80) = (90 - 80)\left(\dfrac{1}{15}\right) = .667$

b. $P(80 < x < 85) = (85 - 80)\left(\dfrac{1}{15}\right) = .333$

c. $E(x) = \mu = \dfrac{c+d}{2} = \dfrac{75+90}{2} = 82.5°F$

5.119 $c = 0, d = 4$

$$f(x) = \begin{cases} \dfrac{1}{d-c} = \dfrac{1}{4-0} = \dfrac{1}{4} & 0 \le x \le 4 \\ 0 & \text{otherwise} \end{cases}$$

$$\mu = \dfrac{c+d}{2} = \dfrac{0+4}{2} = 2, \ \sigma = \dfrac{d-c}{\sqrt{12}} = \dfrac{4-0}{\sqrt{12}} = 1.155$$

$$15 \text{ seconds} = \frac{15}{60} = .25 \text{ minutes}$$

It takes .25 minutes to go from floor 2 to floor 1. Thus, we must find the probability that the waiting time is less than $1.5 - .25 = 1.25$.

$$P(x < 1.25) = (1.25 - 0)\frac{1}{4} = 1.25\left(\frac{1}{4}\right) = .3125$$

5.121 Let x = velocity of a galaxy located within the galaxy cluster A2142. Then x is a normal random variable with mean $\mu = 27,117$ km/s and standard deviation $\sigma = 1,280$ km/s.

$$P(x \le 24,350) = P\left(z \le \frac{24,350 - 27,117}{1,280}\right) = P(z \le -2.16) = .5 - .4846 = .0154$$

Since the probability of observing a galaxy from the galaxy cluster A2142 with a velocity of 24,350 km/s or slower is so small ($p = .0154$), it would be very unlikely that the galaxy observed came from the galaxy cluster A2142.

5.123   a.   Using Table IV, Appendix A, with $\mu = 76.8$ and $\sigma = 9.2$.

$$P(x > 90) = P\left(z > \frac{90 - 76.8}{9.2}\right) = P(z > 1.43) = .5 - P(0 < z < 1.43)$$
$$= .5 - .4236 = .0764$$

Thus, the percentage of compounds formed from the plant extract that have a collagen amount greater than 90 grams is 7.64%.

   b. $P(x_L < x < x_U) = .8000$. Suppose we pick x_L and x_U so that the interval is symmetric around the mean.

$$\text{If } P(x_L < x < x_U) = .8000, \text{ then } P\left(\frac{x_L - 76.8}{9.2} < z < \frac{x_U - 76.8}{9.2}\right)$$
$$= P(z_L < z < z_U) = .8000$$

Then $P(z_L < z < 0) = P(0 < z < z_U) = .4000$. Looking up .4000 in Table IV, the z-score is 1.28. Thus, $z_L = -1.28$ and $z_U = 1.28$. Now, we must convert z_L and z_U back to x scores.

$$z_L = \frac{x_L - 76.8}{9.2} \Rightarrow -1.28 = \frac{x_L - 76.8}{9.2} \Rightarrow x_L = 9.2(-1.28) + 76.8 = 65.024$$

$$z_U = \frac{x_U - 76.8}{9.2} \Rightarrow 1.28 = \frac{x_U - 76.8}{9.2} \Rightarrow x_L = 9.2(1.28) + 76.8 = 88.576$$

Thus, a symmetric interval that contains 80% of the compounds is 65.024 to 88.576.

5.125 From Table IV, Appendix A, with $\mu = 6.3$ and $\sigma = .6$

a. $P(x < 5) = P\left(z < \dfrac{5 - 6.3}{.6}\right) = P(z < -2.17) = .5 - .4850 = .0150$

Thus, the percentage of days when the oxygen content is undesirable is 1.5%.

b. We would expect the oxygen contents to fall within 2 standard deviations of the mean, or

$$\mu \pm 2\sigma \Rightarrow 6.3 \pm 2(.6) \Rightarrow 6.3 \pm 1.2 \Rightarrow (5.1, 7.5)$$

5.127 a. (i) $P(0 < z < 1.2) \approx z(4.4 - z)/10 = 1.2(4.4 - 1.2)/10 = .384$
(ii) $P(0 < z < 2.5) \approx .49$
(iii) $P(z > .8) = .5 - P(0 < z < .8) \approx .5 - .8(4.4 - .8)/10 = .5 - .288 = .212$
(iv) $P(z < 1.0) = .5 + P(0 < z < 1.0) = .5 + 1(4.4 - 1)/10 = .5 + .34 = .84$

b. Using Table IV, Appendix A:
(i) $P(0 < z < 1.2) = .3849$
(ii) $P(0 < z < 2.5) = .4938$
(iii) $P(z > .8) = .5 - P(0 < z < .8) = .5 - .2881 = .2119$
(iv) $P(z < 1.0) = .5 + P(0 < z < 1.0) = .5 + .3413 = .8413$

c. For each part, the absolute error is:
(i) Error $= |.384 - .3869| = .0029$
(ii) Error $= |.49 - .4938| = .0038$
(iii) Error $= |.212 - .2119| = .0001$
(iv) Error $= |.84 - .8413| = .0013$

In all cases, the absolute error is less than .0052.

5.129 Since we know for a mound-shaped distribution that approximately 95% of the data lies within two standard deviations of the mean, by symmetry approximately 2.5% would fall below 2 standard deviations below the mean and approximately 2.5% would fall more than 2 standard deviations above the mean. Therefore, the amount of time allotted should be two standard deviations above the mean. This is:

$$\mu + 2\sigma = 40 + 2(6) = 52 \text{ minutes}$$

5.131 Let $x =$ number of defective CDs in a sample of 1600. Then x is a binomial random variable with $n = 1600$ and $p = .006$. To see if the normal approximation is appropriate, we check:

$$np \pm 3\sqrt{npq} \Rightarrow 1600(.006) \pm 3\sqrt{1600(.006)(.994)}$$
$$\Rightarrow 9.6 \pm 3(3.089) \Rightarrow 9.6 \pm 9.267 \Rightarrow (.333, 18.867)$$

Since this interval falls in the interval 0 to $n = 1600$, the normal approximation is appropriate.

$$P(x \geq 12) \approx P\left(z \geq \frac{(12 - .5) - 9.6}{3.089}\right)$$

$$= P(z \geq .62)$$
$$= .5 - .2324 = .2676$$

Since the probability of seeing 12 or more defective disks is not small ($p = .2676$), it would not be unusual if 99.4% of the disks are defect free. This does not cast doubt on the manufacturer's claim.

5.133   Using Table IV, Appendix A, with $\mu = .27$ and $\sigma = .04$,

$$P(x \leq .14) = P\left(z \leq \frac{.14 - .27}{.04}\right) = P(z < -3.25) \approx .5 - .5 = .0000$$

Since the probability of observing a reading of .14 or smaller is so small ($p \approx .0000$) if the pressure is .1 MPa, it would be extremely unlikely that this reading was obtained at a pressure of .1 MPa.

5.135   a.   Class I (very bright) consists of those with IQs above the 95th percentile. Thus, there would be .05 of the people in Class I.

Class II (bright) consists of those with IQs between the 75th and 95th percentile. Thus, there would be $.95 - .75 = .20$ of the people in Class II.

Class III (normal) consists of those with IQs between the 25th and 75th percentile. Thus, there would be $.75 - .25 = .50$ of the people in Class III.

Class IV (dull) consists of those with IQs between the 5th and 25th percentile. Thus, there would be $.25 - .05 = .20$ of the people in Class IV.

Class V (very dull) consists of those with IQs below the 5th percentile. Thus, there would be .05 of the people in Class V.

b.   Suppose we pick a pair of percentiles and compute the corresponding z-scores. Suppose we compute the z-scores for the 50th and 55th percentiles.

The z-score corresponding to the 50th percentile is $z = 0$. The z-score corresponding to the 55th percentile is:

$$P(z < z_0) = .55 \Rightarrow z_0 = .13$$

Now, suppose we pick another pair of percentiles that are also 5 points apart. Suppose we compute the z-scores for the 94th and 99th percentiles.

The z-score corresponding to the 94th percentile is:

$$P(z < z_0) = .94 \Rightarrow z_0 = 1.555$$

The z-score corresponding to the 99th percentile is:

$$P(z < z_0) = .99 \Rightarrow z_0 = 2.33$$

The z-scores corresponding to the 50th and 55th percentiles are 0 and .13. The difference is $.13 - 0 = .13$. The z-scores corresponding to the 94th and 99th percentiles are 1.555 and 2.33. The difference is $2.33 - 1.555 = .775$. Even though the differences in the percentiles are the same, the differences in the z-scores are much different. The information in the z-scores is more informative.

c.   If the distribution of the IQs is skewed to the right, then the tail to the right is much longer than the tail to the left. If the distribution of the IQs is skewed to the left, then the tail to the left is much longer than the tail to the right. However, the proportions in the 5 cognitive classes would not differ, regardless of the shape of the distribution.

Class I (very bright) consists of those with IQs above the 95th percentile. Thus, there would be .05 of the people in Class I.

Class II (bright) consists of those with IQs between the 75th and 95th percentile. Thus, there would be $.95 - .75 = .20$ of the people in Class II.

Class III (normal) consists of those with IQs between the 25th and 75th percentile. Thus, there would be $.75 - .25 = .50$ of the people in Class III.

Class IV (dull) consists of those with IQs between the 5th and 25th percentile. Thus, there would be $.25 - .05 = .20$ of the people in Class IV.

Class V (very dull) consists of those with IQs below the 5th percentile. Thus, there would be .05 of the people in Class V.

Sampling Distributions

6.1 A population parameter is a numerical descriptive measure of a population. Because it is based on the observations in a population, its value is almost always unknown.

A sample statistic is a numerical descriptive measure of a sample. It is calculated from the observations in the sample.

6.3 a–b. The different samples of $n = 2$ with replacement and their means are:

Possible Samples	$\bar{x}$	Possible Samples	$\bar{x}$
0, 0	0	4, 0	2
0, 2	1	4, 2	3
0, 4	2	4, 4	4
0, 6	3	4, 6	5
2, 0	1	6, 0	3
2, 2	2	6, 2	4
2, 4	3	6, 4	5
2, 6	4	6, 6	6

c. Since each sample is equally likely, the probability of any 1 being selected is

$$\frac{1}{4}\left(\frac{1}{4}\right) = \frac{1}{16}$$

d. $P(\bar{x} = 0) = \dfrac{1}{16}$

$P(\bar{x} = 1) = \dfrac{1}{16} + \dfrac{1}{16} = \dfrac{2}{16}$

$P(\bar{x} = 2) = \dfrac{1}{16} + \dfrac{1}{16} + \dfrac{1}{16} = \dfrac{3}{16}$

$P(\bar{x} = 3) = \dfrac{1}{16} + \dfrac{1}{16} + \dfrac{1}{16} + \dfrac{1}{16} = \dfrac{4}{16}$

$P(\bar{x} = 4) = \dfrac{1}{16} + \dfrac{1}{16} + \dfrac{1}{16} = \dfrac{3}{16}$

$P(\bar{x} = 5) = \dfrac{1}{16} + \dfrac{1}{16} = \dfrac{2}{16}$

$P(\bar{x} = 6) = \dfrac{1}{16}$

$\bar{x}$	$p(\bar{x})$
0	1/16
1	2/16
2	3/16
3	4/16
4	3/16
5	2/16
6	1/16

e.

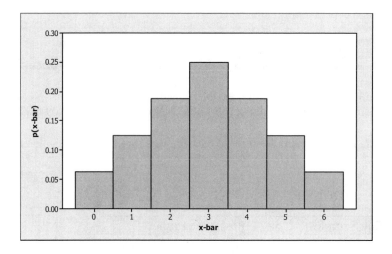

6.5   If the observations are independent of each other, then

$P(1, 1) = p(1)p(1) = .2(.2) = .04$
$P(1, 2) = p(1)p(2) = .2(.3) = .06$
$P(1, 3) = p(1)p(3) = .2(.2) = .04$
    etc.

a.

Possible Samples	$\overline{x}$	$p(\overline{x})$	Possible Samples	$\overline{x}$	$p(\overline{x})$
1, 1	1	.04	3, 4	3.5	.04
1, 2	1.5	.06	3, 5	4	.02
1, 3	2	.04	4, 1	2.5	.04
1, 4	2.5	.04	4, 2	3	.06
1, 5	3	.02	4, 3	3.5	.04
2, 1	1.5	.06	4, 4	4	.04
2, 2	2	.09	4, 5	4.5	.02
2, 3	2.5	.06	5, 1	3	.02
2, 4	3	.06	5, 2	3.5	.03
2, 5	3.5	.03	5, 3	4	.02
3, 1	2	.04	5, 4	4.5	.02
3, 2	2.5	.06	5, 5	5	.01
3, 3	3	.04			

Summing the probabilities, the probability distribution of $\overline{x}$ is:

$\overline{x}$	$p(\overline{x})$
1	.04
1.5	.12
2	.17
2.5	.20
3	.20
3.5	.14
4	.08
4.5	.04
5	.01

b.

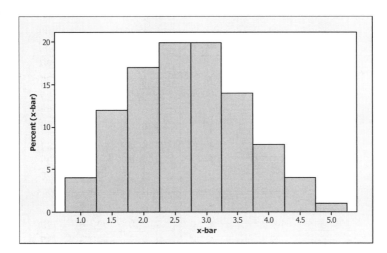

c. $P(\bar{x} \geq 4.5) = .04 + .01 = .05$

d.   No. The probability of observing $\bar{x} = 4.5$ or larger is small (.05).

6.7   a.   For a sample of size $n = 2$, the sample mean and sample median are exactly the same. Thus, the sampling distribution of the sample median is the same as that for the sample mean (see Exercise 6.5**a**).

        b.   The probability histogram for the sample median is identical to that for the sample mean (see Exercise 6.5**b**).

6.11   If the sampling distribution of a sample statistic has a mean equal to the population parameter the statistic is intended to estimate, the statistic is said to be an unbiased estimate of the parameter. If the mean of the sampling distribution is not equal to the parameter, the statistic is said to be a biased estimate of the parameter.

6.13   The properties of an ideal estimator are unbiased and minimum variance. Ideally, when we are estimating a parameter, we would like to use an unbiased estimator. In addition, of all unbiased estimators, we would like to choose the estimator with the minimum variance.

6.15   a. $\mu = \sum xp(x) = 2\left(\dfrac{1}{3}\right) + 4\left(\dfrac{1}{3}\right) + 9\left(\dfrac{1}{3}\right) = \dfrac{15}{3} = 5$

b.   The possible samples of size $n = 3$, the sample means, and the probabilities are:

Possible Samples	$\bar{x}$	$p(\bar{x})$	m	Possible Samples	$\bar{x}$	$p(\bar{x})$	m
2, 2, 2	2	1/27	2	4, 4, 4	4	1/27	4
2, 2, 4	8/3	1/27	2	4, 4, 9	17/3	1/27	4
2, 2, 9	13/3	1/27	2	4, 9, 2	5	1/27	4
2, 4, 2	8/3	1/27	2	4, 9, 4	17/3	1/27	4
2, 4, 4	10/3	1/27	4	4, 9, 9	22/3	1/27	9
2, 4, 9	5	1/27	4	9, 2, 2	13/3	1/27	2
2, 9, 2	13/3	1/27	2	9, 2, 4	5	1/27	4
2, 9, 4	5	1/27	4	9, 2, 9	20/3	1/27	9
2, 9, 9	20/3	1/27	9	9, 4, 2	5	1/27	4
4, 2, 2	8/3	1/27	2	9, 4, 4	17/3	1/27	4
4, 2, 4	10/3	1/27	4	9, 4, 9	22/3	1/27	9
4, 2, 9	5	1/27	4	9, 9, 2	20/3	1/27	9
4, 4, 2	10/3	1/27	4	9, 9, 4	22/3	1/27	9
				9, 9, 9	9	1/27	9

The sampling distribution of $\bar{x}$ is:

$\bar{x}$	$p(\bar{x})$
2	1/27
8/3	3/27
10/3	3/27
4	1/27
13/3	3/27
5	6/27
17/3	3/27
20/3	3/27
22/3	3/27
9	1/27
	27/27

$$E(\bar{x}) = \sum \bar{x}p(\bar{x}) = 2\left(\frac{1}{27}\right) + \frac{8}{3}\left(\frac{3}{27}\right) + \frac{10}{3}\left(\frac{3}{27}\right) + 4\left(\frac{1}{27}\right) + \frac{13}{3}\left(\frac{3}{27}\right)$$

$$+ 5\left(\frac{6}{27}\right) + \frac{17}{3}\left(\frac{3}{27}\right) + \frac{20}{3}\left(\frac{3}{27}\right) + \frac{22}{3}\left(\frac{3}{27}\right) + 9\left(\frac{1}{27}\right)$$

$$= \frac{2}{27} + \frac{8}{27} + \frac{10}{27} + \frac{4}{27} + \frac{13}{27} + \frac{30}{27} + \frac{17}{27} + \frac{20}{27} + \frac{22}{27} + \frac{9}{27}$$

$$= \frac{135}{27} = 5$$

Since $\mu = 5$ in part **a**, and $E(\bar{x}) = \mu = 5$, $\bar{x}$ is an unbiased estimator of μ.

c.   The median was calculated for each sample and is shown in the table in part **b**. The sampling distribution of m is:

m	$p(m)$
2	7/27
4	13/27
9	7/27
	27/27

$$E(m) = \sum mp(m) = 2\left(\frac{7}{27}\right) + 4\left(\frac{13}{27}\right) + 9\left(\frac{7}{27}\right) = \frac{14}{27} + \frac{52}{27} + \frac{63}{27} = \frac{129}{27} = 4.778$$

The $E(m) = 4.778 \neq \mu = 5$. Thus, m is a biased estimator of μ.

d.   Use the sample mean, $\bar{x}$. It is an unbiased estimator.

6.19   a.   Refer to the solution to Exercise 6.9. The values of s^2 and the corresponding probabilities are listed below:

$$s^2 = \frac{\sum (x^2) - \dfrac{\left(\sum x\right)^2}{n}}{n-1}$$

For sample 1, 1, $s^2 = \dfrac{2 - \dfrac{2^2}{2}}{1} = 0$

For sample 1, 2, $s^2 = \dfrac{5 - \dfrac{3^2}{2}}{1} = .5$

The rest of the values are calculated and shown:

s^2	$p(s^2)$	s^2	$p(s^2)$
0.0	.04	0.5	.04
0.5	.06	2.0	.02
2.0	.04	4.5	.04
4.5	.04	2.0	.06
8.0	.02	0.5	.04
0.5	.06	0.0	.04
0.0	.09	0.5	.02
0.5	.06	8.0	.02
2.0	.06	4.5	.03
4.5	.03	2.0	.02
2.0	.04	0.5	.02
0.5	.06	0.0	.01
0.0	.04		

The sampling distribution of s^2 is:

s^2	$p(s^2)$
0.0	.22
0.5	.36
2.0	.24
4.5	.14
8.0	.04

b. $\sigma^2 = \sum(x-\mu)^2 p(x) = (1-2.7)^2(.2) + (2-2.7)^2(.3) + (3-2.7)^2(.2)$
$$+ (4-2.7)^2(.2) + (5-2.7)^2(.1)$$
$$= 1.61$$

c. $E(s^2) = \sum s^2 p(s^2) = 0(.22) + .5(.36) + 2(.24) + 4.5(.14) + 8(.04) = 1.61$

d. The sampling distribution of s is listed below, where $s = \sqrt{s^2}$:

s	$p(s)$
0.000	.22
0.707	.36
1.414	.24
2.121	.14
2.828	.04

e. $E(s) = \sum s p(s) = 0(.22) + .707(.36) + 1.414(.24) + 2.121(.14) + 2.828(.04)$
$$= 1.00394$$

Since $E(s) = 1.00394$ is not equal to $\sigma = \sqrt{\sigma^2} = \sqrt{1.61} = 1.269$, s is a biased estimator of σ.

6.21   The symbol $\mu_{\bar{x}}$ represents the mean of the sampling distribution of $\bar{x}$. The symbol $\sigma_{\bar{x}}$ represents the standard deviation of the sampling distribution of $\bar{x}$.

6.23   The standard deviation of the sampling distribution of $\bar{x}$, $\sigma_{\bar{x}}$, is the standard deviation of the population from which the sample is selected divided by $\sqrt{n}$.

6.25   The Central Limit Theorem states: Consider a random sample of n observations selected from a population (*any* population) with mean μ and standard deviation σ. Then, when n is sufficiently large, the sampling distribution of $\bar{x}$ will be approximately a normal distribution with mean $\mu_{\bar{x}} = \mu$ and standard deviation $\sigma_{\bar{x}} = \sigma/\sqrt{n}$. The larger the sample size, the better will be the normal approximation to the sampling distribution of $\bar{x}$.

6.27   a. $\mu_{\bar{x}} = \mu = 100, \sigma_{\bar{x}} = \dfrac{\sigma}{\sqrt{n}} = \dfrac{\sqrt{100}}{\sqrt{4}} = 5$

       b. $\mu_{\bar{x}} = \mu = 100, \sigma_{\bar{x}} = \dfrac{\sigma}{\sqrt{n}} = \dfrac{\sqrt{100}}{\sqrt{25}} = 2$

       c. $\mu_{\bar{x}} = \mu = 100, \sigma_{\bar{x}} = \dfrac{\sigma}{\sqrt{n}} = \dfrac{\sqrt{100}}{\sqrt{100}} = 1$

       d. $\mu_{\bar{x}} = \mu = 100, \sigma_{\bar{x}} = \dfrac{\sigma}{\sqrt{n}} = \dfrac{\sqrt{100}}{\sqrt{50}} = 1.414$

       e. $\mu_{\bar{x}} = \mu = 100, \sigma_{\bar{x}} = \dfrac{\sigma}{\sqrt{n}} = \dfrac{\sqrt{100}}{\sqrt{500}} = .447$

       f. $\mu_{\bar{x}} = \mu = 100, \sigma_{\bar{x}} = \dfrac{\sigma}{\sqrt{n}} = \dfrac{\sqrt{100}}{\sqrt{1000}} = .316$

6.29   a. $\mu = \sum xp(x) = 1(.1) + 2(.4) + 3(.4) + 8(.1) = 2.9$

$\sigma^2 = \sum (x - \mu)^2 p(x) = (1 - 2.9)^2(.1) + (2 - 2.9)^2(.4) + (3 - 2.9)^2(.4) + (8 - 2.9)^2(.1)$
$$= .361 + .324 + .004 + 2.601 = 3.29$$

$\sigma = \sqrt{3.29} = 1.814$

       b.   The possible samples, values of $\bar{x}$, and associated probabilities are listed:

Possible Samples	$\bar{x}$	$p(\bar{x})$	Possible Samples	$\bar{x}$	$p(\bar{x})$
1, 1	1	.01	3, 1	2	.04
1, 2	1.5	.04	3, 2	2.5	.16
1, 3	2	.04	3, 3	3	.16
1, 8	4.5	.01	3, 8	5.5	.04
2, 1	1.5	.04	8, 1	4.5	.01
2, 2	2	.16	8, 2	5	.04
2, 3	2.5	.16	8, 3	5.5	.04
2, 8	5	.04	8, 8	8	.01

$P(1, 1) = p(1)p(1) = .1(.1) = .01$
$P(1, 2) = p(1)p(2) = .1(.4) = .04$
$P(1, 3) = p(1)p(3) = .1(.4) = .04$
   etc.

The sampling distribution of $\bar{x}$ is:

$\bar{x}$	$p(\bar{x})$
1	.01
1.5	.08
2	.24
2.5	.32
3	.16
4.5	.02
5	.08
5.5	.08
8	.01
	1.00

c. $\mu_{\bar{x}} = E(\bar{x}) = \sum \bar{x}p(\bar{x}) = 1(.01) + 1.5(.08) + 2(.24) + 2.5(.32) + 3(.16) + 4.5(.02)$
$$+ 5(.08) + 5.5(.08) + 8(.01)$$
$$= 2.9 = \mu$$

$\sigma_{\bar{x}}^2 = \sum (\bar{x} - \mu_{\bar{x}})^2 p(\bar{x}) = (1 - 2.9)^2(.01) + (1.5 - 2.9)^2(.08) + (2 - 2.9)^2(.24)$
$$+ (2.5 - 2.9)^2(.32) + (3 - 2.9)^2(.16) + (4.5 - 2.9)^2(.02)$$
$$+ (5 - 2.9)^2(.08) + (5.5 - 2.9)^2(.08) + (8 - 2.9)^2(.01)$$
$$= .0361 + .1568 + .1944 + .0512 + .0016 + .0512 + .3528$$
$$+ .5408 + .2601$$
$$= 1.645$$

$\sigma_{\bar{x}} = \sqrt{1.645} = 1.283$

$\sigma_{\bar{x}} = \sigma/\sqrt{n} = 1.814/\sqrt{2} = 1.283$

6.31 a. $\mu_{\bar{x}} = \mu = 30$, $\sigma_{\bar{x}} = \dfrac{\sigma}{\sqrt{n}} = \dfrac{16}{\sqrt{100}} = 1.6$

b. By the Central Limit Theorem, the sampling distribution of $\bar{x}$ is approximately normal.

c. $P(\bar{x} \geq 28) = P\left(z \geq \dfrac{28 - 30}{1.6}\right) = P(z \geq -1.25) = .5 + .3944 = .8944$

d. $P(22.1 \leq \bar{x} \leq 26.8) = P\left(\dfrac{22.1 - 30}{1.6} \leq z \leq \dfrac{26.8 - 30}{1.6}\right) = P(-4.94 \leq z \leq -2)$
$$= .5 - .4772 = .0228$$

e. $P(\bar{x} \leq 28.2) = P\left(z \leq \dfrac{28.2 - 30}{1.6}\right) = P(z \leq -1.13) = .5 - .3708 = .1292$

f. $P(\bar{x} \geq 27.0) = P\left(z \geq \dfrac{27.0-30}{1.6}\right) = P(z \geq -1.88) = .5 + .4699 = .9699$

6.35   a. $\mu_{\bar{x}}$ is the mean of the sampling distribution of $\bar{x}$. $\mu_{\bar{x}} = \mu = 79$.

   b. $\sigma_{\bar{x}}$ is the standard deviation of the sampling distribution of $\bar{x}$. $\sigma_{\bar{x}} = \dfrac{\sigma}{\sqrt{n}} = \dfrac{23}{\sqrt{100}} = 2.3$

   c.   By the Central Limit Theorem, the sampling distribution of $\bar{x}$ is approximately normal.

   d. $z = \dfrac{\bar{x} - \mu_{\bar{x}}}{\sigma_{\bar{x}}} = \dfrac{80 - 79}{2.3} = 0.43$

   e. $P(\bar{x} > 80) = P(z > 0.43) = .5 - .1664 = .3336$ (Using Table IV, Appendix A.)

6.37   Let $\bar{x}$ = sample mean score change. By the Central Limit Theorem, the sampling distribution of $\bar{x}$ is approximately normal with

   with $\mu_{\bar{x}} = \mu = 19$ and $\sigma_{\bar{x}} = \dfrac{\sigma}{\sqrt{n}} = \dfrac{65}{\sqrt{100}} = 6.5$.

   b. $P(\bar{x} < 10) = P\left(z < \dfrac{10-19}{6.5}\right) = P(z < -1.38) = .5 - .4162 = .0838$

(using Table IV, Appendix A)

6.39   a. $\mu_{\bar{x}} = \mu = 5.1$; $\sigma_{\bar{x}} = \dfrac{\sigma}{\sqrt{n}} = \dfrac{6.1}{\sqrt{150}} = .4981$

   b.   Because the sample size is large, $n = 150$, the Central Limit Theorem says that the sampling distribution of $\bar{x}$ is approximately normal.

   c. $P(\bar{x} > 5.5) = P\left(z > \dfrac{5.5-5.1}{.4981}\right) = P(z > .80) = .5 - .2881 = .2119$

(using Table IV, Appendix A)

   d. $P(4 < \bar{x} < 5) = P\left(\dfrac{4-5.1}{.4981} < z < \dfrac{5-5.1}{.4981}\right) = P(-2.21 < z < -.20)$

$= .4864 - .0793 = .4071$
(using Table IV, Appendix A)

6.41   By the Central Limit Theorem, the sampling distribution of $\bar{x}$ is approximately normal.

$\mu_{\bar{x}} = \mu = 7$; $\sigma_{\bar{x}} = \dfrac{\sigma}{\sqrt{n}} = \dfrac{2}{\sqrt{100}} = .2$

   a. $P(\bar{x} \leq 6.4) = P\left(z \leq \dfrac{6.4-7}{.2}\right) = P(z \leq -3.00) = .5 - .4987 = .0013$

b. Since the probability of observing the sample mean 6.4 or less is only .0013, it would be reasonable to conclude that the program did decrease the mean number of sick days taken by the company's employees.

6.43 **Handrubbing**

$$\mu_{\bar{x}} = \mu = 35, \quad \sigma_{\bar{x}} = \frac{\sigma}{\sqrt{n}} = \frac{59}{\sqrt{50}} = 8.344$$

$$P(\bar{x} < 30) = P\left(z < \frac{30 - 35}{8.344}\right) = P(z < -.60) = .5 - .2257 = .2743$$

(Using Table IV, Appendix A.)

Handwashing

$$\mu_{\bar{x}} = \mu = 69, \quad \sigma_{\bar{x}} = \frac{\sigma}{\sqrt{n}} = \frac{106}{\sqrt{50}} = 14.991$$

$$P(\bar{x} < 30) = P\left(z < \frac{30 - 69}{14.991}\right) = P(z < -2.60) = .5 - .4953 = .0047$$

(Using Table IV, Appendix A.)

This sample of workers probably came from the handrubbing group. The probability of seeing a mean of 30 or smaller for this group is .2743, while the probability of observing a mean of 30 or less for the handwashers is .0047. This would be an extremely rare event if the workers were handwashers because the probability is so small. It would not be a very unusual event for the handrubbers because the probability is not that small.

6.45 The statement "The sample mean, $\bar{x}$, will always be equal to μ_x" is false. The sample mean is used to estimate the population mean, but the probability that it is equal to the population mean is 0.

6.47 The statement "The standard error of $\bar{x}$ will always be small than σ" is true. The standard error of $\bar{x}$ is $\sigma_{\bar{x}} = \frac{\sigma}{\sqrt{n}}$. Thus, the standard error of $\bar{x}$ will always be smaller than σ.

6.49 a. "The sampling distribution of the sample statistic A" is the probability distribution of the variable A.

b. "A" is an unbiased estimator of α because the mean of the sampling distribution of A is α.

c. If both A and B are unbiased estimators of α, then the statistic whose standard deviation is smaller is a better estimator of α.

d. No. The Central Limit Theorem applies only to the sample mean. If A is the sample mean, $\bar{x}$, and n is sufficiently large, then the Central Limit Theorem will apply. However, both A and B cannot be sample means. Thus, we cannot apply the Central Limit Theorem to both A and B.

6.51 By the Central Limit Theorem, the sampling distribution of $\bar{x}$ is approximately normal.

$$\mu_{\bar{x}} = \mu = 19.6, \ \sigma_{\bar{x}} = \frac{3.2}{\sqrt{68}} = .388$$

a. $P(\bar{x} \leq 19.6) = P\left(z \leq \frac{19.6 - 19.6}{.388}\right) = P(z \leq 0) = .5$ \hspace{1em} (using Table IV, Appendix A)

b. $P(\bar{x} \leq 19) = P\left(z \leq \frac{19 - 19.6}{.388}\right) = P(z \leq -1.55) = .5 - .4394 = .0606$

(using Table IV, Appendix A)

c. $P(\bar{x} \geq 20.1) = P\left(z \geq \frac{20.1 - 19.6}{.388}\right) = P(z \geq 1.29) = .5 - .4015 = .0985$

(using Table IV, Appendix A)

d. $P(19.2 < \bar{x} < 20.6) = P\left(\frac{19.2 - 19.6}{.388} < z < \frac{20.6 - 19.6}{.388}\right)$

$= P(-1.03 < z < 2.58) = .3485 + .4951 = .8436$
(using Table IV, Appendix A)

6.55 Given: $\mu = 100$ and $\sigma = 10$

n	1	5	10	20	30	40	50
$\dfrac{\sigma}{\sqrt{n}}$	10	4.472	3.162	2.236	1.826	1.581	1.414

The graph of $\sigma/\sqrt{n}$ against n is given here:

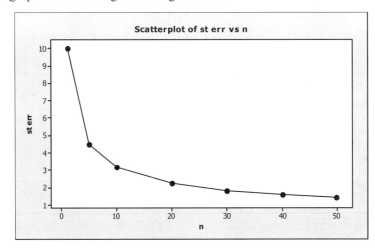

6.57　a.　$\mu_{\bar{x}} = \mu = 89.34;\ \sigma_{\bar{x}} = \dfrac{\sigma}{\sqrt{n}} = \dfrac{7.74}{\sqrt{35}} = 1.3083$

b.

86.72　88.03　89.34　90.65　91.96

c.　$P(\bar{x} > 88) = P\left(z > \dfrac{88 - 89.34}{1.3083}\right) = P(z > -1.02) = .5 + .3461 = .8461$

(using Table IV, Appendix A)

d.　$P(\bar{x} < 87) = P\left(z < \dfrac{87 - 89.34}{1.3083}\right) = P(z < -1.79) = .5 - .4633 = .0367$

(using Table IV, Appendix A)

6.59　a.　$\mu_{\bar{x}} = \mu = 1.3,\ \sigma_{\bar{x}} = \sigma/\sqrt{n} = 1.7/\sqrt{50} = .240$

b.　Yes. By the Central Limit Theorem, the distribution of $\bar{x}$ is approximately normal for n sufficiently large. For this problem, $n = 50$ is sufficiently large.

c.　$P(\bar{x} < 1) = P\left(z < \dfrac{1 - 1.3}{.24}\right) = P(z < -1.25) = .5 - .3944 = .1056$

(using Table IV, Appendix A)

d.　$P(\bar{x} > 1.9) = P\left(z > \dfrac{1.9 - 1.3}{.24}\right) = P(z > 2.5) = .5 - .4938 = .0062$

(using Table IV, Appendix A)

6.61　From Exercise 6.60, $\sigma = .001$. We must assume the Central Limit theorem applies (n is only 25). Thus, the distribution of $\bar{x}$ is approximately normal with $\mu_{\bar{x}} = \mu = .501$ and $\sigma_{\bar{x}} = \sigma/\sqrt{n} = .001/\sqrt{25} = .0002$. Using Table IV, Appendix A,

$$P(\bar{x} < .4994) + P(\bar{x} > .5006) = P\left(z < \dfrac{.4994 - .501}{.0002}\right) + P\left(z < \dfrac{.5006 - .501}{.0002}\right)$$
$$= P(z < -8) + P(z > -2)$$
$$= (.5 - .5) + (.5 + .4772) = .9772$$

6.63　By the Central Limit Theorem, the sampling distribution of $\bar{x}$ is approximately normal.

$$\mu_{\bar{x}} = \mu = 75;\ \sigma_{\bar{x}} = \dfrac{\sigma}{\sqrt{n}} = \dfrac{10}{\sqrt{36}} = 1.6667$$

a. $P(\bar{x} > 79) = P\left(z > \dfrac{79-75}{1.6667}\right) = P(z > 2.4) = .5 - .4918 = .008$

(using Table IV, Appendix A)

b. We must assume the sample size of $n = 36$ is sufficiently large so that the Central Limit Theorem applies.

6.65　a. Discrete. There are only 3 possible outcomes for the response: 1, 1.5, or 2.

b. By the Central Limit Theorem, the sampling distribution of $\bar{x}$ is approximately normal $(n = 651)$ with $\mu_{\bar{x}} = \mu = 1.50$ and $\sigma_{\bar{x}} = \sigma/\sqrt{n} = .45/\sqrt{651} = .01764$. There are no assumptions necessary.

c. $P(\bar{x} \le 1.45) = P\left(z \le \dfrac{1.45-1.5}{.01764}\right) = P(z \le -2.83) = .5 - .4977 = .0023$

(using Table IV, Appendix A)

d. $P(\bar{x} \le 1.36) = P\left(z \le \dfrac{1.36-1.5}{.01764}\right) = P(z \le -7.94) \approx .5 - .5 = 0$

(using Table IV, Appendix A)

Since this probability is so small (≈ 0), it is very unlikely that the population mean is 1.50, but probably is less than 1.50.

6.67　Even though the number of flaws per piece of siding has a Poisson distribution, the Central Limit Theorem implies that the distribution of the sample mean will be approximately normal with $\mu_{\bar{x}} = \mu = 2.5$ and $\sigma_{\bar{x}} = \dfrac{\sigma}{\sqrt{n}} = \dfrac{\sqrt{2.5}}{\sqrt{35}} = .2673$. Therefore,

$P(\bar{x} > 2.1) + P\left(z > \dfrac{2.1-2.5}{\sqrt{2.5}/\sqrt{35}}\right) = P(z > -1.50) = .5 + .4332 = .9332$

(using Table IV, Appendix A)

6.69　a. By the Central Limit Theorem, the distribution of $\bar{x}$ is approximately normal, with $\mu_{\bar{x}} = \mu = 157$ and $\sigma_{\bar{x}} = \sigma/\sqrt{n} = 3/\sqrt{40} = .474$.

The sample mean is 1.3 psi below 157 or $\bar{x} = 157 - 1.3 = 155.7$

$P(\bar{x} \le 155.7) = P\left(z \le \dfrac{155.7-157}{.474}\right) = P(z \le -2.74) = .5 - .4969 = .0031$

(using Table IV, Appendix A)

If the claim is true, it is very unlikely (probability $= .0031$) to observe a sample mean 1.3 psi below 157 psi. Thus, the actual population mean is probably not 157 but something lower.

b. $P(\bar{x} \leq 155.7) = P\left(z \leq \dfrac{155.7 - 156}{.474}\right) = P(z \leq -.63) = .5 - .2357 = .2643$

(using Table IV, Appendix A)

The observed sample is more likely if $\mu = 156$ rather than 157.

$$P(\bar{x} \leq 155.7) = P\left(z \leq \dfrac{155.7 - 158}{.474}\right) = P(z \leq -4.85) = .5 - .5 = 0$$

The observed sample is less likely if $\mu = 158$ rather than 157.

c. $\sigma_{\bar{x}} = \sigma/\sqrt{n} = 2/\sqrt{40} = .316 \qquad \mu_{\bar{x}} = 157$

$$P(\bar{x} \leq 155.7) = P\left(z \leq \dfrac{155.7 - 157}{.316}\right) = P(z \leq -4.11) = .5 - .5 = 0$$

(using Table IV, Appendix A)

The observed sample is less likely if $\sigma = 2$ rather than 3.

$\sigma_{\bar{x}} = \sigma/\sqrt{n} = 6/\sqrt{40} = .949 \qquad \mu_{\bar{x}} = 157$

$$P(\bar{x} \leq 155.7) = P\left(z \leq \dfrac{155.7 - 157}{.949}\right) = P(z \leq -1.37) = .5 - .4147 = .0853$$

(using Table IV, Appendix A)

The observed sample is more likely if $\sigma = 6$ rather than 3.

Inferences Based on a Single Sample: Estimation with Confidence Intervals

7.1   The unknown population parameter (e.g., mean or proportion) that we are interested in estimating is called the target parameter.

7.3   An interval estimator estimates μ with a range of values, while a point estimator estimates μ with a single point.

7.5   Yes. As long as the sample size is sufficiently large, the Central Limit Theorem says the distribution of $\bar{x}$ is approximately normal regardless of the original distribution.

7.7   a.   For $\alpha = .10$, $\alpha/2 = .10/2 = .05$. $z_{\alpha/2} = z_{.05}$ is the z-score with .05 of the area to the right of it. The area between 0 and $z_{.05}$ is $.5 - .05 = .4500$. Using Table IV, Appendix A, $z_{.05} = 1.645$.

        b.   For $\alpha = .01$, $\alpha/2 = .01/2 = .005$. $z_{\alpha/2} = z_{.005}$ is the z-score with .005 of the area to the right of it. The area between 0 and $z_{.005}$ is $.5 - .005 = .4950$. Using Table IV, Appendix A, $z_{.005} = 2.58$.

        c.   For $\alpha = .05$, $\alpha/2 = .05/2 = .025$. $z_{\alpha/2} = z_{.025}$ is the z-score with .025 of the area to the right of it. The area between 0 and $z_{.025}$ is $.5 - .025 = .4750$. Using Table IV, Appendix A, $z_{.025} = 1.96$.

        d.   For $\alpha = .20$, $\alpha/2 = .20/2 = .10$. $z_{\alpha/2} = z_{.10}$ is the z-score with .10 of the area to the right of it. The area between 0 and $z_{.10}$ is $.5 - .10 = .4000$. Using Table IV, Appendix A, $z_{.10} = 1.28$.

7.9   a.   For confidence coefficient .95, $\alpha = .05$ and $\alpha/2 = .05/2 = .025$. From Table IV, Appendix A, $z_{.025} = 1.96$. The confidence interval is:

$$\bar{x} \pm z_{.025}\frac{s}{\sqrt{n}} \Rightarrow 28 \pm 1.96\frac{\sqrt{12}}{\sqrt{75}} \Rightarrow 28 \pm .784 \Rightarrow (27.216, 28.784)$$

        b. $\bar{x} \pm z_{.025}\dfrac{s}{\sqrt{n}} \Rightarrow 102 \pm 1.96\dfrac{\sqrt{22}}{\sqrt{200}} \Rightarrow 102 \pm .65 \Rightarrow (101.35, 102.65)$

        c. $\bar{x} \pm z_{.025}\dfrac{s}{\sqrt{n}} \Rightarrow 15 \pm 1.96\dfrac{.3}{\sqrt{100}} \Rightarrow 15 \pm .0588 \Rightarrow (14.9412, 15.0588)$

        d. $\bar{x} \pm z_{.025}\dfrac{s}{\sqrt{n}} \Rightarrow 4.05 \pm 1.96\dfrac{.83}{\sqrt{100}} \Rightarrow 4.05 \pm .163 \Rightarrow (3.887, 4.213)$

        e.   No. Since the sample size in each part was large (n ranged from 75 to 200), the Central Limit Theorem indicates that the sampling distribution of $\bar{x}$ is approximately normal.

7.11 a. For confidence coefficient .95, $\alpha = .05$ and $\alpha/2 = .05/2 = .025$. From Table IV, Appendix A, $z_{.025} = 1.96$. The confidence interval is:

$$\bar{x} \pm z_{\alpha/2}\frac{s}{\sqrt{n}} \Rightarrow 83.2 \pm 1.96\frac{6.4}{\sqrt{100}} \Rightarrow 83.2 \pm 1.25 \Rightarrow (81.95,\ 84.45)$$

b. The confidence coefficient of .95 means that in repeated sampling, 95% of all confidence intervals constructed will include μ.

c. For confidence coefficient .99, $\alpha = .01$ and $\alpha/2 = .01/2 = .005$. From Table IV, Appendix A, $z_{.005} = 2.58$. The confidence interval is:

$$\bar{x} \pm z_{\alpha/2}\frac{s}{\sqrt{n}} \Rightarrow 83.2 \pm 2.58\frac{6.4}{\sqrt{100}} \Rightarrow 83.2 \pm 1.65 \Rightarrow (81.55,\ 84.85)$$

d. As the confidence coefficient increases, the width of the confidence interval also increases.

e. Yes. Since the sample size is 100, the Central Limit Theorem applies. This ensures the distribution of $\bar{x}$ is normal, regardless of the original distribution.

7.13 a. The point estimate for the average number of latex gloves used per week by all healthcare workers with latex allergy is $\bar{x} = 19.3$.

b. For confidence coefficient .95, $\alpha = .05$ and $\alpha/2 = .05/2 = .025$. From Table IV, Appendix A, $z_{.025} = 1.96$. The 95% confidence interval is:

$$\bar{x} \pm z_{.025}\sigma_{\bar{x}} \Rightarrow \bar{x} \pm 1.96\frac{\sigma}{\sqrt{n}} \Rightarrow 19.3 \pm 1.96\frac{11.9}{\sqrt{46}} \Rightarrow 19.3 \pm 3.44 \Rightarrow (15.86,\ \ 22.74)$$

c. We are 95% confident that the average number of latex gloves used pr week by all healthcare workers with a latex allergy is between 15.86 and 22.74.

d. We must assume that we have a random sample from the target population and that the sample size is sufficiently large.

7.15 a. The target parameter is the mean egg length for all New Zealand birds.

b. Using MINITAB, 50 uniform random numbers were generated between 1 and 132. Those random numbers were:

3, 9, 12, 13, 14, 15, 17, 22, 23, 24, 25, 26, 27, 29, 37, 39, 45, 49, 50, 51, 52, 54, 60, 65, 68, 70, 71, 75, 93, 95, 96, 97, 98, 99, 101, 105, 108, 109, 110, 112, 118, 119, 120, 123, 126, 127, 128, 129, 130, 131

The egg lengths corresponding to these numbers were then selected. The 50 egg lengths are:

57, 44, 31, 36, 61, 67, 69, 48, 58, 61, 59, 65, 66, 46, 56, 64, 49, 40, 58, 30, 28, 43, 45, 42, 52, 40, 46, 74, 26, 23, 23, 19.5, 20, 23.5, 17, 19, 40, 35, 29, 45, 110, 124, 160, 205, 192, 125, 195, 218, 236, 94

c.   Using MINITAB, the descriptive statistics are:

Descriptive Statistics: Egg Length

```
Variable       N  N*    Mean  SE Mean  StDev  Minimum     Q1  Median     Q3
Egg Length    50   0   68.28     7.87  55.65    17.00  34.00   48.50  67.50

Variable      Maximum
Egg Length     236.00
```

The mean is $\bar{x} = 68.28$ and the standard deviation is $s = 55.65$.

d.   For confidence coefficient .99, $\alpha = .01$ and $\alpha/2 = .01/2 = .005$. From Table IV, Appendix A, $z_{.005} = 2.575$. The 99% confidence interval is:

$$\bar{x} \pm z_{.005}\sigma_{\bar{x}} \Rightarrow \bar{x} \pm 2.575\frac{\sigma}{\sqrt{n}} \Rightarrow 68.28 \pm 2.575\frac{55.65}{\sqrt{50}} \Rightarrow 68.28 \pm 20.27 \Rightarrow (48.01, \ 88.55)$$

e.   We are 99% confident that the mean egg length of the bird species of New Zealand is between 48.01 and 88.55 mm.

7.17 a.   For confidence coefficient .99, $\alpha = .01$ and $\alpha/2 = .01/2 = .005$. From Table IV, Appendix A, $z_{.005} = 2.58$. The confidence interval is:

$$\bar{x} \pm z_{\alpha/2}\frac{s}{\sqrt{n}} \Rightarrow 1.13 \pm 2.58\frac{2.21}{\sqrt{72}} \Rightarrow 1.13 \pm .672 \Rightarrow (.458, \ 1.802)$$

We are 99% confident that the true mean number of pecks made by chickens pecking at blue string is between .458 and 1.802.

b.   Yes, there is evidence that chickens are more apt to peck at white string. The mean number of pecks for white string is 7.5. Since 7.5 is not in the 99% confidence interval for the mean number of pecks at blue string, it is not a likely value for the true mean for blue string.

7.19 a.   For confidence coefficient .95, $\alpha = .05$ and $\alpha/2 = .05/2 = .025$. From Table IV, Appendix A, $z_{.025} = 1.96$. The confidence interval is:

$$\bar{x} \pm z_{\alpha/2}\frac{s}{\sqrt{n}} \Rightarrow 19 \pm 1.96\frac{65}{\sqrt{265}} \Rightarrow 19 \pm 7.826 \Rightarrow (11.174, \ 26.826)$$

b.   For confidence coefficient .95, $\alpha = .05$ and $\alpha/2 = .05/2 = .025$. From Table IV, Appendix A, $z_{.025} = 1.96$. The confidence interval is:

$$\bar{x} \pm z_{\alpha/2}\frac{s}{\sqrt{n}} \Rightarrow 7 \pm 1.96\frac{49}{\sqrt{265}} \Rightarrow 7 \pm 5.90 \Rightarrow (1.10, \ 12.90)$$

c.   The SAT-Mathematics test would be more likely to have a mean change of 15 because 15 is in the 95% confidence interval for the mean change in SAT-Mathematics. Since 15 is in the confidence interval, it is a likely value. The value 15 is not in the 95% confidence interval for the SAT-Verbal. Thus, it is not a likely value.

Inferences Based on a Single Sample: Estimation with Confidence Intervals   173

7.21   Using MINITAB, the descriptive statistics are:

Descriptive Statistics: Corr

Variable	N	N*	Mean	SE Mean	StDev	Minimum	Q1	Median	Q3
Corr	34	0	0.4224	0.0343	0.1998	-0.0800	0.2925	0.4300	0.6000

Variable	Maximum
Corr	0.7400

For confidence coefficient .95, $\alpha = .05$ and $\alpha/2 = .05/2 = .025$. From Table IV, Appendix A, $z_{.025} = 1.96$. The 95% confidence interval is:

$$\bar{x} \pm z_{.025}\sigma_{\bar{x}} \Rightarrow \bar{x} \pm 1.96\frac{\sigma}{\sqrt{n}} \Rightarrow .4224 \pm 1.96\frac{.1998}{\sqrt{34}} \Rightarrow .4224 \pm .0672 \Rightarrow (.3552, \ .4896)$$

We are 95% confident that the mean correlation coefficient between appraisal participation and a subordinate's satisfaction with the appraisal is between .3552 and .4896.

7.23   a.   For confidence coefficient .95, $\alpha = .05$ and $\alpha/2 = .025$. From Table IV, Appendix A, $z_{.025} = 1.96$. The confidence interval is:

$$\bar{x} \pm z_{\alpha/2}\frac{s}{\sqrt{n}}$$

Younger: $4.17 \pm 1.96\frac{.75}{\sqrt{241}} \Rightarrow 4.17 \pm .095 \Rightarrow (4.075, 4.265)$

We are 95% confident that the mean job satisfaction score for all adults in the younger age group is between 4.075 and 4.265.

Middle-Age: $4.04 \pm 1.96\frac{.81}{\sqrt{768}} \Rightarrow 4.04 \pm .057 \Rightarrow (3.983, 4.097)$

We are 95% confident that the mean job satisfaction score for all adults in the middle-age age group is between 3.983 and 4.097.

Older: $4.31 \pm 1.96\frac{.82}{\sqrt{677}} \Rightarrow 4.31 \pm .062 \Rightarrow (4.248, 4.372)$

We are 95% confident that the mean job satisfaction score for all adults in the older age group is between 4.248 and 4.372.

b.   Let y = number of 95% confidence intervals that do not contain the population mean in 3 trials. Then y is a binomial random variable with $n = 3$ and $p = .05$.

$$P(y \geq 1) = 1 - P(y = 0) = 1 - \binom{3}{0}.05^0.95^3 = 1 - .857375 = .142625$$

Thus, it is more likely that at least one of three intervals will not contain the population mean than it is for a single confidence interval to miss the population mean.

The probability that a single confidence interval will not contain the population mean is .05.

7.25   The two problems (and corresponding solutions) with using a small sample to estimate μ are:

1. The shape of the sampling distribution of the sample mean $\bar{x}$ now depends on the shape of the population that is sampled. The Central Limit Theorem no longer applies since the sample size is small.

2. The population standard deviation σ is almost always unknown. Although it is still true that $\sigma_{\bar{x}} = \sigma / \sqrt{n}$, the sample standard deviation s may provide a poor approximation for σ when the sample size is small.

7.27   a.   If x is normally distributed, the sampling distribution of is normal, regardless of the sample size.

        b.   If nothing is known about the distribution of x, the sampling distribution of is approximately normal if n is sufficiently large. If n is not large, the distribution of is unknown if the distribution of x is not known.

7.29   a. $P(t \geq t_0) = .025$ where df $= 10$
$$t_0 = 2.228$$

        b. $P(t \geq t_0) = .01$ where df $= 17$
$$t_0 = 2.567$$

        c. $P(t \leq t_0) = .005$ where df $= 6$

            Because of symmetry, the statement can be rewritten
$$P(t \geq -t_0) = .005 \text{ where df} = 6$$
$$t_0 = -3.707$$

        d. $P(t \leq t_0) = .05$ where df $= 13$
$$t_0 = -1.771$$

7.31   First, we must compute $\bar{x}$ and s.

$$\bar{x} = \frac{\sum x}{n} = \frac{30}{6} = 5$$

$$s^2 = \frac{\sum x^2 - \frac{\left(\sum x\right)^2}{n}}{n-1} = \frac{176 - \frac{(30)^2}{6}}{6-1} = \frac{26}{5} = 5.2$$

$$s = \sqrt{5.2} = 2.2804$$

        a.   For confidence coefficient .90, $\alpha = 1 - .90 = .10$ and $\alpha/2 = .10/2 = .05$. From Table VI, Appendix A, with df $= n - 1 = 6 - 1 = 5$, $t_{.05} = 2.015$. The 90% confidence interval is:

$$\bar{x} \pm t_{.05} \frac{s}{\sqrt{n}} \Rightarrow 5 \pm 2.015 \frac{2.2804}{\sqrt{6}} \Rightarrow 5 \pm 1.876 \Rightarrow (3.124, 6.876)$$

Inferences Based on a Single Sample: Estimation with Confidence Intervals   175

b. For confidence coefficient .95, $\alpha = 1 - .95 = .05$ and $\alpha/2 = .05/2 = .025$. From Table VI, Appendix A, with df $= n - 1 = 6 - 1 = 5$, $t_{.025} = 2.571$. The 95% confidence interval is:

$$\bar{x} \pm t_{.025}\frac{s}{\sqrt{n}} \Rightarrow 5 \pm 2.571\frac{2.2804}{\sqrt{6}} \Rightarrow 5 \pm 2.394 \Rightarrow (2.606, 7.394)$$

c. For confidence coefficient .99, $\alpha = 1 - .99 = .01$ and $\alpha/2 = .01/2 = .005$. From Table VI, Appendix A, with df $= n - 1 = 6 - 1 = 5$, $t_{.005} = 4.032$. The 99% confidence interval is:

$$\bar{x} \pm t_{.005}\frac{s}{\sqrt{n}} \Rightarrow 5 \pm 4.032\frac{2.2804}{\sqrt{6}} \Rightarrow 5 \pm 3.754 \Rightarrow (1.246, 8.754)$$

d. a) For confidence coefficient .90, $\alpha = 1 - .90 = .10$ and $\alpha/2 = .10/2 = .05$. From Table VI, Appendix A, with df $= n - 1 = 25 - 1 = 24$, $t_{.05} = 1.711$. The 90% confidence interval is:

$$\bar{x} \pm t_{.05}\frac{s}{\sqrt{n}} \Rightarrow 5 \pm 1.711\frac{2.2804}{\sqrt{25}} \Rightarrow 5 \pm .780 \Rightarrow (4.220, 5.780)$$

b) For confidence coefficient .95, $\alpha = 1 - .95 = .05$ and $\alpha/2 = .05/2 = .025$. From Table VI, Appendix A, with df $= n - 1 = 25 - 1 = 24$, $t_{.025} = 2.064$. The 95% confidence interval is:

$$\bar{x} \pm t_{.025}\frac{s}{\sqrt{n}} \Rightarrow 5 \pm 2.064\frac{2.2804}{\sqrt{25}} \Rightarrow 5 \pm .941 \Rightarrow (4.059, 5.941)$$

c) For confidence coefficient .99, $\alpha = 1 - .99 = .01$ and $\alpha/2 = .01/2 = .005$. From Table VI, Appendix A, with df $= n - 1 = 25 - 1 = 24$, $t_{.005} = 2.797$. The 99% confidence interval is:

$$\bar{x} \pm t_{.005}\frac{s}{\sqrt{n}} \Rightarrow 5 \pm 2.797\frac{2.2804}{\sqrt{25}} \Rightarrow 5 \pm 1.276 \Rightarrow (3.724, 6.276)$$

Increasing the sample size decreases the width of the confidence interval.

7.33 a. The point estimate for the mean amount of cesium in lichen specimens collected in Alaska is $\bar{x} = .009027$.

b. For confidence coefficient .95, $\alpha = .05$ and $\alpha/2 = .05/2 = .025$. From Table VI, Appendix A, with df $= n - 1 = 9 - 1 = 8$, $t_{.025} = 2.306$.

c. The 95% confidence interval is:

$$\bar{x} \pm t_{.025}\frac{s}{\sqrt{n}} \Rightarrow .009027 \pm 2.306\frac{.004854}{\sqrt{9}} \Rightarrow .009027 \pm .003731 \Rightarrow (.005296, .012758)$$

d. This interval is the same as that found on the printout.

e.   We are 95% confident that the mean amount of cesium in lichen specimens collected in Alaska is between .005296 and .012758 microcuries per milliliter.

7.35   a.   First, we must compute some preliminary statistics:

$$\bar{x} = \frac{\sum x}{n} = \frac{28.856}{10} = 2.8856$$

$$s^2 = \frac{\sum x^2 - \frac{\left(\sum x\right)^2}{n}}{n-1} = \frac{221.90161 - \frac{(28.856)^2}{10}}{10-1} = 15.4039$$

$$s = \sqrt{s^2} = \sqrt{15.4039} = 3.925$$

For confidence coefficient .99, $\alpha = .01$ and $\alpha/2 = .01/2 = .005$. From Table VI, Appendix A, with df $= n - 1 = 10 - 1 = 9$, $t_{.005} = 3.250$. The confidence interval is:

$$\bar{x} \pm t_{.005} \frac{s}{\sqrt{n}} \Rightarrow 2.8856 \pm 3.250 \frac{3.925}{\sqrt{10}} \Rightarrow 2.8856 \pm 4.034 \Rightarrow (-1.148, 6.919)$$

b.   First, we must compute some preliminary statistics:

$$\bar{x} = \frac{\sum x}{n} = \frac{4.083}{10} = .4083$$

$$s^2 = \frac{\sum x^2 - \frac{\left(\sum x\right)^2}{n}}{n-1} = \frac{2.227425 - \frac{(4.083)^2}{10}}{10-1} = .06226$$

$$s = \sqrt{s^2} = \sqrt{.06226} = .2495$$

For confidence coefficient .99, $\alpha = .01$ and $\alpha/2 = .01/2 = .005$. From Table VI, Appendix A, with df $= n - 1 = 10 - 1 = 9$, $t_{.005} = 3.250$. The confidence interval is:

$$\bar{x} \pm t_{.005} \Rightarrow .4083 \pm 3.250 \frac{.2495}{\sqrt{10}} \Rightarrow .4083 \pm .2564 \Rightarrow (.1519, .6647)$$

c.   We are 99% confident that the mean lead level in water specimens from Crystal Lake Manors is between −1.148 and 6.919.

We are 99% confident that the mean copper level in water specimens from Crystal Lake Manors is between .1519 and .6647.

d.   The phrase "99% confident" means that if repeated samples of size n were selected and 99% confidence intervals constructed for the mean, 99% of all intervals constructed would contain the mean.

7.37   a.   The population is the set of all DOT permanent count stations in the state of Florida.

   b.   Yes. There are several types of routes included in the sample. There are 3 recreational areas, 7 rural areas, 5 small cities, and 5 urban areas.

   c.   The 95% confidence interval for the mean traffic count at the 30th highest hour is (1,633, 2,779). We are 95% confident that the mean traffic count at the 30th highest hour is between 1,633 and 2,779.

   d.   We must assume that the distribution of the traffic counts at the 30th highest hour is normal. From the stem-and-leaf display, the data look fairly mound-shaped. Thus, the assumption of normality is probably met.

   e.   The 95% confidence interval for the mean traffic count at the 100th highest hour is (1,533, 2,659). We are 95% confident that the mean traffic count at the 100th highest hour is between 1,533 and 2,659.

   We must assume that the distribution of the traffic counts at the 100th highest hour is normal. From the stem-and-leaf display, the data look fairly mound-shaped. Thus, the assumption of normality is probably met.

7.39   a.   Some preliminary calculations are:

$$\bar{x} = \frac{\sum x}{n} = \frac{160.9}{22} = 7.314$$

$$s^2 = \frac{\sum x^2 - \frac{\left(\sum x\right)^2}{n}}{n-1} = \frac{1,389.1 - \frac{160.9^2}{22}}{22-1} = 10.1112$$

$$s = \sqrt{10.1112} = 3.180$$

   For confidence coefficient .95, $\alpha = .05$ and $\alpha/2 = .05/2 = .025$. From Table VI, Appendix A with df $= n - 1 = 22 - 1 = 21$, $t_{.025} = 2.080$. The 95% confidence interval is:

$$\bar{x} \pm t_{\alpha/2} \frac{s}{\sqrt{n}} \Rightarrow 7.314 \pm 2.080 \frac{3.180}{\sqrt{22}} \Rightarrow 7.314 \pm 1.410 \Rightarrow (5.904,\ 8.724)$$

   b.   We are 95% confident that the mean PMI for all human brain specimens obtained at autopsy is between 5.904 and 8.724.

   c.   We must assume that the population of all PMI's is normally distributed. From the dot plot in Exercise 2.25, the distribution does not appear to be normal.

   d.   "95% confidence" means that if repeated samples of size n were selected from the population and 95% confidence intervals formed for μ, 95% of the intervals formed will contain the true mean and 5% will not.

7.41   a.   For confidence coefficient .95, $\alpha = .05$, and $\alpha/2 = .05/2 = .025$. From Table VI, Appendix A, with df $= n - 1 = 15 - 1 = 14$, $t_{.025} = 2.145$. The confidence interval is:

$$\bar{x} \pm t_{.025}\frac{s}{\sqrt{n}} \Rightarrow 37.3 \pm 2.145\frac{13.9}{\sqrt{15}} \Rightarrow 37.3 \pm 7.70 \Rightarrow (29.60, 45.00)$$

b.   We are 95% confident that the true mean adrenocorticotropin level in sleepers one-hour prior to anticipated waking is between 29.60 and 45.00

c.   Suppose we assume that the true mean adrenocorticotropin level of sleepers three hours before anticipated wake-up time is 25.5. Since the 95% confidence interval for the true mean adrenocorticotropin level in sleepers one-hour prior to anticipated waking (29.60, 45.00) does not contain 25.5, there is evidence to indicate that the true mean adrenocorticotropin level of sleepers three hours before anticipated wake-up time is different from that of sleepers one-hour prior to anticipated waking.

7.43   An unbiased estimator is one in which the mean of the sampling distribution is the parameter of interest, i.e., $E(\hat{p}) = p$.

7.45   a.   The sample size is large enough if $\hat{p} \pm 3\sigma_{\hat{p}}$ does not include 0 or 1.

$$\hat{p} \pm 3\sigma_{\hat{p}} \approx .64 \pm 3\sqrt{\frac{.64(.36)}{196}} \Rightarrow .64 \pm .013 \Rightarrow (.537, .743)$$

Since this interval does not contain 0 or 1, the sample size is sufficiently large.

b.   For confidence coefficient .95, $\alpha = .05$ and $\alpha/2 = .025$. From Table IV, Appendix A, $z_{.025} = 1.96$. The confidence interval is:

$$\hat{p} \pm z_{.025}\sqrt{\frac{\hat{p}\hat{q}}{n}} \Rightarrow .64 \pm 1.96\sqrt{\frac{.64(.36)}{196}} \Rightarrow .64 \pm .067 \Rightarrow (.573, .707)$$

c.   We are 95% confident the true value of p is between .372 and .468.

d.   "95% confidence" means that if repeated samples of size 196 were selected from the population and 95% confidence intervals formed, 95% of all confidence intervals will contain the true value of p.

7.47   The sample size is sufficiently large if $\hat{p} \pm 3\sigma_{\hat{p}}$ does not include 0 or 1.

a. $\hat{p} \pm 3\sigma_{\hat{p}} \approx .05 \pm 3\sqrt{\dfrac{.05(.95)}{500}} \Rightarrow .05 \pm .029 \Rightarrow (.021, .079)$

Since this interval does not contain 0 or 1, the sample size is sufficiently large.

b. $\hat{p} \pm 3\sigma_{\hat{p}} \approx .05 \pm 3\sqrt{\dfrac{.05(.95)}{100}} \Rightarrow .05 \pm .065 \Rightarrow (-.015, .115)$

Since the interval contains 0, the sample size is not sufficiently large.

c. $\hat{p} \pm 3\sigma_{\hat{p}} \approx .5 \pm 3\sqrt{\dfrac{.5(.5)}{10}} \Rightarrow .5 \pm .474 \Rightarrow (.026, .974)$

Since this interval does not contain 0 or 1, the sample size is sufficiently large.

d. $\hat{p} \pm 3\sigma_{\hat{p}} \approx .3 \pm 3\sqrt{\dfrac{.3(.7)}{10}} \Rightarrow .3 \pm .435 \Rightarrow (-.135, .735)$

Since the interval contains 0, the sample size is not sufficiently large.

7.49 a. The point estimate of p, the true driver phone cell use rate, is $\hat{p} = \dfrac{x}{n} = \dfrac{35}{1,165} = .030$.

  b. To see if the sample size is sufficiently large:

$$\hat{p} \pm 3\sigma_{\hat{p}} \approx \hat{p} \pm 3\sqrt{\dfrac{\hat{p}\hat{q}}{n}} \Rightarrow .030 \pm 3\sqrt{\dfrac{.030(.970)}{1,165}} \Rightarrow .030 \pm .015 \Rightarrow (.015, .045)$$

Since this interval is wholly contained in the interval $(0, 1)$, we may conclude that the normal approximation is reasonable.

For confidence coefficient .95, $\alpha = .05$ and $\alpha/2 = .05/2 = .025$. From Table IV, Appendix A, $z_{.025} = 1.96$. The 95% confidence interval is:

$$\hat{p} \pm z_{.025}\sigma_{\hat{p}} \Rightarrow \hat{p} \pm 1.96\sqrt{\dfrac{\hat{p}\hat{q}}{n}} \Rightarrow .030 \pm 1.96\sqrt{\dfrac{.030(.970)}{1,165}} \Rightarrow .030 \pm .010 \Rightarrow (.020, .040)$$

  c. We are 95% confident that the true driver phone cell use rate is between .020 and .040.

7.51 First, we compute $\hat{p}$: $\hat{p} = \dfrac{x}{n} = \dfrac{183}{837} = .219$

To see if the sample size is sufficiently large:

$$\hat{p} \pm 3\sigma_{\hat{p}} \approx \hat{p} \pm 3\sqrt{\dfrac{\hat{p}\hat{q}}{n}} \Rightarrow .219 \pm 3\sqrt{\dfrac{.219(.781)}{837}} \Rightarrow .219 \pm .043 \Rightarrow (.176, .262)$$

Since the interval is wholly contained in the interval $(0,1)$, we may conclude that the normal approximation is reasonable.

For confidence coefficient .90, $\alpha = .10$ and $\alpha/2 = .10/2 = .05$. From Table IV, Appendix A, $z_{.05} = 1.645$. The confidence interval is:

$$\hat{p} \pm z_{.05}\sqrt{\dfrac{pq}{n}} \approx \hat{p} \pm 1.645\sqrt{\dfrac{\hat{p}\hat{q}}{n}} \Rightarrow .219 \pm 1.645\sqrt{\dfrac{.219(.781)}{837}} \Rightarrow .219 \pm .024 \Rightarrow (.195, .243)$$

7.53   a.   First, we compute $\hat{p}$: $\hat{p} = \dfrac{x}{n} = \dfrac{14}{38} = .368$

To see if the sample size is sufficiently large:

$$\hat{p} \pm 3\sigma_{\hat{p}} \approx \hat{p} \pm 3\sqrt{\dfrac{\hat{p}\hat{q}}{n}} \Rightarrow .368 \pm 3\sqrt{\dfrac{.368(.632)}{38}} \Rightarrow .368 \pm .235 \Rightarrow (.133, .603)$$

Since the interval is wholly contained in the interval $(0,1)$, we may conclude that the normal approximation is reasonable.

For confidence coefficient .90, $\alpha = .10$ and $\alpha/2 = .10/2 = .05$. From Table IV, Appendix A, $z_{.05} = 1.645$. The confidence interval is:

$$\hat{p} \pm z_{.05}\sqrt{\dfrac{pq}{n}} \approx \hat{p} \pm 1.645\sqrt{\dfrac{\hat{p}\hat{q}}{n}} \Rightarrow .368 \pm 1.645\sqrt{\dfrac{.368(.632)}{38}} \Rightarrow .368 \pm .129 \Rightarrow (.239, .497)$$

We are 90% confident that the true dropout rate for exercises who vary their routine in workouts is between .239 and .497.

b.   First, we compute $\hat{p}$: $\hat{p} = \dfrac{x}{n} = \dfrac{23}{38} = .605$

To see if the sample size is sufficiently large:

$$\hat{p} \pm 3\sigma_{\hat{p}} \approx \hat{p} \pm 3\sqrt{\dfrac{\hat{p}\hat{q}}{n}} \Rightarrow .605 \pm 3\sqrt{\dfrac{.605(.395)}{38}} \Rightarrow .605 \pm .238 \Rightarrow (.367, .843)$$

Since the interval is wholly contained in the interval $(0,1)$, we may conclude that the normal approximation is reasonable.

For confidence coefficient .90, $\alpha = .10$ and $\alpha/2 = .10/2 = .05$. From Table IV, Appendix A, $z_{.05} = 1.645$. The confidence interval is:

$$\hat{p} \pm z_{.05}\sqrt{\dfrac{pq}{n}} \approx \hat{p} \pm 1.645\sqrt{\dfrac{\hat{p}\hat{q}}{n}} \Rightarrow .605 \pm 1.645\sqrt{\dfrac{.605(.395)}{38}} \Rightarrow .605 \pm .130 \Rightarrow (.475, .735)$$

We are 90% confident that the true dropout rate for exercises who have no set schedule for their workouts is between .475 and .735.

7.55   a.   The point estimate of p is $\hat{p} = x/n = 35/55 = .636$.

b.   We must check to see if the sample size is sufficiently large:

$$\hat{p} \pm 3\sigma_{\hat{p}} \approx \hat{p} \pm 3\sqrt{\dfrac{\hat{p}\hat{q}}{n}} \Rightarrow .636 \pm 3\sqrt{\dfrac{.636(.364)}{55}} \Rightarrow .636 \pm .195 \Rightarrow (.441, .831)$$

Since the interval is wholly contained in the interval (0, 1) we may assume that the normal approximation is reasonable.

For confidence coefficient, .99, $\alpha = .01$ and $\alpha/2 = .01/2 = .005$. From Table IV, Appendix A, $z_{.005} = 2.58$. The confidence interval is:

$$\hat{p} \pm z_{.005}\sqrt{\frac{\hat{p}\hat{q}}{n}} \Rightarrow .636 \pm 2.58\sqrt{\frac{.636(.364)}{55}} \Rightarrow .636 \pm .167 \Rightarrow (.469, .803)$$

c. We are 99% confident that the true proportion of fatal accidents involving children is between .469 and .803.

d. The sample proportion of children killed by air bags who were not wearing seat belts or were improperly restrained is 24/35 = .686. This is rather large proportion. Whether a child is killed by an airbag could be related to whether or not he/she was properly restrained or not. Thus, the number of children killed by air bags could possibly be reduced if the child were properly restrained.

7.57 a. First we must compute $\hat{p}$: $\hat{p} = \frac{x}{n} = \frac{97}{185} = .524$

To see if the sample size is sufficiently large:

$$\hat{p} \pm 3\sigma_{\hat{p}} \approx \hat{p} \pm 3\sqrt{\frac{\hat{p}\hat{q}}{n}} \Rightarrow .524 \pm 3\sqrt{\frac{.524(.476)}{185}} \Rightarrow .524 \pm .110 \Rightarrow (.414, .634)$$

Since this interval is wholly contained in the interval (0, 1), we may conclude that the normal approximation is reasonable.

For confidence coefficient .99, $\alpha = .01$ and $\alpha/2 = .01/2 = .005$. From Table IV, Appendix A, $z_{.005} = 2.58$. The confidence interval is:

$$\hat{p} \pm z_{.005}\sqrt{\frac{pq}{n}} \approx \hat{p} \pm 2.58\sqrt{\frac{\hat{p}\hat{q}}{n}} \Rightarrow .524 \pm 2.58\sqrt{\frac{.524(.476)}{185}} \Rightarrow .524 \pm .095$$
$$\Rightarrow (.429, .619)$$

b. We are 99% confident that the true proportion of bottlenose dolphin signature whistles that are Type "a" whistles is between .429 and .619.

7.59 The point estimate for the proportion of health care workers with latex allergy who suspect that he/she has the allergy is $\hat{p} = \frac{x}{n} = \frac{36}{83} = .434$.

To see if the sample size is sufficiently large:

$$\hat{p} \pm 3\sigma_{\hat{p}} \approx \hat{p} \pm 3\sqrt{\frac{\hat{p}\hat{q}}{n}} \Rightarrow .434 \pm 3\sqrt{\frac{.434(.566)}{83}} \Rightarrow .434 \pm .163 \Rightarrow (.271, .597)$$

Since this interval is wholly contained in the interval (0, 1), we may conclude that the normal approximation is reasonable.

Since no confidence limit is given, we will use 95%. For confidence coefficient .95, $\alpha = .05$ and $\alpha/2 = .05/2 = .025$. From Table IV, Appendix A, $z_{.025} = 1.96$. The 95% confidence interval is:

$$\hat{p} \pm z_{.025}\sigma_{\hat{p}} \Rightarrow \hat{p} \pm 1.96\sqrt{\frac{\hat{p}\hat{q}}{n}} \Rightarrow .434 \pm 1.96\sqrt{\frac{.434(.566)}{83}} \Rightarrow .434 \pm .107 \Rightarrow (.327, .541)$$

We are 95% confident that the proportion of health care workers with latex allergy who suspect that he/she has the allergy is between .327 and .541.

7.61   The statement "For a specified sampling error SE, increasing the confidence level (1 - α) will lead to a larger n when determining sample size" is True.

7.63   To compute the necessary sample size, use

$$n = \frac{(z_{\alpha/2})^2 \sigma^2}{(SE)^2} \text{ where } \alpha = 1 - .95 = .05 \text{ and } \alpha/2 = .05/2 = .025$$

From Table IV, Appendix A, $z_{.025} = 1.96$. Thus,

$$n = \frac{(1.96)^2(5.4)}{.2^2} = 518.616 \approx 519$$

You would need to take 519 samples.

7.65   a.   Range = $39 - 31 = 8$. $\sigma \approx \dfrac{\text{Range}}{4} = \dfrac{8}{4} = 2$

For confidence coefficient .90, $\alpha = .10$ and $\alpha/2 = .05$. From Table IV, Appendix A, $z_{.05} = 1.645$.

The sample size is $n = \dfrac{z_{\alpha/2}^2 \sigma^2}{(SE)^2} = \dfrac{1.645^2(2^2)}{.15^2} = 481.07 \approx 482$

b. $\sigma \approx \dfrac{\text{Range}}{6} = \dfrac{8}{6} = 1.333$

The sample size is $n = \dfrac{z_{\alpha/2}^2 \sigma^2}{(SE)^2} = \dfrac{1.645^2(1.333^2)}{.15^2} = 213.7 \approx 214$

7.67   For confidence coefficient .90, $\alpha = .10$ and $\alpha/2 = .05$. From Table IV, Appendix A, $z_{.05} = 1.645$.

We know $\hat{p}$ is in the middle of the interval, so $\hat{p} = \dfrac{.54 + .26}{2} = .4$

The confidence interval is $\hat{p} \pm z_{.05}\sqrt{\dfrac{\hat{p}\hat{q}}{n}} \Rightarrow .4 \pm 1.645\sqrt{\dfrac{.4(.6)}{n}}$

We know $.4 - 1.645\sqrt{\dfrac{.4(.6)}{n}} = .26$

$\Rightarrow .4 - \dfrac{.8059}{\sqrt{n}} = .26$

$\Rightarrow .4 - .26 = \dfrac{.8059}{\sqrt{n}} \Rightarrow \sqrt{n} = \dfrac{.8059}{.14} = 5.756$

$\Rightarrow n = 5.756^2 = 33.1 \approx 34$

7.69   a.   The width of a confidence interval is $2(SE) = 2z_{\alpha/2}\dfrac{\sigma}{\sqrt{n}}$

For confidence coefficient .95, $\alpha = 1 - .95 = .05$ and $\alpha/2 = .05/2 = .025$. From Table IV, Appendix A, $z_{.025} = 1.96$.

For $n = 16$,
$$W = 2z_{\alpha/2}\frac{\sigma}{\sqrt{n}} = 2(1.96)\frac{1}{\sqrt{16}} = 0.98$$

For $n = 25$,
$$W = 2z_{\alpha/2}\frac{\sigma}{\sqrt{n}} = 2(1.96)\frac{1}{\sqrt{25}} = 0.784$$

For $n = 49$,
$$W = 2z_{\alpha/2}\frac{\sigma}{\sqrt{n}} = 2(1.96)\frac{1}{\sqrt{49}} = 0.56$$

For $n = 100$,
$$W = 2z_{\alpha/2}\frac{\sigma}{\sqrt{n}} = 2(1.96)\frac{1}{\sqrt{100}} = 0.392$$

For $n = 400$,
$$W = 2z_{\alpha/2}\frac{\sigma}{\sqrt{n}} = 2(1.96)\frac{1}{\sqrt{400}} = 0.196$$

b.

7.71   a.   The confidence level desired by the researchers is .90.

b.   The sampling error desired by the researchers is $SE = .05$.

c.   Since no value was given for p, we will use $\hat{p} = \dfrac{x}{n} = \dfrac{64}{106} = .604$.

For confidence coefficient .90, $\alpha = .10$ and $\alpha/2 = .10/2 = .05$. From Table IV, Appendix A, $z_{.05} = 1.645$.

The sample size is $n = \dfrac{(z_{.05})^2 \, pq}{(SE)^2} = \dfrac{1.645^2 (.604)(.396)}{.05^2} = 258.9 \approx 259$.

7.73   For confidence coefficient .95, $\alpha = .05$ and $\alpha/2 = .05/2 = .025$. From Table IV, Appendix A, $z_{.025} = 1.96$.

The sample size is $n = \dfrac{(z_{.025})^2 \sigma^2}{(SE)^2} = \dfrac{1.96^2 (5)^2}{1^2} = 96.04 \approx 97$.

7.75   For confidence coefficient .99, $\alpha = .01$ and $\alpha/2 = .01/2 = .005$. From Table IV, Appendix A, $z_{.005} = 2.58$. From the previous estimate, we will use $\hat{p} = .333$ to estimate p.

$$n = \dfrac{z_{\alpha/2}^2 \, pq}{(SE)^2} = \dfrac{2.58^2 (.333)(.667)}{.01^2} = 14{,}784.5966 \approx 14{,}785$$

7.77   From Exercise 7.36, $s = .2316$. For confidence coefficient .95, $\alpha = .05$ and $\alpha/2 = .05/2 = .025$. From Table IV, Appendix A, $z_{.025} = 1.96$.

$$n = \dfrac{z_{\alpha/2}^2 \sigma^2}{(SE)^2} = \dfrac{1.96^2 (.2316)^2}{.04^2} = 128.786 \approx 129$$

7.79   For confidence coefficient .90, $\alpha = .10$ and $\alpha/2 = .05$. From Table IV, Appendix A, $z_{.05} = 1.645$.

The sample size is $n = \dfrac{(z_{\alpha/2})^2 \sigma^2}{(SE)^2} = \dfrac{(1.645)^2 (10^2)}{1^2} = 270.6 \approx 271$

7.81   a.   The target parameter for the average score on the SAT is μ.

b.   The target parameter for the mean time waiting at a supermarket checkout lane is μ.

c.   The target parameter for the proportion of voters in favor of legalizing marijuana is p.

d.   The target parameter for the percentage of NFL players who have ever made the Pro Bowl is p.

e.   The target parameter for the dropout rate of American college students is p.

7.83   a.   For a small sample from a normal distribution with unknown standard deviation, we use the t statistic. For confidence coefficient .95, $\alpha = 1 - .95 = .05$ and $\alpha/2 = .05/2 = .025$. From Table VI, Appendix A, with df $= n - 1 = 21 - 1 = 20$, $t_{.025} = 2.086$.

      b.   For a large sample from a distribution with an unknown standard deviation, we can estimate the population standard deviation with s and use the z statistic. For confidence coefficient .95, $\alpha = 1 - .95 = .05$ and $\alpha/2 = .05/2 = .025$. From Table IV, Appendix A, $z_{.025} = 1.96$.

      c.   For a small sample from a normal distribution with known standard deviation, we use the z statistic. For confidence coefficient .95, $\alpha = 1 - .95 = .05$ and $\alpha/2 = .05/2 = .025$. From Table IV, Appendix A, $z_{.025} = 1.96$.

      d.   For a large sample from a distribution about which nothing is known, we can estimate the population standard deviation with s and use the z statistic. For confidence coefficient .95, $\alpha = 1 - .95 = .05$ and $\alpha/2 = .05/2 = .025$. From Table IV, Appendix A, $z_{.025} = 1.96$.

      e.   For a small sample from a distribution about which nothing is known, we can use neither z nor t.

7.85   a.   The point estimate for the proportion of measurements in the population with characteristic A is $\hat{p} = \dfrac{x}{n} = \dfrac{227}{400} = .5675$.

To see if the sample size is sufficiently large:

$$\hat{p} \pm 3\sigma_{\hat{p}} \approx \hat{p} \pm 3\sqrt{\frac{\hat{p}\hat{q}}{n}} \Rightarrow .5675 \pm 3\sqrt{\frac{.5675(.4325)}{400}} \Rightarrow .5675 \pm .0743 \Rightarrow (.4932, \ .6418)$$

Since this interval is wholly contained in the interval $(0, 1)$, we may conclude that the normal approximation is reasonable.

For confidence coefficient .95, $\alpha = .05$ and $\alpha/2 = .05/2 = .025$. From Table IV, Appendix A, $z_{.025} = 1.96$. The 95% confidence interval is:

$$\hat{p} \pm z_{.025}\sigma_{\hat{p}} \Rightarrow \hat{p} \pm 1.96\sqrt{\frac{\hat{p}\hat{q}}{n}} \Rightarrow .5675 \pm 1.96\sqrt{\frac{.5675(.4325)}{400}}$$
$$\Rightarrow .5675 \pm .0486 \Rightarrow (.5189, \ .6161)$$

We are 95% confident that the proportion of measurements in the population with characteristic A is between .5189 and .6161.

      b.   We will use $\hat{p} = .5675$ to estimate p.

For confidence coefficient .95, $\alpha = .05$ and $\alpha/2 = .05/2 = .025$. From Table IV, Appendix A, $z_{.025} = 1.96$.

The sample size is $n = \dfrac{(z_{.025})^2 pq}{(SE)^2} = \dfrac{1.96^2(.5675)(.4325)}{.02^2} = 2{,}357.2 \approx 2{,}358$.

7.87   The parameters of interest for the problems are:

(1)   The question requires a categorical response. One parameter of interest might be the proportion, p, of all Americans over 18 years of age who think their health is generally very good or excellent.

(2)   A parameter of interest might be the mean number of days, μ, in the previous 30 days that all Americans over 18 years of age felt that their physical health was not good because of injury or illness.

(3)   A parameter of interest might be the mean number of days, μ, in the previous 30 days that all Americans over 18 years of age felt that their mental health was not good because of stress, depression, or problems with emotions.

(4)   A parameter of interest might be the mean number of days, μ, in the previous 30 days that all Americans over 18 years of age felt that their physical or mental health prevented them from performing their usual activities.

7.89   a.   The 95% confidence interval is (19.7, 20.3). We are 95% confident that the mean number of cigarettes smoked per day by all smokers is between 19.7 and 20.3.

b.   Since the sample size is so large ($n = 11,000$), no assumptions are necessary. The Central Limit Theorem indicates that the sampling distribution of $\bar{x}$ is approximately normal.

c.   Since the entire 95% confidence interval is above the value of 15, the claim made by the tobacco industry researcher is probably not true.

7.91   Using MINITAB, the descriptive statistics are:

Descriptive Statistics: SeedWt

Variable	N	N*	Mean	SE Mean	StDev	Minimum	Q1	Median	Q3	Maximum
SeedWt	16	0	1.373	0.258	1.034	0.201	0.475	1.347	2.009	3.751

For confidence coefficient .99, $\alpha = .01$ and $\alpha/2 = .01/2 = .005$. From Table VI, Appendix A, with df $= n - 1 = 16 - 1 = 15$, $t_{.005} = 2.947$.

The 99% confidence interval is:

$$\bar{x} \pm t_{0.05}\frac{s}{\sqrt{n}} \Rightarrow 1.373 \pm 2.947\frac{1.034}{\sqrt{16}} \Rightarrow 1.373 \pm .762 \Rightarrow (.611, \ 2.135)$$

We are 99% confident that the average weight of dry seeds in the crops of spinifex pigeons inhabiting the Western Australian desert is between .611 and 2.135 grams.

7.93   The 95% confidence interval is (.045, .091). We are 95% confident that the true proportion of people who were/are homeless is between .045 and .091.

7.95 a. First, we compute $\hat{p}$: $\hat{p} = \dfrac{x}{n} = \dfrac{665}{1007} = .660$

To see if the sample size is sufficiently large:

$$\hat{p} \pm 3\sigma_{\hat{p}} \approx \hat{p} \pm 3\sqrt{\dfrac{\hat{p}\hat{q}}{n}} \Rightarrow .660 \pm 3\sqrt{\dfrac{.660(.340)}{1007}} \Rightarrow .660 \pm .045 \Rightarrow (.615, .705)$$

Since the interval is wholly contained in the interval (0,1), we may conclude that the normal approximation is reasonable.

For confidence coefficient .95, $\alpha = .05$ and $\alpha/2 = .05/2 = .025$. From Table IV, Appendix A, $z_{.025} = 1.96$. The confidence interval is:

$$\hat{p} \pm z_{.025}\sqrt{\dfrac{pq}{n}} \approx \hat{p} \pm 1.96\sqrt{\dfrac{\hat{p}\hat{q}}{n}} \Rightarrow .660 \pm 1.96\sqrt{\dfrac{.660(.340)}{1007}} \Rightarrow .660 \pm .029 \Rightarrow (.631, .689)$$

We are 95% confident that the proportion of U.S. workers who take their lunch to work is between .631 and .689.

b. First, we compute $\hat{p}$: $\hat{p} = \dfrac{x}{n} = \dfrac{200}{665} = .301$

To see if the sample size is sufficiently large:

$$\hat{p} \pm 3\sigma_{\hat{p}} \approx \hat{p} \pm 3\sqrt{\dfrac{\hat{p}\hat{q}}{n}} \Rightarrow .301 \pm 3\sqrt{\dfrac{.301(.699)}{665}} \Rightarrow .301 \pm .053 \Rightarrow (.248, .354)$$

Since the interval is wholly contained in the interval (0,1), we may conclude that the normal approximation is reasonable.

For confidence coefficient .95, $\alpha = .05$ and $\alpha/2 = .05/2 = .025$. From Table IV, Appendix A, $z_{.025} = 1.96$. The confidence interval is:

$$\hat{p} \pm z_{.025}\sqrt{\dfrac{pq}{n}} \approx \hat{p} \pm 1.96\sqrt{\dfrac{\hat{p}\hat{q}}{n}} \Rightarrow .301 \pm 1.96\sqrt{\dfrac{.301(.699)}{665}} \Rightarrow .301 \pm .035 \Rightarrow (.266, .336)$$

We are 95% confident that the proportion of U.S. workers who take their lunch to work who brown-bag their lunch is between .266 and .336.

7.97 a. For confidence coefficient .99, $\alpha = .01$ and $\alpha/2 = .01/2 = .005$. From Table IV, Appendix A, $z_{.005} = 2.58$. The confidence interval is:

$$\bar{x} \pm z_{.005}\dfrac{s}{\sqrt{n}} \Rightarrow .044 \pm 2.58\dfrac{.884}{\sqrt{197}} \Rightarrow .044 \pm .162 \Rightarrow (-.118, .206)$$

We are 99% confident that the mean inbreeding coefficient for this species of wasps is between −.118 and .206.

b. A coefficient of 0 indicates that the wasp has no tendency to inbreed. Since 0 is in the 99% confidence interval, it is a likely value for the true mean inbreeding coefficient. Thus, there is no evidence to indicate that this species of wasps has a tendency to inbreed.

7.99   a. Using MINITAB, the descriptive statistics are:

Descriptive Statistics: CPU Time

```
Variable    N   N*   Mean  SE Mean  StDev  Minimum    Q1  Median    Q3  Maximum
CPU Time   52    0  0.812   0.209   1.505   0.0360  0.136   0.275  0.595    8.788
```

For confidence coefficient .95, $\alpha = .05$ and $\alpha/2 = .05/2 = .025$. From Table IV, Appendix A, $z_{.025} = 1.96$. The 95% confidence interval is:

$$\bar{x} \pm z_{.025}\sigma_{\bar{x}} \Rightarrow \bar{x} \pm 1.96\frac{\sigma}{\sqrt{n}} \Rightarrow .812 \pm 1.96\frac{1.505}{\sqrt{52}} \Rightarrow .812 \pm .409 \Rightarrow (.403,\ 1.221)$$

We are 95% confident that the mean solution time for the hybrid algorithm is between .403 and 1.221.

b. The sample size needed would be $n = \dfrac{(z_{.025})^2 \sigma^2}{(SE)^2} = \dfrac{1.96^2(1.505)^2}{.25^2} = 139.2 \approx 140$.

7.101   For all parts to this problem, we will use a 95% confidence interval. For confidence coefficient, .95, $\alpha = .05$ and $\alpha/2 = .05/2 = .025$. From Table IV, Appendix A, $z_{.025} = 1.96$.

a. Some preliminary calculations:

$\hat{p} = x/n = 14/37 = .378$

We must check to see if the sample size is sufficiently large:

$$\hat{p} \pm 3\sigma_{\hat{p}} \approx \hat{p} \pm 3\sqrt{\frac{\hat{p}\hat{q}}{n}} \Rightarrow .378 \pm 3\sqrt{\frac{.378(.622)}{37}} \Rightarrow .378 \pm .239 \Rightarrow (.139, .617)$$

Since the interval is wholly contained in the interval (0, 1), we may assume that the normal approximation is reasonable.

The confidence interval is:

$$\hat{p} \pm z_{.025}\sqrt{\frac{\hat{p}\hat{q}}{n}} \Rightarrow .378 \pm 1.96\sqrt{\frac{.378(.622)}{37}} \Rightarrow .378 \pm .156 \Rightarrow (.222, .534)$$

We are 95% confident that the true proportion of suicides at the jail that are committed by inmates charged with murder/manslaughter is between .222 and .534.

b. Some preliminary calculations:

$\hat{p} = x/n = 26/37 = .703$

We must check to see if the sample size is sufficiently large:

$$\hat{p} \pm 3\sigma_{\hat{p}} \approx \hat{p} \pm 3\sqrt{\frac{\hat{p}\hat{q}}{n}} \Rightarrow .703 \pm 3\sqrt{\frac{.703(.297)}{37}} \Rightarrow .703 \pm .225 \Rightarrow (.478, .928)$$

Since the interval is wholly contained in the interval (0, 1), we may assume that the normal approximation is reasonable.
The confidence interval is:

$$\hat{p} \pm z_{.025}\sqrt{\frac{\hat{p}\hat{q}}{n}} \Rightarrow .703 \pm 1.96\sqrt{\frac{.703(.297)}{37}} \Rightarrow .703 \pm .147 \Rightarrow (.556, .850)$$

We are 95% confident that the true proportion of suicides at the jail that are committed by inmates charged with murder/manslaughter is between .556 and .850.

c.   Some preliminary calculations are:

$$\bar{x} = \frac{\sum x}{n} = \frac{1532}{37} = 41.405$$

$$s^2 = \frac{\sum x^2 - \frac{\left(\sum x\right)^2}{n}}{n-1} = \frac{223,606 - \frac{(1532)^2}{37}}{37-1} = 4,449.2477$$

$$s = \sqrt{s^2} = \sqrt{4,449.2477} = 66.703$$

The confidence interval is:

$$\bar{x} \pm z_{.05}\frac{s}{\sqrt{n}} \Rightarrow 41.405 \pm 1.96\frac{66.703}{\sqrt{37}} \Rightarrow 41.405 \pm 21.493 \Rightarrow (19.912, 62.898)$$

We are 95% confident that the true average length of time an inmate is in jail before committing suicide is between 19.912 and 62.898 days.

d.   Some preliminary calculations:

$$\hat{p} = x/n = 14/37 = .378$$

We must check to see if the sample size is sufficiently large:

$$\hat{p} \pm 3\sigma_{\hat{p}} \approx \hat{p} \pm 3\sqrt{\frac{\hat{p}\hat{q}}{n}} \Rightarrow .378 \pm 3\sqrt{\frac{.378(.622)}{37}} \Rightarrow .378 \pm .239 \Rightarrow (.139, .617)$$

Since the interval is wholly contained in the interval (0, 1), we may assume that the normal approximation is reasonable.

The confidence interval is:

$$\hat{p} \pm z_{.025}\sqrt{\frac{\hat{p}\hat{q}}{n}} \Rightarrow .378 \pm 1.96\sqrt{\frac{.378(.622)}{37}} \Rightarrow .378 \pm .156 \Rightarrow (.222, .534)$$

We are 95% confident that the true proportion of suicides that are committed by white inmates is between .222 and .534. The percentage would be between 22.2% and 53.4%.

7.103   a.   The point estimate for the fraction of the entire market who refuse to purchase bars is:

$$\hat{p} = \frac{x}{n} = \frac{23}{244} = .094$$

b.   To see if the sample size is sufficient:

$$\hat{p} \pm 3\sqrt{\frac{\hat{p}\hat{q}}{n}} \Rightarrow .094 \pm 3\sqrt{\frac{(.094)(.906)}{244}} \Rightarrow .094 \pm .056 \Rightarrow (.038, .150)$$

Since the interval above is contained in the interval (0, 1), the sample size is sufficiently large.

c.   For confidence coefficient .95, $\alpha = 1 - .95 = .05$ and $\alpha/2 = .05/2 = .025$. From Table IV, Appendix A, $z_{.025} = 1.96$. The confidence interval is:

$$\hat{p} \pm z_{.025}\sqrt{\frac{\hat{p}\hat{q}}{n}} \Rightarrow .094 \pm 1.96\sqrt{\frac{.094(.906)}{244}} \Rightarrow .094 \pm .037 \Rightarrow (.057, .131)$$

d.   The best estimate of the true fraction of the entire market who refuse to purchase bars six months after the poisoning is .094. We are 95% confident the true fraction of the entire market who refuse to purchase bars six months after the poisoning is between .057 and .131.

7.105   a.   For confidence coefficient .99, $\alpha = .01$ and $\alpha/2 = .01/2 = .005$. From Table VI, Appendix A, with df $= n - 1 = 3 - 1 = 2$, $t_{.005} = 9.925$. The confidence interval is:

$$\bar{x} \pm t_{.005}\frac{s}{\sqrt{n}} \Rightarrow 49.3 \pm 9.925\frac{1.5}{\sqrt{3}} \Rightarrow 49.3 \pm 8.60 \Rightarrow (40.70, 57.90)$$

b.   We are 99% confident that the mean percentage of B(a)p removed from all soil specimens using the poison is between 40.70% and 57.90%.

c.   We must assume that the distribution of the percentages of B(a)p removed from all soil specimens using the poison is normal.

d.   For confidence coefficient .99, $\alpha = .01$ and $\alpha/2 = .01/2 = .005$. From Table IV, Appendix A, $z_{.005} = 2.58$.

$$n = \frac{z_{\alpha/2}^2 \sigma^2}{(SE)^2} = \frac{1.96^2 (1.5)^2}{.5^2} = 34.57 \approx 35$$

7.107 a. From Chebyshev's Rule, we know that at least $1-\dfrac{1}{k^2}$ of the observations will fall within k standard deviations of the mean. We need to find k so that $1-\dfrac{1}{k^2}=.60$.

$$1-\frac{1}{k^2}=.60 \Rightarrow .40=\frac{1}{k^2}\Rightarrow k^2=\frac{1}{.40}=2.5\Rightarrow k=\sqrt{2.5}=1.58$$

$$s=\frac{80^{th}\text{ percentile}-60^{th}\text{ percentile}}{k}=\frac{73,000-35,100}{1.58}=23,987.34$$

For confidence coefficient .98, $\alpha=.02$ and $\alpha/2=.02/2=.01$. From Table IV, Appendix A, $z_{.01}=2.33$. The sample size required is:

$$n=\frac{(z_{.01})^2\sigma^2}{(SE)^2}=\frac{2.33^2(23,987.34)^2}{2,000^2}=780.9\approx781$$

b. See part **a**.

c. We must assume that any sample selected will be random.

7.109 a. As long as the sample is random (and thus representative), a reliable estimate of the mean weight of all the scallops can be obtained.

b. The government is using only the sample mean to make a decision. Rather than using a point estimate, they should probably use a confidence interval to estimate the true mean weight of the scallops.

c. We will form a 95% confidence interval for the mean weight of the scallops. Using MINITAB, the descriptive statistics are:

Descriptive Statistics: Weight

```
Variable   N   N*    Mean   SE Mean    StDev   Minimum      Q1   Median     Q3
Weight     18   0   0.9317   0.0178   0.0753    0.8400   0.8800   0.9100   9800

Variable   Maximum
Weight      1.1400
```

For confidence coefficient .95, $\alpha=.05$ and $\alpha/2=.05/2=.025$. From Table VI, Appendix A, with df $=n-1=18-1=17$, $t_{.025}=2.110$.

The 95% confidence interval is:

$$\bar{x}\pm t_{.025}\frac{s}{\sqrt{n}}\Rightarrow.9317\pm2.110\frac{.0753}{\sqrt{18}}\Rightarrow.9317\pm.0374\Rightarrow(.8943,\ .9691)$$

We are 95% confident that the true mean weight of the scallops is between .8943 and .9691. Recall that the weights have been scaled so that a mean weight of 1 corresponds to 1/36 of a pound. Since the above confidence interval does not include 1, we have sufficient evidence to indicate that the minimum weight restriction was violated.

Inferences Based on a Single Sample: Tests of Hypotheses

8.1   The null hypothesis is the "status quo" hypothesis, while the alternative hypothesis is the research hypothesis.

8.3   The "level of significance" of a test is α. This is the probability that the test statistic will fall in the rejection region when the null hypothesis is true.

8.5   The four possible results are:

      1.   Rejecting the null hypothesis when it is true. This would be a Type I error.
      2.   Accepting the null hypothesis when it is true. This would be a correct decision.
      3.   Rejecting the null hypothesis when it is false. This would be a correct decision.
      4.   Accepting the null hypothesis when it is false. This would be a Type II error.

8.7   When you reject the null hypothesis in favor of the alternative hypothesis, this does not prove the alternative hypothesis is correct. We are $100(1 - \alpha)\%$ confident that there is sufficient evidence to conclude that the alternative hypothesis is correct.

      If we were to repeatedly draw samples from the population and perform the test each time, approximately $100(1 - \alpha)\%$ of the tests performed would yield the correct decision.

8.9   Let p = proportion of liars correctly detected by the new thermal imaging camera. To determine if the camera can correctly detect liars 75% of the time, we test:

H_0: $p = .75$
H_a: $p \neq .75$

8.11   a.   To determine if the percentage of senior women who use herbal therapies to prevent or treat health problems is different from 45%, we test:

H_0: $p = .45$
H_a: $p \neq .45$

      b.   To determine if the average number of herbal products used in a year by senior women who use herbal therapies is different from 2.5, we test:

H_0: $\mu = 2.5$
H_a: $\mu \neq 2.5$

8.13   To determine if the percentage of all cocaine-exposed babies who suffer no major problems is greater than 75%, we test:

H_0: $p = .75$
H_a: $p > .75$

8.15   a.   To determine if the average level of mercury uptake in wading birds in the Everglades today is less than 15 parts per million, we test:

H_0: $\mu = 15$
H_a: $\mu < 15$

b. A Type I error is rejecting H_0 when H_0 is true. In terms of this problem, we would be concluding that the average level of mercury uptake in wading birds in the Everglades today is less than 15 parts per million, when in fact, the average level of mercury uptake in wading birds in the Everglades today is equal to 15 parts per million.

c. A Type II error is accepting H_0 when H_0 is false. In terms of this problem, we would be concluding that the average level of mercury uptake in wading birds in the Everglades today is equal to 15 parts per million, when in fact, the average level of mercury uptake in wading birds in the Everglades today is less than 15 parts per million.

8.17 a. The null hypothesis is:

H_0: No intrusion occurs

b. The alternative hypothesis is:

H_a: Intrusion occurs

c. α = Probability of a Type I error = Probability of rejecting H_0 when it is true = P(system provides warning when no intrusion occurs) = $1 / 1000 = .001$.

β = Probability of a Type II error = Probability of accepting H_0 when it is false = P(system does not provide warning when an intrusion occurs) = $500 / 1000 = .5$.

8.19 There are 2 conditions required for a valid large-sample hypothesis test for μ. They are:

1. A random sample is selected from a target population.
2. The sample size n is large, i.e., $n \geq 30$. (Due to the Central Limit Theorem, this condition guarantees that the test statistic will be approximately normal regardless of the shape of the underlying probability distribution of the population.)

8.21 a. Probability of Type I error
= $P(z > 1.96) = .5 - .4750 = .0250$
(From Table IV, Appendix A)

b. Probability of Type I error
= $P(z > 1.645) = .5 - .4500 = .05$
(From Table IV, Appendix A)

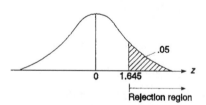

c. Probability of Type I error
= $P(z > 2.58) = .5 - .4951 = .0049$
(From Table IV, Appendix A)

d. Probability of Type I error
= $P(z < -1.28) = .5 - .3997 = .1003$
(From Table IV, Appendix A)

e. Probability of Type I error
= $P(z < -1.645) + P(z > 1.645)$
= $.5 - .4500 + .5 - .4500 = .05 + .05 = .10$
(From Table IV, Appendix A)

f. Probability of Type I error
= $P(z < -2.58) + P(z > 2.58)$
= $.5 - .4951 + .5 - .4951 = .0049 + .0049$
= $.0098$ (From Table IV, Appendix A)

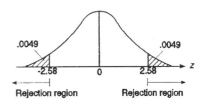

8.23 a. $H_0: \mu = 100$
$H_a: \mu > 100$

The test statistic is $z = \dfrac{\bar{x} - \mu_0}{\sigma_{\bar{x}}} = \dfrac{\bar{x} - \mu_0}{\sigma / \sqrt{n}} = \dfrac{110 - 100}{60 / \sqrt{100}} = 1.67$

The rejection region requires $\alpha = .05$ in the upper tail of the z distribution. From Table IV, Appendix A, $z_{.05} = 1.645$. The rejection region is $z > 1.645$.

Since the observed value of the test statistic falls in the rejection region, ($z = 1.67 > 1.645$), H_0 is rejected. There is sufficient evidence to indicate the true population mean is greater than 100 at $\alpha = .05$.

b. $H_0: \mu = 100$
$H_a: \mu \neq 100$

The test statistic is $z = \dfrac{\bar{x} - \mu_0}{\sigma_{\bar{x}}} = \dfrac{110 - 100}{60 / \sqrt{100}} = 1.67$

The rejection region requires $\alpha/2 = .05/2 = .025$ in each tail of the z distribution. From Table IV, Appendix A, $z_{.025} = 1.96$. The rejection region is $z < -1.96$ or $z > 1.96$.

Since the observed value of the test statistic does not fall in the rejection region, ($z = 1.67 \not> 1.96$), H_0 is not rejected. There is insufficient evidence to indicate μ does not equal 100 at $\alpha = .05$.

c.   In part **a**, we rejected H_0 and concluded the mean was greater than 100. In part **b**, we did not reject H_0. There was insufficient evidence to conclude the mean was different from 100. Because the alternative hypothesis in part **a** is more specific than the one in **b**, it is easier to reject H_0.

8.25   a.   A Type I error would be to conclude that the mean response for the population of all New York City public school children is not 3 when, in fact, the mean response is equal to 3.

A Type II error would be to conclude that the mean response for the population of all New York City public school children is equal to 3 when, in fact, the mean response is not equal to 3.

b.   To determine if the mean response for the population of all New York City public school children is different from 3, we test:

H_0: $\mu = 3$
H_a: $\mu \neq 3$

The test statistic is $z = \dfrac{\bar{x} - \mu_o}{\sigma_{\bar{x}}} = \dfrac{2.15 - 3}{\dfrac{1.05}{\sqrt{11,160}}} = -85.52$

The rejection region requires $\alpha/2 = .05/2 = .025$ in each tail of the z distribution. From Table IV, Appendix A, $z_{.025} = 1.96$. The rejection region is $z < -1.96$ or $z > 1.96$.

Since the observed value of the test statistic falls in the rejection region ($z = -85.52 < -1.96$), H_0 is rejected. There is sufficient evidence to indicate the mean response for the population of all New York City public school children different from 3 at $\alpha = .05$.

c.   To determine if the mean response for the population of all New York City public school children is different from 3, we test:

H_0: $\mu = 3$
H_a: $\mu \neq 3$

The test statistic is $z = \dfrac{\bar{x} - \mu_o}{\sigma_{\bar{x}}} = \dfrac{2.15 - 3}{\dfrac{1.05}{\sqrt{11,160}}} = -85.52$

The rejection region requires $\alpha/2 = .10/2 = .05$ in each tail of the z distribution. From Table IV, Appendix A, $z_{.05} = 1.645$. The rejection region is $z < -1.645$ or $z > 1.645$.

Since the observed value of the test statistic falls in the rejection region ($z = -85.52 < -1.645$), H_0 is rejected. There is sufficient evidence to indicate the mean response for the population of all New York City public school children different from 3 at $\alpha = .10$.

8.27   To determine if the mean alkalinity level of water in the tributary exceeds 50 mpl, we test:

H_0: $\mu = 50$
H_a: $\mu > 50$

The test statistic is $z = \dfrac{\bar{x} - \mu_0}{\sigma_{\bar{x}}} = \dfrac{67.8 - 50}{14.4/\sqrt{100}} = 12.36$

The rejection region requires $\alpha = .01$ in the upper tail of the z distribution. From Table IV, Appendix A, $z_{.01} = 2.33$. The rejection region is $z > 2.33$.

Since the observed value of the test statistic falls in the rejection region ($z = 12.36 > 2.33$), H_0 is rejected. There is sufficient evidence to indicate that the mean alkalinity level of water in the tributary exceeds 50 mpl at $\alpha = .01$.

8.29   a.   To determine if the true mean PTSD score of all World War II avaiator POWs is less than 16, we test:

H_0: $\mu = 16$
H_a: $\mu < 16$

b.   The test statistic is $z = z = \dfrac{\bar{x} - \mu_o}{\sigma_{\bar{x}}} = \dfrac{9.00 - 16}{9.32/\sqrt{33}} = -4.31$

The rejection region requires $\alpha = .10$ in the lower tail of the z distribution. From Table IV, Appendix A, $z_{.10} = 1.28$. The rejection region is $z < -1.28$.

Since the observed value of the test statistic falls in the rejection region ($z = -4.31 < -1.28$), H_0 is rejected. There is sufficient evidence to indicate that the true mean PTSD score of all World War II aviator POWs is less than 16 at $\alpha = .10$.

c.   Only 33 of the total 239 World War II aviator POWs volunteered to participate in the study. These POWs were self-selected, not random. Usually those who self-select themselves tend to have strong feelings about the subject. They may not be representative of the entire group.

8.31   a.   Using MINITAB, the descriptive statistics are:

Descriptive Statistics: Bones

Variable	N	N*	Mean	SE Mean	StDev	Minimum	Q1	Median	Q3	Maximum
Bones	41	0	9.258	0.188	1.204	6.230	8.615	9.200	9.935	12.000

To determine if the population mean ratio of all bones of this particular species differs from 8.5, we test:

H_0: $\mu = 8.5$
H_a: $\mu \neq 8.5$

The test statistic is $z = \dfrac{\bar{x} - \mu_0}{\sigma_{\bar{x}}} = \dfrac{9.258 - 8.5}{1.204/\sqrt{41}} = 4.03$

Inferences Based on a Single Sample: Tests of Hypotheses

The rejection region requires $\alpha/2 = .01/2 = .005$ in each tail of the z distribution. From Table IV, Appendix A, $z_{.005} = 2.58$. The rejection region is $z < -2.58$ or $z > 2.58$.

Since the observed value of the test statistic falls in the rejection region ($z = 4.03 > 2.58$), H_0 is rejected. There is sufficient evidence to indicate that the true population mean ratio of all bones of this particular species differs from 8.5 at $\alpha = .01$.

b.   The practical implications of the test in part **a** is that the species from which these particular bones came from is probably not species A.

8.33   a.   Since the hypothesized value of μ_M ($\$60,000$) falls in the 95% confidence interval, it is not an unusual value. There is no evidence to reject it. There is no evidence to indicate that the mean salary of all males with post-graduate degrees differs from $\$60,000$.

b.   To determine if the mean salary of all males with post-graduate degrees differs from $\$60,000$, we test:

H_0: $\mu_M = 60,000$
H_a: $\mu_M \neq 60,000$

The test statistic is $z = \dfrac{\bar{x} - \mu_0}{\sigma_{\bar{x}}} = \dfrac{61,340 - 60,000}{2,185} = 0.61$

The rejection region requires $\alpha/2 = .05/2 = .025$ in each tail of the z distribution. From Table IV, Appendix A, $z_{.025} = 1.96$. The rejection region is $z < -1.96$ or $z > 1.96$.

Since the observed value of the test statistic does not fall in the rejection region ($z = 0.61 \not> 1.96$), H_0 is not rejected. There is insufficient evidence to indicate the mean salary of all males with post-graduate degrees differs from $\$60,000$ at $\alpha = .05$.

c.   The inferences in parts **a** and **b** agree because the same values are used for both. The z value used in the 95% confidence interval is the same z used for the rejection region. The value of $\bar{x}$ and $s_{\bar{x}}$ are the same in both the confidence interval and the test statistic.

d.   Since the hypothesized value of μ_F ($\$33,000$) falls in the 95% confidence interval, it is not an unusual value. There is no evidence to reject it. There is no evidence to indicate that the mean salary of all females with post-graduate degrees differs from $\$33,000$.

e.   To determine if the mean salary of all females with post-graduate degrees differs from $\$33,000$, we test:
H_0: $\mu_M = 33,000$
H_a: $\mu_M \neq 33,000$

The test statistic is $z = \dfrac{\bar{x} - \mu_0}{\sigma_{\bar{x}}} = \dfrac{32,227 - 33,000}{932} = -0.83$

The rejection region requires $\alpha/2 = .05/2 = .025$ in each tail of the z distribution. From Table IV, Appendix A, $z_{.025} = 1.96$. The rejection region is $z < -1.96$ or $z > 1.96$.

Since the observed value of the test statistic does not fall in the rejection region ($z = -0.83 \not< -1.96$), H_0 is not rejected. There is insufficient evidence to indicate the mean salary of all females with post-graduate degrees differs from \$33,000 at $\alpha = .05$.

f. The inferences in parts **d** and **e** agree because the same values are used for both. The z value used in the 95% confidence interval is the same z used for the rejection region. The value of $\bar{x}$ and $s_{\bar{x}}$ are the same in both the confidence interval and the test statistic.

8.35   a. To determine if the mean social interaction score of all Connecticut mental health patients differs from 3, we test:

H_0: $\mu = 3$
H_a: $\mu \neq 3$

The test statistic is $z = \dfrac{\bar{x} - \mu_0}{\sigma_{\bar{x}}} = \dfrac{2.95 - 3}{1.10/\sqrt{6,681}} = -3.72$

The rejection region requires $\alpha/2 = .01/2 = .005$ in each tail of the z distribution. From Table IV, Appendix A, $z_{.005} = 2.58$. The rejection region is $z < -2.58$ or $z > 2.58$.

Since the observed value of the test statistic falls in the rejection region ($z = -3.72 < -2.58$), H_0 is rejected. There is sufficient evidence to indicate that the mean social interaction score of all Connecticut mental health patients differs from 3 at $\alpha = .01$.

b. From the test in part a, we found that the mean social interaction score was statistically different from 3. However, the sample mean score was 2.95. Practically speaking, 2.95 is very similar to 3.0. The very large sample size, $n = 6,681$, makes it very easy to find statistical significance, even when no practical significance exists.

c. Because the variable of interest is measured on a 5-point scale, it is very unlikely that the population of the ratings will be normal. However, because the sample size was extremely large, ($n = 6,681$), the Central Limit Theorem will apply. Thus, the distribution of $\bar{x}$ will be normal, regardless of the distribution of x. Thus, the analysis used above is appropriate.

8.37   In general, small p-values support the alternative hypothesis, H_a. The p-value is the probability of observing your test statistic or anything more unusual, given H_0 is true. If the p-value is small, it would be very unusual to observe your test statistic, given H_0 is true. This would indicate that H_0 is probably false and H_a is probably true.

8.39   a.   Since the *p*-value = .10 is greater than α = .05, H_0 is not rejected.

b.   Since the *p*-value = .05 is less than α = .10, H_0 is rejected.

c.   Since the *p*-value = .001 is less than α = .01, H_0 is rejected.

d.   Since the *p*-value = .05 is greater than α = .025, H_0 is not rejected.

e.   Since the *p*-value = .45 is greater than α = .10, H_0 is not rejected.

8.41   *p*-value = $P(z \geq 2.17) = .5 - P(0 < z < 2.17) = .5 - .4850 = .0150$

(using Table IV, Appendix A)

8.43 $z = \dfrac{\bar{x} - \mu_0}{\sigma_{\bar{x}}} = \dfrac{49.4 - 50}{4.1 / \sqrt{100}} = -1.46$

p-value = $P(z \geq -1.46) = .5 + .4279 = .9279$

There is no evidence to reject H_0 for $\alpha \leq .10$.

8.45   a.   The *p*-value reported by SPSS is for a two-tailed test. Thus, $P(z \leq -1.63) + P(z \geq 1.63)$ = .1032. For this one-tailed test, the *p*-value = $P(z \leq -1.63) = .1032/2 = .0516$.

Since the *p*-value = .0516 > α = .05, H_0 is not rejected. There is insufficient evidence to indicate $\mu < 75$ at α = .05.

b.   For this one-tailed test, the *p*-value = $P(z \leq 1.63)$. Since $P(z \leq -1.63) = .1032/2 = .0516$, $P(z \leq 1.63) = 1 - .0516 = .9484$.

Since the *p*-value = .9484 > α = .10, H_0 is not rejected. There is insufficient evidence to indicate $\mu < 75$ at α = .10.

c.   For this one-tailed test, the *p*-value = $P(z \geq 1.63) = .1032/2 = .0516$.

Since the *p*-value = .0516 < α = .10, H_0 is rejected. There is sufficient evidence to indicate $\mu > 75$ at α = .10.

d.   For this two-tailed test, the *p*-value = .1032.

Since the *p*-value = .1032 > α = .01, H_0 is not rejected. There is insufficient evidence to indicate $\mu \neq 75$ at α = .01.

8.47   a.   From Exercise 8.26, $z = -.40$. The *p*-value is $p = P(z \leq -.40) = .5 - .1554 = .3446$ (using Table IV, Appendix A).

b.   The *p*-value is $p = .3446$. Since this is greater than α = .01, H_0 is not rejected. There is insufficient evidence to indicate the mean number of latex gloves used per week by hospital employees diagnosed with a latex allergy from exposure to the powder on latex gloves is less than 20 at α = .01.

8.49   From the printout, the p-value < .0001. Since the p-value < .0001 < α = .01, H_0 is rejected. There is sufficient evidence to indicate that the true population mean ratio of all bones of this particular species differs from 8.5 at α = .01.

8.51   a.   The test statistic is $z = \dfrac{\bar{x} - \mu_0}{\sigma_{\bar{x}}} = \dfrac{10.2 - 0}{31.3/\sqrt{50}} = 2.3$

        b.   To determine if the mean level of feminization differs from 0%, we test:

              H_0: $\mu = 0$
              H_a: $\mu \neq 0$

              Since the alternative hypothesis contains $\neq$, this is a two-tailed test. The p-value is
              $p = P(z \leq -2.3) + P(z \geq 2.3) = .5 - P(-2.3 < z < 0) + .5 - P(0 < z < 2.3) = .5 - .4893 + .5 - .4893 = .0214.$

        b.   The test statistic is $z = \dfrac{\bar{x} - \mu_0}{\sigma_{\bar{x}}} = \dfrac{15 - 0}{25.1/\sqrt{50}} = 4.22.$

              Since the alternative hypothesis contains $\neq$, this is a two-tailed test. The p-value is
              $p = P(z \leq -4.22) + P(z \geq 4.22) = .5 - P(-4.22 < z < 0) + .5 - P(0 < z < 4.22) \approx .5 - .5 + .5 - .5 = 0.$

8.53   We should use the t distribution in testing a hypothesis about a population mean if the sample size is small, the population being sampled from is normal, and the variance of the population is unknown.

8.55   a. $P(t > 1.440) = .10$
              (Using Table VI, Appendix A, with df = 6)

        b. $P(t < -1.782) = .05$
              (Using Table VI, Appendix A, with df = 12)

        c. $P(t < -2.060) = P(t > 2.060) = .025$
              (Using Table VI, Appendix A, with df = 25)

8.57   a.   The rejection region requires $\alpha/2 = .05/2 = .025$ in each tail of the t distribution with df = $n - 1 = 14 - 1 = 13$. From Table VI, Appendix A, $t_{.025} = 2.160$. The rejection region is $t < -2.160$ or $t > 2.160$.

        b.   The rejection region requires $\alpha = .01$ in the upper tail of the t distribution with df = $n - 1 = 24 - 1 = 23$. From Table VI, Appendix A, $t_{.01} = 2.500$. The rejection region is $t > 2.500$.

c. The rejection region requires $\alpha = .10$ in the upper tail of the t distribution with df $= n - 1 = 9 - 1 = 8$. From Table VI, Appendix A, $t_{.10} = 1.397$. The rejection region is $t > 1.397$.

d. The rejection region requires $\alpha = .01$ in the lower tail of the t distribution with df $= n - 1 = 12 - 1 = 11$. From Table VI, Appendix A, $t_{.01} = 2.718$. The rejection region is $t < -2.718$.

e. The rejection region requires $\alpha/2 = .10/2 = .05$ in each tail of the t distribution with df $= n - 1 = 20 - 1 = 19$. From Table VI, Appendix A, $t_{.05} = 1.729$. The rejection region is $t < -1.729$ or $t > 1.729$.

f. The rejection region requires $\alpha = .05$ in the lower tail of the t distribution with df $= n - 1 = 4 - 1 = 3$. From Table VI, Appendix A, $t_{.05} = 2.353$. The rejection region is $t < -2.353$.

8.59 a. H_0: $\mu = 6$
H_a: $\mu < 6$

The test statistic is $t = \dfrac{\bar{x} - \mu_0}{s/\sqrt{n}} = \dfrac{4.8 - 6}{1.3/\sqrt{5}} = -2.064$.

The necessary assumption is that the population is normal.

The rejection region requires $\alpha = .05$ in the lower tail of the t distribution with df $= n - 1 = 5 - 1 = 4$. From Table VI, Appendix A, $t_{.05} = 2.132$. The rejection region is $t < -2.132$.

Since the observed value of the test statistic does not fall in the rejection region ($t = -2.064 \Leftrightarrow -2.132$), H_0 is not rejected. There is insufficient evidence to indicate the mean is less than 6 at $\alpha = .05$.

b. H_0: $\mu = 6$
H_a: $\mu \neq 6$

The test statistic is $t = -2.064$ (from **a**).

The assumption is the same as in **a**.

The rejection region requires $\alpha/2 = .05/2 = .025$ in each tail of the t distribution with df $= n - 1 = 5 - 1 = 4$. From Table VI, Appendix A, $t_{.025} = 2.776$. The rejection region is $t < -2.776$ or $t > 2.776$.

Since the observed value of the test statistic does not fall in the rejection region ($t = -2.064 \not< -2.776$), H_0 is not rejected. There is insufficient evidence to indicate the mean is different from 6 at $\alpha = .05$.

c. For part **a**, the p-value $= P(t \le -2.064)$.

From Table VI, with df $= 4$, $.05 < P(t \le -2.064) < .10$ or $.05 < p$-value $< .10$.

For part **b**, the p-value $= P(t \le -2.064) + P(t \ge 2.064)$.

From Table VI, with df $= 4$, $2(.05) < p$-value $< 2(.10)$ or $.10 < p$-value $< .20$.

8.61 a. To determine if the mean breaking strength of the new bonding adhesive is less than 5.70 Mpa, we test:

H_0: $\mu = 5.70$
H_a: $\mu < 5.70$

b. The rejection region requires $\alpha = .01$ in the lower tail of the t distribution with df $= n - 1$ $= 10 - 1 = 9$. From Table VI, Appendix A, $t_{.01} = 2.821$. The rejection region is $t < -2.821$.

c. The test statistic is $t = \dfrac{\bar{x} - \mu_0}{\dfrac{s}{\sqrt{n}}} = \dfrac{5.07 - 5.70}{\dfrac{.46}{\sqrt{10}}} = -4.33$.

d. Since the observed value of the test statistic falls in the rejection region $(t = -4.33 < -2.821)$, H_0 is rejected. There is sufficient evidence to indicate that the mean breaking strength of the new bonding adhesive is less than 5.70 Mpa at $\alpha = .01$.

e. The conditions required for this test is a random sample from the target population and the population from which the sample is selected is approximately normal.

8.63 To determine if the mean Dental Anxiety Scale score for college students differs from 11, we test:

H_0: $\mu = 11$
H_a: $\mu \ne 11$

The test statistic is $t = \dfrac{\bar{x} - \mu_0}{s/\sqrt{n}} = \dfrac{10.7 - 11}{3.6/\sqrt{27}} = -.43$

The rejection region requires $\alpha/2 = .05/2 = .025$ in each tail of the t distribution with df $= n - 1 = 27 - 1 = 26$. From Table VI, Appendix A, $t_{.025} = 2.056$. The rejection region is $t < -2.056$ or $t > 2.056$.

Since the observed value of the test statistic does not fall in the rejection region $(t = -.43 \not< -2.056)$, H_0 is not rejected. There is insufficient evidence to indicate the mean Dental Anxiety Scale score for college students differs from 11 at $\alpha = .05$.

8.65   To determine if the mean amount of cesium in lichen specimens differs from .003, we test:

H_0: $\mu = .003$
H_a: $\mu \neq .003$

From the printout, the test statistic is t = 3.72 and the *p*-value is *p* = .006.

Since the p-value is less than α ($p = .006 < \alpha = .10$), H_0 is rejected. There is sufficient evidence to indicate the mean amount of cesium in lichen specimens differs from .003 at $\alpha = .10$.

In order for the above test to be valid, the sample of observations must come from a normal distribution. The stem-and-leaf display indicates that the sample is somewhat mound-shaped. Thus, the condition is met.

8.67   To determine if the true mean crack intensity of the Mississippi highway exceeds the AASHTO recommended maximum, we test:

H_0: $\mu = .100$
H_a: $\mu > .100$

The test statistic is $t = \dfrac{\bar{x} - \mu_0}{s/\sqrt{n}} = \dfrac{.210 - .100}{\sqrt{.011}/\sqrt{8}} = 2.97$

The rejection region requires $\alpha = .01$ in the upper tail of the *t* distribution with df $= n - 1$ $= 8 - 1 = 7$. From Table VI, Appendix A, $t_{.01} = 2.998$. The rejection region is $t > 2.998$.

Since the observed value of the test statistic does not fall in the rejection region ($t = 2.97 \not> 2.998$), H_0 is not rejected. There is insufficient evidence to indicate that the true mean crack intensity of the Mississippi highway exceeds the AASHTO recommended maximum at $\alpha = .01$.

8.69   To determine if the true mean PST score of all patients with mild to moderate traumatic brain injury exceeds the "normal" value of 40, we test:

H_0: $\mu = 40$
H_a: $\mu > 40$

The test statistic is $t = \dfrac{\bar{x} - \mu_0}{s/\sqrt{n}} = \dfrac{48.43 - 48}{20.76/\sqrt{23}} = 1.95$

The rejection region requires $\alpha = .05$ in the upper tail of the *t* distribution with df $= n - 1$ $= 23 - 1 = 22$. From Table VI, Appendix A, $t_{.05} = 1.717$. The rejection region is $t > 1.717$.

Since the observed value of the test statistic falls in the rejection region ($t = 1.95 > 1.717$), H_0 is rejected. There is sufficient evidence to indicate that the true mean PST score of all patients with mild to moderate traumatic brain injury exceeds the "normal" value of 40 at $\alpha = .05$.

8.71   Typically, qualitative data are associated with making inferences about a population proportion.

8.73   The sample size is large enough if the interval $p_0 \pm 3\sigma_{\hat{p}}$ is contained in the interval $(0, 1)$.

a. $p_0 \pm 3\sqrt{\dfrac{p_0 q_0}{n}} \Rightarrow .05 \pm 3\sqrt{\dfrac{(.05)(.95)}{500}} \Rightarrow .05 \pm .029 \Rightarrow (.021, .079)$

Since the interval is contained in the interval $(0, 1)$, the sample size is large enough.

b. $p_0 \pm 3\sqrt{\dfrac{p_0 q_0}{n}} \Rightarrow .99 \pm 3\sqrt{\dfrac{(.99)(.01)}{100}} \Rightarrow .99 \pm .030 \Rightarrow (.960, 1.020)$

Since the interval is not contained in the interval $(0, 1)$, the sample size is not large enough.

c. $p_0 \pm 3\sqrt{\dfrac{p_0 q_0}{n}} \Rightarrow .2 \pm 3\sqrt{\dfrac{(.2)(.8)}{50}} \Rightarrow .2 \pm .170 \Rightarrow (.030, .370)$

Since the interval is contained in the interval $(0, 1)$, the sample size is large enough.

d. $p_0 \pm 3\sqrt{\dfrac{p_0 q_0}{n}} \Rightarrow .2 \pm 3\sqrt{\dfrac{(.2)(.8)}{20}} \Rightarrow .2 \pm .268 \Rightarrow (-.068, 468)$

Since the interval is not contained in the interval $(0, 1)$, the sample size is not large enough.

e. $p_0 \pm 3\sqrt{\dfrac{p_0 q_0}{n}} \Rightarrow .4 \pm 3\sqrt{\dfrac{(.4)(.6)}{10}} \Rightarrow .4 \pm .465 \Rightarrow (-.065, .865)$

Since the interval is not contained in the interval $(0, 1)$, the sample size is not large enough.

8.75   a. $z = \dfrac{\hat{p} - p_0}{\sqrt{\dfrac{p_0 q_0}{n}}} = \dfrac{.84 - .9}{\sqrt{\dfrac{.9(.1)}{100}}} = -2.00$

b.   The denominator in Exercise 8.74 is $\sqrt{\dfrac{.75(.25)}{100}} = .0433$ as compared to $\sqrt{\dfrac{.9(.1)}{100}} = .03$ in part **a**. Since the denominator in this problem is smaller, the absolute value of z is larger.

c.   The rejection region requires $\alpha = .05$ in the lower tail of the z distribution. From Table IV, Appendix A, $z_{.05} = 1.645$. The rejection region is $z < -1.645$.

Since the observed value of the test statistic falls in the rejection region $(z = -2.00 < -1.645)$, H_0 is rejected. There is sufficient evidence to indicate the population proportion is less than .9 at $\alpha = .05$.

d.   The p-value $= P(z \leq -2.00) = .5 - .4772 = .0228$ (from Table IV, Appendix A).

8.77   From Exercise 7.48, $n = 50$ and since p is the proportion of consumers who do not like the snack food, will be:

$$\hat{p} = \frac{\text{Number of 0's in sample}}{n} = \frac{29}{50} = .58$$

Inferences Based on a Single Sample: Tests of Hypotheses   205

First, check to see if the normal approximation will be adequate:

$$p_0 \pm 3\sigma_{\hat{p}} \Rightarrow p_0 \pm 3\sqrt{\frac{pq}{n}} \approx p_0 \pm 3\sqrt{\frac{p_0 q_0}{n}} \Rightarrow .5 \pm 3\sqrt{\frac{.5(1-.5)}{50}} \Rightarrow .5 \pm .2121$$

$$\Rightarrow (.2879, .7121)$$

Since the interval lies completely in the interval (0, 1), the normal approximation will be adequate.

a. H_0: $p = .5$
    H_a: $p > .5$

The test statistic is $z = \dfrac{\hat{p} - p_0}{\sigma_{\hat{p}}} = \dfrac{\hat{p} - p_0}{\sqrt{\dfrac{p_0 q_0}{n}}} = \dfrac{.58 - .5}{\sqrt{\dfrac{.5(1-.5)}{50}}} = 1.13$

The rejection region requires $\alpha = .10$ in the upper tail of the z distribution. From Table IV, Appendix A, $z_{.10} = 1.28$. The rejection region is $z > 1.28$.

Since the observed value of the test statistic does not fall in the rejection region ($z = 1.13 \ngtr 1.28$), H_0 is not rejected. There is insufficient evidence to indicate the proportion of customers who do not like the snack food is greater than .5 at $\alpha = .10$.

b. p-value $= P(z \geq 1.13) = .5 - .3708 = .1292$

8.79 a. The point estimate for p is $\hat{p} = \dfrac{x}{n} = \dfrac{7}{163} = .043$.

b. To determine if the proportion of unauthorized uses of business websites in 2001 that came from inside the company has changed since 1999, we test:

H_0: $p = .07$
H_a: $p \neq .07$

c. The test statistic is $z = \dfrac{\hat{p} - p_0}{\sqrt{\dfrac{p_0 q_0}{n}}} = \dfrac{.034 - .07}{\sqrt{\dfrac{.07(.93)}{163}}} = -1.80$

d. The rejection region requires $\alpha/2 = .05/2 = .025$ in each tail of the z distribution. From Table IV, Appendix A, $z_{.025} = 1.96$. The rejection region is $z < -1.96$ or $z > 1.96$.

e. First, check to see if the normal approximation will be adequate:

$$p_0 \pm 3\sigma_{\hat{p}} \Rightarrow p_0 \pm 3\sqrt{\frac{pq}{n}} \approx p_0 \pm 3\sqrt{\frac{p_0 q_0}{n}} \Rightarrow .07 \pm 3\sqrt{\frac{.07(.93)}{163}} \Rightarrow .07 \pm .060 \Rightarrow (.010, .130)$$

Since the interval is completely in the interval (0, 1), the normal approximation will be adequate.

Since the observed value of the test statistic does not fall in the rejection region ($z = -1.80 \not< -1.96$), H_0 is not rejected. There is insufficient evidence to indicate the proportion of unauthorized uses of business websites in 2001 that came from inside the company has changed since 1999 at $\alpha = .05$.

f. The p-value is

$$p = P(z \le -1.80) + P(z \ge 1.80) = (.5 - .4641) + (.5 - .4641) = .0359 + .0359 = .0718$$

Since the p-value is greater than $\alpha\,(p = .0718 > .05)$, H_0 is not rejected. This is the same conclusion as in part **e**.

8.81   Some preliminary calculations:

$$\hat{p} = \frac{x}{n} = \frac{401}{835} = .48$$

First we check to see if the normal approximation is adequate:

$$p_0 \pm 3\sigma_{\hat{p}} \Rightarrow p_0 \pm 3\sqrt{\frac{pq}{n}} \approx p_0 \pm 3\sqrt{\frac{p_0 q_0}{n}} \Rightarrow .45 \pm 3\sqrt{\frac{.45(.55)}{835}} \Rightarrow .45 \pm .052 \Rightarrow (.398, .502)$$

Since the interval falls completely in the interval $(0, 1)$, the normal distribution will be adequate.

To determine if more than 45% of male youths are raised in a single-parent family, we test:

H_0: $p = .45$
H_a: $p > .45$

The test statistic is $z = \dfrac{\hat{p} - p_0}{\sqrt{\dfrac{p_0 q_0}{n}}} = \dfrac{.48 - .45}{\sqrt{\dfrac{.45(.55)}{835}}} = 1.74$

The rejection region requires $\alpha = .05$ in the upper tail of the z distribution. From Table IV, Appendix A, $z_{.05} = 1.645$. The rejection region is $z > 1.645$.

Since the observed value of the test statistic falls in the rejection region ($z = 1.74 > 1.645$), H_0 is rejected. There is sufficient evidence that more than 45% of male youths are raised in a single-parent family at $\alpha = .05$.

8.83   The point estimate for p is $\hat{p} = \dfrac{x}{n} = \dfrac{71 + 68}{678} = \dfrac{139}{678} = .205$

First, check to see if the normal approximation will be adequate:

$$p_o \pm 3\sigma_{\hat{p}} \Rightarrow p_o \pm 3\sqrt{\frac{pq}{n}} \approx p_o \pm 3\sqrt{\frac{p_o q_o}{n}} \Rightarrow .25 \pm 3\sqrt{\frac{.25(.75)}{678}} \Rightarrow .25 \pm .05 \Rightarrow (.20, .30)$$

Since the interval is completely in the interval (0, 1), the normal approximation will be adequate.

To determine if the true percentage of appealed civil cases that are actually reversed is less than 25%, we test:

H_0: $p = .25$
H_a: $p < .25$

The test statistic is $z = \dfrac{\hat{p} - p_0}{\sqrt{\dfrac{p_0 q_0}{n}}} = \dfrac{.205 - .25}{\sqrt{\dfrac{.25(.75)}{678}}} = -2.71$

The rejection region requires $\alpha = .01$ in the lower tail of the z distribution. From Table IV, Appendix A, $z_{.01} = 2.33$. The rejection region is $z < -2.33$.

Since the observed value of the test statistic falls in the rejection region ($z = -2.71 < -2.33$), H_0 is rejected. There is sufficient evidence to indicate the true percentage of appealed civil cases that are actually reversed is less than 25% at $\alpha = .01$.

8.85   The point estimate for p is $\hat{p} = \dfrac{x}{n} = \dfrac{85}{124} = .685$

First, check to see if the normal approximation will be adequate:

$$p_0 \pm 3\sigma_{\hat{p}} \Rightarrow p_0 \pm 3\sqrt{\dfrac{pq}{n}} \approx p_0 \pm 3\sqrt{\dfrac{p_0 q_0}{n}} \Rightarrow .167 \pm 3\sqrt{\dfrac{.167(.833)}{124}} \Rightarrow .167 \pm .100 \Rightarrow (.067, \ .267)$$

Since the interval is completely in the interval (0, 1), the normal approximation will be adequate.

To determine if the students will tend to choose the three-grill display so that Grill #2 is a compromise between a more and a less desirable grill ($p > .167$), we test:

H_0: $p = .167$
H_a: $p > .167$

The test statistic is $z = \dfrac{\hat{p} - p_0}{\sqrt{\dfrac{p_0 q_0}{n}}} = \dfrac{.685 - .167}{\sqrt{\dfrac{.167(.822)}{124}}} = 15.46$

The rejection region requires $\alpha = .05$ in the upper tail of the z distribution. From Table IV, Appendix A, $z_{.05} = 1.645$. The rejection region is $z > 1.645$.

Since the observed value of the test statistic falls in the rejection region ($z = 15.46 > 1.645$), H_0 is rejected. There is sufficient evidence to indicate the students will tend to choose the three-grill display so that Grill #2 is a compromise between a more and a less desirable grill ($p > .167$) at $\alpha = .05$.

8.87   a.   The point estimate for p is $\hat{p} = \dfrac{x}{n} = \dfrac{24}{33} = .727$

First, check to see if the normal approximation will be adequate:

$$p_0 \pm 3\sigma_{\hat{p}} \Rightarrow p_0 \pm 3\sqrt{\dfrac{pq}{n}} \approx p_0 \pm 3\sqrt{\dfrac{p_0 q_0}{n}} \Rightarrow .60 \pm 3\sqrt{\dfrac{.60(.40)}{33}} \Rightarrow .60 \pm .256 \Rightarrow (.344, \ .856)$$

Since the interval is completely in the interval (0, 1), the normal approximation will be adequate.

To determine if the cream will improve the skin of more than 60% of middle-aged women, we test:

H_0: $p = .60$
H_a: $p > .60$

The test statistic is $z = \dfrac{\hat{p} - p_0}{\sqrt{\dfrac{p_0 q_0}{n}}} = \dfrac{.727 - .60}{\sqrt{\dfrac{.60(.40)}{33}}} = 1.49$

The rejection region requires $\alpha = .05$ in the upper tail of the z distribution. From Table IV, Appendix A, $z_{.05} = 1.645$. The rejection region is $z > 1.645$.

Since the observed value of the test statistic does not fall in the rejection region ($z = 1.49 \not> 1.645$), H_0 is not rejected. There is insufficient evidence to indicate the cream will improve the skin of more than 60% of middle-aged women at $\alpha = .05$.

b.   The p-value of the test is:

$$p = P(z \geq 1.49) = .5 - .4319 = .0681$$

Since the p-value is not less than α (p = .0681 $\not<$ .05), H_0 is not rejected. There is insufficient evidence to indicate the cream will improve the skin of more than 60% of middle-aged women at $\alpha = .05$.

8.89   Let p = proportion of patients taking the pill who reported an improved condition.

First we check to see if the normal approximation is adequate:

$$p_0 \pm 3\sigma_{\hat{p}} \Rightarrow p_0 \pm 3\sqrt{\dfrac{p_0 q_0}{n}} \Rightarrow .5 \pm 3\sqrt{\dfrac{.5(.5)}{7000}} \Rightarrow .5 \pm .018 \Rightarrow (.482, .518)$$

Since the interval falls completely in the interval (0, 1), the normal distribution will be adequate.

To determine if there really is a placebo effect at the clinic, we test:

H_0: $p = .5$
H_a: $p > .5$

The test statistic is $z = \dfrac{\hat{p} - p_0}{\sqrt{\dfrac{p_0 q_0}{n}}} = \dfrac{.7 - .5}{\sqrt{\dfrac{.5(.5)}{7000}}} = 33.47$

The rejection region requires $\alpha = .05$ in the upper tail of the z distribution. From Table IV, Appendix A, $z_{.05} = 1.645$. The rejection region is $z > 1.645$.

Since the observed value of the test statistic falls in the rejection region ($z = 33.47 > 1.645$), H_0 is rejected. There is sufficient evidence to indicate that there really is a placebo effect at the clinic at $\alpha = .05$.

8.91   a.   The power of a test is equal to $1 - \beta$. As β increases, the power decreases.

8.93   a.

b. $z = \dfrac{\bar{x}_0 - \mu_0}{\sigma_{\bar{x}}} \Rightarrow \bar{x}_0 = \mu_0 + z_\alpha \sigma_{\bar{x}} = \mu_0 + z_\alpha \dfrac{\sigma}{\sqrt{n}}$ where $z_\alpha = z_{.05} = 1.645$ from Table IV, Appendix A.

Thus, $\bar{x}_0 = 1000 + 1.645 \dfrac{120}{\sqrt{36}} = 1032.9$.

c.

d. $\beta = P(\bar{x}_0 < 1032.9$ when $\mu = 1020) = P\left(z < \dfrac{1032.9 - 1020}{120/\sqrt{36}}\right) = P(z < .65)$

$= .5 + .2422 = .7422$

e.   Power $= 1 - \beta = 1 - .7422 = .2578$

8.95 a. The sampling distribution of $\bar{x}$ will be approximately normal (by the Central Limit Theorem) with $\mu_{\bar{x}} = \mu = 50$ and $\sigma_{\bar{x}} = \dfrac{\sigma}{\sqrt{n}} = \dfrac{20}{\sqrt{64}} = 2.5$.

b. The sampling distribution of $\bar{x}$ will be approximately normal (by the Central Limit Theorem) with $\mu_{\bar{x}} = \mu = 45$ and $\sigma_{\bar{x}} = \dfrac{\sigma}{\sqrt{n}} = \dfrac{20}{\sqrt{64}} = 2.5$.

c. First, find $\bar{x}_0$ so that $P(\bar{x} < \bar{x}_0) = .10$.

$$P(\bar{x} < \bar{x}_0) = P\left(z < \dfrac{\bar{x}_0 - 50}{20/\sqrt{64}}\right) = P\left(z < \dfrac{\bar{x}_0 - 50}{2.5}\right) = P(z < z_0) = .10$$

From Table IV, Appendix A, $z_{.10} = -1.28$

$$z_0 = \dfrac{\bar{x}_0 - 50}{2.5} \Rightarrow -1.28 = \dfrac{\bar{x}_0 - 50}{2.5} \Rightarrow \bar{x}_0 = 46.8$$

Now, find $\beta = P(\bar{x} > 46.8 \text{ when } \mu = 45) = P\left(z > \dfrac{46.8 - 45}{20/\sqrt{64}}\right) = P(z > .72)$

$$= .5 - .2642 = .2358$$

d. Power $= 1 - \beta = 1 - .2358 = .7642$

8.97 a. The sampling distribution of $\bar{x}$ will be approximately normal (by the Central Limit Theorem) with $\mu_{\bar{x}} = \mu = 10$ and $\sigma_{\bar{x}} = \dfrac{\sigma}{\sqrt{n}} = \dfrac{1.00}{\sqrt{100}} = 0.1$.

b. The sampling distribution of $\bar{x}$ will be approximately normal (CLT) with $\mu_{\bar{x}} = \mu = 9.9$ and $\sigma_{\bar{x}} = \dfrac{\sigma}{\sqrt{n}} = \dfrac{1.00}{\sqrt{100}} = 0.1$.

c. First, find $\bar{x}_{O,L}$ and $\bar{x}_{O,U}$ such that $P(\bar{x} < \bar{x}_{O,L}) = P(\bar{x} > \bar{x}_{O,U}) = .025$

$$P(\bar{x} < \bar{x}_{O,L}) = P\left(z < \dfrac{\bar{x}_{O,L} - 10}{.1}\right) = P(z < z_{O,L}) = .025$$

From Table IV, Appendix A, $z_{O,L} = -1.96$

Thus, $z_{O,L} = \dfrac{\bar{x}_{O,L} - 10}{.1} \Rightarrow \bar{x}_{O,L} = -1.96(.1) + 10 = 9.804$

$$P(\bar{x} > \bar{x}_{O,U}) = P\left(z > \dfrac{\bar{x}_{O,U} - 10}{.1}\right) = P(z > z_{O,U}) = .025$$

Inferences Based on a Single Sample: Tests of Hypotheses

From Table IV, Appendix A, $z_{0,U} = 1.96$

Thus, $z_{0,U} = \dfrac{\bar{x}_{0,U} - 10}{.1} \Rightarrow \bar{x}_{0,U} = 1.96(.1) + 10 = 10.196$

Now, find $\beta = P(9.804 < \bar{x} < 10.196 \text{ when } \mu = 9.9)$

$$= P\left(\dfrac{9.804 - 9.9}{1/\sqrt{100}} < z < \dfrac{10.196 - 9.9}{1/\sqrt{100}}\right) = P(-.96 < z < 2.96)$$

$$= .3315 + .4985 = .8300$$

d. $\beta = P(9.804 < \bar{x} < 10.196 \text{ when } \mu = 10.1)$

$$= P\left(\dfrac{9.804 - 10.1}{1/\sqrt{100}} < z < \dfrac{10.196 - 10.1}{1/\sqrt{100}}\right) = P(-2.96 < z < .96)$$

$$= .4985 + .3315 = .8300$$

8.99   a.   First, find $\bar{x}_0$ such that $P(\bar{x} < \bar{x}_0) = .10$

$$P(\bar{x} < \bar{x}_0) = P\left(z < \dfrac{\bar{x}_0 - 16}{9.32/\sqrt{100}}\right) = P(z < z_0) = .10$$

From Table IV, Appendix A, $z_{.10} = -1.28$

Thus, $z_0 = \dfrac{\bar{x}_0 - 16}{9.32/\sqrt{100}} \Rightarrow \bar{x}_0 = -1.28(1.622) + 16 = 14.81$

For $\mu = 15.5$, the power is:

$$\text{Power} = P(\bar{x} < 14.81) = P\left(z < \dfrac{14.81 - 15.5}{9.32/\sqrt{100}}\right) = P(z < -.74) = .5 - .2704$$

$$= .2296$$

For $\mu = 15.0$, the power is:

$$\text{Power} = P(\bar{x} < 14.81) = P\left(z < \dfrac{14.81 - 15.0}{9.32/\sqrt{100}}\right) = P(z < -.20) = .5 - .0793$$

$$= .4207$$

For $\mu = 14.5$, the power is:

$$\text{Power} = P(\bar{x} < 14.81) = P\left(z < \dfrac{14.81 - 14.5}{9.32/\sqrt{100}}\right) = P(z < .33) = .5 - .1293$$

$$= .6293$$

For $\mu = 14.0$, the power is:

$$\text{Power} = P(\bar{x} < 14.81) = P\left(z < \frac{14.81 - 14.0}{9.32/\sqrt{100}}\right) = P(z < .87) = .5 - .3078$$
$$= .8078$$

For $\mu = 13.5$, the power is:

$$\text{Power} = P(\bar{x} < 14.81) = P\left(z < \frac{14.81 - 13.5}{9.32/\sqrt{100}}\right) = P(z < 1.41) = .5 + .4207$$
$$= .9207$$

b.   The plot of the power is:

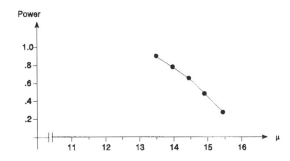

8.101   First, find $\bar{x}_0$ such that $P(\bar{x} < \bar{x}_0) = .05$.

$$P(\bar{x} < \bar{x}_0) = P\left(z < \frac{\bar{x}_0 - 10}{1.2/\sqrt{48}}\right) = P(z < z_0) = .05.$$

From Table IV, Appendix A, $z_0 = -1.645$.

Thus, $z_0 = \dfrac{\bar{x}_0 - 10}{1.2/\sqrt{48}} \Rightarrow \bar{x}_0 = -1.645(.173) + 10 = 9.715$

The probability of a Type II error is:

$$\beta = P(\bar{x} \geq 9.715 \,|\, \mu = 9.5) = P\left(z \geq \frac{9.715 - 9.5}{1.2/\sqrt{48}}\right) = P(z \geq 1.24) = .5 - .3295$$
$$= .1075$$

8.103   The conditions required for a valid test for σ^2 are:

1.   A random sample is selected from the target population.
2.   The population from which the sample is selected has a distribution that is approximately normal.

8.105   The statement "When the sample size n is large, no assumptions about the population are necessary to test the population variance σ^2" is false. The population from which the sample is drawn must be approximately normal.

8.107 a.   df $= n - 1 = 16 - 1 = 15$; reject H_0 if $\chi^2 < 6.26214$ or $\chi^2 > 27.4884$

   b.   df $= n - 1 = 23 - 1 = 22$; reject H_0 if $\chi^2 > 40.2894$

   c.   df $= n - 1 = 15 - 1 = 14$; reject H_0 if $\chi^2 > 21.0642$

   d.   df $= n - 1 = 13 - 1 = 12$; reject H_0 if $\chi^2 < 3.57056$

   e.   df $= n - 1 = 7 - 1 = 6$; reject H_0 if $\chi^2 < 1.63539$ or $\chi^2 > 12.5916$

   f.   df $= n - 1 = 25 - 1 = 24$; reject H_0 if $\chi^2 < 13.8484$

8.109 a. H_0: $\sigma^2 = 1$
             H_a: $\sigma^2 > 1$
             The test statistic is $\chi^2 = \dfrac{(100-1)(1.84)}{1} = 182.16$

             The rejection region requires $\alpha = .05$ in the upper tail of the χ^2 distribution with df $=$
             $n - 1 = 100 - 1 = 99$. From Table VII, Appendix A, $\chi^2_{.05} \approx 124.324$. The rejection
             region is $\chi^2 > 124.324$.

             Since the observed value of the test statistic falls in the rejection region ($\chi^2 = 182.16 >$
             124.324), H_0 is rejected. There is sufficient evidence to indicate the variance is larger
             than 1 at $\alpha = .05$.

   b.   In part **b** of Exercise 8.108, the test statistic was $\chi^2 = 11.04$. In Exercise 8.108, we did
        not reject H_0, but we did in this Exercise. As the sample size increases, it becomes
        easier to reject H_0.

8.111 a.   To determine if the true standard deviation of the point-spread errors exceed 15
             (variance exceeds 225), we test:

             H_0: $\sigma^2 = 225$
             H_a: $\sigma^2 > 225$

   b.   The test statistic is $\chi^2 = \dfrac{(n-1)s^2}{\sigma_0^2} = \dfrac{(240-1)13.3^2}{225} = 187.896$

   c.   The rejection region requires α in the upper tail of the χ^2 distribution with df $= n - 1$
        $= 240 - 1 = 239$. The maximum value of df in Table VII is 100. Thus, we cannot find
        the rejection region using Table VII. Using a statistical package, the p-value associated
        with $\chi^2 = 187.896$ is .9938.

        Since the p-value is so large, there is no evidence to reject H_0. There is insufficient
        evidence to indicate that the true standard deviation of the point-spread errors exceed 15
        for any reasonable value of α.

(Since the observed variance (or standard deviation) is less than the hypothesized value of the variance (or standard deviation) under H_0, there is no way H_0 will be rejected for any reasonable value of α.)

8.113   To determine if the variance of birthweights of babies delivered by cocaine-dependent women is less than 200,000, we test:

H_0: $\sigma^2 = 200,000$
H_a: $\sigma^2 < 200,000$

The test statistic is $\chi^2 = \dfrac{(n-1)s^2}{\sigma_0^2} = \dfrac{(16-1)410^2}{200,000} = 12.6075$

The rejection region requires $\alpha = .01$ in the lower tail of the χ^2 distribution with df $= n - 1 = 16 - 1 = 15$. From Table VII, Appendix A, $\chi_{.99}^2 = 5.22935$. The rejection region is $\chi^2 < 5.22935$.

Since the observed value of the test statistic does not fall in the rejection region ($\chi^2 = 12.6075$ $\not< 5.22935$), H_0 is not rejected. There is insufficient evidence to indicate that the variance of birthweights of babies delivered by cocaine-dependent women is less than 200,000 at $\alpha = .01$.

8.115   To determine if the standard deviation of the percent recovery using the new method differs from 15, we test:

H_0: $\sigma^2 = 15^2 = 225$
H_a: $\sigma^2 \neq 225$

The statistic is $\chi^2 = \dfrac{(n-1)s^2}{\sigma_0^2} = \dfrac{(7-1)9^2}{225} = 2.16$

The rejection region requires $\alpha/2 = .10/2 = .05$ in each tail of the χ^2 distribution with df $= n - 1 = 7 - 1 = 6$. From Table VII, Appendix A, $\chi_{.05}^2 = 12.5916$ and $\chi_{.95}^2 = 1.63539$. The rejection region is $\chi^2 < 1.63539$ or $\chi^2 > 12.5916$.

Since the observed value of the test statistic does not fall in the rejection region ($\chi^2 = 2.16 \not< 1.63539$ and $\chi^2 = 2.16 \not> 12.5916$), H_0 is not rejected. There is insufficient evidence to indicate that the standard deviation of the percent recovery using the new method differs from 15 (or the variance differs from 225) at $\alpha = .10$.

8.117   a.   Some preliminary calculations:

$$s^2 = \dfrac{\sum x^2 - \dfrac{(\sum x)^2}{n}}{n-1} = \dfrac{29345.78 - \dfrac{(342.6)^2}{4}}{4-1} = .6967$$

To determine if the variation in the CO_2 concentration measurements using the LRM method differs from 1, we test:

H_0: $\sigma^2 = 1$
H_a: $\sigma^2 \neq 1$

The test statistic is $\chi^2 = \dfrac{(n-1)s^2}{\sigma_0^2} = \dfrac{(4-1).6967^2}{1} = 2.09$

Since no α was given we will use $\alpha = .05$. The rejection region requires $\alpha/2 = .05/2 = .025$ in each tail of the χ^2 distribution with df $= n - 1 = 4 - 1 = 3$. From Table VII, Appendix A, $\chi_{.025}^2 = 9.34840$ and $\chi_{.975}^2 = 0.215795$. The rejection region is $\chi^2 < 0.215795$ or $\chi^2 > 9.34840$.

Since the observed value of the test statistic does not fall in the rejection region ($\chi^2 = 2.09 \not< 0.215795$ and $\chi^2 = 2.09 \not> 9.34840$), H_0 is not rejected. There is insufficient evidence to indicate that the variation in the CO_2 concentration measurements using the LRM method differs from 1 at $\alpha = .05$.

b.   We must assume that the population of CO_2 amounts are normally distributed.

8.119   The smaller the p-value associated with a test of hypothesis, the stronger the support for the **alternative** hypothesis. The p-value is the probability of observing your test statistic or anything more unusual, given the null hypothesis is true. If this value is small, it would be very unusual to observe this test statistic if the null hypothesis were true. Thus, it would indicate the alternative hypothesis is true.

8.121   The elements of the test of hypothesis that should be specified prior to analyzing the data are: null hypothesis, alternative hypothesis, and significance level.

8.123   The larger the p-value associated with a test of hypothesis, the stronger the support for the **null** hypothesis. The p-value is the probability of observing your test statistic or anything more unusual, given the null hypothesis is true. If this value is large, it would not be very unusual to observe this test statistic if the null hypothesis were true. Thus, it would lend support that the null hypothesis is true.

8.125   a. H_a: $p = .35$
            H_a: $p < .35$

The test statistic is $z = \dfrac{\hat{p} - p_0}{\sqrt{\dfrac{p_0 q_0}{n}}} = \dfrac{.29 - .35}{\sqrt{\dfrac{.35(.65)}{200}}} = -1.78$

The rejection region requires $\alpha = .05$ in the lower tail of the z distribution. From Table IV, Appendix A, $z_{.05} = 1.645$. The rejection region is $z < -1.645$.

Since the observed value of the test statistic falls in the rejection region ($z = -1.78 < -1.645$), H_0 is rejected. There is sufficient evidence to indicate $p < .35$ at $\alpha = .05$.

b. H_0: $p = .35$
H_a: $p \neq .35$

The test statistic is $z = -1.78$ (from **a**).

The rejection region requires $\alpha/2 = .05/2 = .025$ in each tail of the z distribution. From Table IV, Appendix A, $t_{.025} = 1.96$. The rejection region is $z < -1.96$ or $z > 1.96$.

Since the observed value of the test statistic does not fall in the rejection region ($z = -1.78 \not< -1.96$), H_0 is not rejected. There is insufficient evidence to indicate p is different from .35 at $\alpha = .05$.

c. For confidence coefficient .95, $\alpha = .05$ and $\alpha/2 = .025$. From Table IV, Appendix A, $z_{.025} = 1.96$. The confidence interval is:

$$\hat{p} \pm z_{.025}\sqrt{\frac{\hat{p}\hat{q}}{n}} \Rightarrow .29 \pm 1.96\sqrt{\frac{.29(.71)}{200}} \Rightarrow .29 \pm .063 \Rightarrow (.227, .353)$$

d. For confidence coefficient .99, $\alpha = .01$ and $\alpha/2 = .005$. From Table IV, Appendix A, $z_{.005} = 2.58$. The confidence interval is:

$$\hat{p} \pm z_{.005}\sqrt{\frac{\hat{p}\hat{q}}{n}} \Rightarrow .29 \pm 2.58\sqrt{\frac{.29(.71)}{200}} \Rightarrow .29 \pm .083 \Rightarrow (.207, .373)$$

e. $n = \frac{(z_{\alpha/2})^2 pq}{B^2} = \frac{2.58^2(.29)(.71)}{.05^2} = 548.2 \approx 549$

(We will use $\hat{p} = .29$ to estimate the value of p.)

8.127 a. H_0: $\sigma^2 = 30$
H_a: $\sigma^2 > 30$

The test statistic is $\chi^2 = \frac{(n-1)s^2}{\sigma_0^2} = \frac{(41-1)(6.9)^2}{30} = 63.48$

The rejection region requires $\alpha = .05$ in the upper tail of the χ^2 distribution with df $= n - 1 = 40$. From Table VII, Appendix A, $\chi^2_{.05} = 55.7585$. The rejection region is $\chi^2 > 55.7585$.

Since the observed value of the test statistic falls in the rejection region ($\chi^2 = 63.48 > 55.7585$), H_0 is rejected. There is sufficient evidence to indicate the variance is larger than 30 at $\alpha = .05$.

b. H_0: $\sigma^2 = 30$
H_a: $\sigma^2 \neq 30$

The test statistic is $\chi^2 = 63.48$ (from part **a**).

The rejection region requires $\alpha/2 = .05/2 = .025$ in each tail of the χ^2 distribution with df $= n - 1 = 40$. From Table VII, Appendix A, $\chi^2_{.025} = 59.3417$ and $\chi^2_{.975} = 24.4331$. The rejection region is $\chi^2 < 24.4331$ or $\chi^2 > 59.3417$.

Since the observed value of the test statistic falls in the rejection region ($\chi^2 = 63.48 > 59.3417$), H_0 is rejected. There is sufficient evidence to indicate the variance is not 30 at $\alpha = .05$.

8.129   a.   Since the company must give proof the drug is safe, the null hypothesis would be the drug is unsafe. The alternative hypothesis would be the drug is safe.

b.   A Type I error would be concluding the drug is safe when it is not safe. A Type II error would be concluding the drug is not safe when it is. α is the probability of concluding the drug is safe when it is not. β is the probability of concluding the drug is not safe when it is.

c.   In this problem, it would be more important for α to be small. We would want the probability of concluding the drug is safe when it is not to be as small as possible.

8.131   a.   To determine if the true mean score of all sleep-deprived subjects is less than 80, we test:

$$H_0:\ \mu = 80$$
$$H_a:\ \mu < 80$$

The test statistic is $t = \dfrac{\bar{x}_0 - \mu_0}{s/\sqrt{n}} = \dfrac{63 - 80}{17/\sqrt{12}} = -3.46$

The rejection region requires $\alpha = .05$ in the lower tail of the t distribution with df $= n - 1 = 12 - 1 = 11$. From Table VI, Appendix A, $t_{.05} = 1.796$. The rejection region is $t < -1.796$.

Since the observed value of the test statistic falls in the rejection region ($t = -3.46 < -1.796$), H_0 is rejected. There is sufficient evidence to indicate that the true mean score of all sleep-deprived subjects is less than 80 at $\alpha = .05$.

b.   We must assume that the overall test scores of sleep-deprived students are normally distributed.

8.133   a.   Let $p =$ proportion of the subjects who felt that the masculinization of face shape decreased attractiveness of the male face. If there is no preference for the unaltered or morphed male face, then $p = .5$.

For this problem, $\hat{p} = x/n = 58/67 = .866$.

First we check to see if the normal approximation is adequate:

$$p_0 \pm 3\sigma_{\hat{p}} \Rightarrow p_0 \pm 3\sqrt{\dfrac{p_0 q_0}{n}} \Rightarrow .5 \pm 3\sqrt{\dfrac{.5(.5)}{67}} \Rightarrow .5 \pm .183 \Rightarrow (.317, .683)$$

Since the interval falls completely in the interval $(0, 1)$, the normal distribution will be adequate.

To determine if the subjects showed a preference for either the unaltered or morphed face, we test:

H_0: $p = .5$
H_a: $p \neq .5$

b.   The test statistic is $z = \dfrac{\hat{p} - p_0}{\sqrt{\dfrac{p_0 q_0}{n}}} = \dfrac{.866 - .50}{\sqrt{\dfrac{.50(.50)}{67}}} = 5.99$

c.   By definition, the p-value is the probability of observing our test statistic or anything more unusual, given H_0 is true. For this problem, $p = P(z \leq -5.99) + P(z \geq 5.99)$ $= .5 - P(-5.99 < z < 0) + .5 - P(0 < z < 5.99) \approx .5 - .5 + .5 - .5 = 0$. This corresponds to what is listed in the Exercise.

d.   The rejection region requires $\alpha/2 = .01/2 = .005$ in each tail of the z distribution. From Table IV, Appendix A, $z_{.005} = 2.575$. The rejection region is $z < -2.575$ or $z > 2.575$.

Since the observed value of the test statistic falls in the rejection region ($z = 5.99 > 2.575$), H_0 is rejected. There is sufficient evidence to indicate that the subjects showed a preference for either the unaltered or morphed face at $\alpha = .01$.

8.135   a.   If we wish to test the research hypothesis that the mean GHQ score for all unemployed men exceeds 10, we test:

H_0: $\mu = 10$
H_a: $\mu > 10$

This is a one-tailed test. We are only interested in rejecting H_0 if the mean GHQ score for all unemployed men is greater than 10.

b.   The rejection region requires $\alpha = .05$ in the upper tail of the z distribution. From Table IV, Appendix A, $z_{.05} = 1.645$. The rejection region is $z > 1.645$.

c.   The test statistic is $z = \dfrac{\bar{x} - \mu_0}{\sigma_{\bar{x}}} = \dfrac{10.94 - 10.0}{5.10 / \sqrt{49}} = 1.29$

Since the observed value of the test statistic does not fall in the rejection region ($z = 1.29 \not> 1.645$), H_0 is not rejected. There is insufficient evidence to indicate the mean GHQ score for all unemployed men is greater than 10 at $\alpha = .05$.

8.137   Using MINITAB, the descriptive statistics are:

Descriptive Statistics: Weight

Variable	N	N*	Mean	SE Mean	StDev	Minimum	Q1	Median	Q3	Maximum
Weight	16	0	1.373	0.258	1.034	0.201	0.475	1.347	2.009	3.751

To determine whether the mean weight in the crops of all spinifex pigeons differs from 1 gram, we test:

H_0: $\mu = 1$
H_a: $\mu \neq 1$

The test statistic is $t = \dfrac{\bar{x} - \mu_0}{s/\sqrt{n}} = \dfrac{1.373 - 1}{1.034/\sqrt{16}} = 1.44$

The rejection region requires $\alpha/2 = .05/2 = .025$ in each tail of the t distribution with df = $n - 1 = 16 - 1 = 15$. From Table VI, Appendix A, $t_{.025} = 2.131$. The rejection region is $t < -2.131$ and $t > 2.131$.

Since the observed value of the test statistic does not fall in the rejection region ($t = 1.44 \not> 2.131$), H_0 is not rejected. There is insufficient evidence to indicate the mean weight in the crops of all spinifex pigeons differs from 1 gram at $\alpha = .05$.

We must assume that the population being sampled from is normal. The stem-and-leaf display of the data is:

Stem-and-Leaf Display: Weight

```
Stem-and-leaf of Weight   N  = 16
Leaf Unit = 0.10

  4   0   2234
  7   0   588
 (4)  1   3344
  5   1   6
  4   2   1
  3   2   59
  1   3
  1   3   7
```

The data do not appear to be mound-shaped. Thus, the test above may not be valid.

8.139   a.   To determine if the true mean inbreeding coefficient μ for this species of wasp exceeds 0, we test:

H_0: $\mu = 0$
H_a: $\mu > 0$

The test statistic is $z = \dfrac{\bar{x} - \mu_0}{\sigma_{\bar{x}}} = \dfrac{.044 - 0}{.884/\sqrt{197}} = 0.70$

The rejection region requires $\alpha = .05$ in the upper tail of the z distribution. From Table IV, Appendix A, $z_{.05} = 1.645$. The rejection region is $z > 1.645$.

Since the observed value of the test statistic does not fall in the rejection region ($z = 0.70 \not> 1.645$), H_0 is not rejected. There is insufficient evidence to indicate that the true mean inbreeding coefficient μ for this species of wasp exceeds 0 at $\alpha = .05$.

b.   This result agrees with that of Exercise 7.97. The confidence interval in Exercise 7.97 was $(-.118, .206)$. Since this interval contains 0, there is no evidence to indicate that the mean is different from 0. This is the same conclusion that was reached in part **a**.

8.141   a.   To determine if the production process should be halted, we test:

H_0: $\mu = 3$
H_a: $\mu > 3$

where μ = mean amount of PCB in the effluent.

The test statistic is $z = \dfrac{\bar{x} - \mu_0}{\sigma_{\bar{x}}} = \dfrac{3.1 - 3}{.5/\sqrt{50}} = 1.41$

The rejection region requires $\alpha = .01$ in the upper tail of the z distribution. From Table IV, Appendix A, $z_{.01} = 2.33$. The rejection region is $z > 2.33$.

Since the observed value of the test statistic does not fall in the rejection region, ($z = 1.41 \not> 2.33$), H_0 is not rejected. There is insufficient evidence to indicate the mean amount of PCB in the effluent is more than 3 parts per million at $\alpha = .01$. Do not halt the manufacturing process.

b.   As plant manager, I do not want to shut down the plant unnecessarily. Therefore, I want $\alpha = P(\text{shut down plant when } \mu = 3)$ to be small.

8.143   a.   No, it increases the risk of falsely rejecting H_0, i.e., closing the plant unnecessarily.

b.   First, find $\bar{x}_0$ such that $P(\bar{x} > \bar{x}_0) = P(z > z_0) = .05$.

From Table IV, Appendix A, $z_0 = 1.645$

$$z = \frac{\bar{x} - \mu_0}{\sigma/\sqrt{n}} \Rightarrow 1.645 = \frac{\bar{x}_0 - 3}{.5/\sqrt{50}} \Rightarrow \bar{x}_0 = 3.116$$

Then, compute

$$\beta = P(\bar{x}_0 \le 3.116 \text{ when } \mu = 3.1) = P\left(z \le \frac{3.116 - 3.1}{.5/\sqrt{50}}\right) = P(z \le .23)$$

$$= .5 + .0910 = .5910$$

Power $= 1 - \beta = 1 - .5910 = .4090$

c.   The power of the test increases as α increases.

8.145   First, check to see if the normal approximation is adequate:

$$p_0 \pm 3\sigma_{\hat{p}} \Rightarrow p_0 \pm 3\sqrt{\frac{p_0 q_0}{n}} \Rightarrow .5 \pm 3\sqrt{\frac{(.5)(.5)}{2,237}} \Rightarrow .5 \pm .032 \Rightarrow (.468, .532)$$

Since the interval falls completely in the interval $(0, 1)$, the normal distribution will be adequate.

$$\hat{p} = \frac{x}{n} = \frac{1,630}{2,237} = .729$$

To determine if the true percentage of engineering Ph.D. degrees awarded to foreign nationals exceeds 50%, we test:

H_0: $p = .5$
H_a: $p > .5$

The test statistic is $z = \dfrac{\hat{p} - p_0}{\sqrt{\dfrac{p_0 q_0}{n}}} = \dfrac{.729 - .5}{\sqrt{\dfrac{(.5)(.5)}{2,237}}} = 21.66$

The rejection region requires $\alpha = .01$ in the upper tail of the z distribution. From Table IV, Appendix A, $z_{.01} = 2.33$. The rejection region is $z > 2.33$.

Since the observed value of the test statistic falls in the rejection region ($z = 21.66 > 2.33$), H_0 is rejected. There is sufficient evidence to indicate that the true percentage of engineering Ph.D. degrees awarded to foreign nationals exceeds 50% at $\alpha = .01$.

8.147   a.   A Type I error is rejecting the null hypothesis when it is true. In this problem, we would be concluding that the individual is a liar when, in fact, the individual is telling the truth.

A Type II error is accepting the null hypothesis when it is false. In this problem, we would be concluding that the individual is telling the truth when, in fact, the individual is a liar.

b.   The probability of a Type I error would be the probability of concluding the individual is a liar when he/she is telling the truth. From the problem, it stated that the polygraph would indicate that of 500 individuals who were telling the truth, 185 would be liars. Thus, an estimate of the probability of a Type I error would be $185/500 = .37$.

The probability of a Type II error would be the probability of concluding the individual is telling the truth when he/she is a liar. From the problem, it stated that the polygraph would indicate that of 500 individuals who were liars, 120 would be telling the truth. Thus, an estimate of the probability of a Type II error would be $120/500 = .24$.

8.149 a.   To determine if the mean size of all California homes built in late 1999 exceeds the national average, we test:

H_0: $\mu = 2{,}230$
H_a: $\mu > 2{,}230$

The test statistic is $z = \dfrac{\bar{x} - \mu_0}{\sigma_{\bar{x}}} = \dfrac{2{,}347 - 2{,}230}{\dfrac{257}{\sqrt{100}}} = 4.55$

The rejection region requires $\alpha = .01$ in the upper tail of the z distribution. From Table IV, Appendix A, $z_{.01} = 2.33$. The rejection region is $z > 2.33$.

Since the observed value of the test statistic falls in the rejection region ($z = 4.55 > 2.33$), H_0 is rejected. There is sufficient evidence to indicate the mean size of all California homes built in late 1999 exceeds the national average at $\alpha = .01$.

b.   First, we must find $\bar{x}_0$ such that $P(\bar{x} > \bar{x}_0) = .01$.

$$P(\bar{x} > \bar{x}_0) = P\left(z > \dfrac{\bar{x}_0 - 2{,}230}{\dfrac{257}{\sqrt{100}}} \right) = P(z > z_0) = .01. \text{ From Table IV, Appendix A, } z_0 = 2.33.$$

Thus, $z_0 = \dfrac{\bar{x}_0 - 2{,}230}{\dfrac{257}{\sqrt{100}}} = 2.33 \Rightarrow \bar{x}_0 = 2.33\left(\dfrac{257}{\sqrt{100}} \right) + 2{,}230 = 2{,}289.881$.

For $\mu_0 = 2{,}330$,

$$\beta = P(\bar{x} < 2{,}289.881) = P\left(z < \dfrac{2{,}289.881 - 2{,}330}{\dfrac{257}{\sqrt{100}}} \right)$$

$$= P(z < -1.56) = .5 - .4406 = .0594$$

This type error is a Type II error.

c.   For $\mu_0 = 2{,}330$,

$$\alpha = P(\bar{x} > 2{,}289.881) = P\left(z > \dfrac{2{,}289.881 - 2{,}330}{\dfrac{257}{\sqrt{100}}} \right)$$

$$= P(z > -1.56) = .5 + .4406 = .9406$$

This type error is a Type I error.

d.   First, find $\bar{x}_0$ such that $P(\bar{x} > \bar{x}_0) = .01$.

$$P(\bar{x} > \bar{x}_0) = P\left(z > \frac{\bar{x}_0 - 2,230}{\frac{257}{\sqrt{100}}}\right) = P(z > z_0) = .01$$

From Table IV, Appendix A, $z_0 = 2.33$.

Thus, $z_0 = \dfrac{\bar{x} - 2,230}{\frac{257}{\sqrt{100}}} \Rightarrow \bar{x}_0 = 2.33(25.7) + 2,230 = 2,289.881$

For $\mu_a = 2,330$, the power is:

$$\text{Power} = P(\bar{x} > 2,289.881) = P\left(z > \frac{2,289.881 - 2,330}{\frac{257}{\sqrt{100}}}\right) = P(z > -1.56) = .5 + .4406 = .9406$$

e.   For $\mu_a = 2,280$, the power is:

$$\text{Power} = P(\bar{x} > 2,289.881) = P\left(z > \frac{2,289.881 - 2,280}{\frac{257}{\sqrt{100}}}\right) = P(z > .38) = .5 - .1480 = .3520$$

8.151 a.   We want to show that more than 17,000 of the 18,200 signatures are valid. Thus, we want to show that the proportion of valid signatures is greater than $17,000/18,200 = .934$.

From the Exercise, $\hat{p} = 98/100 = .98$.

First, we check to see if the normal approximation is adequate:

$$p_0 \pm 3\sigma_{\hat{p}} \Rightarrow p_0 \pm 3\sqrt{\frac{p_0 q_0}{n}} \Rightarrow .934 \pm 3\sqrt{\frac{.934(.066)}{100}} \Rightarrow .934 \pm .074 \Rightarrow (.860, 1.008)$$

Since the interval does not fall completely in the interval $(0, 1)$, the normal distribution may not be adequate.

To determine if more than .934 of the signatures are valid, we test:

H_0: $p = .934$
H_a: $p > .934$

The test statistic is $z = \dfrac{\hat{p} - p_0}{\sqrt{\dfrac{p_0 q_0}{n}}} = \dfrac{.98 - .934}{\sqrt{\dfrac{.934(.066)}{100}}} = 1.85$

Since no α is given in the problem, we will choose $\alpha = .05$. The rejection region requires $\alpha = .05$ in the upper tail of the z distribution. From Table IV, Appendix A, $z_{.05} = 1.645$. The rejection region is $z > 1.645$.

Since the observed value of the test statistic falls in the rejection region ($z = 1.85 > 1.645$), H_0 is rejected. There is sufficient evidence to indicate that the true proportion of valid signatures is greater than .934 at $\alpha = .05$. This indicates that more than 17,000 of the 18,200 signatures are valid.

b. We want to show that more than 16,000 of the 18,200 signatures are valid. Thus, we want to show that the proportion of valid signatures is greater than $16,000/18,200 = .879$.

Again, from the Exercise, $\hat{p} = 98/100 = .98$.

First we check to see if the normal approximation is adequate:

$$p_0 \pm 3\sigma_{\hat{p}} \Rightarrow p_0 \pm 3\sqrt{\dfrac{p_0 q_0}{n}} \Rightarrow .879 \pm 3\sqrt{\dfrac{.879(.121)}{100}} \Rightarrow .879 \pm .098 \Rightarrow (.781, .977)$$

Since the interval is completely in the interval $(0, 1)$, the normal distribution will be adequate.

To determine if more than .879 of the signatures are valid, we test:

H_0: $p = .879$
H_a: $p > .879$

The test statistic is $z = \dfrac{\hat{p} - p_0}{\sqrt{\dfrac{p_0 q_0}{n}}} = \dfrac{.98 - .879}{\sqrt{\dfrac{.879(.121)}{100}}} = 3.09$

Since no α is given in the problem, we will choose $\alpha = .05$. The rejection region requires $\alpha = .05$ in the upper tail of the z distribution. From Table IV, Appendix A, $z_{.05} = 1.645$. The rejection region is $z > 1.645$.

Since the observed value of the test statistic falls in the rejection region ($z = 3.09 > 1.645$), H_0 is rejected. There is sufficient evidence to indicate that the true proportion of valid signatures is greater than .879 at $\alpha = .05$. This indicates that more than 16,000 of the 18,200 signatures are valid.

Inferences Based on Two Samples: Confidence Intervals and Tests of Hypotheses

9.1 When the samples are large, the sampling distribution of $(\bar{x}_1 - \bar{x}_2)$ is approximately normal by the Central Limit Theorem. The mean of the sampling distribution is $(\mu_1 - \mu_2)$ and the standard deviation is $\sqrt{\dfrac{\sigma_1^2}{n_1} + \dfrac{\sigma_2^2}{n_2}}$.

9.3   a.   No. Both populations must be normal.

      b.   No. Both populations variances must be equal.

      c.   No. Both populations must be normal.

      d.   Yes.

      e.   No. Both populations must be normal.

9.5 The confidence interval for $(\mu_1 - \mu_2)$ is $(-10, -4)$. The correct inference is **b** – $(\mu_1 < \mu_2)$. Since all the values in the interval are negative, there is evidence that $(\mu_1 < \mu_2)$.

9.7   a. $\mu_{\bar{x}_1} = \mu_1 = 14$

$$\sigma_{\bar{x}_1} = \frac{\sigma_1}{\sqrt{n_1}} = \frac{4}{\sqrt{100}} = .4$$

      b. $\mu_{\bar{x}_2} = \mu_2 = 10$

$$\sigma_{\bar{x}_2} = \frac{\sigma_2}{\sqrt{n_2}} = \frac{3}{\sqrt{100}} = .3$$

      c. $\mu_{\bar{x}_1 - \bar{x}_2} = \mu_1 - \mu_2 = 14 - 10 = 4$

$$\sigma_{\bar{x}_1 - \bar{x}_2} = \sqrt{\frac{\sigma_1^2}{n_1} + \frac{\sigma_2^2}{n_2}} = \sqrt{\frac{4^2}{100} + \frac{3^2}{100}} = \sqrt{\frac{25}{100}} = .5$$

      d.   Since $n_1 \geq 30$ and $n_2 \geq 30$, the sampling distribution of $\bar{x}_1 - \bar{x}_2$ is approximately normal by the Central Limit Theorem.

9.9   Some preliminary calculations are:

$$\bar{x}_1 = \frac{\sum x_1}{n_1} = \frac{11.8}{5} = 2.36 \qquad s_1^2 = \frac{\sum x_1^2 - \frac{\left(\sum x_1\right)^2}{n_1}}{n_1 - 1} = \frac{30.78 - \frac{(11.8)^2}{5}}{5-1} = .733$$

$$\bar{x}_2 = \frac{\sum x_2}{n_2} = \frac{14.4}{4} = 3.6 \qquad s_2^2 = \frac{\sum x_2^2 - \frac{\left(\sum x_2\right)^2}{n_2}}{n_2 - 1} = \frac{53.1 - \frac{(14.4)^2}{4}}{4-1} = .42$$

a. $s_p^2 = \frac{(n_1 - 1)s_1^2 + (n_2 - 1)s_2^2}{n_1 + n_2 - 2} = \frac{(5-1).773 + (4-1).42}{5+4-2} = \frac{4.192}{7} = .5989$

b. $H_0: \mu_1 - \mu_2 = 0$
      $H_a: \mu_1 - \mu_2 < 0$

The test statistic is $t = \dfrac{(\bar{x}_1 - \bar{x}_2) - D_0}{\sqrt{s_p^2\left(\dfrac{1}{n_1} + \dfrac{1}{n_2}\right)}} = \dfrac{(2.36 - 3.6) - 0}{\sqrt{.5989\left(\dfrac{1}{5} + \dfrac{1}{4}\right)}} = \dfrac{-1.24}{.5191} = -2.39$

The rejection region requires $\alpha = .10$ in the lower tail of the t distribution with df = $n_1 + n_2 - 2 = 5 + 4 - 2 = 7$. From Table VI, Appendix A, $t_{.10} = 1.415$. The rejection region is $t < -1.415$.

Since the test statistic falls in the rejection region ($t = -2.39 < -1.415$), H_0 is rejected. There is sufficient evidence to indicate that $\mu_2 > \mu_1$ at $\alpha = .10$.

c.   A small sample confidence interval is needed because $n_1 = 5 < 30$ and $n_2 = 4 < 30$.

For confidence coefficient .90, $\alpha = .10$ and $\alpha/2 = .05$. From Table VI, Appendix A, with df = $n_1 + n_2 - 2 = 5 + 4 - 2 = 7$, $t_{.05} = 1.895$. The 90% confidence interval for $(\mu_1 - \mu_2)$ is:

$$(\bar{x}_1 - \bar{x}_2) \pm t_{.05}\sqrt{s_p^2\left(\frac{1}{n_1} + \frac{1}{n_2}\right)} \Rightarrow (2.36 - 3.6) \pm 1.895\sqrt{.5989\left(\frac{1}{5} + \frac{1}{4}\right)}$$

$$\Rightarrow -1.24 \pm .98 \Rightarrow (-2.22, -0.26)$$

d.   The confidence interval in part **c** provides more information about $(\mu_1 - \mu_2)$ than the test of hypothesis in part **b**. The test in part **b** only tells us that μ_2 is greater than μ_1. However, the confidence interval estimates what the difference is between μ_1 and μ_2.

9.11   a.   The p-value is $p = .115$.

Since the p-value is not small, there is no evidence to reject H_0. There is no evidence to indicate that the population means are different for $\alpha \le .10$.

b.   The p-value would be half of the p-value in part **a**. The p-value = $1/2(.1150) = .0575$.

There is no evidence to reject H_0 for $\alpha = .05$. There is no evidence to indicate that the mean for population 1 is less than the mean for population 2 for $\alpha = .05$.

There is evidence to reject H_0 for $\alpha > .0575$. There is evidence to indicate that the mean for population 1 is less than the mean for population 2 for $\alpha > .0575$.

9.13 a. Let μ_1 = mean number of books read by students who earned an "A" grade and μ_2 = mean number of books read by students who earned a "B or C" grade. The parameter of interest for this problem is $\mu_1 - \mu_2$, the difference in the mean number of books read between the students who received an "A" grade and those who received a "B or C" grade.

b. Using MINITAB, the descriptive statistics are:

Descriptive Statistics: No. Books

Variable	Grade2	N	N*	Mean	SE Mean	StDev	Minimum	Q1	Median	Q3
No. Books	A	8	0	37.00	3.08	8.70	24.00	31.00	36.50	41.50
	B-C	6	0	24.50	3.48	8.53	16.00	19.00	21.50	31.00

Variable	Grade2	Maximum
No. Books	A	53.00
	B-C	40.00

Some preliminary calculations are:

$$s_p^2 = \frac{(n_1 - 1)s_1^2 + (n_2 - 1)s_2^2}{n_1 + n_2 - 2} = \frac{(8-1)8.7^2 + (6-1)8.53^2}{8+6-2} = 74.470$$

For confidence coefficient .95, $\alpha = .05$ and $\alpha/2 = .05/2 = .025$. From Table VI, Appendix A, with df $= n_1 + n_2 - 2 = 8 + 6 - 2 = 12$, $t_{.025} = 2.179$. The confidence interval is:

$$(\bar{x}_1 - \bar{x}_2) \pm t_{.025}\sqrt{s_p^2\left(\frac{1}{n_1} + \frac{1}{n_2}\right)} \Rightarrow (37 - 24.5) \pm 2.179\sqrt{74.47\left(\frac{1}{8} + \frac{1}{6}\right)}$$

$$\Rightarrow 12.5 \pm 10.155 \Rightarrow (2.345, \ 22.655)$$

c. We are 95% confident that the true difference in the mean number of books read between the students who received an "A" grade and those who received a "B or C" grade is between 2.345 and 22.655.

d. In Exercise 2.31, the stem-and-leaf display indicated that the students who earned A's tended to read more books than those who earned B's or C's. This agrees with the confidence interval in part b. Because all the values in the confidence interval are positive, the mean number of books read by the students earning A's is larger than the mean number read by students earning B's or C's.

9.15   a.   Let μ_1 = mean height of Australian boys who repeated a grade and μ_2 = mean height of Australian boys who never repeated a grade.
To determine if the average height of Australian boys who repeated a grade is less than the average height of boys who never repeated, we test:

H_0: $\mu_1 = \mu_2$
H_a: $\mu_1 < \mu_2$

   b.   The test statistic is $z = \dfrac{\bar{x}_1 - \bar{x}_2}{\sqrt{\dfrac{s_1^2}{n_1} + \dfrac{s_2^2}{n_2}}} = \dfrac{-.04 - .30}{\sqrt{\dfrac{1.17^2}{86} + \dfrac{.97^2}{1346}}} = -2.64$

The rejection region requires $\alpha = .05$ in the lower tail of the z distribution. From Table IV, Appendix A, $z_{.05} = 1.645$. The rejection region is $z < -1.645$.

Since the observed value of the test statistic falls in the rejection region ($z = -2.64 < -1.645$), H_0 is rejected. There is sufficient evidence to indicate that the average height of Australian boys who repeated a grade is less than the average height of boys who never repeated at $\alpha = .05$.

   c.   Let μ_1 = mean height of Australian girls who repeated a grade and μ_2 = mean height of Australian girls who never repeated a grade.

To determine if the average height of Australian girls who repeated a grade is less than the average height of girls who never repeated, we test:

H_0: $\mu_1 = \mu_2$
H_a: $\mu_1 < \mu_2$

The test statistic is $z = \dfrac{\bar{x}_1 - \bar{x}_2}{\sqrt{\dfrac{s_1^2}{n_1} + \dfrac{s_2^2}{n_2}}} = \dfrac{.26 - .22}{\sqrt{\dfrac{.94^2}{43} + \dfrac{1.04^2}{1366}}} = .27$

The rejection region requires $\alpha = .05$ in the lower tail of the z distribution. From Table IV, Appendix A, $z_{.05} = 1.645$. The rejection region is $z < -1.645$.

Since the observed value of the test statistic does not fall in the rejection region ($z = .27 \nless -1.645$), H_0 is not rejected. There is insufficient evidence to indicate that the average height of Australian girls who repeated a grade is less than the average height of girls who never repeated at $\alpha = .05$.

9.17   a.   Let μ_1 = mean response of noontime watchers and μ_2 = mean response of non-noontime watchers.

To determine whether the mean response of noontime watchers differs from the mean response of non-noontime watchers, we test:

H_0: $\mu_1 = \mu_2$
H_a: $\mu_1 \neq \mu_2$

Inferences Based on Two Samples: Confidence Intervals and Tests of Hypotheses

b. Since the observed p-value is less than α ($p = .02 < \alpha = .05$), H_0 is rejected. There is sufficient evidence to indicate the mean response of noontime watchers differs from the mean response of non-noontime watchers at $\alpha = .05$.

c. Since the observed p-value is not less than α ($p = .02 > \alpha = .01$), H_0 is not rejected. There is insufficient evidence to indicate the mean response of noontime watchers differs from the mean response of non-noontime watchers at $\alpha = .01$.

d. The 2 sample means are 3.3 and 3.4. Even though there is a statistical difference between the 2 populations means, there is little practical difference. The sample means are very similar.

9.19   Let μ_1 = mean FNE scores for bulimic students and μ_2 = mean FNE score for normal students.

Some preliminary calculations are:

$$\overline{x}_1 = \frac{\sum x_1}{n_1} = \frac{196}{11} = 17.82$$

$$s_1^2 = \frac{\sum x_1^2 - \frac{\left(\sum x_1\right)^2}{n_1}}{n_1 - 1} = \frac{3,734 - \frac{196^2}{11}}{11 - 1} = 24.1636$$

$$s_1 = \sqrt{s_1^2} = \sqrt{24.1636} = 4.916$$

$$\overline{x}_2 = \frac{\sum x_2}{n_2} = \frac{198}{14} = 14.14$$

$$s_2^2 = \frac{\sum x_2^2 - \frac{\left(\sum x_2\right)^2}{n_2}}{n_2 - 1} = \frac{3,164 - \frac{198^2}{14}}{14 - 1} = 27.9780$$

$$s_2 = \sqrt{s_2^2} = \sqrt{27.9780} = 5.289$$

$$s_p^2 = \frac{(n_1 - 1)s_1^2 + (n_2 - 1)s_2^2}{n_1 + n_2 - 2} = \frac{(11 - 1)24.1636 + (14 - 1)27.9780}{11 + 14 - 2} = 26.3196$$

a. For confidence coefficient .95, $\alpha = .05$ and $\alpha/2 = .05/2 = .025$. From Table VI, Appendix A, with df $= n_1 + n_2 - 2 = 11 + 14 - 2 = 23$, $t_{.025} = 2.069$. The confidence interval is:

$$\left(\overline{x}_1 - \overline{x}_2\right) \pm t_{.025}\sqrt{s_p^2\left(\frac{1}{n_1} + \frac{1}{n_2}\right)} \Rightarrow (17.82 - 14.14) \pm 2.069\sqrt{26.3196\left(\frac{1}{11} + \frac{1}{14}\right)}$$

$$\Rightarrow 3.68 \pm 4.277 \Rightarrow (-.597, 7.957)$$

We are 95% confident that the difference in mean FNE scores for bulimic and normal students is between −.597 and 7.957,

b. We must assume that the distribution of FNE scores for the bulimic students and the distribution of the FNE scores for the normal students are normally distributed. We must also assume that the variances of the two populations are equal.

Both sample distributions look somewhat mound-shaped and the sample variances are fairly close in value. Thus, both assumptions appear to be reasonably satisfied.

9.21   a.   Using MINITAB, the output for comparing the mean level of family involvement in science homework assignments of TIPS and ATIPS students is:

```
Two sample T for GSHWS

COND          N      Mean     StDev    SE Mean
ATIPS         98     1.43     1.06      0.11
TIPS         128     2.55     1.27      0.11

95% CI for mu (ATIPS) - mu (TIPS ): ( -1.43,  -0.82)
T-Test mu (ATIPS) = mu (TIPS ) (vs not =): T = -7.24 P = 0.0000 DF = 222
```

Let μ_1 = mean level of involvement in science homework assignments for TIPS students and μ_2 = mean level of involvement in science homework assignments for ATIPS students.
To compare the mean level of family involvement in science homework assignments of TIPS and ATIPS students, we test:

H_0: $\mu_1 = \mu_2$
H_a: $\mu_1 \neq \mu_2$

From the printout, the test statistic is $t = -7.24$ and the p-value is $p = 0.0000$. Since the p-value is less than α ($p = 0.0000 < .05$), H_0 is rejected. There is sufficient evidence to indicate a difference in the mean level of family involvement in science homework assignments between TIPS and ATIPS students at $\alpha = .05$.

b.   Using MINITAB, the output for comparing the mean level of family involvement in mathematics homework assignments of TIPS and ATIPS students is:

```
Two sample T for MTHHWS

COND          N      Mean     StDev    SE Mean
ATIPS         98     1.48     1.22      0.12
TIPS         128     1.56     1.27      0.11

95% CI for mu (ATIPS) - mu (TIPS ): ( -0.41,   0.25)
T-Test mu (ATIPS) = mu (TIPS ) (vs not =): T = -0.50  P = 0.62  DF = 212
```

Let μ_1 = mean level of involvement in mathematics homework assignments for TIPS students and μ_2 = mean level of involvement in mathematics homework assignments for ATIPS students.

To compare the mean level of family involvement in mathematics homework assignments of TIPS and ATIPS students, we test:

$H_0: \mu_1 = \mu_2$
$H_a: \mu_1 \neq \mu_2$

From the printout, the test statistic is $t = -0.50$ and the p-value is $p = 0.62$. Since the p-value is not less than α ($p = 0.62 > .05$), H_0 is not rejected. There is insufficient evidence to indicate a difference in the mean level of family involvement in mathematics homework assignments between TIPS and ATIPS students at $\alpha = .05$.

c. Using MINITAB, the output for comparing the mean level of family involvement in language arts homework assignments of TIPS and ATIPS students is:

```
Two sample T for LAHWS

COND           N      Mean     StDev    SE Mean
ATIPS          98     1.01     1.09      0.11
TIPS           128    1.20     1.12      0.099

95% CI for mu (ATIPS) - mu (TIPS ): ( -0.48,   0.106)
T-Test mu (ATIPS) = mu (TIPS ) (vs not =): T = -1.25   P = 0.21   DF = 211
```

Let μ_1 = mean level of involvement in language arts homework assignments for TIPS students and μ_2 = mean level of involvement in language arts homework assignments for ATIPS students.
To compare the mean level of family involvement in language arts homework assignments of TIPS and ATIPS students, we test:

$H_0: \mu_1 = \mu_2$
$H_a: \mu_1 \neq \mu_2$

From the printout, the test statistic is $t = -1.25$ and the p-value is $p = 0.21$. Since the p-value is not less than α ($p = 0.21 > .05$), H_0 is not rejected. There is insufficient evidence to indicate a difference in the mean level of family involvement in language arts homework assignments between TIPS and ATIPS students at $\alpha = .05$.

d. Since both sample sizes are greater than 30, the only assumption necessary is:

1. The samples are random and independent.

From the information given, there is no reason to dispute this assumption.

9.23 Using MINITAB, the descriptive statistics are:

Descriptive Statistics: Species

```
Variable  Region        N   N*    Mean   SE Mean   StDev   Minimum    Q1    Median
Species   Dry Steppe    5   0    14.00    9.53     21.31     3.00    3.00     5.00
          Gobi Desert   6   0    11.83    7.44     18.21     4.00    4.00     4.50

Variable  Region            Q3   Maximum
Species   Dry Steppe     29.50     52.00
          Gobi Desert    16.00     49.00
```

Let μ_1 = average number of ant species found in the Dry Steppe and μ_2 = average number of ant species found in the Gobi Desert.

$$s_p^2 = \frac{(n_1-1)s_1^2 + (n_2-1)s_2^2}{n_1+n_2-2} = \frac{(5-1)21.31^2 + (6-1)18.21^2}{5+6-2} = 386.0539$$

To determine if there is a difference in the average number of ant species found at sites in the two regions, we test:

H_0: $\mu_1 = \mu_2$
H_a: $\mu_1 \neq \mu_2$

The test statistic is $t = \dfrac{(\bar{x}_1 - \bar{x}_2) - D_o}{\sqrt{s_p^2\left(\dfrac{1}{n_1} + \dfrac{1}{n_2}\right)}} = \dfrac{(14-11.83)-0}{\sqrt{386.0539\left(\dfrac{1}{5} + \dfrac{1}{6}\right)}} = 0.18$

The rejection region requires $\alpha/2 = .05/2 = .025$ in each tail of the t-distribution with df $= n_1 + n_2 - 2 = 5 + 6 - 2 = 9$. From Table VI, Appendix B, $t_{.025} = 2.262$. The rejection region is $t < -2.262$ or $t > 2.262$.

Since the observed value of the test statistic does not fall in the rejection region ($t = 0.18 \ngtr 2.262$), H_0 is not rejected. There is insufficient evidence to indicate a difference in the average number of ant species found at sites in the two regions at $\alpha = .05$.

9.25   a.   Let μ_1 = mean MFS score for the violent event group and μ_2 = mean MFS score for the avoided-violent event group. The target parameter of interest is $\mu_1 - \mu_2$ = difference in the mean MFS score between the 2 groups.

b.   We are given the sample mean scores for the two groups. However, in order to determine if there is a difference in the 2 population means, we also need to know the population standard deviations for the 2 groups or the sample standard deviations for the 2 groups. This information was not provided.

c.   The p-value of the test is

$$p = P(z \leq -1.21) + P(z \geq 1.21) = (.5 - .3869) + (.5 - .3869) = .1131 + .1131 = .2262$$

d.   Since the observed p-value is greater than α ($p = .2262 > \alpha = .10$), H_0 is not rejected. There is insufficient evidence to indicate a difference in the mean MFS score between the violent event group and the avoided-violent event group at $\alpha = .10$.

Inferences Based on Two Samples: Confidence Intervals and Tests of Hypotheses

9.27 Let μ_1 = mean DIQ score for SLI children and μ_2 = mean DIQ score for YND children.

Some preliminary calculations are:

$$\bar{x}_1 = \frac{\sum x_1}{n_1} = \frac{936}{10} = 93.6$$

$$s_1^2 = \frac{\sum x_1^2 - \frac{\left(\sum x_1\right)^2}{n_1}}{n_1 - 1} = \frac{88352 - \frac{(936)^2}{10}}{10 - 1} = 82.4889$$

$$\bar{x}_2 = \frac{\sum x_2}{n_2} = \frac{953}{10} = 95.3$$

$$s_2^2 = \frac{\sum x_2^2 - \frac{\left(\sum x_2\right)^2}{n_2}}{n_1 - 1} = \frac{91329 - \frac{(953)^2}{10}}{10 - 1} = 56.4556$$

$$s_p^2 = \frac{(n_1 - 1)s_1^2 + (n_2 - 1)^2 s_2^2}{n_1 + n_2 - 2} = \frac{(10 - 1)82.4889 + (10 - 1)56.4556}{10 + 10 - 2} = 69.4723$$

To determine if the mean DIQ scores differ for the two groups, we test:

H_0: $\mu_1 - \mu_2 = 0$
H_a: $\mu_1 - \mu_2 \neq 0$

The test statistic is $t = \dfrac{\bar{x}_1 - \bar{x}_2 - 0}{\sqrt{s_p^2\left(\dfrac{1}{n_1} + \dfrac{1}{n_2}\right)}} = \dfrac{(93.6 - 95.3) - 0}{\sqrt{69.4723\left(\dfrac{1}{10} + \dfrac{1}{10}\right)}} = -0.46$

The rejection region requires $\alpha/2 = .10/2 = .05$ in each tail of the t distribution with df $= n_1 + n_2 - 2 = 10 + 10 - 2 = 18$. From Table VI, Appendix A, $t_{.05} = 1.734$. The rejection region is $t < -1.734$ or $t > 1.734$.

Since the observed value of the test statistic does not fall in the rejection region ($t = -.46 \not< -1.734$), H_0 is not rejected. There is insufficient evidence to indicate that the mean DIQ scores differ for the two groups at $\alpha = .10$.

9.29 a. From the information given, we have no idea what the standard deviations are. Whether the population means are different or not depends on how variable the data are.

b. Let μ_1 = mean pain intensity rating for blacks and μ_2 = mean pain intensity rating for whites.

To determine if blacks, on average, have a higher pain intensity rating than whites, we test:
$H_0: \mu_1 = \mu_2$
$H_a: \mu_1 > \mu_2$

The rejection region requires $\alpha = .05$ in the upper tail of the z distribution. From Table IV, Appendix A, $z_{.05} = 1.645$. Thus, in order to reject H_0, the test statistic would have to be greater than 1.645.

Substituting known values into the test statistic, we can solve for s_p.

$$z = \frac{\bar{x}_1 - \bar{x}_2}{\sqrt{s_p^2\left(\dfrac{1}{n_1} + \dfrac{1}{n_2}\right)}} > 1.645$$

$$\Rightarrow \frac{8.2 - 6.9}{\sqrt{s_p^2\left(\dfrac{1}{55} + \dfrac{1}{159}\right)}} > 1.645$$

$$\Rightarrow 1.3 > 1.645(s_p)\sqrt{\left(\dfrac{1}{55} + \dfrac{1}{159}\right)}$$

$$\Rightarrow \frac{1.3}{1.645(.1564)} > s_p$$

$$\Rightarrow 5.053 > s_p$$

Thus, if both s_1 and s_2 were less than 5.053, then we would conclude that blacks, on average would have a higher pain intensity than whites. (It is possible that either s_1 or s_2 could be greater than 5.053 and we would still reject H_0. As long as $s_p < 5.053$, we would reject H_0.)

c. From part **b**, we know we would reject H_0 if $s_p < 5.053$. Thus, we would not reject H_0 if $s_p \geq 5.053$. This could happen if both s_1 and s_2 are greater than 5.053. (It is possible that either s_1 or s_2 could be less than 5.053 and we would still reject H_0. As long as $s_p \geq 5.053$, we would reject H_0.)

9.31 In a paired difference experiment, the observations should be paired before collecting the data.

9.33 a. The rejection region requires $\alpha = .05$ in the upper tail of the t distribution with df $= n_D - 1 = 10 - 1 = 9$. From Table VI, Appendix A, $t_{.05} = 1.833$. The rejection region is $t > 1.833$.

b. From Table VI, with df $= n_D - 1 = 20 - 1 = 19$, $t_{.10} = 1.328$. The rejection region is $t > 1.328$.

c. From Table VI, with df $= n_D - 1 = 5 - 1 = 4$, $t_{.025} = 2.776$. The rejection region is $t > 2.776$.

d. From Table VI, with df $= n_D - 1 = 9 - 1 = 8$, $t_{.01} = 2.896$. The rejection region is $t > 2.896$.

9.35 a.

Pair	Difference
1	3
2	2
3	2
4	4
5	0
6	1

$$\bar{x}_D = \frac{\sum x_D}{n} = \frac{12}{6} = 2$$

$$s_D^2 = \frac{\sum x_D^2 - \frac{\left(\sum x_D\right)^2}{n_D}}{n_D - 1} = \frac{\left(34 - \frac{(12)^2}{6}\right)}{5} = 2$$

b. $\mu_D = \mu_1 - \mu_2$

c.   For confidence coefficient .95, $\alpha = .05$ and $\alpha/2 = .025$. From Table VI, Appendix A, with df = $n_D - 1 = 6 - 1 = 5$, $t_{.025} = 2.571$. The confidence interval is:

$$\bar{x}_D \pm t_{\alpha/2}\frac{s_D}{\sqrt{n_D}} \Rightarrow 2 \pm 2.571\frac{\sqrt{2}}{\sqrt{6}} \Rightarrow 2 \pm 1.484 \Rightarrow (.516, 3.484)$$

d. H_0: $\mu_D = 0$
     H_a: $\mu_D \neq 0$

The test statistic is $t = \dfrac{\bar{x}_D}{s_D/\sqrt{n_D}} = \dfrac{2}{\sqrt{2}/\sqrt{6}} = 3.46$

The rejection region requires $\alpha/2 = .05/2 = .025$ in each tail of the t distribution with df = $n_D - 1 = 6 - 1 = 5$. From Table VI, Appendix A, $t_{.025} = 2.571$. The rejection region is $t < -2.571$ or $t > 2.571$.

Since the observed value of the test statistic falls in the rejection region ($t = 3.46 > 2.571$), H_0 is rejected. There is sufficient evidence to indicate that the mean difference is different from 0 at $\alpha = .05$.

9.37 a. H_0: $\mu_D = 10$
          H_a: $\mu_D \neq 10$

The test statistic is $z = \dfrac{\bar{x}_D - 0}{s_D / \sqrt{n_D}} = \dfrac{11.7 - 10}{6 / \sqrt{40}} = 1.79$

The rejection region requires $\alpha/2 = .05/2 = .025$ in each tail of the z distribution. From Table IV, Appendix A, $z_{.025} = 1.96$. The rejection region is $z < -1.96$ or $z > 1.96$.

Since the observed value of the test statistic does not fall in the rejection region ($z = 1.79 \not> 1.96$), H_0 is not rejected. There is insufficient evidence to indicate the difference in the population means is different from 10 at $\alpha = .05$.

b. The p-value is

$$p = P(z \leq -1.79) + P(z \geq 1.79) = (.5 - .4633) + (.5 - .4633) = .0367 + .0367 = .0734$$

9.39 a. Let μ_1 = mean BOLD score for the first session and μ_2 = mean BOLD score when the placebo was applied. The target parameter is $\mu_D = \mu_1 - \mu_2$, the difference in the mean BOLD scores between the first session and the session involving the placebo.

b. A paired difference design was used to collect the data. Each experimental person had two observations measured on it.

c. To determine if there was a placebo effect, we test:

H_o: $\mu_D = 0$
H_a: $\mu_D > 0$

d. The test statistic is $t = \dfrac{\bar{x}_D - 0}{s_D / \sqrt{n_D}} = \dfrac{0.21 - 0}{.47 / \sqrt{24}} = 2.19$

Since no α value was given, we will use $\alpha = .05$. The rejection region requires $\alpha = .05$ in the upper tail of the t distribution with df $= n_D - 1 = 24 - 1 = 23$. From Table VI, Appendix A, $t_{.025} = 1.714$. The rejection region is $t > 1.714$.

Since the observed value of the test statistic falls in the rejection region ($t = 2.19 > 1.714$), H_0 is rejected. There is sufficient evidence to indicate that there is a placebo effect at $\alpha = .05$.

e. Since the p-value is less than α ($p = .02 < \alpha = .05$), H_0 is rejected. There is sufficient evidence to indicate that there is a placebo effect at $\alpha = .05$.

9.41 a. First, some preliminary calculations:

| | Testosterone Levels | | |
Patient	Pretreatment	After 6 months of Depro-Provera	D = P – A
1	849	96	753
2	903	41	862
3	890	31	859
4	1,092	124	968
5	362	46	316
6	900	53	847
7	1,006	113	893
8	672	174	498

$$\bar{x}_D = \frac{\sum x_D}{n_D} = \frac{5{,}996}{8} = 749.5$$

$$s_D^2 = \frac{\sum x_D^2 - \frac{\left(\sum x_D\right)^2}{n_D}}{n_D - 1} = \frac{4{,}847{,}676 - \frac{5{,}996^2}{8}}{8 - 1} = 50{,}524.857$$

For confidence coefficient .99, $\alpha = .01$ and $\alpha/2 = .01/2 = .005$. From Table VI, Appendix A, with df $= n_D - 1 = 8 - 1 = 7$, $t_{.005} = 3.499$. The confidence interval is:

$$\bar{x}_D \pm t_{.005} \frac{s_D}{\sqrt{n_D}} \Rightarrow 749.5 \pm 3.499 \frac{\sqrt{50{,}524.857}}{\sqrt{8}} \Rightarrow 749.5 \pm 278.068$$

$$\Rightarrow (471.432, 1027.568)$$

We are 99% confident that the true mean difference between the pretreatment and after-treatment testosterone levels of young male TBI patients is between 471.432 and 1,027.568.

b. Since 0 is not in the confidence interval, there is evidence that there is a difference in the testosterone levels pre and post treatment. Thus, there is evidence that Depo-Provera is effective in reducing testosterone levels in young male TBI patients.

9.43 a. Let $\mu_1 =$ mean reading response times for the tongue-twister list and $\mu_2 =$ mean reading response times for the control list. Then $\mu_D = \mu_1 - \mu_2$.

To compare the mean reading response times for the tongue-twister and control lists, we test:

H_0: $\mu_D = 0$
H_a: $\mu_D \neq 0$

The test statistic is $z = \dfrac{\bar{x}_D - 0}{s_D / \sqrt{n}} = \dfrac{.25 - 0}{.78 / \sqrt{42}} = 2.08$

The p-value is $P(z \leq -2.08) + P(z \geq 2.08) = (.5000 - .4812) + (.5000 - .4812) = .0188 + .0188 = .0376$.

c. Since the observed p-value is less than α $(p = .0376 < .05)$, H_0 is rejected. There is sufficient evidence to conclude that the mean reading response times differ for the tongue-twister and control lists at $\alpha = .05$.

9.45   a.   Since all the data were collected from twins, the observations from each pair are not independent of each other. Thus, the data were collected as paired data. If the data are collected as paired data, they must be analyzed as paired data.

b.   Let μ_1 = mean level of overall leisure activity for the control group and μ_2 = mean level of overall leisure activity for the demented group. The target parameter is $\mu_D = \mu_1 - \mu_2$, the difference in the mean level of overall leisure activity for the control group and the demented group.

Using MINITAB, the descriptive statistics are:

Descriptive Statistics: Diff

Variable	N	N*	Mean	SE Mean	StDev	Minimum	Q1	Median	Q3
Diff	107	0	1.953	0.975	10.082	-28.000	-4.000	2.000	9.000

Variable	Maximum
Diff	29.000

We will use a 95% confidence interval to estimate the difference in the mean level of leisure activity between the control group and the demented group. For confidence coefficient .95, $\alpha = .05$ and $\alpha/2 = .05/2 = .025$. From Table IV, appendix A, $z_{.025} = 1.96$. The 95% confidence interval is:

$$\bar{x}_D \pm z_{.025}\frac{s_D}{\sqrt{n_D}} \Rightarrow 1.953 \pm 1.96\frac{10.082}{\sqrt{107}} \Rightarrow 1.953 \pm 1.910 \Rightarrow (0.043,\ 3.863)$$

We are 95% confident that the difference in the mean level of leisure activity between the control group and the demented group is between 0.043 and 3.863. Since 0 is not contained in this interval, there is evidence of a difference in the mean level of leisure activity between the control group and the demented group at $\alpha = .05$. Since all the values are positive, there is evidence that the mean level of leisure activity for the control group is larger than that for the demented group.

9.47   Let μ_1 = mean homophone confusion errors for time 1 and μ_2 = mean homophone confusion errors for time 2. Then $\mu_D = \mu_1 - \mu_2$.

To determine if Alzheimer's patients show a significant increase in mean homophone confusion errors over time, we test:

H_0: $\mu_D = 0$
H_a: $\mu_D \neq 0$

The test statistic is t = -2.306.

The p-value is $p = .0163$. Since the p-value is small, there is sufficient evidence to indicate an increase in mean homophone confusion errors from time 1 to time 2

We must assume that the population of differences is normally distributed and that the sample was randomly selected. A stem-and-leaf display of the data indicate that the data are mound-shaped. It appears that these assumptions are valid.

9.49   a.   The distribution of x_1 is binomial with n_1 trials and the probability of success, p_1.
            The distribution of x_2 is binomial with n_2 trials and the probability of success, p_2.

        b.   For large samples, the sampling distribution of $(\hat{p}_1 - \hat{p}_2)$ is approximately normal with

            mean $(p_1 - p_2)$, and standard deviation $\sigma_{\hat{p}_1 - \hat{p}_2} = \sqrt{\dfrac{p_1 q_1}{n_1} + \dfrac{p_2 q_2}{n_2}}$.

9.51   The conditions required for a large-sample inference about $(p_1 - p_2)$ are:

        1.   The two samples are randomly selected in an independent manner from the two
              target populations.
        2.   The sample sizes, n_1 and n_2, are both large so that the sampling distribution of
              $(\hat{p}_1 - \hat{p}_2)$ will be approximately normal. (This condition will be satisfied if both
              intervals, $\hat{p}_1 \pm 3\sigma_{\hat{p}_1}$ and $\hat{p}_2 \pm 3\sigma_{\hat{p}_2}$, fall between 0 and 1.)

9.53   a.   The rejection region requires $\alpha = .01$ in the lower tail of the z distribution. From Table
            IV, Appendix A, $z_{.01} = 2.33$. The rejection region is $z < -2.33$.

        b.   The rejection region requires $\alpha = .025$ in the lower tail of the z distribution. From Table
            IV, Appendix A, $z_{.025} = 1.96$. The rejection region is $z < -1.96$.

        c.   The rejection region requires $\alpha = .05$ in the lower tail of the z distribution. From Table
            IV, Appendix A, $z_{.05} = 1.645$. The rejection region is $z < -1.645$.

        d.   The rejection region requires $\alpha = .10$ in the lower tail of the z distribution. From Table
            IV, Appendix A, $z_{.10} = 1.28$. The rejection region is $z < -1.28$.

9.55   For confidence coefficient .95, $\alpha = 1 - .95 = .05$ and $\alpha/2 = .05/2 = .025$. From Table IV,
        Appendix A, $z_{.025} = 1.96$. The 95% confidence interval for $p_1 - p_2$ is approximately:

        a. $(\hat{p}_1 - \hat{p}_2) \pm z_{\alpha/2} \sqrt{\dfrac{\hat{p}_1 \hat{q}_1}{n_1} + \dfrac{\hat{p}_2 \hat{q}_2}{n_2}}$

              $\Rightarrow (.65 - .58) \pm 1.96 \sqrt{\dfrac{.65(1-.65)}{400} + \dfrac{.58(1-.58)}{400}} \Rightarrow .07 \pm .067 \Rightarrow (.003, .137)$

        b. $(\hat{p}_1 - \hat{p}_2) \pm z_{\alpha/2} \sqrt{\dfrac{\hat{p}_1 \hat{q}_1}{n_1} + \dfrac{\hat{p}_2 \hat{q}_2}{n_2}}$

              $\Rightarrow (.31 - .25) \pm 1.96 \sqrt{\dfrac{.31(1-.31)}{180} + \dfrac{.25(1-.25)}{250}} \Rightarrow .06 \pm .086 \Rightarrow (-026, .146)$

        c. $(\hat{p}_1 - \hat{p}_2) \pm z_{\alpha/2} \sqrt{\dfrac{\hat{p}_1 \hat{q}_1}{n_1} + \dfrac{\hat{p}_2 \hat{q}_2}{n_2}}$

              $\Rightarrow (.46 - .61) \pm 1.96 \sqrt{\dfrac{.46(1-.46)}{100} + \dfrac{.61(1-.61)}{120}} \Rightarrow -.15 \pm .131 \Rightarrow (-.281, -.019)$

9.57 H_0: $(p_1 - p_2) = .1$

H_a: $(p_1 - p_2) > .1$

Since D_0 is not equal to 0, the test statistic is:

$$z = \frac{(\hat{p}_1 - \hat{p}_2) - D_0}{\sqrt{\dfrac{p_1 q_1}{n_1} + \dfrac{p_2 q_2}{n_2}}} = \frac{(\hat{p}_1 - \hat{p}_2) - D_0}{\sqrt{\dfrac{\hat{p}_1 \hat{q}_1}{n_1} + \dfrac{\hat{p}_2 \hat{q}_2}{n_2}}} = \frac{(.4 - .2) - .1}{\sqrt{\dfrac{.4(1 - .4)}{50} + \dfrac{.2(1 - .2)}{60}}} = \frac{.1}{.0864} = 1.16$$

The rejection region requires $\alpha = .05$ in the upper tail of the z distribution. From Table IV, Appendix A, $z_{.05} = 1.645$. The rejection region is $z > 1.645$.

Since the observed value of the test statistic does not fall in the rejection region ($z = 1.16 \not> 1.645$), H_0 is not rejected. There is insufficient evidence to show $(p_1 - p_2) > .1$ at $\alpha = .05$.

9.59 a. $\hat{p}_1 = \dfrac{x_1}{n_1} = \dfrac{29}{189} = .153$

b. $\hat{p}_2 = \dfrac{x_2}{n_2} = \dfrac{32}{149} = .215$

c.   For confidence coefficient .90, $\alpha = .10$ and $\alpha/2 = .10/2 = .05$. From Table IV, Appendix A, $z_{.05} = 1.645$. The 90% confidence interval is:

$$(\hat{p}_1 - \hat{p}_2) \pm z_{.05}\sqrt{\frac{\hat{p}_1 \hat{q}_1}{n_1} + \frac{\hat{p}_2 \hat{q}_2}{n_2}} \Rightarrow (.153 - .215) \pm 1.645\sqrt{\frac{.153(.847)}{189} + \frac{.215(.785)}{149}}$$

$$\Rightarrow -.062 \pm .070 \Rightarrow (-.132, \quad .008)$$

d.   We are 90% confident that the difference in the true proportion of super-experienced bidders who fall prey to the winner's curse and the true proportion of less-experienced bidders who fall prey to the winner's curse is between −0.132 and 0.008.

9.61 a.   The observed proportion of St. John's wort patients who were in remission is:

$$\hat{p}_1 = \frac{x_1}{n_1} = \frac{14}{98} = .143$$

b.   The observed proportion of placebo patients who were in remission is:

$$\hat{p}_2 = \frac{x_2}{n_2} = \frac{5}{102} = .049$$

c.	To determine if the proportion of St. John wort patients in remission exceeds the proportion of placebo patients in remission, we test:

H_0: $p_1 = p_2$
H_a: $p_1 > p_2$

The test statistic is $z = \dfrac{\hat{p}_1 - \hat{p}_2}{\sqrt{\hat{p}\hat{q}\left(\dfrac{1}{n_1} + \dfrac{1}{n_2}\right)}} = \dfrac{.143 - .049}{\sqrt{.095(.905)\left(\dfrac{1}{98} + \dfrac{1}{102}\right)}} = 2.27$

The rejection region requires $\alpha = .01$ in the upper tail of the z distribution. From Table IV, Appendix A, $z_{.01} = 2.33$. The rejection region is $z > 2.33$.

Since the observed value of the test statistic does not fall in the rejection region ($z = 2.27 \not> 2.33$), H_0 is not rejected. There is insufficient evidence to indicate the proportion of St. John wort patients in remission exceeds the proportion of placebo patients in remission at $\alpha = .01$.

d.	The hypotheses and test statistic are the same as in part **c**.

The rejection region requires $\alpha = .10$ in the upper tail of the z distribution. From Table IV, Appendix A, $z_{.10} = 1.28$. The rejection region is $z > 1.28$.

Since the observed value of the test statistic falls in the rejection region ($z = 2.27 > 1.28$), H_0 is rejected. There is sufficient evidence to indicate the proportion of St. John wort patients in remission exceeds the proportion of placebo patients in remission $\alpha = .10$.

e.	By changing the value of α in this problem, the conclusion changes. When α is small ($\alpha = .01$), we did not reject H_0. When α increases ($\alpha = .10$), we rejected H_0. As α increases, the chance of making a Type I error increase, but the chance of a Type II error decrease.

9.63	Let p_1 = proportion of larvae that died in containers containing high carbon dioxide levels and p_2 = proportion of larvae that died in containers containing normal carbon dioxide levels. The parameter of interest for this problem is $p_1 - p_2$, or the difference in the death rates for the two groups.

Some preliminary calculations are:

$\hat{p}_1 = \dfrac{x_1 + x_2}{n_1 + n_2} = \dfrac{.10(80) + .50(80)}{80 + 80} = .075 \qquad \hat{q} = 1 - \hat{p} = 1 - .075 = .925$

To determine if an increased level of carbon dioxide is effective in killing a higher percentage of leaf-eating larvae, we test:

H_0: $p_1 - p_2 = 0$
H_a: $p_1 - p_2 > 0$

The test statistic is $z = \dfrac{(\hat{p}_1 - \hat{p}_2) - 0}{\sqrt{\hat{p}\hat{q}\left(\dfrac{1}{80} + \dfrac{1}{80}\right)}} = \dfrac{(.10 - .05) - 0}{\sqrt{.075(.925)\left(\dfrac{1}{80} + \dfrac{1}{80}\right)}} = 1.201$

The rejection region requires $\alpha = .01$ in the upper tail of the z distribution. From Table IV, Appendix A, $z_{.01} = 2.33$. The rejection region is $z > 2.33$.

Since the observed value of the test statistic does not fall in the rejection region ($z = 1.201 \ngtr 2.33$), H_0 is not rejected. There is insufficient evidence to indicate that an increased level of carbon dioxide is effective in killing a higher percentage of leaf-eating larvae at $\alpha = .01$.

9.65   Let p_1 = recall rate of the 60 to 72 year-old seniors and p_2 = recall rate of the 73 to 83 year-old seniors.

Some preliminary calculations are:

$\hat{p}_1 = \dfrac{x_1}{n_1} = \dfrac{31}{40} = .775$ $\qquad$ $\hat{p}_2 = \dfrac{x_2}{n_2} = \dfrac{22}{40} = .55$ $\qquad$ $\hat{p} = \dfrac{x_1 + x_2}{n_1 + n_2} = \dfrac{31 + 22}{40 + 40} = .6625$

To determine if the recall rates of the two groups differ, we test:

H_0: $p_1 = p_2$
H_a: $p_1 \neq p_2$

The test statistic is $z = \dfrac{(\hat{p}_1 - \hat{p}_2) - 0}{\sqrt{\hat{p}\hat{q}\left(\dfrac{1}{n_1} + \dfrac{1}{n_2}\right)}} = \dfrac{(.775 - .55) - 0}{\sqrt{.6625(.3375)\left(\dfrac{1}{40} + \dfrac{1}{40}\right)}} = 2.13$

The rejection region requires $\alpha/2 = .05/2 = .025$ in each tail of the z distribution. From Table IV, Appendix A, $z_{.025} = 1.96$. The rejection region is $z < -1.96$ or $z > 1.96$.

Since the observed value of the test statistic falls in the rejection region ($z = 2.13 > 1.96$), H_0 is rejected. There is sufficient evidence to indicate the recall rates of the two groups differ at $\alpha = .05$.

9.67 Let p_1 = proportion of flightless birds of extinct species and p_2 = proportion of flightless birds of non-extinct species.

Some preliminary calculations are:

$$\hat{p}_1 = \frac{x_1}{n_1} = \frac{21}{38} = .553 \qquad \hat{p}_2 = \frac{x_2}{n_2} = \frac{7}{78} = .090 \qquad \hat{p} = \frac{x_1 + x_2}{n_1 + n_2} = \frac{21 + 7}{38 + 78} = .241$$

To determine if the proportion of flightless birds for the extinct species is greater than that for the non-extinct species, we test:

H_0: $p_1 = p_2$
H_a: $p_1 > p_2$

The test statistic is $z = \dfrac{(\hat{p}_1 - \hat{p}_2) - 0}{\sqrt{\hat{p}\hat{q}\left(\dfrac{1}{n_1} + \dfrac{1}{n_2}\right)}} = \dfrac{(.553 - .090) - 0}{\sqrt{.241(.759)\left(\dfrac{1}{38} + \dfrac{1}{78}\right)}} = 5.47$

The rejection region requires $\alpha = .01$ in the upper tail of the z distribution. From Table IV, Appendix A, $z_{.01} = 2.33$. The rejection region is $z > 2.33$.

Since the observed value of the test statistic falls in the rejection region ($z = 5.47 > 2.33$), H_0 is rejected. There is sufficient evidence to indicate the proportion of flightless birds for the extinct species is greater than that for the non-extinct species $\alpha = .01$.

9.69 a. Let p_1 = true proportion of women who acknowledge having food cravings and p_2 = true proportion of men who acknowledge having food cravings.

To determine if the true proportion of women who acknowledge having food cravings exceeds the corresponding proportion of men, we test:

H_o: $p_1 = p_2$
H_a: $p_1 > p_2$

The test statistic would be $z = \dfrac{(\hat{p}_1 - \hat{p}_2) - 0}{\sqrt{\hat{p}\hat{q}\left(\dfrac{1}{n_1} + \dfrac{1}{n_2}\right)}}$

The rejection region requires $\alpha = .01$ in the upper tail of the z distribution. From Table IV, Appendix A, $z_{.01} = 2.33$. The rejection region is $z > 2.33$.

We need to find $n_1 = n_2$ so that the test statistic falls in the rejection region or $z > 2.33$. We know that $\hat{p}_1 = .97$ and $\hat{p}_2 = .67$. Assuming $n_1 = n_2 = n$,

$$\hat{p} = \frac{\hat{p}_1 + \hat{p}_2}{2} = \frac{.97 + .67}{2} = .82$$

$$z = \frac{(\hat{p}_1 - \hat{p}_2) - 0}{\sqrt{\hat{p}\hat{q}\left(\frac{1}{n_1} + \frac{1}{n_2}\right)}} = \frac{(.97 - .67) - 0}{\sqrt{.82(.18)\left(\frac{1}{n} + \frac{1}{n}\right)}} = 2.33$$

$$\Rightarrow .30 = 2.33\sqrt{.82(.18)\left(\frac{1}{n} + \frac{1}{n}\right)}$$

$$\Rightarrow .30 = 2.33\sqrt{.1476\left(\frac{2}{n}\right)} \Rightarrow .30 = 2.33\sqrt{\frac{.2952}{n}}$$

$$\Rightarrow .30^2 n = 2.33^2(.2952) \Rightarrow n = \frac{2.33^2(.2952)}{.3^2} = 17.807 \approx 18$$

We would need at least 18 observations from each group.

b.   This study involved Students at McMaster University students. It is very dangerous to generalize the results of this study to the general adult population of North America. The sample of students used may not be representative of the population of interest.

9.71   We can estimate the values of p_1 and p_2 based on prior samples, by using an educated guess of the values, or most conservatively, estimating p_1 and p_2 with .5.

9.73 $$n_1 = n_2 = \frac{(z_{\alpha/2})^2(\sigma_1^2 + \sigma_2^2)}{(SE)^2}$$

For confidence coefficient .95, $\alpha = 1 - .95 = .05$ and $\alpha/2 = .05/2 = .025$. From Table IV, Appendix A, $z_{.025} = 1.96$.

$$n_1 = n_2 = \frac{1.96^2(15+15)}{2.2^2} = 23.8 \approx 24$$

9.75   a.   For confidence coefficient .99, $\alpha = 1 - .99 = .01$ and $\alpha/2 = .01/2 = .005$. From Table IV, Appendix A, $z_{.005} = 2.58$.

$$n_1 = n_2 = \frac{(z_{\alpha/2})^2(p_1 q_1 + p_2 q_2)}{(SE)^2} = \frac{2.58^2(.4(1-.4) + .7(1-.7))}{.01^2}$$

$$= \frac{2.99538}{.0001} = 29,953.8 \approx 29,954$$

b.   For confidence coefficient .90, $\alpha = 1 - .90 = .10$ and $\alpha/2 = .10/2 = .05$. From Table IV, Appendix A, $z_{.05} = 1.645$. Since we have no prior information about the proportions, we use $p_1 = p_2 = .5$ to get a conservative estimate. For a width of .05, the standard error is .5.

$$n_1 = n_2 = \frac{(z_{\alpha/2})^2(p_1 q_1 + p_2 q_2)}{(SE)^2} = \frac{(1.645)^2(.5(1-.5) + .5(1-.5))}{.025^2} = 2164.82 \approx 2165$$

c. From part **b**, $z_{.05} = 1.645$.

$$n_1 = n_2 = \frac{(z_{\alpha/2})^2 (p_1 q_1 + p_2 q_2)}{(SE)^2} = \frac{1.645^2 (.2(1-.2)+.3(1-.3))}{.03^2}$$

$$= \frac{1.00123}{.0009} = 1112.48 \approx 1113$$

9.77 For confidence coefficient .95, $\alpha = .05$ and $\alpha/2 = .05/2 = .025$. From Table IV, Appendix A, $z_{.025} = 1.96$.

$$n_1 = n_2 = \frac{(z_{\alpha/2})^2 (\sigma_B^2 + \sigma_N^2)}{(SE)} = \frac{1.96^2 (25 + 25)}{2^2} = 48.02 \approx 49$$

9.79 For confidence coefficient .90, $\alpha = .10$ and $\alpha/2 = .10/2 = .05$. From Table IV, Appendix A, $z_{.05} = 1.645$.

$$n_1 = n_2 = \frac{(z_{\alpha/2})^2 (p_1 q_1 + p_2 q_2)}{(SE)^2} = \frac{1.645^2 (.4(.6) + .6(.4))}{.1^2} = 129.889 \approx 130$$

9.81 For confidence coefficient .95, $\alpha = .05$ and $\alpha/2 = .025$. From Table IV, Appendix A, $z_{.025} = 1.96$.

$$n_1 = n_2 = \frac{(z_{\alpha/2})^2 (\sigma_1^2 + \sigma_2^2)}{(SE)^2} = \frac{1.96^2 (15^2 + 15^2)}{1^2} = 1728.72 \approx 1729$$

9.83 For confidence coefficient .9, $\alpha = 1 - .9 = .1$ and $\alpha/2 = .1/2 = .05$. From Table IV, Appendix A, $z_{.05} = 1.645$.

$$n_1 = n_2 = \frac{(z_{\alpha/2})^2 (\sigma_1^2 + \sigma_2^2)}{(SE)^2} = \frac{1.645^2 (5^2 + 5^2)}{1^2} = 135.3 \Rightarrow 136$$

9.85 The conditions required for valid inferences about σ_1^2 / σ_2^2 are:

1. The two sampled populations are normally distributed.
2. The samples are randomly and independently selected from their respective populations.

9.87 The statement "H_0: $\sigma_1^2 = \sigma_2^2$ is equivalent to H_0: $\sigma_1^2 / \sigma_2^2 = 0$" is false. The correct statement is:

H_0: $\sigma_1^2 = \sigma_2^2$ is equivalent to H_0: $\sigma_1^2 / \sigma_2^2 = 1$.

9.89   a.   With $v_1 = 2$ and $v_2 = 30$,
$$P(F \geq 4.18) = .025 \quad \text{(Table X, Appendix A)}$$

b.   With $v_1 = 24$ and $v_2 = 10$,
$$P(F \geq 1.94) = .10 \quad \text{(Table VIII, Appendix A)}$$

Thus, $P(F < 1.94) = 1 - P(F \geq 1.94) = 1 - .10 = .90$

c.   With $v_1 = 9$ and $v_2 = 1$,
$$P(F \geq 6022) = .01 \quad \text{(Table XI, Appendix A)}$$

Thus, $P(F < 6022) = 1 - P(F \geq 6022) = 1 - .01 = .99$

d.   With $v_1 = 30$ and $v_2 = 30$,
$$P(F \geq 1.84) = .05 \quad \text{(Table IX, Appendix A)}$$

9.91   The test statistic for each of these is:

$$F = \frac{\text{Larger sample variance}}{\text{Smaller sample variance}}$$

a.   The rejection region requires $\alpha/2 = .20/2 = .10$ in the upper tail of the F distribution. If $s_1^2 > s_2^2$, numerator df $= v_1 = 8$ and denominator df $= v_2 = 40$. From Table VIII, Appendix A, $F_{.10} = 1.83$. The rejection region is $F > 1.83$. If $s_1^2 < s_2^2$, numerator df $= v_2 = 40$ and denominator df $= v_1 = 8$. From Table VIII, Appendix A, $F_{.10} = 2.36$. The rejection region is $F > 2.36$.

b.   The rejection region requires $\alpha/2 = .10/2 = .05$ in the upper tail of the F distribution. If $s_1^2 > s_2^2$, numerator df $= v_1 = 8$ and denominator df $= v_2 = 40$. From Table IX, Appendix A, $F_{.05} = 2.18$. The rejection region is $F > 2.18$. If $s_1^2 < s_2^2$, numerator df $= v_2 = 40$ and denominator df $= v_1 = 8$. From Table IX, Appendix A, $F_{.05} = 3.04$. The rejection region is $F > 3.04$.

c.   The rejection region requires $\alpha/2 = .05/2 = .025$ in the upper tail of the F distribution. If $s_1^2 > s_2^2$, numerator df $= v_1 = 8$ and denominator df $= v_2 = 40$. From Table X, Appendix A, $F_{.025} = 2.53$. The rejection region is $F > 2.53$. If $s_1^2 < s_2^2$, numerator df $= v_2 = 40$ and denominator df $= v_1 = 8$. From Table X, Appendix A, $F_{.025} = 3.84$. The rejection region is $F > 3.84$.

d.   The rejection region requires $\alpha/2 = .02/2 = .01$ in the upper tail of the F distribution. If $s_1^2 > s_2^2$, numerator df $= v_1 = 8$ and denominator df $= v_2 = 40$. From Table XI, Appendix A, $F_{.01} = 2.99$. The rejection region is $F > 2.99$. If $s_1^2 < s_2^2$, numerator df $= v_2 = 40$ and denominator df $= v_1 = 8$. From Table XI, Appendix A, $F_{.01} = 5.12$. The rejection region is $F > 5.12$.

9.93   a. H_0: $\sigma_1^2 = \sigma_2^2$

H_a: $\sigma_1^2 \neq \sigma_2^2$

The test statistic is $F = \dfrac{\text{Larger sample variance}}{\text{Smaller sample variance}} = \dfrac{s_2^2}{s_1^2} = \dfrac{9.85}{2.87} = 3.43$

The rejection region requires $\alpha/2 = .05/2 = .025$ in the upper tail of the F distribution with numerator df $\nu_1 = n_2 - 1 = 25 - 1 = 24$ and denominator df $\nu_2 = n_1 - 1 = 16 - 1 = 15$. From Table X, Appendix A, $F_{.025} = 2.70$. The rejection region is $F > 2.70$.

Since the observed value of the test statistic falls in the rejection region ($F = 3.43 > 2.70$), H_0 is rejected. There is sufficient evidence to indicate $\sigma_1^2 \neq \sigma_2^2$ at $\alpha = .05$.

   b.   The p-value for the test is $p = 2P(F \geq 3.43)$. Using Table XI, Appendix A, with df $\nu_1 = n_2 - 1 = 25 - 1 = 24$ and df $\nu_2 = n_1 - 1 = 16 - 1 = 15$, $P(F > 3.29) = .01$. Thus, the p-value is $2P(F \geq 3.43) < 2(.01) = .02$ or $p < .02$.

9.95   a.   To determine whether σ_M^2 is less than σ_F^2, we test:

H_0: $\sigma_M^2 = \sigma_F^2$

H_a: $\sigma_M^2 < \sigma_F^2$

   b.   The test statistic is $F = \dfrac{s_F^2}{s_M^2} = \dfrac{6.94^2}{6.73^2} = 1.063$.

   c.   The rejection region requires $\alpha = .10$ in the upper tail of the F distribution with $\nu_1 = n_F - 1 = 114 - 1 = 113$ and $\nu_2 = n_M - 1 = 127 - 1 = 126$. From Table VIII, Appendix A, $F_{.10} \approx 1.26$. The rejection region is $F > 1.26$.

   d.   The p-value is $p = P(F \geq 1.063)$. Using Table VIII with $\nu_1 = n_F - 1 = 114 - 1 = 113$ and $\nu_2 = n_M - 1 = 127 - 1 = 126$, $P(F > 1.26) = .10$. Thus, the p-value is $p = P(F \geq 1.063) > .10$.

   e.   Since the observed value of the test statistic does not fall in the rejection region ($F = 1.063 \not> 1.26$), H_0 is not rejected. There is insufficient evidence to indicate σ_M^2 is less than σ_F^2 at $\alpha = .10$.

   f.   The conditions necessary for the test results to be valid are:

     1.   The two sampled populations are normally distributed.
     2.   The samples are randomly and independently selected from their respective populations.

9.97 Let σ_B^2 = variance of the FNE scores for bulimic students and σ_N^2 = variance of the FNE scores for normal students.

From Exercise 9.19, $s_B^2 = 24.1636$ and $s_N^2 = 27.9780$

To determine if the variances are equal, we test:

H_0: $\sigma_B^2 = \sigma_N^2$

H_a: $\sigma_B^2 \neq \sigma_N^2$

The test statistic is $F = \dfrac{\text{Larger sample variance}}{\text{Smaller sample variance}} = \dfrac{s_N^2}{s_B^2} = \dfrac{27.9780}{24.1636} = 1.16$

The rejection region requires $\alpha/2 = .05/2 = .025$ in the upper tail of the F distribution with numerator df $v_2 = n_2 - 1 = 14 - 1 = 13$ and denominator df $v_1 = n_1 - 1 = 11 - 1 = 10$. From Table X, Appendix A, $F_{.025} \approx 3.62$. The rejection region is $F > 3.62$.

Since the observed value of the test statistic does not fall in the rejection region ($F = 1.16 \not> 3.62$), H_0 is not rejected. There is insufficient evidence that the two variances are different at $\alpha = .05$. It appears that the assumption of equal variances is valid.

9.99 a. Using MINITAB, the descriptive statistics are:

Descriptive Statistics: Text-line, Witness-line, Intersection

Variable	N	Mean	Median	TrMean	StDev	SE Mean
Text-lin	3	0.3830	0.3740	0.3830	0.0531	0.0306
Witness-	6	0.3042	0.2955	0.3042	0.1015	0.0415
Intersec	5	0.3290	0.3190	0.3290	0.0443	0.0198

Variable	Minimum	Maximum	Q1	Q3
Text-lin	0.3350	0.4400	0.3350	0.4400
Witness-	0.1880	0.4390	0.2045	0.4075
Intersec	0.2850	0.3930	0.2900	0.3730

Let σ_1^2 = variance of zinc measurements for the text-line, σ_2^2 = variance of zinc measurements for the witness-line, and σ_3^2 = variance of zinc measurements for the intersection.

To determine if the variation in zinc measurements for the text-line and the variation in zinc measurements for the intersection differ, we test:

H_0: $\sigma_1^2 = \sigma_3^2$

H_a: $\sigma_1^2 \neq \sigma_3^2$

The test statistic is $F = \dfrac{\text{Larger sample variance}}{\text{Smaller sample variance}} = \dfrac{s_1^2}{s_3^2} = \dfrac{.0531^2}{.0443^2} = 1.437$

The rejection region requires $\alpha/2 = .05/2 = .025$ in the upper tail of the F distribution with $v_1 = n_1 - 1 = 3 - 1 = 2$ and $v_2 = n_3 - 1 = 5 - 1 = 4$. Using Table X, Appendix A, $F_{.025} = 10.65$. The rejection region is $F > 10.65$.

Since the observed value of the test statistic does not fall in the rejection region ($F = 1.437 \not> 10.65$), H_0 is not rejected. There is insufficient evidence to indicate the variation in zinc measurements for the text-line and the variation in zinc measurements for the intersection differ at $\alpha = .05$.

b. To determine if the variation in zinc measurements for the witness-line and the variation in zinc measurements for the intersection differ, we test:

H_0: $\sigma_2^2 = \sigma_3^2$
H_a: $\sigma_2^2 \neq \sigma_3^2$

The test statistic is $F = \dfrac{\text{Larger sample variance}}{\text{Smaller sample variance}} = \dfrac{s_2^2}{s_3^2} = \dfrac{.1015^2}{.0443^2} = 5.250$

The rejection region requires $\alpha/2 = .05/2 = .025$ in the upper tail of the F distribution with $v_1 = n_2 - 1 = 6 - 1 = 5$ and $v_2 = n_3 - 1 = 5 - 1 = 4$. Using Table X, Appendix A, $F_{.025} = 9.36$. The rejection region is $F > 9.36$.

Since the observed value of the test statistic does not fall in the rejection region ($F = 5.250 \not> 9.36$), H_0 is not rejected. There is insufficient evidence to indicate the variation in zinc measurements for the witness-line and the variation in zinc measurements for the intersection differ at $\alpha = .05$.

c. The largest sample variance is $s_2^2 = .1015^2$ and the smallest sample variance is $s_3^2 = .0443^2$. Since the test indicated there was no difference between the variances of the two populations, we can infer that there is no difference among all three variances.

d. The conditions necessary for the test results to be valid are:

1. The two sampled populations are normally distributed.
2. The samples are randomly and independently selected from their respective populations.

Since there are so few observations per group, it is very difficult to check these assumptions.

9.101 Let σ_1^2 = variance of the effective population size of the outcrossing snails and σ_2^2 = variance of the effective population size of the selfing snails. To determine if the variances for the two groups differ, we test:

H_0: $\sigma_1^2 = \sigma_2^2$
H_a: $\sigma_1^2 \neq \sigma_2^2$

The test statistic is $F = \dfrac{\text{Larger sample variance}}{\text{Smaller sample variance}} = \dfrac{s_1^2}{s_2^2} = \dfrac{1,932^2}{1,890^2} = 1.045$

Since α is not given, we will use $\alpha = .05$. The rejection region requires $\alpha/2 = .05/2 = .025$ in the upper tail of the F distribution with $v_1 = n_1 - 1 = 17 - 1 = 16$ and $v_2 = n_2 - 1 = 5 - 1 = 4$. From Table X, Appendix A, $F_{.025} \approx 8.66$. The rejection region is $F > 8.66$.

Since the observed value of the test statistic does not fall in the rejection region ($F = 1.045 \not> 8.66$), H_0 is not rejected. There is insufficient evidence to indicate the variances for the two groups differ at $\alpha = .05$.

9.103 a. To compare average SAT scores of males and females, the target parameter is $\mu_1 - \mu_2$.

b. To compare the difference between mean waiting times at two supermarket checkout lines, the target parameter is $\mu_1 - \mu_2$.

c. To compare proportions of Democrats and Republicans who favor legalization of marijuana, the target parameter is $p_1 - p_2$.

d. To compare variation in salaries of NBA players picked in the 1st round and the 2nd round, the target parameter is $\sigma_1^2 \big/ \sigma_2^2$.

e. To compare the difference in dropout rates of college student-athletes and regular students, the target parameter is $p_1 - p_2$.

9.105 a. $$s_p^2 = \frac{(n_1 - 1)s_1^2 + (n_1 - 1)s_2^2}{n_1 + n_2 - 2} = \frac{11(74.2) + 13(60.5)}{12 + 14 - 2} = 66.7792$$

H_0: $\mu_1 - \mu_2 = 0$
H_a: $\mu_1 - \mu_2 > 0$

The test statistic is $t = \dfrac{(\bar{x}_1 - \bar{x}_2) - 0}{\sqrt{s_p^2\left(\dfrac{1}{n_1} + \dfrac{1}{n_2}\right)}} = \dfrac{(17.8 - 15.3) - 0}{\sqrt{66.7792\left(\dfrac{1}{12} + \dfrac{1}{14}\right)}} = .78$

The rejection region requires $\alpha = .05$ in the upper tail of the t distribution with df $= n_1 + n_2 - 2 = 12 + 14 - 2 = 24$. From Table VI, Appendix A, for df $= 24$, $t_{.05} = 1.711$. The rejection region is $t > 1.711$.

Since the observed value of the test statistic does not fall in the rejection region ($t = 0.78 \not> 1.711$), H_0 is not rejected. There is insufficient evidence to indicate that $\mu_1 > \mu_2$ at $\alpha = .05$.

b. For confidence coefficient .99, $\alpha = .01$ and $\alpha/2 = .01/2 = .005$. From Table VI, Appendix A, with df $= n_1 + n_2 - 2 = 12 + 14 - 2 = 24$, $t_{.005} = 2.797$. The confidence interval is:

$$(\bar{x}_1 - \bar{x}_2) \pm t_{.005}\sqrt{s_p^2\left(\frac{1}{n_1} + \frac{1}{n_2}\right)} \Rightarrow (17.8 - 15.3) \pm 2.797\sqrt{66.7792\left(\frac{1}{12} + \frac{1}{14}\right)}$$
$$\Rightarrow 2.50 \pm 8.99 \Rightarrow (-6.49, 11.49)$$

c.　For confidence coefficient .99, $\alpha = .01$ and $\alpha/2 = .01/2 = .005$. From Table IV, Appendix A, $z_{.005} = 2.58$.

$$n_1 = n_2 = \frac{\left(z_{\alpha/2}\right)^2 \left(\sigma_1^2 + \sigma_2^2\right)}{(SE)^2} = \frac{(2.58)^2 (74.2 + 60.5)}{2^2} = 224.15 \approx 225$$

9.107　a.　For confidence coefficient .90, $\alpha = .10$ and $\alpha/2 = .05$. From Table IV, Appendix A, $z_{.05} = 1.645$. The confidence interval is:

$$(\bar{x}_1 - \bar{x}_2) \pm z_{.05} \sqrt{\frac{s_1^2}{n_1} + \frac{s_2^2}{n_2}} \Rightarrow (12.2 - 8.3) \pm 1.645 \sqrt{\frac{2.1}{135} + \frac{3.0}{148}}$$

$$\Rightarrow 3.90 \pm .31 \Rightarrow (3.59, 4.21)$$

b.　H_0: $\mu_1 - \mu_2 = 0$
H_a: $\mu_1 - \mu_2 \neq 0$

The test statistic is $z = \dfrac{(\bar{x}_1 - \bar{x}_2) - 0}{\sqrt{\dfrac{s_1^2}{n_1} + \dfrac{s_2^2}{n_2}}} = \dfrac{(12.2 - 8.3) - 0}{\sqrt{\dfrac{2.1}{135} + \dfrac{3.0}{148}}} = 20.60$

The rejection region requires $\alpha/2 = .01/2 = .005$ in each tail of the z distribution. From Table IV, Appendix A, $z_{.005} = 2.58$. The rejection region is $z < -2.58$ or $z > 2.58$.

Since the observed value of the test statistic falls in the rejection region ($20.60 > 2.58$), H_0 is rejected. There is sufficient evidence to indicate that $\mu_1 \neq \mu_2$ at $\alpha = .01$.

c.　For confidence coefficient .90, $\alpha = .10$ and $\alpha/2 = .05$. From Table IV, Appendix A, $z_{.05} = 1.645$.

$$n_1 = n_2 = \frac{\left(z_{\alpha/2}\right)^2 \left(\sigma_1^2 + \sigma_2^2\right)}{(SE)^2} = \frac{(1.645)^2 (2.1 + 3.0)}{.2^2} = 345.02 \approx 346$$

9.109　a.　This is a paired difference experiment.

Pair	Difference (Pop. 1 – Pop. 2)
1	6
2	4
3	4
4	3
5	2

$$\bar{x}_D = \frac{\sum x_D}{n_D} = \frac{19}{5} = 3.8 \qquad s_D^2 = \frac{\sum x_D^2 - \dfrac{\left(\sum x_D\right)^2}{n_D}}{n_D - 1} = \frac{81 - \dfrac{19^2}{5}}{5 - 1} = 2.2$$

$$s_D = \sqrt{2.2} = 1.4832$$

$$H_0: \mu_D = 0$$
$$H_a: \mu_D \neq 0$$

The test statistic is $t = \dfrac{\bar{x}_D - 0}{s_D / \sqrt{n_D}} = \dfrac{3.8 - 0}{1.4832 / \sqrt{5}} = 5.73$

The rejection region requires $\alpha/2 = .05/2 = .025$ in each tail of the t distribution with df $= n - 1 = 5 - 1 = 4$. From Table VI, Appendix A, $t_{.025} = 2.776$. The rejection region is $t < -2.776$ or $t > 2.776$.

Since the observed value of the test statistic falls in the rejection region ($5.73 > 2.776$), H_0 is rejected. There is sufficient evidence to indicate that the population means are different at $\alpha = .05$.

b. For confidence coefficient .95, $\alpha = .05$ and $\alpha/2 = .025$. Therefore, we would use the same t value as above, $t_{.025} = 2.776$. The confidence interval is:

$$\bar{x}_D \pm t_{\alpha/2} \frac{s_D}{\sqrt{n_D}} \Rightarrow 3.8 \pm 2.776 \frac{1.4832}{\sqrt{5}} \Rightarrow 3.8 \pm 1.84 \Rightarrow (1.96, 5.64)$$

c. The sample of differences must be randomly selected from a population of differences which has a normal distribution.

9.111 From the printout, the 95% confidence interval for the difference in mean seabird densities of oiled and unoiled transects is $(-2.93, 2.49)$. We are 95% confident that the true difference in mean seabird densities of oiled and unoiled transects is between -2.93 and 2.49. Since 0 is contained in the interval, there is no evidence to indicate that the mean seabird densities are different for the oiled and unoiled transects.

9.113 a. The variable measured for this experiment is the time needed to match the picture with the sentence.

b. The experimental units are the climbers.

c. Since the same climbers were timed at the base camp and at a camp 5 miles above sea level, the data should be analyzed as a paired experiment.

9.115 a. Let μ_1 = mean trait for senior year in high school and μ_2 = mean trait during sophomore year of college. Also, let $\mu_D = \mu_1 - \mu_2$. To determine if there is a decrease in the mean self-concept of females between the senior year in high school and the sophomore year in college, we test:

$$H_0: \mu_D = 0$$
$$H_a: \mu_D > 0$$

b.	Since the same female students were used in each study, the data should be analyzed as paired differences. The samples are not independent.

c.	Since the number of pairs is $n_0 = 133$, no assumptions about the population of differences is necessary. We still assume that a random sample of differences is selected.

d.	Leadership: The p-value > .05. There is no evidence to reject H_0 for $\alpha = .05$. There is no evidence to indicate that there is a decrease in mean self-concept of females on leadership between the senior year in high school and the sophomore year in college for $\alpha = .05$.

Popularity: The p-value < .05. There is evidence to reject H_0 for $\alpha = .05$. There is evidence to indicate that there is a decrease in mean self-concept of females on popularity between the senior year in high school and the sophomore year in college for $\alpha = .05$.

Intellectual self-confidence: The p-value < .05. There is evidence to reject H_0 for $\alpha = .05$. There is evidence to indicate that there is a decrease in mean self-concept of females on intellectual self-concept between the senior year in high school and the sophomore year in college for $\alpha = .05$.

9.117	a.	Let p_1 = proportion of sun-shaded eggs that hatch and p_2 = proportion of unshaded eggs that hatch.

Some preliminary calculations are:

$$\hat{p}_1 = \frac{x_1}{n_1} = \frac{34}{70} = .486; \qquad \hat{p}_2 = \frac{x_2}{n_2} = \frac{31}{80} = .388; \qquad \hat{p} = \frac{x_1 + x_2}{n_1 + n_2} = \frac{34 + 31}{70 + 80} = .433$$

To compare the hatching rates of the two groups of Pacific tree frog eggs, we test:

$H_0: p_1 - p_2 = 0$
$H_a: p_1 - p_2 \neq 0$

b.	The test statistic is $z = \dfrac{(\hat{p}_1 - \hat{p}_2) - 0}{\sqrt{\hat{p}\hat{q}\left(\dfrac{1}{n_1} + \dfrac{1}{n_2}\right)}} = \dfrac{(.486 - .388) - 0}{\sqrt{.433(.567)\left(\dfrac{1}{70} + \dfrac{1}{80}\right)}} = 1.21$

The rejection region requires $\alpha/2 = .01/2 = .005$ in each tail of the z distribution. From Table IV, Appendix A, $z_{.005} = 2.58$. The rejection region is $z < -2.58$ or $z > 2.58$.

Since the observed value of the test statistic does not fall in the rejection region ($z = 1.21 \not> 2.58$), H_0 is not rejected. There is insufficient evidence to indicate the hatching rates of the two groups of Pacific tree frog eggs differ at $\alpha = .01$.

9.119 a. For each measure, let μ_1 = mean job satisfaction for day-shift nurses and μ_2 = mean job satisfaction for night-shift nurses. To determine whether a difference in job satisfaction exists between day-shift and night-shift nurses, we test:

$$H_0: \mu_1 - \mu_2 = 0$$
$$H_a: \mu_1 - \mu_2 \neq 0$$

b. Hours of work: The p-value = .813. Since the p-value is so large, there is no evidence to reject H_0. There is insufficient evidence to indicate a difference in mean job satisfaction exists between day-shift and night-shift nurses on hours of work for $\alpha \leq .10$.

Free time: The p-value = .047. Since the p-value is so small, there is evidence to reject H_0. There is sufficient evidence to indicate a difference in mean job satisfaction exists between day-shift and night-shift nurses on free time for $\alpha > .047$.

Breaks: The p-value = .0073. Since the p-value is so small, there is evidence to reject H_0. There is sufficient evidence to indicate a difference in mean job satisfaction exists between day-shift and night-shift nurses on breaks for $\alpha > .0073$.

c. We must make the following assumptions for each measure:

1. The job satisfaction scores for both day-shift and night-shift nurses are normally distributed.
2. The variances of job satisfaction scores for both day-shift and night-shift nurses are equal.
3. Random and independent samples were selected from both populations of job satisfaction scores.

9.121 a. Since we want to compare the means of two independent groups, we would use a two sample test of hypothesis for independent samples. Since the sample sizes are small (21 for each), we would use a small sample test.

b. We must assume that both populations being sampled from are approximately normally distributed and that the population variances of the two groups are equal.

c. No. We need to know the common variance of the two groups or an estimate of it.

d. Since the p-value was so large ($p = .79$), H_0 would not be rejected for any reasonable value of α. There is insufficient evidence to indicate a difference in the mean scores for the two groups on the question dealing with clean/sterile gloves at $\alpha \leq .10$.

e. Since the p-value was so small ($p = .02$), H_0 is rejected for any $\alpha > .02$. There is sufficient evidence to indicate a difference in the mean scores for the two groups on the question dealing with a stethoscope at $\alpha > .02$.

9.123   Some preliminary calculations:

Patient	Panic Attacks per Week Placebo	Inositol	$D = Pl - In$	Patient	Panic Attacks per Week Placebo	Inositol	$D = Pl - In$
1	0	0	0	12	0	2	−2
2	2	1	1	13	3	1	2
3	0	3	−3	14	3	1	2
4	1	2	−1	15	3	4	−1
5	0	0	0	16	4	2	2
6	10	5	5	17	6	4	2
7	2	0	2	18	15	21	−6
8	6	4	2	19	28	8	20
9	1	1	0	20	30	0	30
10	1	0	1	21	13	0	13
11	1	3	−2				

$$\bar{x}_D = \frac{\sum x_D}{n_D} = \frac{67}{21} = 3.19$$

$$s_D^2 = \frac{\sum x_D^2 - \frac{\left(\sum x_D\right)^2}{n_D}}{n_D - 1} = \frac{\left(1{,}575 - \frac{67^2}{21}\right)}{21 - 1} = 68.0619$$

To determine if there is a difference in the mean number of panic attacks between the placebo and the drug Inositol, we test:

H_0: $\mu_D = 0$
H_a: $\mu_D \neq 0$

The test statistic is $t = \dfrac{\bar{x}_D - 0}{s_D / \sqrt{n_D}} = \dfrac{3.19 - 0}{\sqrt{68.0619} / \sqrt{21}} = 1.77$

Since no α was given, we will use $\alpha = .05$. The rejection region requires $\alpha/2 = .05/2 = .025$ in each tail of the t distribution with df $= n_D - 1 = 21 - 1 = 20$. From Table VI, Appendix A, $t_{.025} = 2.086$. The rejection region is $t < -2.086$ or $t > 2.086$.

Since the observed value of the test statistic does not fall in the rejection region ($t = 1.77 \not> 2.086$), H_0 is not rejected. There is insufficient evidence to indicate that there is a difference in the mean number of panic attacks between the placebo and the drug Inositol at $\alpha = .05$. There is no evidence that the drug is effective.

9.125   Let p_1 = proportion of inositol-fed infants who suffer from retinopathy of prematurity and p_2 = proportion of infants on the standard diet who suffer from retinopathy of prematurity.

Some preliminary calculations are:

$$\hat{p}_1 = \frac{x_1}{n_1} = \frac{14}{110} = .127; \quad \hat{p}_2 = \frac{x_2}{n_2} = \frac{29}{110} = .264; \quad \hat{p} = \frac{x_1 + x_2}{n_1 + n_2} = \frac{14 + 29}{110 + 110} = .195$$

To determine if the proportion of infants suffering from retinopathy is less for the inositol-fed group than for the group fed the standard diet, we test:

H_0: $p_1 - p_2 = 0$

H_a: $p_1 - p_2 < 0$

The test statistic is $z = \dfrac{(\hat{p}_1 - \hat{p}_2) - 0}{\sqrt{\hat{p}\hat{q}\left(\dfrac{1}{n_1} + \dfrac{1}{n_2}\right)}} = \dfrac{(.127 - .264) - 0}{\sqrt{.195(.805)\left(\dfrac{1}{110} + \dfrac{1}{110}\right)}} = -2.56$

The rejection region requires $\alpha = .01$ in the lower tail of the z distribution. From Table IV, Appendix A, $z_{.01} = 2.33$. The rejection region is $z < -2.33$.

Since the observed value of the test statistic falls in the rejection region ($z = -2.56 < -2.33$), H_0 is rejected. There is sufficient evidence to indicate the proportion of infants suffering from retinopathy is less for the inositol-fed group than for the group fed the standard diet at $\alpha = .01$.

9.127   Let μ_1 = mean rating for music majors and μ_2 = mean rating of nonmusic majors.

For confidence coefficient .95, $\alpha = .05$ and $\alpha/2 = .05/2 = .025$. From Table IV, Appendix A, $z_{.025} = 1.96$. The confidence interval is:

$$(\bar{x}_1 - \bar{x}_2) \pm z_{.025}\sqrt{\frac{s_1^2}{n_1} + \frac{s_2^2}{n_2}} \Rightarrow (4.26 - 4.59) \pm 1.96\sqrt{\frac{.81^2}{100} + \frac{.78^2}{100}}$$

$$\Rightarrow -.33 \pm .220 \Rightarrow (-.550, -.110)$$

We are 95% confident that the difference in the mean rating between music majors and nonmusic majors is between $-.55$ and $-.11$.

9.129   a.   Some preliminary calculations are:

$$s_1^2 = \frac{\sum x_1^2 - \dfrac{\left(\sum x_1\right)^2}{n_1}}{n_1 - 1} = \frac{4209 - \dfrac{(145)^2}{5}}{5 - 1} = 1$$

$$s_2^2 = \frac{\sum x_2^2 - \dfrac{\left(\sum x_2\right)^2}{n_2}}{n_2 - 1} = \frac{4540 - \dfrac{(150)^2}{5}}{5 - 1} = 10$$

Let σ_1^2 = variance of measurements for instrument 1 and σ_2^2 = variance of measurements for instrument 2.

To determine if the variances of the measurements for the two instruments differ, we test:

$$H_0: \sigma_1^2 = \sigma_2^2$$
$$H_a: \sigma_1^2 \neq \sigma_2^2$$

The test statistic is $F = \dfrac{\text{Larger sample variance}}{\text{Smaller sample variance}} = \dfrac{s_2^2}{s_1^2} = \dfrac{10}{1} = 10$

Since no α was given, we will use $\alpha = .05$. The rejection region requires $\alpha/2 = .05/2 = .025$ in the upper tail of the F distribution with numerator df $v_1 = n_2 - 1 = 5 - 1 = 4$ and denominator df $v_2 = n_1 - 1 = 5 - 1 = 4$. From Table X, Appendix A, $F_{.025} = 9.60$. The rejection region is $F > 9.60$.

Since the observed value of the test statistic falls in the rejection reigon ($F = 10 > 9.60$), H_0 is rejected. There is sufficient evidence to indicate the variances of the measurements for the two instruments differ at $\alpha = .05$.

c. We must assume that the samples are randomly and independently selected from populations that are normally distributed.

9.131 Let $p_1 =$ proportion of patients receiving Zyban who were not smoking one year later and $p_2 =$ proportion of patients not receiving Zyban who were not smoking one year later.

Some preliminary calculations are:

$$\hat{p}_1 = \frac{x_1}{n_1} = \frac{71}{309} = .230 \qquad\qquad \hat{p}_2 = \frac{x_2}{n_2} = \frac{37}{306} = .121$$

$$\hat{p} = \frac{x_1 + x_2}{n_1 + n_2} = \frac{71 + 37}{309 + 306} = .176 \qquad \hat{q} = 1 = \hat{p} = 1 - .176 = .824$$

To determine if the antidepressant drug Zyban helped cigarette smokers kick their habit, we test:

$$H_0: p_1 - p_2 = 0$$
$$H_a: p_1 - p_2 > 0$$

The test statistic is $z = \dfrac{(\hat{p}_1 - \hat{p}_2) - 0}{\sqrt{\hat{p}\hat{q}\left(\dfrac{1}{n_1} + \dfrac{1}{n_2}\right)}} = \dfrac{(.230 - .121) - 0}{\sqrt{.176(.824)\left(\dfrac{1}{309} + \dfrac{1}{306}\right)}} = 3.55$

The rejection region requires $\alpha = .05$ in the upper tail of the z distribution. From Table IV, Appendix A, $z_{.05} = 1.645$. The rejection region is $z > 1.645$.

Since the observed value of the test statistic falls in the rejection region ($z = 3.55 > 1.645$), H_0 is rejected. There is sufficient evidence to indicate that the antidepressant drub Zyban helped cigarette smokers kick their habit at $\alpha = .05$.

9.135   Using MINITAB, the descriptive statistics are:

Descriptive Statistics: CREATIVE, INFO, DECPERS, SKILLS, TASKID, AGE, EDYRS

Variable	GROUP	N	N*	Mean	SE Mean	StDev	Minimum	Q1	Median	Q3	Maximum
CREATIVE	NOSPILL	67	0	4.4478	0.0648	0.5304	3.0000	4.0000	4.0000	5.0000	5.0000
	SPILLOV	47	0	5.2553	0.0643	0.4408	5.0000	5.0000	5.0000	6.0000	6.0000
INFO	NOSPILL	67	0	4.657	0.272	2.226	1.000	3.000	5.000	7.000	7.000
	SPILLOV	47	0	5.213	0.251	1.719	1.000	4.000	5.000	7.000	7.000
DECPERS	NOSPILL	67	0	2.746	0.240	1.964	1.000	1.000	2.000	5.000	7.000
	SPILLOV	47	0	3.319	0.295	2.023	1.000	1.000	3.000	5.000	7.000
SKILLS	NOSPILL	67	0	4.821	0.134	1.100	2.000	4.000	5.000	5.000	7.000
	SPILLOV	47	0	5.851	0.169	1.161	2.000	5.000	6.000	7.000	7.000
TASKID	NOSPILL	67	0	4.239	0.141	1.156	1.000	3.000	4.000	5.000	7.000
	SPILLOV	47	0	4.809	0.296	2.028	1.000	3.000	5.000	7.000	7.000
AGE	NOSPILL	67	0	45.343	0.974	7.971	21.000	41.000	45.000	50.000	63.000
	SPILLOV	47	0	46.298	0.841	5.767	30.000	44.000	47.000	51.000	54.000
EDYRS	NOSPILL	67	0	13.224	0.160	1.312	12.000	12.000	13.000	14.000	18.000
	SPILLOV	47	0	13.085	0.155	1.060	12.000	12.000	13.000	14.000	16.000

Let μ_1 = mean characteristic for the workers with positive spillover and μ_2 = mean characteristic for the workers with no spillover. To determine if there is a difference in the mean characteristic between the positive spillover group and the no spillover group, we test:

H_0: $\mu_1 = \mu_2$
H_a: $\mu_1 \neq \mu_2$

The test statistic is $z = \dfrac{\bar{x}_1 - \bar{x}_2}{\sqrt{\left(\dfrac{s_1^2}{n_1} + \dfrac{s_2^2}{n_2}\right)}}$

Since no α was given, we will run all tests at $\alpha = .05$. The rejection region requires $\alpha/2 = .05/2 = .025$ in each tail of the z distribution. From Table IV, Appendix A, $z_{.025} = 1.96$. The rejection region is $z < -1.96$ or $z > 1.96$.

Use of Creative Ideas:

The test statistic is $z = \dfrac{\bar{x}_1 - \bar{x}_2}{\sqrt{\left(\dfrac{s_1^2}{n_1} + \dfrac{s_2^2}{n_2}\right)}} = \dfrac{5.2553 - 4.4478}{\sqrt{\dfrac{.4408^2}{47} + \dfrac{.5304^2}{67}}} = 8.85$

Since the observed value of the test statistic falls in the rejection region ($z = 8.85 > 1.96$), H_0 is rejected. There is sufficient evidence to indicate a difference in the mean use of creative ideas between the positive spillover group and the no spillover group at $\alpha = .05$.

Utilization of Information:

The test statistic is $z = \dfrac{\bar{x}_1 - \bar{x}_2}{\sqrt{\left(\dfrac{s_1^2}{n_1} + \dfrac{s_2^2}{n_2}\right)}} = \dfrac{5.213 - 4.657}{\sqrt{\dfrac{1.719^2}{47} + \dfrac{2.226^2}{67}}} = 1.50$

Since the observed value of the test statistic does not fall in the rejection region ($z = 1.50 \not> 1.96$), H_0 is not rejected. There is insufficient evidence to indicate a difference in the mean utilization of information between the positive spillover group and the no spillover group at $\alpha = .05$.

Decisions Regarding Personnel Matters:

The test statistic is $z = \dfrac{\bar{x}_1 - \bar{x}_2}{\sqrt{\left(\dfrac{s_1^2}{n_1} + \dfrac{s_2^2}{n_2}\right)}} = \dfrac{3.319 - 2.746}{\sqrt{\dfrac{2.023^2}{47} + \dfrac{1.964^2}{67}}} = 1.51$

Since the observed value of the test statistic does not fall in the rejection region ($z = 1.51 \not> 1.96$), H_0 is not rejected. There is insufficient evidence to indicate a difference in the mean participation in decisions regarding personnel matters between the positive spillover group and the no spillover group at $\alpha = .05$.

Good Use of Job Skills:

The test statistic is $z = \dfrac{\bar{x}_1 - \bar{x}_2}{\sqrt{\left(\dfrac{s_1^2}{n_1} + \dfrac{s_2^2}{n_2}\right)}} = \dfrac{5.851 - 4.821}{\sqrt{\dfrac{1.161^2}{47} + \dfrac{1.100^2}{67}}} = 4.76$

Since the observed value of the test statistic falls in the rejection region ($z = 4.76 \not> 1.96$), H_0 is rejected. There is sufficient evidence to indicate a difference in the mean good use of skills between the positive spillover group and the no spillover group at $\alpha = .05$.

Task Identity:

The test statistic is $z = \dfrac{\bar{x}_1 - \bar{x}_2}{\sqrt{\left(\dfrac{s_1^2}{n_1} + \dfrac{s_2^2}{n_2}\right)}} = \dfrac{4.809 - 4.239}{\sqrt{\dfrac{2.028^2}{47} + \dfrac{1.156^2}{67}}} = 1.74$

Since the observed value of the test statistic does not fall in the rejection region ($z = 1.74 \not> 1.96$), H_0 is not rejected. There is insufficient evidence to indicate a difference in the mean task identity between the positive spillover group and the no spillover group at $\alpha = .05$.

Of the 5 job-related characteristics, there are only 2 that have significantly different means for the 2 groups. They are "use of creative ideas" and "good use of skills". For both of these characteristics, the mean for the positive spillover group was significantly higher than the mean for the no spillover group.

Analysis of Variance: Comparing More than Two Means

10.1 Since only one factor is utilized, the treatments are the four levels (A, B, C, D) of the qualitative factor.

10.3 One has no control over the levels of the factors in an observational experiment. One does have control of the levels of the factors in a designed experiment.

10.5 a. This is an observational experiment. The economist has no control over the factor levels or unemployment rates.

   b. This is a designed experiment. The psychologist selects the feedback programs of interest and randomly assigns five rats to each program.

   c. This is a designed experiment. The marketer has control of the selection of the national publications.

   d. This is an observational experiment. The load on the generators is not controlled by the utility.

   e. This is an observational experiment. One has no control over the distance of the haul, the goods hauled, or the price of diesel fuel.

   f. This is an observational experiment. The student does not control which state is assigned to a portion of the country.

10.7 a. The response variable is the age when cancer is first detected.

   b. The experimental units are the people.

   c. The factor in the study is type of screening method. There are 2 levels of screening method.

   d. The treatments are the same as the factor levels in this problem. There are 2 factor levels or treatments: CT scan or chest X-ray.

10.9 a. The experimental units are the cockatiels.

   b. This experiment is a designed experiment. The birds were randomly divided into 3 groups and each group received a different treatment.

   c. There is one factor in this study. The factor is the group.

   d. There are three levels of the group variable – Group 1 received purified water, Group 2 received purified water and liquid sucrose, and Group 3 received purified water and liquid sodium chloride.

e. There are 3 treatments in the study. Because there is only one factor, the treatments are the same as the factor levels.

f. The response variable is the water consumption.

10.11 a. The ethical behavior of the salesperson.

b. There are two factors (with two levels at each factor):
Type of sales job (high tech versus low tech) and
Sales task (new account development).

c. The treatments are the $2 \times 2 = 4$ factor-level combinations of type of sales job and sales task.

d. The college students are the experimental units.

10.13 For a completely randomized design, independent random samples are selected for each treatment.

10.15 The conditions required for a valid ANOVA F-test in a completely randomized design are:

1. The samples are randomly selected in an independent manner from k treatment populations.

2. All k sampled populations have distributions that are approximately normal.

3. The k population variances are equal (i.e., $\sigma_1^2 = \sigma_2^2 = ... = \sigma_k^2$)

10.17 a. Using Table IX, $F_{.05} = 6.59$ with $v_1 = 3$, $v_2 = 4$.

b. Using Table XI, $F_{.01} = 16.69$ with $v_1 = 3$, $v_2 = 4$.

c. Using Table VIII, $F_{.10} = 1.61$ with $v_1 = 20$, $v_2 = 40$.

d. Using Table X, $F_{.025} = 3.87$ with $v_1 = 12$, $v_2 = 9$.

10.19 In the second dot diagram **b**, the difference between the sample means is small relative to the variability within the sample observations. In the first dot diagram **a**, the values in each of the samples are grouped together with a range of 4, while in the second diagram **b**, the range of values is 8.

10.21 For each dot diagram, we want to test:

H_0: $\mu_1 = \mu_2$
H_a: $\mu_1 \neq \mu_2$

From Exercise 10.20,

Diagram a	Diagram b
$\bar{x}_1 = 9$	$\bar{x}_1 = 9$
$\bar{x}_2 = 14$	$\bar{x}_2 = 14$
$s_1^2 = 2$	$s_1^2 = 14.4$
$s_2^2 = 2$	$s_2^2 = 14.4$

a.

Diagram a	Diagram b
$s_p^2 = \dfrac{s_1^2 + s_2^2}{2}$	$s_p^2 = \dfrac{s_1^2 + s_2^2}{2}$
$= \dfrac{2+2}{2} = 2 \quad (n_1 = n_2)$	$= \dfrac{14.4 + 14.4}{2} = 14.4 \quad (n_1 = n_2)$
In Exercise 10.20, MSE = 2	In Exercise 10.20, MSE = 14.4

The pooled variance for the two-sample t test is the same as the MSE for the F test.

b.

Diagram a	Diagram b
$t = \dfrac{\bar{x}_1 - \bar{x}_2}{\sqrt{s_p^2\left(\dfrac{1}{n_1} + \dfrac{1}{n_2}\right)}} = \dfrac{9-14}{\sqrt{2\left(\dfrac{1}{6} + \dfrac{1}{6}\right)}}$	$t = \dfrac{\bar{x}_1 - \bar{x}_2}{\sqrt{s_p^2\left(\dfrac{1}{n_1} + \dfrac{1}{n_2}\right)}} = \dfrac{9-14}{\sqrt{14.4\left(\dfrac{1}{6} + \dfrac{1}{6}\right)}}$
$= -6.12$	$= -2.28$
In Exercise 10.20, $F = 37.5$	In Exercise 10.20, $F = 5.21$

The test statistic for the F test is the square of the test statistic for the t test.

c.

Diagram a	Diagram b
For the t test, the rejection region requires $\alpha/2 = .05/2 = .025$ in each tail of the t distribution with df $= n_1 + n_2 - 2 = 6 + 6 - 2 = 10$. From Table VI, Appendix A, $t_{.025} = 2.228$.	For the t test, the rejection region is the same as Diagram **a** since we are using the same α, n_1, and n_2 for both tests.

The rejection region is $t < -2.228$ or $t > 2.228$.

In Exercise 10.20, the rejection region for both diagrams using the F test is $F > 4.96$.

The tabled F value equals the square of the tabled t value.

d.

Diagram a	**Diagram b**
For the t test, since the test statistic falls in the rejection region ($t = 6.12 < -2.228$), we would reject H_0. In Exercise 10.20 using the F test, we rejected H_0.	For the t test, since the test statistic falls in the rejection region ($t = -2.28 < -2.228$), we would reject H_0. In Exercise 10.20 using the F test, we rejected H_0.

e. Assumptions for the t test:

1. Both populations have relative frequency distributions that are approximately normal.
2. The two population variances are equal.
3. Samples are selected randomly and independently from the populations.

Assumptions for the F test:

1. Both population probability distributions are normal.
2. The two population variances are equal.
3. Samples are selected randomly and independently from the respective populations.

The assumptions are the same for both tests.

10.23 For all parts, the hypotheses are:

H_0: $\mu_1 = \mu_2 = \mu_3 = \mu_4 = \mu_5$
H_a: At least two treatment means differ

The rejection region for all parts is the same.

The rejection region requires $\alpha = .10$ in the upper tail of the F distribution with $v_1 = k - 1 = 5 - 1 = 4$ and $v_2 = n - k = 30 - 5 = 25$. From Table VIII, Appendix A, $F_{.10} = 2.18$. The rejection region is $F > 2.18$.

a. $SST = .2(500) = 100$ $SSE = SS(Total) - SST = 500 - 100 = 400$

$$MST = \frac{SST}{k-1} = \frac{100}{5-1} = 25 \qquad MSE = \frac{SSE}{n-k} = \frac{400}{30-5} = 16$$

$$F = \frac{MST}{MSE} = \frac{25}{16} = 1.5625$$

Since the observed value of the test statistic does not fall in the rejection region ($F = 1.5625 \ngtr 2.18$), H_0 is not rejected. There is insufficient evidence to indicate differences among the treatment means at $\alpha = .10$.

b. $SST = .5(500) = 250$ $SSE = SS(Total) - SST = 500 - 250 = 250$

$$MST = \frac{SST}{k-1} = \frac{250}{5-1} = 62.5 \qquad MSE = \frac{SSE}{n-k} = \frac{250}{30-5} = 10$$

$$F = \frac{MST}{MSE} = \frac{62.5}{10} = 6.25$$

Since the observed value of the test statistic falls in the rejection region ($F = 6.25 >$ 2.18), H_0 is rejected. There is sufficient evidence to indicate differences among the treatment means at $\alpha = .10$.

c. $SST = .8(500) = 400$ $SSE = SS(Total) - SST = 500 - 400 = 100$

$$MST = \frac{SST}{k-1} = \frac{400}{5-1} = 100 \qquad\qquad MSE = \frac{SSE}{n-k} = \frac{100}{30-5} = 4$$

$$F = \frac{MST}{MSE} = \frac{100}{4} = 25$$

Since the observed value of the test statistic falls in the rejection region, ($F = 25 > 2.18$), H_0 is rejected. There is sufficient evidence to indicate differences among the treatment means at $\alpha = .10$.

d. The F ratio increases as the treatment sum of squares increases.

10.25 a. Some preliminary calculations are:

$$CM = \frac{\left(\sum y_i\right)^2}{n} = \frac{40.9^2}{13} = 128.6777$$

$$SS(Total) = \sum y_i^2 - CM = 159.43 - 128.6777 = 30.7523$$

$$SST = \sum \frac{T_i^2}{n_i} - CM = \frac{17.2^2}{5} + \frac{19.5^2}{5} + \frac{4.2^2}{3} - 128.6777$$

$$= 141.098 - 128.6777 = 12.4203$$

$$SSE = SS(Total) - SST = 30.7523 - 12.4203 = 18.332$$

$$MST = \frac{SST}{k-1} = \frac{12.4203}{3-1} = 6.21015 \qquad MSE = \frac{SSE}{n-k} = \frac{18.332}{13-3} = 1.8332$$

$$F = \frac{MST}{MSE} = \frac{6.21015}{1.8332} = 3.39$$

Source	df	SS	MS	F
Treatments	2	12.4203	6.21015	3.39
Error	10	18.3320	1.8332	
Total	12	30.7523		

b. H_0: $\mu_1 = \mu_2 = \mu_3$
  H_a: At least two treatment means differ

The test statistic is $F = 3.39$.

The rejection region requires $\alpha = .01$ in the upper tail of the F distribution with $v_1 = k - 1 = 3 - 1 = 2$ and $v_2 = n - k = 13 - 3 = 10$. From Table XI, Appendix A, $F_{.01} = 7.56$. The rejection region is $F > 7.56$.

Since the observed value of the test statistic does not fall in the rejection region ($F = 3.39 \not> 7.56$), H_0 is not rejected. There is insufficient evidence to indicate a difference in the treatment means at $\alpha = .01$.

10.27 a. The experimental design used is a completely randomized design.

b. There are 4 treatments in this experiment. The four treatments are the 4 "colonies" to which the robots were assigned – 3, 6, 9, or 12 robots per colony.

c. To determine if the mean energy expended (per robot) of the four different colony sizes differed, we test:

H_0: $\mu_1 = \mu_2 = \mu_3 = \mu_4$
H_a: At least two treatment means differ

d. The test statistic is $F = 7.70$. The p-value is $p < .001$. Since the p-value is less than $\alpha = .05$, H_0 is rejected. There is sufficient evidence to indicate that mean energy expended (per robot) of the four different colony sizes differed at $\alpha = .05$

10.29 a. To determine if the average heights of male Australian school children differ among the age groups, we test:

H_0: $\mu_1 = \mu_2 = \mu_3$
H_a: At least two treatment means differ

b. The test statistic is $F = 4.57$. The p-value is $p = .01$. Since the p-value is less than α ($p = .01 < .05$), H_0 is rejected. There is sufficient evidence to indicate the average heights of male Australian school children differ among the age groups at $\alpha = .05$.

c. To determine if the average heights of female Australian school children differ among the age groups, we test:

H_0: $\mu_1 = \mu_2 = \mu_3$
H_a: At least two treatment means differ

The test statistic is $F = 0.85$. The p-value is $p = .43$. Since the p-value is not less than α ($p = .43 > .05$), H_0 is not rejected. There is insufficient evidence to indicate the average heights of female Australian school children differ among the age groups at $\alpha = .05$.

d. For the boys, differences were found in the mean standardized heights among the three tertiles. For the girls, no differences were found in the mean standardized heights among the three tertiles.

10.31 To determine if a driver's propensity to engage in road rage is related to his/her income, we test:

H_o: $\mu_1 = \mu_2 = \mu_3$
H_a: At least two means differ

The test statistic is $F = 3.90$.

Analysis of Variance: Comparing More Than Two Means

The p-value is $p < .01$. Since the p-value is so small, H_0 would be rejected for any reasonable value of α. There is sufficient evidence to indicate that a driver's propensity to engage in road rage is related to his/her income at $\alpha \geq .01$.

We have just concluded that the mean road rage score is related to income group. For the Under \$30,000 group, the mean road rage score is 4.60. For the \$30,000 to \$60,000 group, the mean road rage score is 5.08. For the Over \$60,000 group, the mean road rage score is 5.15. Thus, as the income increases, the mean road rage score also increases.

10.33   a.   The subjects were randomly divided into 3 treatment groups with one group receiving an injection of scopolamine, another group receiving an injection of glycopyrrolate, and the third group receiving nothing. Thus, this is a completely randomized design.

       b.   There are 3 treatments: injection of scopolamine, injection of glycopyrrolate, and nothing. The response variable is the number of pairs recalled.

       c.   Using MINITAB, the descriptive statistics are:

Descriptive Statistics: Scopolamine, Placebo, No Drug

Variable	N	N*	Mean	SE Mean	StDev	Minimum	Q1	Median	Q3
Scopolamine	12	0	6.167	0.366	1.267	4.000	5.250	6.000	7.500
Placebo	8	0	9.375	0.532	1.506	7.000	8.250	9.500	10.000
No Drug	8	0	10.625	0.532	1.506	8.000	9.250	11.000	12.000

Variable	Maximum
Scopolamine	8.000
Placebo	12.000
No Drug	12.000

The sample means for the 3 groups are: 6.167, 9.375, and 10.625. There is not sufficient information to support the researcher's theory. We need to take into account the variability within each group.

       d.   Using MINITAB, the ANOVA table is:

One-way ANOVA: Scopolamine, Placebo, No Drug

Source	DF	SS	MS	F	P
Factor	2	107.01	53.51	27.07	0.000
Error	25	49.42	1.98		
Total	27	156.43			

$S = 1.406$ $R\text{-}Sq = 68.41\%$ $R\text{-}Sq(adj) = 65.88\%$

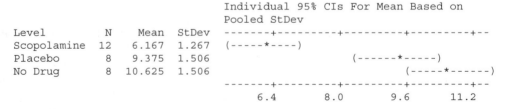

```
                                    Individual 95% CIs For Mean Based on
                                    Pooled StDev
Level         N    Mean   StDev   -------+---------+---------+---------+--
Scopolamine  12   6.167   1.267   (-----*----)
Placebo       8   9.375   1.506                     (------*-----)
No Drug       8  10.625   1.506                           (-----*------)
                                  -------+---------+---------+---------+--
                                       6.4       8.0       9.6      11.2
```

Pooled StDev = 1.406

To determine if the mean number of words recalled differed among the 3 groups, we test:

H_0: $\mu_1 = \mu_2 = \mu_3$
H_a: At least two means differ

The test statistic is $F = 27.07$.

The p-value is $p = .000$. Since the p-value is so small, H_0 would be rejected for any reasonable value of α. There is sufficient evidence to indicate the mean number of words recalled differed among the 3 groups at $\alpha = .05$.

Prior to the experiment, the researchers theorized that the mean number of word pairs recalled for the scopolamine group would be less that the corresponding means for the other 2 groups. From the printout, the sample mean for the scopolamine group is 6.167. The means for the placebo group and the nothing group are 9.375 and 10.625.

Since the sample mean for the scopolamine group is much smaller than the other two, it appears that the researchers' theory was correct.

10.35   Using MINITAB, the ANOVA table is:

Source	df	SS	MS	F	P
Expressions	5	23.09	4.62	3.96	0.007
Error	30	34.99	1.17		
Total	35	58.07			

To determine if differences exist among the mean dominance ratings of the six facial expressions, we test:

H_0: $\mu_1 = \mu_2 = \mu_3 = \mu_4 = \mu_5 = \mu_6$
H_a: At least two treatment means differ

where μ_i represents the mean dominance rating for facial expression i.
The test statistic is $F = 3.96$.

The rejection region requires $\alpha = .10$ in the upper tail of the F distribution with $v_1 = k - 1 = 6 - 1 = 5$ and $v_2 = n - k = 36 - 6 = 30$. Using Table VIII, Appendix A, $F_{.10} = 2.05$. The rejection region is $F > 2.05$.

Since the observed value of the test statistic falls in the rejection region ($F = 3.96 > 2.05$), H_0 is rejected. There is sufficient evidence to indicate that differences exists among the mean dominance rating for facial expressions at $\alpha = .10$.

10.37   The experiment-wise error rate is the probability of declaring at least one pair of means different when they are not among all comparisons in the experiment.

10.39   a.   The confidence interval $(-10, 5)$ for $(\mu_1 - \mu_2)$ means that we are confident that the difference between $\mu_1 - \mu_2$ is between -10, and 5. Since this interval spans both positive and negative numbers, we cannot conclude that either mean is significantly larger.

Analysis of Variance: Comparing More Than Two Means   **269**

b.	The confidence interval $(-10, -5)$ for $(\mu_1 - \mu_2)$ means that we are confident that the difference between $\mu_1 - \mu_2$ is between -10, and -5. Since this interval spans only negative numbers, we can conclude that μ_2 is significantly larger than μ_1.

c.	The confidence interval $(5, 10)$ for $(\mu_1 - \mu_2)$ means that we are confident that the difference between $\mu_1 - \mu_2$ is between 5, and 10. Since this interval spans only positive numbers, we can conclude that μ_1 is significantly larger than μ_2.

10.41	The number of pairwise comparisons is equal to $k(k-1)/2$.

    a.	For $k = 3$, the number of comparisons is $3(3-1)/2 = 3$.

    b.	For $k = 5$, the number of comparisons is $5(5-1)/2 = 10$.

    c.	For $k = 4$, the number of comparisons is $4(4-1)/2 = 6$.

    d.	For $k = 10$, the number of comparisons is $10(10-1)/2 = 45$.

10.43	$(\mu_1 - \mu_2)$: $(2, 15)$	Since all values in the interval are positive, μ_1 is significantly greater than μ_2.

    $(\mu_1 - \mu_3)$: $(4, 7)$	Since all values in the interval are positive, μ_1 is significantly greater than μ_3.

    $(\mu_1 - \mu_4)$: $(-10, 3)$	Since 0 is in the interval, μ_1 is not significantly different from μ_4. However, since the center of the interval is less than 0, μ_4 is larger than μ_1.

    $(\mu_2 - \mu_3)$: $(-5, 11)$	Since 0 is in the interval, μ_2 is not significantly different from μ_3. However, since the center of the interval is greater than 0, μ_2 is larger than μ_3.

    $(\mu_2 - \mu_4)$: $(-12, -6)$	Since all values in the interval are negative, μ_4 is significantly greater than μ_2.

    $(\mu_3 - \mu_4)$: $(-8, -5)$	Since all values in the interval are negative, μ_4 is significantly greater than μ_3.

Thus, the largest mean is μ_4 followed by μ_1, μ_2, and μ_3.

10.45	a.	There are $c = \dfrac{k(k-1)}{2} = \dfrac{4(4-1)}{2} = 6$ pairwise comparisons.

    b.	There are no significant differences in the mean energy expended among the colony sizes of 3, 6, and 9. However, the mean energy expended for the colony containing 12 robots was significantly less than that for all other colony sizes.

10.47 a. Yes, there is a significant difference between the standardized height means for the oldest and youngest boys because their sample means are not connected.

b. Yes, there is a significant difference between the standardized height means for the oldest and middle-aged boys because their sample means are not connected.

c. No, there is not a significant difference between the standardized height means for the middle-aged and youngest boys because their sample means are connected.

d. The experiment-wise error rate for the inferences made in parts **a-c** is $\alpha = .05$.

e. No differences were found among the means of the three groups of girls. Therefore, we do not need to find where the differences are.

10.49 a. To determine if there are differences in the mean dental fear scores among the three groups, we test:

H_0: $\mu_1 = \mu_2 = \mu_3$
H_a: At least two treatment means differ

The test statistic is $F = 4.43$ and the p-value is $p < .05$. If we use $\alpha = .05$, then the rejection region will be p-value $< .05$. Since the p-value is less than .05, we reject H_0. There is sufficient evidence to indicate there are differences in the mean dental fear scores among the three groups at $\alpha = .05$.

b. First, we arrange the means in order from the largest to the smallest. Then we draw a line between the means that are not significantly different. The results are:

Questionnaire   53.8

Slide   43.1 |
                       |
Control   41.8 |

10.51 From Exercise 10.33, we rejected H_0 and concluded that the mean number of words recalled differed among the groups. The group means are:

Scopolamine 6.167, Placebo 9.375, and No drug 10.625.

Using MINITAB, the results of the Tukey multiple comparison procedure are:

```
Tukey 95% Simultaneous Confidence Intervals
All Pairwise Comparisons

Individual confidence level = 98.02%

Scopolamine subtracted from:

           Lower   Center   Upper   --+---------+---------+---------+-------
Placebo    1.611   3.208    4.806                     (------*-----)
No Drug    2.861   4.458    6.056                        (------*-----)
                                    --+---------+---------+---------+-------
                                    -2.5       0.0       2.5       5.0
```

```
Placebo subtracted from:

                Lower  Center  Upper     --+---------+---------+---------+-------
No Drug       -0.500   1.250   3.000                     (------*------)
                                         --+---------+---------+---------+-------
```

The confidence interval comparing the difference between the mean number of word pairs recalled between the Placebo group and the Scopolamine group is (1.611, 4.806). Since this interval does not contain 0, it implies that there is a significant difference in the mean number of word pairs recalled between these two groups. Because the differences are positive, the mean number of word pairs recalled by the Placebo group is greater than the mean number of word pairs recalled by the Scopolamine group.

The confidence interval comparing the difference between the mean number of word pairs recalled between the No Drug group and the Scopolamine group is (2.861, 6.056). Since this interval does not contain 0, it implies that there is a significant difference in the mean number of word pairs recalled between these two groups. Because the differences are positive, the mean number of word pairs recalled by the No Drug group is greater than the mean number of word pairs recalled by the Scopolamine group.

The confidence interval comparing the difference between the mean number of word pairs recalled between the No Drug group and the Placebo group is (-0.500, 3.000). Since this interval contains 0, it implies that there is no significant difference in the mean number of word pairs recalled between these two groups.

The researchers' theory was that the mean number of word pairs recalled by the scopolamine group would be less than the means for the other two groups. This theory is supported by the results.

10.53 $\alpha^* = \dfrac{2\alpha}{k(k-1)} = \dfrac{2(.03)}{3(3-1)} = .01$

$t_{\alpha^*/2} = t_{.01/2} = t_{.005} \approx 2.7$ (From Table VI, Appendix A, with df = 38)

$s = \sqrt{\text{MSE}} = \sqrt{2.03} \approx 1.42$

CBT-WLT and CBT-IPT:

$(0.2 - 1.9) \pm 2.7(1.42)\sqrt{\dfrac{1}{17} + \dfrac{1}{13}} \Rightarrow -1.7 \pm 1.41 \Rightarrow (-3.11, -0.29)$

CBT-WLT and Control:

$(0.2 - 2.9) \pm 2.7(1.42)\sqrt{\dfrac{1}{17} + \dfrac{1}{11}} \Rightarrow -2.7 \pm 1.48 \Rightarrow (-4.18, -1.22)$

CBT-IPT and Control:

$(1.9 - 2.9) \pm 2.7(1.42)\sqrt{\dfrac{1}{13} + \dfrac{1}{11}} \Rightarrow -1.0 \pm 1.57 \Rightarrow (-2.57, 0.57)$

We are 97% confident that the intervals collectively contain all the differences between the true means. The interval that contains 0 (CBT-IPT) does not support a conclusion that the true means differ. If both endpoints are negative, as in the cases of the other two intervals, the implications are that

1) the mean for CBT-IPT exceeds that of CBT-WLT and
2) the mean for Control exceeds that of CBT-WLT

A convenient summary of the results is below, where the treatment means are listed from highest to lowest with a solid line connecting those that are not significantly different.

Control	CBT-IPT	CBT-WLT
2.9	1.9	0.2

10.55 A paired difference experiment is a randomized block design with only 2 experimental units per block. In the paired difference design, the pairs are the blocks. However, a randomized block design is not limited to 2 experimental units per block.

10.57 a. There are 3 blocks used since Block df $= b - 1 = 2$ and 5 treatments since the treatment df $= k - 1 = 4$.

b. There were 15 observations since the Total df $= n - 1 = 14$.

c. H_0: $\mu_1 = \mu_2 = \mu_3 = \mu_4 = \mu_5$
H_a: At least two treatment means differ

d. The test statistic is $F = \dfrac{MST}{MSE} = 9.109$

e. The rejection region requires $\alpha = .01$ in the upper tail of the F distribution with $v_1 = k - 1 = 5 - 1 = 4$ and $v_2 = n - k - b + 1 = 15 - 5 - 3 + 1 = 8$. From Table XI, Appendix A, $F_{.01} = 7.01$. The rejection region is $F > 7.01$.

f. Since the observed value of the test statistic falls in the rejection region ($F = 9.109 > 7.01$), H_0 is rejected. There is sufficient evidence to indicate that at least two treatment means differ at $\alpha = .01$.

g. The assumptions necessary to assure the validity of the test are as follows:

1. The probability distributions of observations corresponding to all the block-treatment combinations are normal.
2. The variances of all the probability distributions are equal.
3. The b blocks are randomly selected and all k treatments are applied (in random order) to each block.

10.59 a. The ANOVA Table is as follows:

Source	df	SS	MS	F	p
Treatment	2	12.0317	6.0158	50.96	0.000
Block	3	71.7492	23.9164	202.59	0.000
Error	6	.7083	.1181		
Total	11	84.4892			

b. To determine if the treatment means differ, we test:

H_0: $\mu_A = \mu_B = \mu_C$
H_a: At least two treatment means differ

The test statistic is $F = \dfrac{MST}{MSE} = 50.986$

The rejection region requires $\alpha = .05$ in the upper tail of the F distribution with $v_1 = k - 1 = 3 - 1 = 2$ and $v_2 = n - k - b + 1 = 12 - 3 - 4 + 1 = 6$. From Table IX, Appendix A, $F_{.05} = 5.14$. The rejection region is $F > 5.14$.

Since the observed value of the test statistic falls in the rejection region ($F = 50.958 > 5.14$), H_0 is rejected. There is sufficient evidence to indicate that the treatment means differ at $\alpha = .05$.

c. To see if the blocking was effective, we test:

H_0: $\mu_1 = \mu_2 = \mu_3 = \mu_4$
H_a: At least two block means differ

The test statistic is $F = \dfrac{MSB}{MSE} = 202.586$

The rejection region requires $\alpha = .05$ in the upper tail of the F distribution with $v_1 = b - 1 = 4 - 1 = 3$ and $v_2 = n - k - b + 1 = 12 - 3 - 4 + 1 = 6$. From Table IX, Appendix A, $F_{.05} = 4.76$. The rejection region is $F > 4.76$.

Since the observed value of the test statistic falls in the rejection region ($F = 202.586 > 4.76$), H_0 is rejected. There is sufficient evidence to indicate that blocking was effective in reducing the experimental error at $\alpha = .05$.

d. From the printout, we are given the differences in the sample means. The difference between treatment B and treatment A is positive (1.1125). Thus, treatment B has a larger mean than treatment A. The difference between treatment C and treatment A is negative (−1.325). Thus, treatment A has a larger mean than treatment C. The difference between treatment C and treatment B is negative (−2.450). Thus, treatment B has a larger mean than treatment C. Finally, treatment B has the largest mean, treatment A has the next largest, and treatment C has the smallest. Since 0 is not contained in any of the confidence intervals, all the means are statistically different.

e. The assumptions necessary to assure the validity of the inferences above are:

1. The probability distributions of observations corresponding to all the block-treatment combinations are normal.
2. The variances of all the probability distributions are equal.
3. The b blocks are randomly selected and all k treatments are applied (in random order) to each block.

10.61   a.   A randomized block design is preferred over a completely randomized design because there is large variation in the number of oil rigs running among the months. By blocking for months, we can reduce this variation.

      b.   The treatments in the experiment are the states. There are 3 states: California, Utah, and Alaska.

      c.   The blocks in this experiment are the selected months. There are 3 blocks: Nov. 2000, Oct. 2001, and Nov. 2001.

      d.   To determine if there is a difference in the mean number of oil rigs running in each state per month, we test:

H_0: $\mu_C = \mu_U = \mu_A$
H_a: At least two treatment means differ

      e.   From the printout, the test statistics is $F = 38.07$ and the p-value is 0.002.

      f.   From the SPSS output, there is no difference in the mean number of oil rigs running between Alaska and Utah. All other means are different. Thus, the mean number of oil rigs running for California is significantly greater than the mean number of oil rigs running for Alaska and Utah.

10.63   a.   This is a randomized block design. The blocks are the 12 plots of land. The treatments are the three methods used on the shrubs: fire, clipping, and control. The response variable is the mean number of flowers produced. The experimental units are the 36 shrubs.

      b.

Treatment

		Fire	Clipping	Control
	1	Shrub 2	Shrub 1	Shrub 3
	2	Shrub 3	Shrub 2	Shrub 1
Plot	.	.	.	.
	.	.	.	.
	.	.	.	.
	12	Shrub 1	Shrub 3	Shrub 2

      c.   To determine if there is a difference in the mean number of flowers produced among the three treatments, we test:

H_0: $\mu_1 = \mu_2 = \mu_3$
H_a: The mean number of flowers produced differ for at least two of the methods.

The test statistic is $F = 5.42$ and $p = .009$. We can reject the null hypothesis at the $\alpha > .009$ level of significance. At least two of the methods differ with respect to mean number of flowers produced by pawpaws.

d. The means of Control and Clipping do not differ significantly. The means of Clipping and Burning do not differ significantly. The mean of treatment Burning exceeds that of the Control.

10.65 a. The experimenters expected there to be much variation in the number of participants from week to week (more participants at the beginning and fewer as time goes on). Thus, by blocking on weeks, this extraneous source of variation can be controlled.

b. Using MINITAB, the ANOVA results are:

Two-way ANOVA: Walkers versus Week, Group

```
Source   DF      SS      MS      F       P
Group    4    1185.0  296.25  39.87   0.000
Week     5     386.4   77.28  10.40   0.000
Error   20     148.6    7.43
Total   29    1720.0

S = 2.726    R-Sq = 91.36%    R-Sq(adj) = 87.47%


                     Individual 95% CIs For Mean Based on
                     Pooled StDev
Group     Mean    ---------+---------+---------+---------+
1       2.6667    (--*---)
2      17.0000                        (---*---)
3      20.6667                              (--*---)
4      10.5000              (---*--)
5       9.1667             (---*---)
                  ---------+---------+---------+---------+
                      6.0      12.0      18.0      24.0
```

The ANOVA table is:

Source	df	SS	MS	F	p
Prompt	4	1185.0	296.25	39.87	0.000
Week	5	386.4	77.28	10.40	0.000
Error	20	148.6	7.43		
Total	29	1720.0			

c. To determine if a difference exists in the mean number of walkers per week among the five walker groups, we test:

H_0: $\mu_1 = \mu_2 = \mu_3 = \mu_4 = \mu_5$
H_a: At least two treatment means differ

where μ_i represents the mean number of walkers in group i.

The test statistic is $F = 39.87$.

The rejection region requires $\alpha = .05$ in the upper tail of the F distribution with $v_1 = k - 1 = 5 - 1 = 4$ and $v_2 = n - k - b + 1 = 30 - 4 - 6 + 1 = 20$. From Table IX, Appendix A, $F_{.05} = 2.69$. The rejection region is $F > 2.69$.

Since the observed value of the test statistic falls in the rejection region ($F = 39.87 > 2.69$), H_0 is rejected. There is sufficient evidence to indicate differences exist among the mean number of walkers per week among the 5 walker groups at $\alpha = .05$.

d. Using SAS, the Tukey multiple comparison results are:

```
           Tukey's Studentized Range (HSD) Test for walkers

NOTE: This test controls the Type I experimentwise error rate, but it generally has a
                 higher Type II error rate than REGWQ.


                 Alpha                                  0.05
                 Error Degrees of Freedom                 20
                 Error Mean Square                       7.43
                 Critical Value of Studentized Range  4.23186
                 Minimum Significant Difference        4.7092


          Means with the same letter are not significantly different.


     Tukey Grouping           Mean      N    group

                  A         20.667      6    FREQ/HIGH
                  A
                  A         17.000      6    FREQ/LOW

                  B         10.500      6    INFREQ/LOW
                  B
                  B          9.167      6    INFREQ/HIGH

                  C          2.667      6    CONTROL
```

There is no difference in the mean number of walkers between the FREQ/HIGH group and the FREQ/LOW group. There is no difference in the mean number of walkers between the INFREQ/LOW group and the INFREQ/HIGH group.

The mean number of walkers in the Control group is significantly less than the means for the other 4 groups. The mean number of walkers in the INFREQ/LOW and INFRE/HIGH groups is significantly less than the mean number of walkers in the FREQ/LOW and FREQ/HIGH groups.

e. In order for the above inferences to be valid, the following assumptions must hold:

1) The probability distributions of observations corresponding to all block-treatment conditions are normal.
2) The variances of all the probability distributions are equal.
3) The b blocks are randomly selected and all k treatments are applied (in random order) to each block.

10.67   Using MINITAB, the ANOVA results are:

Two-way ANOVA: Temp versus Plant, Student

```
Source   DF      SS       MS      F      P
Plant     2   0.122   0.06100   0.02   0.981
Student   9  18.415   2.04611   0.63   0.754
Error    18  58.038   3.22433
Total    29  76.575

S = 1.796    R-Sq = 24.21%    R-Sq(adj) = 0.00%


                       Individual 95% CIs For Mean Based on
                       Pooled StDev
Plant   Mean   -------+---------+---------+---------+--
Live    95.21  (---------------*----------------)
None    95.20  (---------------*----------------)
Photo   95.34     (---------------*----------------)
               -------+---------+---------+---------+--
                   94.50     95.20     95.90     96.60
```

To determine if there are differences among the mean temperatures among the three treatments, we test:

H_0: $\mu_1 = \mu_2 = \mu_3$
H_a: At least two treatment means differ

The test statistic is $F = 0.02$. The associated p-value is $p = .981$. Since the p-value is very large, there is no evidence of a difference in mean temperature among the three treatments. Since there is no difference, we do not need to compare the means. It appears that the presence of plants or pictures of plants does not reduce stress.

10.69   a.   The data analysis method seems reasonable. There are probably large differences among the infants, which we can control for using a randomized complete block design.

        b.   To determine if the mean listening times differ for the two types of sentences, we test:

                 H_0: $\mu_{consistent} = \mu_{inconsistent}$
                 H_a: $\mu_{consistent} \neq \mu_{inconsistent}$

             The test statistic is $F = 25.7$ and $p < .001$. We can reject the null hypothesis at the $\alpha \geq .001$ significance level. The mean listening times of consistent and inconsistent sentences differ.

        c.   The mean listening time of consistent and inconsistent sentences are paired for each infant.

                 $\sqrt{F} = t$
                 $\sqrt{25.7} = 5.07$

d. $SSE = (n_1 - 1)s_1^2 + (n_2 - 1)s_2^2$

$\qquad = (16 - 1)(2.6)^2 + (16 - 1)(2.16)^2$

$\qquad = 171.384$

$SST = n_1(\bar{x}_1 - \bar{x})^2 + n_2(\bar{x}_2 - \bar{x})^2$

$\qquad = 16(6.3 - 7.65)^2 + 16(9.0 - 7.65)^2$

$\qquad 58.32$

$MSE = \dfrac{SSE}{n-k} = \dfrac{171.384}{32-2} = 5.712$

$MST = \dfrac{SST}{k-1} = \dfrac{58.32}{2-1} = 58.32$

$F = \dfrac{MST}{MSE} = \dfrac{58.32}{5.7128} = 10.21$

This test statistic provides weaker evidence of a difference between treatment means than the test in part b because it was not able to remove that source of variation due to differences among infants.

e. There are only two treatments.

10.71 The conditions that are required for valid inferences for a factorial ANOVA are:

1. The response distribution for each factor-level combination (treatment) is normal.

2. The response variance is constant for all treatments.

3. Random and independent samples of experimental units are associated with each treatment.

10.73 a. There are two factors.

b. No, we cannot tell whether the factors are qualitative or quantitative.

c. Yes. There are 3 levels of factor A and 5 levels of factor B.

d. A treatment would consist of a combination of one level of factor A and one level of factor B. There are a total of $3 \times 5 = 15$ treatments.

e. One problem with only one replicate is there are no degrees of freedom for error. This is overcome by having at least two replicates.

10.75   The ANOVA table is:

Source	df	SS	MS	F
A	2	.8	24.4000	2.00
B	3	5.3	1.7667	8.83
AB	6	9.6	1.6000	8.00
Error	12	2.4	.2000	
Total	23	18.1		

df for A is $a - 1 = 3 - 1 = 2$

df for B is $b - 1 = 4 - 1 = 3$

df for AB is $(a - 1)(b - 1) = 2(3) = 6$

df for Error is $n - ab = 24 - 3(4) = 12$

df for Total is $n - 1 = 24 - 1 = 23$

$SSE = SS(Total) - SSA - SSB - SSAB = 18.1 - .8 - 5.3 - 9.6 = 2.4$

$$MSA = \frac{SSA}{a-1} = \frac{.8}{3-1} = .40 \qquad MSB = \frac{SSB}{b-1} = \frac{5.3}{4-1} = 1.7667$$

$$MSAB = \frac{SSAB}{(a-1)(b-1)} = \frac{9.6}{(3-1)(4-1)} = 1.60$$

$$MSE = \frac{MSE}{n-ab} = \frac{2.4}{24-3(4)} = .2000$$

$$F_A = \frac{MSA}{MSE} = \frac{.4000}{.2000} = 2.00 \qquad\qquad F_B = \frac{MSB}{MSE} = \frac{1.7667}{.2000} = 8.83$$

$$F_{AB} = \frac{MSAB}{MSE} = \frac{1.6000}{.2000} = 8.00$$

b.   Sum of Squares for Treatment $= SSA + SSB + SSAB = .8 = 5.3 + 2.6 = 15.7$.

$$MST = \frac{SST}{ab-1} = \frac{15.7}{3(4)-1} = 1.4273$$

$$F_T = \frac{MST}{MSE} = \frac{1.4273}{.2000} = 7.14$$

To determine if the treatment means differ, we test:

H_0: $\mu_1 = \mu_2 = \cdots = \mu_{12}$
H_a: At least two treatment means differ

The test statistic is $F = 7.14$.

The rejection region requires $\alpha = .05$ in the upper tail of the F distribution with $v_1 = ab - 1 = 3(4) - 1 = 11$ and $v_2 = n - ab = 24 - 3(4) = 12$. From Table IX, Appendix A, $F_{.05} \approx 2.75$. The rejection region is $F > 2.75$.

Since the observed value of the test statistic falls in the rejection region ($F = 7.14 >$ 2.75), H_0 is rejected. There is sufficient evidence to indicate the treatment means differ at $\alpha = .05$.

c. Yes. We need to partition the Treatment Sum of Squares into the Main Effects and Interaction Sum of Squares. Then we test whether factors A and B interact. Depending on the conclusion of the test for interaction, we either test for main effects or compare the treatment means.

d. Two factors are said to interact if the effects of one factor on the dependent variable are not the same at different levels of the second factor. If the factors interact, then tests for main effects are not necessary. We need to compare the treatment means for one factor at each level of the second.

e. To determine if the factors interact, we test:

H_0: Factors A and B do not interact to affect the response mean
H_a: Factors A and B do interact to affect the response mean

The test statistic is $F = \dfrac{\text{MS}AB}{\text{MSE}} = 8.00$

The rejection region requires $\alpha = .05$ in the upper tail of the F distribution with $v_1 = (a-1)(b-1) = (3-1)(4-1) = 6$ and $v_2 = n - ab = 24 - 3(4) = 12$. From Table IX, Appendix A, $F_{.05} = 3.00$. The rejection region is $F > 3.00$.

Since the observed value of the test statistic falls in the rejection region ($F = 8.00 >$ 3.00), H_0 is rejected. There is sufficient evidence to indicate the two factors interact to affect the response mean at $\alpha = .05$.

f. No. Testing for main effects is not warranted. Instead, we compare the treatment means of one factor at each level of the second factor.

10.77 a. $\text{SS}A = .2(1000) = 200$, $\text{SS}B = .1(1000) = 100$, $\text{SS}AB = .1(1000) = 100$
$\text{SSE} = \text{SS(Total)} - \text{SS}A - \text{SS}B - \text{SS}AB = 1000 - 200 - 100 - 100 = 600$
$\text{SST} = \text{SS}A + \text{SS}B + \text{SS}AB = 200 + 100 + 100 = 400$

$$\text{MS}A = \frac{\text{SS}A}{a-1} = \frac{200}{3-1} = 100 \qquad \text{MS}B = \frac{\text{SS}B}{b-1} = \frac{100}{3-1} = 50$$

$$\text{MS}AB = \frac{\text{SS}AB}{(a-1)(b-1)} = \frac{100}{(3-1)(3-1)} = 25$$

$$\text{MSE} = \frac{\text{SSE}}{n-ab} = \frac{600}{27-3(3)} = 33.333 \qquad \text{MST} = \frac{\text{SST}}{ab-1} = \frac{400}{3(3)-1} = 50$$

$$F_A = \frac{\text{MS}A}{\text{MSE}} = \frac{100}{33.333} = 3.00 \qquad F_B = \frac{\text{MS}B}{\text{MSE}} = \frac{50}{33.333} = 1.50$$

$$F_{AB} = \frac{\text{MS}AB}{\text{MSE}} = \frac{25}{33.333} = .75 \qquad F_T = \frac{\text{MST}}{\text{MSE}} = \frac{50}{33.333} = 1.50$$

Source	df	SS	MS	F
A	2	200	100	3.00
B	2	100	50	1.50
AB	4	100	25	.75
Error	18	600	33.333	
Total	26	1000		

To determine whether the treatment means differ, we test:

H_0: $\mu_1 = \mu_2 = \cdots = \mu_9$

H_a: At least two treatment means differ

The test statistic is $F = \dfrac{\text{MST}}{\text{MSE}} = 1.50$

Suppose $\alpha = .05$. The rejection region requires $\alpha = .05$ in the upper tail of the F distribution with $v_1 = ab - 1 = 3(3) - 1 = 8$ and $v_2 = n - ab = 27 - 3(3) = 18$. From Table IX, Appendix A, $F_{.05} = 2.51$. The rejection region is $F > 2.51$.

Since the observed value of the test statistic does not fall in the rejection region ($F = 1.50 \not> 2.51$), H_0 is not rejected. There is insufficient evidence to indicate the treatment means differ at $\alpha = .05$. Since there are no treatment mean differences, we have nothing more to do.

b. $\text{SS}A = .1(1000) = 100$, $\text{SS}B = .1(1000) = 100$, $\text{SS}AB = .5(1000) = 500$

$\text{SSE} = \text{SS(Total)} - \text{SS}A - \text{SS}B - \text{SS}AB = 1000 - 100 - 100 - 500 = 300$

$\text{SST} = \text{SS}A + \text{SS}B + \text{SS}AB = 100 + 100 + 500 = 700$

$\text{MS}A = \dfrac{\text{SS}A}{a-1} = \dfrac{100}{3-1} = 50$ 　　　　 $\text{MS}B = \dfrac{\text{SS}B}{b-1} = \dfrac{100}{3-1} = 50$

$\text{MS}AB = \dfrac{\text{SS}AB}{(a-1)(b-1)} = \dfrac{500}{(3-1)(3-1)} = 125$

$\text{MSE} = \dfrac{\text{SSE}}{n-ab} = \dfrac{300}{27-3(3)} = 16.667$ 　　　 $\text{MST} = \dfrac{\text{SST}}{ab-1} = \dfrac{700}{9-1} = 87.5$

$F_A = \dfrac{\text{MS}A}{\text{MSE}} = \dfrac{50}{16.667} = 3.00$ 　　　 $F_B = \dfrac{\text{MS}B}{\text{MSE}} = \dfrac{50}{16.667} = 3.00$

$F_{AB} = \dfrac{\text{MS}AB}{\text{MSE}} = \dfrac{125}{16.667} = 7.50$ 　　 $F_T = \dfrac{\text{MST}}{\text{MSE}} = \dfrac{87.5}{16.667} = 5.25$

Source	df	SS	MS	F
A	2	100	50	3.00
B	2	100	50	3.00
AB	4	500	125	7.50
Error	18	300	16.667	
Total	26	1000		

To determine if the treatment means differ, we test:

H_0: $\mu_1 = \mu_2 = \cdots = \mu_9$
H_a: At least two treatment means differ

The test statistic is $F = \dfrac{\text{MST}}{\text{MSE}} = 5.25$

The rejection region requires $\alpha = .05$ in the upper tail of the F distribution with $v_1 = ab - 1 = 3(3) - 1 = 8$ and $v_2 = n - ab = 27 - 3(3) = 18$. From Table IX, Appendix A, $F_{.05} = 2.51$. The rejection region is $F > 2.51$.

Since the observed value of the test statistic falls in the rejection region ($F = 5.25 > 2.51$), H_0 is rejected. There is sufficient evidence to indicate the treatment means differ at $\alpha = .05$.

Since the treatment means differ, we next test for interaction between factors A and B. To determine if factors A and B interact, we test:

H_0: Factors A and B do not interact to affect the mean response
H_a: Factors A and B do interact to affect the mean response

The test statistic is $F = \dfrac{\text{MS}AB}{\text{MSE}} = 7.50$

The rejection region requires $\alpha = .05$ in the upper tail of the F distribution with $v_1 = (a - 1)(b - 1) = (3 - 1)(3 - 1) = 4$ and $v_2 = n - ab = 27 - 3(3) = 18$. From Table IX, Appendix A, $F_{.05} = 2.93$. The rejection region is $F > 2.93$.

Since the observed value of the test statistic falls in the rejection region ($F = 7.50 > 2.93$), H_0 is rejected. There is sufficient evidence to indicate the factors A and B interact at $\alpha = .05$. Since interaction is present, no tests for main effects are necessary.

c. $SSA = .4(1000) = 400$, $SSB = .1(1000) = 100$, $SSAB = .2(1000) = 200$
$SSE = SS(\text{Total}) - SSA - SSB - SSAB = 1000 - 400 - 100 - 200 = 300$
$SST = SSA + SSB + SSAB = 400 + 100 + 200 = 700$

$$MSA = \frac{SSA}{a - 1} = \frac{400}{3 - 1} = 50 \qquad\qquad MSB = \frac{SSB}{b - 1} = \frac{100}{3 - 1} = 50$$

$$MSAB = \frac{SSAB}{(a - 1)(b - 1)} = \frac{200}{(3 - 1)(3 - 1)} = 50$$

$$MSE = \frac{SSE}{n - ab} = \frac{300}{27 - 3(3)} = 16.667 \qquad\qquad MST = \frac{SST}{ab - 1} = \frac{700}{3(3) - 1} = 87.5$$

$$F_A = \frac{MSA}{MSE} = \frac{200}{16.667} = 12.00 \qquad\qquad F_B = \frac{MSB}{MSE} = \frac{50}{16.667} \, 3.00$$

$$F_{AB} = \frac{MSAB}{MSE} = \frac{50}{16.667} = 3.00 \qquad\qquad F_T = \frac{MST}{MSE} = \frac{87.5}{16.667} = 5.25$$

Source	df	SS	MS	F
A	2	400	200	12.00
B	2	100	50	3.00
AB	4	200	50	3.00
Error	18	300	16.667	
Total	26	1000		

To determine if the treatment means differ, we test:

H_0: $\mu_1 = \mu_2 = \cdots = \mu_9$
H_a: At least two treatment means differ

The test statistic is $F = \dfrac{\text{MST}}{\text{MSE}} = 5.25$

The rejection region requires $\alpha = .05$ in the upper tail of the F distribution with $v_1 = ab - 1 = 3(3) - 1 = 8$ and $v_2 = n - ab = 27 - 3(3) = 18$. From Table IX, Appendix A, $F_{.05} = 2.51$. The rejection region is $F > 2.51$.

Since the observed value of the test statistic falls in the rejection region ($F = 5.25 > 2.51$), H_0 is rejected. There is sufficient evidence to indicate the treatment means differ at $\alpha = .05$.

Since the treatment means differ, we next test for interaction between factors A and B. To determine if factors A and B interact, we test:

H_0: Factors A and B do not interact to affect the mean response
H_a: Factors A and B do interact to affect the mean response

The test statistic is $F = \dfrac{\text{MS}AB}{\text{MSE}} = 3.00$

The rejection region requires $\alpha = .05$ in the upper tail of the F distribution with $v_1 = (a - 1)(b - 1) = (3 - 1)(3 - 1) = 4$ and $v_2 = n - ab = 27 - 3(3) = 18$. From Table IX, Appendix A, $F_{.05} = 2.93$. The rejection region is $F > 2.93$.

Since the observed value of the test statistic falls in the rejection region ($F = 3.00 > 2.93$), H_0 is rejected. There is sufficient evidence to indicate the factors A and B interact at $\alpha = .05$. Since interaction is present, no tests for main effects are necessary.

d. $SSA = .4(1000) = 400$, $SSB = .4(1000) = 400$, $SSAB = .1(1000) = 100$

$SSE = SS(\text{Total}) - SSA - SSB - SSAB = 1000 - 400 - 400 - 100 = 100$

$SST = SSA + SSB + SSAB = 400 + 400 + 100 = 900$

$MSA = \dfrac{SSA}{a-1} = \dfrac{400}{3-1} = 200$ $\qquad\qquad$ $MSB = \dfrac{SSB}{b-1} = \dfrac{400}{3-1} = 200$

$MSAB = \dfrac{SSAB}{(a-1)(b-1)} = \dfrac{100}{(3-1)(3-1)} = 25$

$$MSE = \frac{SSE}{n-ab} = \frac{100}{27-3(3)} = 5.556 \qquad MST = \frac{SST}{ab-1} = \frac{900}{3(3)-1} = 112.5$$

$$F_A = \frac{MSA}{MSE} = \frac{200}{5.556} = 36.00 \qquad F_B = \frac{MSB}{MSE} = \frac{200}{5.556} = 36.00$$

$$F_{AB} = \frac{MSAB}{MSE} = \frac{25}{5.556} = 4.50 \qquad F_T = \frac{MST}{MSE} = \frac{112.5}{5.556} = 20.25$$

Source	df	SS	MS	F
A	2	400	200	36.00
B	2	400	200	36.00
AB	4	100	25	4.50
Error	18	100	5.556	
Total	26	1000		

To determine if the treatment means differ, we test:

H_0: $\mu_1 = \mu_2 = \cdots = \mu_9$
H_a: At least two treatment means differ

The test statistic is $F = \dfrac{MST}{MSE} = 20.25$

The rejection region requires $\alpha = .05$ in the upper tail of the F distribution with $\nu_1 = ab - 1 = 3(3) - 1 = 8$ and $\nu_2 = n - ab = 27 - 3(3) = 18$. From Table IX, Appendix A, $F_{.05} = 2.51$. The rejection region is $F > 2.51$.

Since the observed value of the test statistic falls in the rejection region ($F = 20.25 > 2.51$), H_0 is rejected. There is sufficient evidence to indicate the treatment means differ at $\alpha = .05$.

Since the treatment means differ, we next test for interaction between factors A and B. To determine if factors A and B interact, we test:

H_0: Factors A and B do not interact to affect the mean response
H_a: Factors A and B do interact to affect the mean response

The test statistic is $F = \dfrac{MSAB}{MSE} = 4.50$

The rejection region requires $\alpha = .05$ in the upper tail of the F distribution with $\nu_1 = (a - 1)(b - 1) = (3 - 1)(3 - 1) = 4$ and $\nu_2 = n - ab = 27 - 3(3) = 18$. From Table IX, Appendix A, $F_{.05} = 2.93$. The rejection region is $F > 2.93$.

Since the observed value of the test statistic falls in the rejection region ($F = 4.50 > 2.93$), H_0 is rejected. There is sufficient evidence to indicate the factors A and B interact at $\alpha = .05$. Since interaction is present, no tests for main effects are necessary.

10.79   a.   This is a 6×6 factorial design.

      b.   There are 2 factors – level of coagulant and acidity level. The factor "level of coagulation" has 6 levels – 5, 10, 20, 50, 100, and 200 milligrams per liter. The factor "acidity level" has 6 levels – 4.0, 5.0, 6.0, 7.0, 8.0, and 9.0. There are $6 \times 6 = 36$ treatments for this study. Each treatment is a combination of one level of coagulation level and acidity level. An example of a treatment is coagulation level 5 and acidity level 4.0.

10.81   a.   There are 2 factors in this experiment. The first factor is wash-up event. There are 3 levels of this factor. The second factor is strata. There are 4 levels of strata: coarse-branching, medium-branching, fine-branching, and hydroid algae.

      b.   There are a total of $3 \times 4 = 12$ treatments in the experiment.

      c.   There are 2 replicates for each treatment in the experiment.

      d.   The total sample size is $12 \times 2 = 24$.

      e.   The response variable is the mussel density (percent per square centimeter).

      f.   The first ANOVA F-test is the test for differences among the treatments. If this test is significant, then the test for interaction follows.

Since not enough information is provided to test for differences among the treatment means, we will test for interaction.

To determine if Event and Strata interact to affect the mean mussel density, we test:

H_0: Event and Strata do not interact
H_a: Event and Strata interact

The test statistic is $F = 1.91$.

The p-value is $p > .05$. Since the p-value $(> .05)$ is not less than $\alpha = .05$, H_0 is not rejected. There is insufficient evidence to indicate Event and Strata interact at $\alpha = .05$.

      g.   Since the interaction is not significant, we will test for the main effects.

Event:

To determine if differences exist in the mean mussel densities among the three events, we test:

H_0: $\mu_1 = \mu_2 = \mu_3$
H_a: At least two event means differ

The test statistic is $F = 0.35$.

The *p*-value is $p > .05$. Since the *p*-value ($> .05$) is not less than $\alpha = .05$, H_0 is not rejected. There is insufficient evidence to indicate differences exist in the mean mussel densities among the three events at $\alpha = .05$.

Strata:

To determine if differences exist in the mean mussel densities among the four strata, we test:

H_0: $\mu_1 = \mu_2 = \mu_3 = \mu_4$
H_a: At least two strata means differ

The test statistic is $F = 217.33$.

The *p*-value is $p < .05$. Since the p-value ($< .05$) is less than $\alpha = .05$, H_0 is rejected. There is sufficient evidence to indicate differences exist in the mean mussel densities among the four strata at $\alpha = .05$.

    h.   The mean density for Strata Hydroid is significantly larger than the mean densities of the other 3 strata. The mean density for Strata Fine is significantly larger than the mean densities of Strata Medium and Strata Coarse. There is no difference in the mean densities of Strata Medium and Strata Coarse.

10.83   a.   A 2×2 factorial design was used for this study. The two factors are color and type of questions, each at 2 levels. There are $2 \times 2 = 4$ treatments. The 4 treatments are "blue, difficult", "blue, simple", "red, difficult", and "red, simple".

    b.   Since the *p*-value is small (*p*-value $< .03$), H_0 is rejected. There is sufficient evidence to indicate that color and type of questions interact to affect mean exam scores. This means that the effect of color on the mean exam scores depends on the difficulty of the questions.

    c.   Using MINITAB, the graph is:

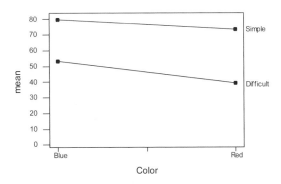

Looking at the graph, the lines are not parallel. The difference between the Blue and Red "simple" questions is not as great as the difference between the Blue and Red "difficult" questions. The effect of color on the exam scores depends on the level of difficulty.

10.85   a.

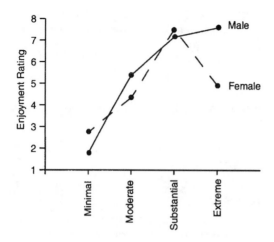

The pattern in the graph suggests interaction between suspense and gender. The difference between the mean ratings of the two genders varies depending on the suspense category. Notice that the lines cross twice.

b.   To determine if interaction exists between suspense and gender, we test:

H_0: Gender and Suspense do not interact
H_a: Gender and Suspense interact

The test statistic is $F = 4.42$ and p-value = .007. We reject the null hypothesis. For any level of significance greater than .007, we can conclude that Gender and Suspense interact to affect the mean rating.

c.   Because the factors interact, there is evidence to indicate the difference between the mean enjoyment levels of males and females are different for different suspense levels.

10.87   a.   Using MINITAB, the ANOVA results are:

ANOVA: Weight versus Diet, Size

```
Factor   Type   Levels  Values
Diet     fixed       2  1, 2
Size     fixed       2  1, 2


Analysis of Variance for Weight

Source     DF       SS       MS       F      P
Diet        1   0.0124   0.0124    0.22  0.645
Size        1   8.0679   8.0679  141.18  0.000
Diet*Size   1   0.0364   0.0364    0.64  0.432
Error      24   1.3715   0.0571
Total      27   9.4883
```

Source	df	SS	MS	F	P
Diet	1	0.0124	0.0124	0.22	0.645
Size	1	8.0679	8.0679	141.18	0.000
Interaction	1	0.0364	0.0364	0.64	0.432
Error	24	1.3715	0.0571		
Total	27	9.4883			

b. To determine if Diet and Size interact, we test:

H_0: The factors Diet and Size do not interact
H_a: Diet and Size interact

The test statistic is $F = .64$ and p-value $= .432$. We do not reject the null hypothesis. For any level of significance lower than $\alpha = .432$, we could not conclude that the factors interact. We therefore test the main effects.

To determine if the mean weight differs for the two diets, we test:

H_0: $\mu_{regular} = \mu_{supplement}$
H_a: $\mu_{regular} \neq \mu_{supplement}$

The test statistic is $F = .22$ and p-value $= .645$. We do not reject the null hypothesis. For any significance level lower than $\alpha = .645$, we cannot conclude that the mean weight of the kidney differed for the two diets.

To determine if the mean weight differs between the two sizes, we test:

H_0: $\mu_{lean} = \mu_{obese}$
H_a: $\mu_{lean} \neq \mu_{obese}$

The test statistic is $F = 141.18$ and p-value $= .000$. We reject the null hypothesis. For any significance level greater than or equal to $\alpha = .000$, we conclude that the mean weight of the kidney differs for the two sizes.

10.89 a. We first calculate the total of $n = 8$ pulling force measurements for each of the four categories by multiplying the means in each category by 8.

	Light	Heavy	Totals
Females	146.4	116.0	262.4
Males	104.0	98.0	202.0
Totals	250.4	214.0	

$$\sum x_i = 146.4 + 116.0 + 104.0 + 98.0 = 464.4$$

b. $CM = \dfrac{\left(\sum x_i\right)^2}{n} = \dfrac{464.4^2}{32} = 6{,}739.605$

c. $SS(Sex) = \dfrac{\sum A_i^2}{br} - CM = \dfrac{262.4^2}{2(8)} + \dfrac{202.0^2}{2(8)} - 6{,}739.605 = 6{,}853.61 - 6{,}739.605$

$$= 114.005$$

$SS(Weight) = \dfrac{\sum B_i^2}{ar} - CM = \dfrac{250.4^2}{2(8)} + \dfrac{214.0^2}{2(8)} - 6{,}739.605 = 6{,}781.01 - 6{,}739.605$

$$= 41.405$$

$SS(Sex \times Weight) = \dfrac{\sum\sum AB_{ij}^2}{r} - SS(Sex) - SS(Weight) - CM$

$$= \dfrac{146.4^2}{8} + \dfrac{116.0^2}{8} + \dfrac{104.0^2}{8} + \dfrac{98.0^2}{8} - 114.005 - 41.405$$

$$- 6{,}739.605 = 18.605$$

d. The sum of squares of deviations within each sample are found by multiplying the variance by $n - 1 = 8 - 1 = 7$.

	Standard Deviation	Variance	SS
Female, Light	6.81	46.3761	324.6327
Female, Heavy	2.93	8.5849	60.0943
Male, Light	5.04	25.4016	177.8112
Male, Heavy	5.70	32.4900	227.4300
			789.9682

e. $SSE = 789.9682$

f. $SS(Total) = SS(Sex) + SS(Weight) + SS(Sex \times Weight) + SSE$

$$= 114.005 + 41.405 + 18.605 + 789.9682 = 963.9832$$

g.

Source	df	SS	MS	F
Sex	1	114.005	114.005	4.04
Weight	1	41.405	41.405	1.47
Sex $\times$ Weight	1	18.605	18.605	.66
Error	28	789.9682	18.21315	
Total	31	963.9832		

h. $SST = SS(Sex) + SS(Weight) + SS(Sex \times Weight) = 114.005 + 41.405 + 18.605$

$$= 174.015$$

$MST = \dfrac{SST}{ab-1} = \dfrac{174.015}{2(2)-1} = 58.005$

$F_T = \dfrac{MST}{MSE} = \dfrac{58.005}{28.21315} = 2.06$

To determine if differences exist among the treatment means, we test:

H_0: $\mu_1 = \mu_2 = \mu_3 = \mu_4$
H_a: At least one treatment mean is different

The test statistic is $F = \dfrac{\text{MST}}{\text{MSE}} = 2.06$

The rejection region requires $\alpha = .05$ in the upper tail of the F distribution with $v_1 = ab - 1 = 2(2) - 1 = 3$ and $v_2 = n - ab = 32 - 2(2) = 28$. From Table IX, Appendix A, $F_{.05} \approx 2.95$. The rejection region is $F > 2.95$.

Since the observed value of the test statistic does not fall in the rejection region ($F = 2.06 \not> 2.95$), H_0 is not rejected. There is insufficient evidence to indicate the treatment means differ at $\alpha = .05$.

Since there is no difference among the treatment means, no further analysis is warranted.

A graph of the means is:

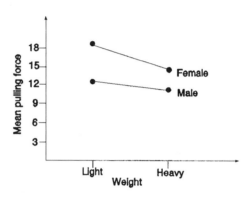

i.   We must assume that:
1)   The response times for each gender-weight categories are normally distributed.
2)   The response time variances are the same for each gender-weight category.
3)   Random and independent samples are drawn from each gender-weight category.

10.91   In a completely randomized design, independent random selection of treatments to be assigned to experimental units is required; in a randomized block design, sets (blocks) of matched experimental units are employed, with an experimental unit in each block randomly assigned a treatment.

10.93   When the overall level of significance of a multiple comparisons procedure is α, the level of significance for each comparison is less than α.

10.95   a.   SS(Treatment) = SS(Total) − SS(Block) − SSE = 22.308 − 10.688 − .288 = 11.332

MS(Treatment) = $\dfrac{\text{SS(Treatment)}}{k-1} = \dfrac{11.332}{4-1} = 3.777$, df = $k - 1 = 3$

MS(Block) = $\dfrac{\text{SS(Block)}}{b-1} = \dfrac{10.688}{5-1} = 2.672$, df = $b - 1 = 4$

MSE = $\dfrac{\text{SSE}}{n-k-b+1} = \dfrac{.288}{20-4-5+1} = .024$, df = $n - k - b + 1 = 12$

Treatment $F = \dfrac{MS(\text{Treatment})}{MSE} = \dfrac{3.777}{.024} = 157.375$

Block $F = \dfrac{MS(\text{Block})}{MSE} = \dfrac{2.672}{.024} = 111.33$

The ANOVA Table is:

Source	df	SS	MS	F
Treatment	3	11.332	3.777	157.38
Block	4	10.688	2.672	111.33
Error	12	.288	.024	
Total	19	22.308		

b. To determine if there is a difference among the treatment means, we test:

H_0: $\mu_A = \mu_B = \mu_C = \mu_D$
H_a: At least two treatment means differ

The test statistic is $F = \dfrac{MS(\text{Treatment})}{MSE} = 157.38$

The rejection region requires $\alpha = .05$ in the upper tail of the F distribution with $v_1 = k - 1 = 4 - 1 = 3$ and $v_2 = n - k - b + 1 = 20 - 4 - 5 + 1 = 12$. From Table IX, Appendix A, $F_{.05} = 3.49$. The rejection region is $F > 3.49$.
Since the observed value of the test statistic falls in the rejection region ($F = 157.38 > 3.49$), H_0 is rejected. There is sufficient evidence to indicate a difference among the treatment means at $\alpha = .05$.

c. Since there is evidence of differences among the treatment means, we need to compare the treatment means. The number of pairwise comparisons is $\dfrac{k(k-1)}{2} = \dfrac{4(4-1)}{2} = 6$.

d. To determine if there are difference among the block means, we test:

H_0: All the block means are the same
H_a: At least two block means differ

The test statistic is $F = \dfrac{MS(\text{Block})}{MSE} = 111.33$

The rejection region requires $\alpha = .05$ in the upper tail of the F distribution with $v_1 = b - 1 = 5 - 1 = 4$ and $v_2 = n - k - b + 1 = 20 - 4 - 5 + 1 = 12$. From Table IX, Appendix A, $F_{.05} = 3.26$. The rejection region is $F > 3.26$.

Since the observed value of the test statistic falls in the rejection region ($F = 111.33 > 3.26$), H_0 is rejected. There is sufficient evidence that the block means differ at $\alpha = .05$.

10.97 a. The data are collected as a completely randomized design because five boxes of each size were randomly selected and tested.

b. Yes. The confidence intervals surrounding each of the means do not overlap. This would indicate that there is a difference in the means for the two sizes.

c. No. Several of the confidence intervals overlap. This would indicate that the mean compression strengths of the sizes that have intervals that overlap are not significantly different.

10.99 To determine if differences in the mean percent of pronoun errors exist among the three groups, we test:

H_0: $\mu_1 = \mu_2 = \mu_3$
H_a: At least two treatment means differ

where μ_i represents the mean percent of pronoun errors for the ith group.

The test statistic is $F = 8.295$.

Since the p-value is so small ($p = .0016$), H_0 is rejected for any $\alpha > .0016$. There is sufficient evidence to indicate a difference in the mean percent of pronoun errors among the three groups.

A multiple comparison was run on the three group means. A line connects the means of the SLI and the YND groups. The mean percent of pronoun errors is not different for these two groups. The mean percent of pronoun errors for the OND group is significantly smaller than the mean percent of pronoun errors for both the SLI and the YND groups.

10.101 a. To determine if the mean scores of the four groups differ, we test:

H_0: $\mu_1 = \mu_2 = \mu_3 = \mu_4$
H_a: At least two treatment means differ

The test statistic is $F = 39.1$.

The rejection region requires $\alpha = .05$ in the upper tail of the F distribution with $\nu_1 = k - 1 = 4 - 1 = 3$ and $\nu_2 = n - k = 278 - 4 = 274$. Using Table IX, Appendix A, $F_{.05} \approx 2.60$. The rejection region is $F > 2.60$.

Since the observed value of the test statistic falls in the rejection region ($F = 39.1 > 2.60$), H_0 is rejected. There is sufficient evidence to indicate a difference in the mean scores among the four groups at $\alpha = .05$.

b. No. No information was provided on the sample means. The test of hypotheses performed in part a just indicates that differences exist, but not where. Further information is needed.

Analysis of Variance: Comparing More Than Two Means   **293**

c.   There is no significant difference in the mean scores between the forensic psychiatric patients and the nonforensic psychiatric patients. There is no significant difference in the mean scores between the honest college students and the "fake bad" college students. However, the mean scores for the two college student groups are significantly greater than the mean scores for the psychiatric patients. Again the higher the score, the more deliberately distorted responses.

10.103 Using MINITAB, the ANOVA results are:

One-way ANOVA: Spillage versus Cause

```
Source  DF      SS    MS     F      P
Cause    3    6576  2192  0.74  0.535
Error   44  130565  2967
Total   47  137140

S = 54.47   R-Sq = 4.80%   R-Sq(adj) = 0.00%
```

```
                                  Individual 95% CIs For Mean Based on
                                  Pooled StDev
Level        N   Mean   StDev   ---+---------+---------+---------+------
Collision   10  76.60   70.36                 (-------------*-------------)
Fire        12  70.92   60.68             (-----------*------------)
Grounding   14  47.79   28.47   (-----------*-----------)
HullFail    12  54.42   56.39      (------------*-----------)
                                  ---+---------+---------+---------+------
                                    25        50        75       100

Pooled StDev = 54.47
```

The ANOVA table is:

Source	df	SS	MS	F	p
Cause	3	6,576	2,192	0.74	0.535
Error	44	130,565	2,967	2,967	
Total	47	137,140			

To determine if differences exist among the mean spillage amounts of the four accident types, we test:

H_0: $\mu_1 = \mu_2 = \mu_3 = \mu_4$
H_a: At least two treatment means differ

The test statistic is $F = 0.74$.

The p-value is $p = .535$. Since the p-value is greater than α ($p = .535 > .01$), H_0 is not rejected. There is insufficient evidence to indicate differences exist among the mean spillage amounts of the four accident types at $\alpha = .01$.

10.105 a.

Source	df	F-value	p-value
Time Period	3	11.25	.0001
Station	9		
Error	27		
Total	39		

b. To determine if the mean biomass densities differ among the three time periods, we test:

H_0: $\mu_1 = \mu_2 = \mu_3 = \mu_4$
H_a: The mean biomass density differ for at least two of the time periods

The test statistic is $F = 11.25$ and $p = .0001$. We can reject the null hypothesis at the $\alpha > .0001$ level of significance. At least two of the time periods differ with respect to the mean biomass of water boatmen nymphs.

c. The time period with the largest mean biomass is either 7/9-7/23 or 7/24-8/8. There is no significant difference between the two means. The time period with the smallest mean biomass is 8/24-8/31.

10.107 a. Experimental units: zircaloy components
Blocks: ingots
Response: pressure required to separate the bonded components
Factor: bonding agent or element
Factor type: qualitative
Treatments: nickel, iron, copper

b. This is a designed experiment. The elements and their assignment to the ingots is under the control of the people running the experiment.

c. Using MINITAB, the ANOVA results are:

Two-way ANOVA: Pressure versus Agent, Ingot

```
Source   DF       SS       MS      F       P
Agent     2   131.901   65.9505   6.36   0.013
Ingot     6   268.290   44.7149   4.31   0.015
Error    12   124.459   10.3716
Total    20   524.650

S = 3.220    R-Sq = 76.28%    R-Sq(adj) = 60.46%

                    Individual 95% CIs For Mean Based on
                    Pooled StDev
Agent       Mean    -----+---------+---------+---------+----
Copper   70.1857    (--------*--------)
Iron     75.9000                       (--------*--------)
Nickel   71.1000       (--------*--------)
                    -----+---------+---------+---------+----
                      69.0      72.0      75.0      78.0
```

d. To determine if differences exist in the mean pressure required among the 3 bonding agents, we test:

H_o: $\mu_1 = \mu_2 = \mu_3$
H_a: At least two treatment means differ.

The test statistic is $F = 6.36$.

The p-value is $p = .013$. Since the p-value is less than α ($p = .013 < .05$), H_0 is rejected. There is sufficient evidence to indicate differences exist in the mean pressure required among the 3 bonding agents at $\alpha = .05$.

e. Using SAS, the Tukey multiple comparisons are:

```
Tukey's Studentized Range (HSD) Test for pressure

NOTE: This test controls the Type I experimentwise error rate, but it generally has a
           higher Type II error rate than REGWQ.


           Alpha                                        0.05
           Error Degrees of Freedom                       12
           Error Mean Square                        10.37159
           Critical Value of Studentized Range       3.77278
           Minimum Significant Difference             4.5923


       Means with the same letter are not significantly different.


       Tukey Grouping           Mean      N    agent

                    A         75.900      7    Iron

                    B         71.100      7    Nickel
                    B
                    B         70.186      7    Copper
```

From the printout, the mean pressure for Iron is significantly greater than the mean pressure for Nickel and Copper. No other differences exist.

f. Assumptions:

1. The probability distributions of the bonding strength for all ingot-element combinations are normal.
2. The variances for all the probability distributions are equal.
3. The samples are selected randomly and independently within blocks.

10.109 a.　Using MINITAB, the ANOVA results are:

ANOVA: Sales versus Price, Display

```
Factor    Type    Levels   Values
Price     fixed        3   1, 2, 3
Display   fixed        3   1, 2, 3

Analysis of Variance for Sales

Source          DF        SS        MS        F       P
Price            2   3089054   1544527   3121.89   0.000
Display          2   1691393    845696   1709.37   0.000
Price*Display    4    510705    127676    258.07   0.000
Error           18      8905       495
Total           26   5300057

S = 22.2428   R-Sq = 99.83%   R-Sq(adj) = 99.76%
```

b.　Some preliminary calculations are:

$$\text{SST} = 3{,}089{,}054 + 1{,}691{,}393 + 510{,}705 = 5{,}291{,}152$$
$$\text{MST} = \frac{5{,}291{,}152}{8} = 661{,}394$$

To determine whether the treatment means differ, we test:

H_0: $\mu_1 = \mu_2 = \cdots = \mu_9$
H_a: At least two treatment means differ

The test statistic is $F = \dfrac{\text{MST}}{\text{MSE}} = \dfrac{661{,}394}{495} = 1336.85$

The rejection region requires $\alpha = .10$ in the upper tail of the F distribution with $v_1 = ab - 1 = 3(3) - 1 = 8$ and $v_2 = n - ab = 27 - 3(3) = 18$. From Table VIII, Appendix A, $F_{.10} = 2.04$. The rejection region is $F > 2.04$.

Since the observed value of the test statistic falls in the rejection region ($F = 1336.85 > 2.04$), H_0 is rejected. There is sufficient evidence to indicate the treatment means differ at $\alpha = .10$.

c.　Since there are differences among the treatment means, we next test for the presence of interaction.

H_0: Factors A and B do not interact to affect the response means
H_a: Factors A and B do interact to affect the response means

The test statistic is $F = \dfrac{\text{MS}AB}{\text{MSE}} = 258.07$

The rejection region requires $\alpha = .10$ in the upper tail of the F distribution with $v_1 = (a - 1)(b - 1) = (3 - 1)(3 - 1) = 4$ and $v_2 = n - ab = 17 - 3(3) = 18$. From Table VIII, Appendix A, $F_{.10} = 2.29$. The rejection region is $F > 2.29$.

Analysis of Variance: Comparing More Than Two Means

Since the observed value of the test statistic falls in the rejection region ($F = 258.07 > 2.29$), H_0 is rejected. There is sufficient evidence to indicate the two factors interact at $\alpha = .10$.

d. The main effect tests are not warranted since interaction is present in part **c**.

e. Since the interaction is significant, the nine treatment means need to be compared. To reduce the number of comparisons, we will compare the means of the prices at each level of the displays.

Using SAS, the Tukey's multiple comparisons are:

```
------------------------------ DISPLAY=NORMAL ------------------------------

                           The ANOVA Procedure

                Tukey's Studentized Range (HSD) Test for SALES

       NOTE: This test controls the Type I experimentwise error rate, but it
             generally has a higher Type II error rate than REGWQ.


                 Alpha                                   0.05
                 Error Degrees of Freedom                   6
                 Error Mean Square                    401.8889
                 Critical Value of Studentized Range  4.33902
                 Minimum Significant Difference         50.221


         Means with the same letter are not significantly different.


         Tukey Grouping          Mean      N    PRICE

                      A        1578.00      3    COST

                      B        1202.67      3    REDUCED

                      C        1014.67      3    REGULAR

------------------------------ DISPLAY=PLUS ------------------------------

                           The ANOVA Procedure

                Tukey's Studentized Range (HSD) Test for SALES

       NOTE: This test controls the Type I experimentwise error rate, but it
             generally has a higher Type II error rate than REGWQ.


                 Alpha                                   0.05
                 Error Degrees of Freedom                   6
                 Error Mean Square                    653.4444
                 Critical Value of Studentized Range  4.33902
                 Minimum Significant Difference         64.038


         Means with the same letter are not significantly different.


         Tukey Grouping          Mean      N    PRICE

                      A        2510.00      3    COST

                      B        1898.67      3    REDUCED

                      C        1215.00      3    REGULAR
```

```
---------------------------- DISPLAY=TWICE ----------------------------

                          The ANOVA Procedure

             Tukey's Studentized Range (HSD) Test for SALES

    NOTE: This test controls the Type I experimentwise error rate, but it
            generally has a higher Type II error rate than REGWQ.

                 Alpha                                 0.05
                 Error Degrees of Freedom                 6
                 Error Mean Square                   428.8889
                 Critical Value of Studentized Range  4.33902
                 Minimum Significant Difference         51.88


          Means with the same letter are not significantly different.


          Tukey Grouping        Mean      N     PRICE

                     A        1828.67      3     COST

                     B        1505.00      3     REDUCED

                     C        1202.67      3     REGULAR
```

For Display = Normal, there are significant differences among mean sales for all prices. The mean sales for those priced at "cost to supermarket" is significantly greater than the mean sales for those priced at "reduced" price and "regular" price. The mean sales for those priced at "reduced" price is significantly greater than those priced at "regular" price.

For Display = Normal Plus, there are significant differences among mean sales for all prices. The mean sales for those priced at "cost to supermarket" is significantly greater than the mean sales for those priced at "reduced" price and "regular" price. The mean sales for those priced at "reduced" price is significantly greater than those priced at "regular" price.

For Display = Twice Normal, there are significant differences among mean sales for all prices. The mean sales for those priced at "cost to supermarket" is significantly greater than the mean sales for those priced at "reduced" price and "regular" price. The mean sales for those priced at "reduced" price is significantly greater than those priced at "regular" price.

10.111 a. df Photoperiod $= a - 1 = 2 - 1 = 1$; df Gender $= b - 1 = 2 - 1 = 1$
df $P \times G = (a - 1)(b - 1) = (2 - 1)(2 - 1) = 1$
df Error $= n - ab = 124 - 2(2) = 120$; df Total $= n - 1 = 124 - 1 = 123$

The ANOVA table is:

Source	df
Photoperiod	1
Gender	1
$P \times G$	1
Error	120
Total	123

b. The test for interaction was not significant. This implies that the weight gain for each gender did not depend on the photoperiod.

c. The p-value for the main effect photoperiod was less than .001. Since this p-value is so small, H_0 is rejected. There is sufficient evidence to indicate that the weight gain differs for the two photoperiods.

The p-value for the main effect gender was less than .001. Since this p-value is so small, H_0 is rejected. There is sufficient evidence to indicate that the weight gain differs for the two genders.

10.113 a. This is a 2×2 factorial experiment.

b. The two factors are the tent type (treated or untreated) and location (inside or outside). There are $2 \times 2 = 4$ treatments. The four treatments are (treated, inside), (treated, outside), (untreated, inside), and (untreated, outside).

c. The response variable is the number of mosquito bites received in a 20 minute interval.

d. There is sufficient evidence to indicate interaction is present. This indicates that the effect of the tent type on the number of mosquito bites depends on whether the person is inside or outside.

Simple Linear Regression

11.1 A deterministic model does not allow for random error or variation, whereas a probabilistic model does. An example where a deterministic model would be appropriate is:

Let y = cost of a 2×4 piece of lumber and
x = length (in feet)

The model would be $y = \beta_1 x$. There should be no variation in price for the same length of wood.

An example where a probabilistic model would be appropriate is:

Let y = sales per month of a commodity and
x = amount of money spent advertising

The model would be $y = \beta_0 + \beta_1 x + \varepsilon$. The sales per month will probably vary even if the amount of money spent on advertising remains the same.

11.3 The "line of means" is the deterministic component in a probabilistic model.

11.5

a.

b.

c.

d.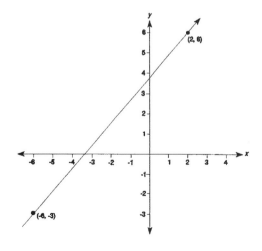

11.7   The two equations are:

$$4 = \beta_0 + \beta_1(-2) \text{ and } 6 = \beta_0 + \beta_1(4)$$

Subtracting the first equation from the second, we get

$$6 = \beta_0 + 4\beta_1$$
$$-(4 = \beta_0 - 2\beta_1)$$
$$\overline{}$$
$$2 = \quad 6\beta_1 \Rightarrow \beta_1 = \frac{2}{6} = \frac{1}{3}$$

Substituting $\beta_1 = \frac{1}{3}$ into the first equation, we get:

$$4 = \beta_0 + \frac{1}{3}(-2) \Rightarrow \beta_0 = 4 + \frac{2}{3} = \frac{14}{3}$$

The equation for the line is $y = \dfrac{14}{3} + \dfrac{1}{3}x$

11.9   To graph a line, we need two points. Pick two values for x, and find the corresponding y values by substituting the values of x into the equation.

a.   Let $x = 0 \Rightarrow y = 4 + (0) = 4$
and $x = 2 \Rightarrow y = 4 + (2) = 6$

b.   Let $x = 0 \Rightarrow y = 5 \Rightarrow 2(0) = 5$
and $x = 2 \Rightarrow y = 5 \Rightarrow 2(2) = 1$

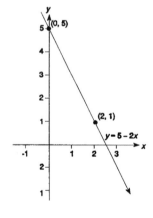

c. Let $x = 0 \Rightarrow y = -4 + 3(0) = -4$
and $x = 2 \Rightarrow y = -4 + 3(2) = 2$

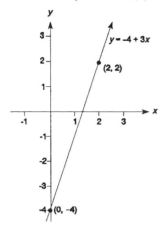

d. Let $x = 0 \Rightarrow y = -2(0) = 0$
and $x = 2 \Rightarrow y = -2(2) = -4$

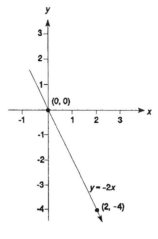

e. Let $x = 0 \Rightarrow y = 0$
and $x = 2 \Rightarrow y = 2$

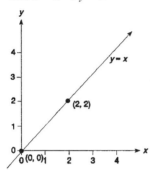

f. Let $x = 0 \Rightarrow y = .5 + 1.5(0) = .5$
and $x = 2 \Rightarrow y = .5 + 1.5(2) = 3.5$

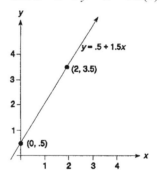

11.11 In regression, the error of prediction is the difference between the observed and predicted values of the dependent variable.

11.13 The statement "The estimates of β_0 and β_1 should be interpreted only within the sampled range of the independent variable, x." is true. We only have information about the relationship between y and x within the observed range of x.

11.15 From Exercise 11.14, $\hat{\beta}_0 = 7.10$ and $\hat{\beta}_1 = -.78$.

The fitted line is $= 7.10 - .78x$. To obtain values for , we substitute values of x into the equation and solve for.

a.

x	y	$\hat{y} = 7.10 - .78x$	$(y - \hat{y})$	$(y - \hat{y})^2$
7	2	1.64	.36	.1296
4	4	3.98	.02	.0004
6	2	2.42	−.42	.1764
2	5	5.54	−.54	.2916
1	7	6.32	.68	.4624
1	6	6.32	−.32	.1024
3	5	4.76	.24	.0576

$$\sum (y - \hat{y}) = 0.02 \qquad \text{SSE} = \sum (y - \hat{y})^2 = 1.2204$$

b.

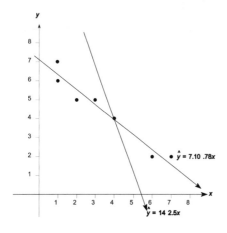

c.

x	y	$\hat{y} = 14 - 2.5x$	$(y - \hat{y})$	$(y - \hat{y})^2$
7	2	−3.5	5.5	30.25
4	4	4	0	0
6	2	−1	3	9
2	5	9	−4	16
1	7	11.5	−4.5	20.25
1	6	11.5	−5.5	30.25
3	5	6.5	−1.5	2.25
			$= -7$	SSE = 108.00

11.17 a.

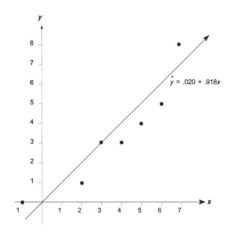

b. As x increases, y tends to increase. Thus, there appears to be a positive, linear relationship between y and x.

c. $\hat{\beta}_1 = \dfrac{SS_{xy}}{SS_{xx}} = \dfrac{39.8571}{43.4286} = .9177616 \approx .918$

$\hat{\beta}_0 = \bar{y} - \hat{\beta}_1 \bar{x} = 3.4286 - .9177616(3.7143) = .0197581 \approx .020$

d. The line appears to fit the data quite well.

e. $\hat{\beta}_0 = .020$ The estimated mean value of y when $x = 0$ is .020.

$\hat{\beta}_1 = .918$ The estimated change in the mean value of y for each unit change in x is .918.

These interpretations are valid only for values of x in the range from -1 to 7.

11.19 Some preliminary calculations are:

$\sum x_i = 13$ $\qquad\qquad \sum y_i = 107$ $\qquad\qquad \sum x_i y_i = 345$

$\sum x_i^2 = 43$ $\qquad\qquad \sum y_i^2 = 3,633$

$SS_{xy} = \sum x_i y_i - \dfrac{\sum x_i \sum y_i}{n} = 345 - \dfrac{13(107)}{5} = 66.8$

$SS_{xx} = \sum x_i^2 - \dfrac{\left(\sum x_i\right)^2}{n} = 43 - \dfrac{13^2}{5} = 9.2$

a. The straight-line model is $y = \beta_0 + \beta_1 x + \varepsilon$

b. $\hat{\beta}_1 = \dfrac{SS_{xy}}{SS_{xx}} = \dfrac{66.8}{9.2} = 7.260869565$

$$\hat{\beta}_0 = \bar{y} - \hat{\beta}_1\bar{x} = \frac{107}{5} - 7.260869565\left(\frac{13}{5}\right) = 2.52173913$$

The least squares prediction equation is $\hat{y} = 2.522 + 7.261x$

   c. $\hat{\beta}_1 = 7.261$. For each additional one day duration, the mean number of arrests is estimated to increase by 7.261.

        $\hat{\beta}_0 = 2.522$. Since x = 0 is not in the observed range of the duration in days, $\hat{\beta}_0$ has no interpretation other than the y-intercept.

11.21   a.   Using MINITAB, the least squares line is:

The slope of the line is positive – as x increases, y also increases.

   b. $\hat{\beta}_0 = 18.13$. Since we have no information as to whether x = 0 is within the observed range, we will assume that it is. Then, the estimate of the mean magnitude when redshift level is 0 is 18.13.

   c. $\hat{\beta}_1 = 6.21$. For each unit increase in redshift level, the mean value of magnitude is estimated to increase by 6.21.

11.23   a.   The straight-line model is $y = \beta_0 + \beta_1 x + \varepsilon$. Based on the theory, we would expect the metal level to decrease as the distance increases. Thus, the slope should be negative.

   b.   Yes. As the distance from the plant increases, the concentration of calcium tends to decrease.

   c.   No. As the distance from the plant increases, the concentration of arsenic tends to increase.

11.25   a.   The straight-line model is $y = \beta_0 + \beta_1 x + \varepsilon$

b. Some preliminary calculations are:

$$\sum x_i = 51.4 \qquad \sum y_i = 45.5 \qquad \sum x_i y_i = 210.49$$
$$\sum x_i^2 = 227.5 \qquad \sum y_i^2 = 214.41$$

$$SS_{xy} = \sum x_i y_i - \frac{\sum x_i \sum y_i}{n} = 210.49 - \frac{51.4(45.5)}{15} = 54.5766667$$

$$SS_{xx} = \sum x_i^2 - \frac{\left(\sum x_i\right)^2}{n} = 227.5 - \frac{51.4^2}{15} = 51.3693333$$

$$\hat{\beta}_1 = \frac{SS_{xy}}{SS_{xx}} = \frac{54.5766667}{51.3693333} = 1.062436734$$

$$\hat{\beta}_0 = \bar{y} - \hat{\beta}_1 \bar{x} = \frac{45.5}{15} - (1.062436734)\left(\frac{51.4}{15}\right) = -.607283208$$

The least squares prediction equation is $\hat{y} = -.607 + 1.062x$

c. Using MINITAB, the graph is:

There appears to be a positive linear relationship between the two variables. As the radar rainfall increases, the rain gauge values also increase.

d. $\hat{\beta}_0 = -.607$. Since $x = 0$ is not in the observed range, $\hat{\beta}_0$ has no meaning other than the y-intercept.

$\hat{\beta}_1 = 1.062$. For each unit increase in radar rainfall, the mean rain gauge rainfall increases by an estimated 1.062.

e. The straight-line model is $y = \beta_0 + \beta_1 x + \varepsilon$

Some preliminary calculations are:

$$\sum x_i = 46.7 \qquad \sum y_i = 45.5 \qquad \sum x_i y_i = 207.89$$
$$\sum x_i^2 = 210.21 \qquad \sum y_i^2 = 214.41$$

$$SS_{xy} = \sum x_i y_i - \frac{\sum x_i \sum y_i}{n} = 207.89 - \frac{46.7(45.5)}{15} = 66.2333333$$

$$SS_{xx} = \sum x_i^2 - \frac{\left(\sum x_i\right)^2}{n} = 210.21 - \frac{46.7^2}{15} = 64.8173333$$

$$\hat{\beta}_1 = \frac{SS_{xy}}{SS_{xx}} = \frac{66.2333333}{64.8173333} = 1.021846008$$

$$\hat{\beta}_0 = \bar{y} - \hat{\beta}_1 \bar{x} = \frac{45.5}{15} - (1.021846008)\left(\frac{46.7}{15}\right) = -.148013904$$

The least squares prediction equation is $\hat{y} = -.148 + 1.022x$

Using MINITAB, the graph is:

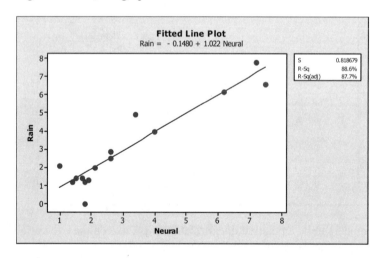

There appears to be a positive linear relationship between the two variables. As the neural rainfall increases, the rain gauge values also increase.

11.27   a.   A scattergram of the data is:

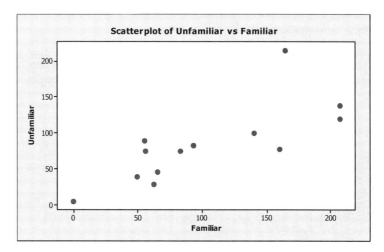

It appears that there is a positive linear relationship between total number of words with unfamiliar partner and with familiar partner.

b.   A straight line model would be $y = \beta_0 + \beta_1 x + \varepsilon$.

c.   Some preliminary calculations are:

$$\sum x_i = 1,341 \qquad \sum y_i = 1,099 \qquad \sum x_i y_i = 145,607$$
$$\sum x_i^2 = 189,963 \qquad \sum y_i^2 = 127,397$$

$$SS_{xy} = \sum x_i y_i - \frac{\sum x_i \sum y_i}{n} = 145,607 - \frac{1,341(1,099)}{13} = 32,240.9231$$

$$SS_{xx} = \sum x_i^2 - \frac{\left(\sum x_i\right)^2}{n} = 189,963 - \frac{1,341^2}{13} = 51,633.6923$$

$$\hat{\beta}_1 = \frac{SS_{xy}}{SS_{xx}} = \frac{32,240.9231}{51,633.6923} = .624416377$$

$$\hat{\beta}_0 = \bar{y} - \hat{\beta}_1 \bar{x} = \frac{1,099}{13} - (.624416377)\left(\frac{1,341}{13}\right) = 20.12751061$$

The least squares prediction equation is $\hat{y} = 20.1275 + .6244x$

d. $\hat{\beta}_0 = 20.1275$. Since $x = 0$ is in the observed range, the mean number of words in conversation with an unfamiliar partner is estimated to be 20.1275 when the number of words in conversation with a familiar partner is 0.

$\hat{\beta}_1 = .62442$. For each additional word in conversation with a familiar partner, the mean number of words in conversation with an unfamiliar partner is estimated to increase by .62442.

11.29 Using MINITAB, the regression analysis is:

```
The regression equation is
y = 5.35 + 0.530 x

Predictor        Coef       StDev          T         P
Constant       5.3480      0.1635      32.71     0.000
x              0.5299      0.9254       0.57     0.575

S = 0.4115      R-Sq = 2.0%       R-Sq(adj) = 0.0%

Analysis of Variance

Source            DF          SS          MS         F         P
Regression         1      0.0555      0.0555      0.33     0.575
Residual Error    16      2.7091      0.1693
Total             17      2.7646
```

The fitted regression line is $\hat{y} = 5.35 + .530x$. Thus, if the takeoff error was reduced by .1 meters, we would estimate that the best jumping distance would change by $.530(-.1) = -.053$ meters.

Generally, we would expect that the smaller the takeoff error, the longer the jump. From this data, the coefficient corresponding to the takeoff error is positive, indicating that there is a positive linear relationship between jumping distance and takeoff error. However, examining the output indicates that there is insufficient evidence of a linear relationship between jumping distance and takeoff error ($t = .57$ and $p = .575$). In addition, the R-square is very small ($R^2 = 2.0\%$), again indicating that takeoff error is not linearly related to jumping distance.

11.31 See Figure 11.7 in the text.

11.33 a. $SSE = SS_{yy} - \hat{\beta}_1 SS_{xy} = 95 - .75(50) = 57.5$

$$s^2 = \frac{SSE}{n-2} = \frac{57.5}{20-2} = 3.19444$$

b. $SS_{yy} = \sum y^2 - \frac{\left(\sum y\right)^2}{n} = 860 - \frac{50^2}{40} = 797.5$

$SSE = SS_{yy} - \hat{\beta}_1 SS_{xy} = 797.5 - .2(2700) = 257.5$

$$s^2 = \frac{SSE}{n-2} = \frac{257.5}{40-2} = 6.776315789 \approx 6.7763$$

c. $SS_{yy} = \sum (y_i - \bar{y})^2 = 58$ $\hat{\beta}_1 = \dfrac{SS_{xy}}{SS_{xx}} = \dfrac{91}{170} = .535294117$

$SSE = SS_{yy} - \hat{\beta}_1 SS_{xy} = 58 - .535294117(91) = 9.2882353 \approx 9.288$

$s^2 = \dfrac{SSE}{n-2} = \dfrac{9.2882353}{10-2} = 1.161029413 \approx 1.1610$

11.35 $SSE = SS_{yy} - \hat{\beta}_1 SS_{xy}$

where $SS_{yy} = \sum y_i^2 - \dfrac{\left(\sum y_i\right)^2}{n}$

For Exercise 11.14,

$\sum y_i^2 = 159$ $\sum y_i = 31$

$SS_{yy} = 159 - \dfrac{31^2}{7} = 159 - 137.2857143 = 21.7142857$

$SS_{xy} = -26.2857143$ $\hat{\beta}_1 = -.779661017$

Therefore, $SSE = 21.7142857 - (-.779661017)(-26.2857143) = 1.22033896 \approx 1.2203$

$s^2 = \dfrac{SSE}{n-2} = \dfrac{1.22033896}{7-2} = .244067792,\ s = \sqrt{.244067792} = .4960$

We would expect most of the observations to fall within $2s$ or $2(.4940)$ or $.988$ units of the least squares prediction line.

For Exercise 11.17,

$\sum x_i = 26$ $\sum y_i = 24$ $\sum x_i y_i = 129$ $\sum x_i^2 = 140$ $\sum y_i^2 = 124$

$SS_{xy} = \sum x_i y_i - \dfrac{\left(\sum x_i \sum y_i\right)}{n} = 129 - \dfrac{(26)(24)}{7} = 129 - 89.14285714 = 39.85714286$

$SS_{xx} = \sum x_i^2 - \dfrac{\left(\sum x_i\right)^2}{n} = 140 - \dfrac{(26)^2}{7} = 140 - 96.57142857 = 43.42857143$

$S_{yy} = \sum y_i^2 - \dfrac{\left(\sum y_i\right)^2}{n} = 124 - \dfrac{(24)^2}{7} = 124 - 82.28571429 = 41.71428571$

$\hat{\beta}_1 = \dfrac{SS_{xy}}{SS_{xx}} = \dfrac{39.85714286}{43.42857143} = .917763157$

$SSE = SS_{yy} - \hat{\beta}_1 SS_{xy} = 41.71428571 - (.917763157)(39.85714286)$

$= 41.71428571 - 36.57941726 = 5.13486841 \approx 5.1349$

$s^2 = \dfrac{SSE}{n-2} = \dfrac{5.13486841}{7-2} = 1.026973682\quad s = \sqrt{1.026973682} = 1.0134$

We would expect most of the observations to fall within $2s$ or $2(1.0134)$ or 2.0268 units of the least squares prediction line.

11.37 a.   From Exercise 11.19,

$$\sum y_i = 107 \qquad \sum y_i^2 = 3{,}633 \qquad SS_{xy} = 66.8 \qquad \hat{\beta}_1 = 7.260869565$$

$$SS_{yy} = \sum y_i^2 - \frac{\left(\sum y_i\right)^2}{n} = 3{,}633 - \frac{107^2}{5} = 1{,}343.2$$

$$SSE = SS_{yy} - \hat{\beta}_1 SS_{xy} = 1{,}343.2 - 7.260869565(66.8) = 858.1739131$$

$$s^2 = \frac{SSE}{n-2} = \frac{858.1739131}{5-2} = 286.057971$$
$$s = \sqrt{s^2} = \sqrt{286.057971} = 16.9132$$

b.   We would expect most of the observations to be within $2s = 2(16.9132) = 33.8264$ of the least squares line.

11.39 a.   From Exercise 11.24,

$$\sum y_i = 3{,}781.1 \qquad \sum y_i^2 = 651{,}612 \qquad SS_{xy} = -3{,}881.9986 \qquad \hat{\beta}_1 = -.305416114$$

$$SS_{yy} = \sum y_i^2 - \frac{\left(\sum y_i\right)^2}{n} = 651{,}612 - \frac{3{,}781.1^2}{22} = 1{,}761.2177$$

$$SSE = SS_{yy} - \hat{\beta}_1 SS_{xy} = 1{,}761.2177 - (-.305416114)(-3{,}881.9986) = 575.592773$$

$$s^2 = \frac{SSE}{n-2} = \frac{575.592773}{22-2} = 28.77963865$$
$$s = \sqrt{s^2} = \sqrt{28.77963865} = 5.364665754$$

We would expect most of the observations to be within $2s = 2(5.3647) = 10.7294$ of the least squares line.

b.   From Exercise 11.24,

$$\sum y_i = 3{,}764.2 \qquad \sum y_i^2 = 645{,}221 \qquad SS_{xy} = -3{,}441.97 \qquad \hat{\beta}_1 = -.270796878$$

$$SS_{yy} = \sum y_i^2 - \frac{\left(\sum y_i\right)^2}{n} = 645{,}221 - \frac{3{,}764.2^2}{22} = 1{,}166.38$$

$$SSE = SS_{yy} - \hat{\beta}_1 SS_{xy} = 1{,}166.38 - (-.270796878)(-3{,}441.97) = 234.3052698$$

$$s^2 = \frac{SSE}{n-2} = \frac{234.3052698}{22-2} = 11.71526349$$

$$s = \sqrt{s^2} = \sqrt{11.71526349} = 3.422756709$$

We would expect most of the observations to be within $2s = 2(3.4228) = 6.8456$ of the least squares line.

b. Since the standard deviation ($s = 3.423$) for the reading scores is smaller than the standard deviation for the math scores ($s = 5.365$), the reading score can be more accurately predicted than the math score.

11.41 a. From Exercise 11.27,

$$\sum y_i = 1,099 \qquad \sum y_i^2 = 127,397 \qquad SS_{xy} = 32,240.9231 \qquad \hat{\beta}_1 = .624416377$$

$$SS_{yy} = \sum y_i^2 - \frac{\left(\sum y_i\right)^2}{n} = 127,397 - \frac{1,099^2}{13} = 34,489.23077$$

$$SSE = SS_{yy} - \hat{\beta}_1 SS_{xy} = 34,489.23077 - (.624416377)(32,240.9231) = 14,357.47038$$

$$s^2 = \frac{SSE}{n-2} = \frac{14,357.47038}{13-2} = 1,305.22458$$
$$s = \sqrt{s^2} = \sqrt{1,305.22458} = 36.12789199$$

b. We would expect most of the observed numbers of words in conversation with an unfamiliar partner to fall within $2s$ or $2(36.1279)$ or 72.26 words of their predicted values.

11.43 In the equation, $E(y) = \beta_0 + \beta_1 x$, the value of β_1 is 0 if x has no linear relationship with y.

11.45 If you are running a one-tailed test of β_1 in simple linear regression, you divide the p-value from the computer printout by 2 to obtain the correct p-value of the one-tailed test.

11.47 a. For confidence coefficient .95, $\alpha = 1 - .95 = .05$ and $\alpha/2 = .05/2 = .025$. From Table VI, Appendix A, with df $= n - 2 = 12 - 2 = 10$, $t_{.025} = 2.228$.

The 95% confidence interval for β_1 is:

$$\hat{\beta}_1 \pm t_{.025} s_{\hat{\beta}_1} \quad \text{where } s_{\hat{\beta}_1} = \frac{s}{\sqrt{SS_{xx}}} = \frac{3}{\sqrt{35}} = .5071$$

$$\Rightarrow 31 \pm 2.228(.5071) \Rightarrow 31 \pm 1.13 \Rightarrow (29.87, 32.13)$$

For confidence coefficient .90, $\alpha = 1 - .90 = .10$ and $\alpha/2 = .10/2 = .05$. From Table VI, Appendix A, with df $= 10$, $t_{.05} = 1.812$.

The 90% confidence interval for β_1 is:

$$\hat{\beta}_1 \pm t_{.05} s_{\hat{\beta}_1} \Rightarrow 31 \pm 1.812(.5071) \Rightarrow 31 \pm .92 \Rightarrow (30.08, 31.92)$$

b. $s^2 = \dfrac{\text{SSE}}{n-2} = \dfrac{1960}{18-2} = 122.5, s = \sqrt{s^2} = 11.0680$

For confidence coefficient, .95, $\alpha = 1 - .95 = .05$ and $\alpha/2 = .05/2 = .025$. From Table VI, Appendix A, with df $= n - 2 = 18 - 2 = 16$, $t_{.025} = 2.120$. The 95% confidence interval for β_1 is:

$$\hat{\beta}_1 \pm t_{.025}\, s_{\hat{\beta}_1} \quad \text{where } s_{\hat{\beta}_1} = \dfrac{s}{\sqrt{\text{SS}_{xx}}} = \dfrac{11.0680}{\sqrt{30}} = 2.0207$$

$$\Rightarrow 64 \pm 2.120(2.0207) \Rightarrow 64 \pm 4.28 \Rightarrow (59.72, 68.28)$$

For confidence coefficient .90, $\alpha = 1 - .90 = .10$ and $\alpha/2 = .10/2 = .05$. From Table VI, Appendix A, with df $= 16$, $t_{.05} = 1.746$.

The 90% confidence interval for β_1 is:

$$\hat{\beta}_1 \pm t_{.05}\, s_{\hat{\beta}_1} \Rightarrow 64 \pm 1.746(2.0207) \Rightarrow 64 \pm 3.53 \Rightarrow (60.47, 67.53)$$

c. $s^2 = \dfrac{\text{SSE}}{n-2} = \dfrac{146}{24-2} = 6.6364, s = \sqrt{s^2} = 2.5761$

For confidence coefficient .95, $\alpha = 1 - .95 = .05$ and $\alpha/2 = .05/2 = .025$. From Table VI, Appendix A, with df $= n - 2 = 24 - 2 = 22$, $t_{.025} = 2.074$. The 95% confidence interval for β_1 is:

$$\hat{\beta}_1 \pm t_{.025}\, s_{\hat{\beta}_1} \quad \text{where } s_{\hat{\beta}_1} = \dfrac{s}{\sqrt{\text{SS}_{xx}}} = \dfrac{2.5761}{\sqrt{64}} = .3220$$

$$\Rightarrow -8.4 \pm 2.074(.322) \Rightarrow -8.4 \pm .67 \Rightarrow (-9.07, -7.73)$$

For confidence coefficient .90, $\alpha = 1 - .90 = .10$ and $\alpha/2 = .10/2 = .05$. From Table VI, Appendix A, with df $= 22$, $t_{.05} = 1.717$.

The 90% confidence interval for β_1 is:

$$\hat{\beta}_1 \pm t_{.05}\, s_{\hat{\beta}_1} \Rightarrow -8.4 \pm 1.717(.322) \Rightarrow -8.4 \pm .55 \Rightarrow (-8.95, -7.85)$$

11.49 a & c. Using MINITAB, a scatterplot of the data is:

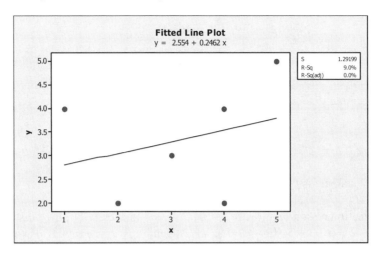

b. Some preliminary calculations are:

$$\sum x_i = 19 \qquad \sum y_i = 20 \qquad \sum x_i y_i = 66$$
$$\sum x_i^2 = 71 \qquad \sum y_i^2 = 74$$

$$SS_{xy} = \sum x_i y_i - \frac{\sum x_i \sum y_i}{n} = 66 - \frac{19(20)}{6} = 2.666666667$$

$$SS_{xx} = \sum x_i^2 - \frac{\left(\sum x_i\right)^2}{n} = 71 - \frac{19^2}{6} = 10.833333333$$

$$\hat{\beta}_1 = \frac{SS_{xy}}{SS_{xx}} = \frac{2.66666667}{10.833333333} = .246153846$$

$$\hat{\beta}_0 = \bar{y} - \hat{\beta}_1 \bar{x} = \frac{20}{6} - (.246153846)\left(\frac{19}{6}\right) = 2.553846155$$

The least squares prediction equation is $\hat{y} = 2.554 + .246x$

d. Some preliminary calculations are:

$$SS_{yy} = \sum y_i^2 - \frac{\left(\sum y_i\right)^2}{n} = 74 - \frac{20^2}{6} = 7.3333333333$$

$$SSE = SS_{yy} - \hat{\beta}_1 SS_{xy} = 7.3333333333 - (.246153846)(2.666666667) = 6.6769$$

$$s^2 = \frac{SSE}{n-2} = \frac{6.6769}{6-2} = 1.6692 \qquad s = \sqrt{s^2} = \sqrt{1.6692} = 1.292$$

The test statistic is $t = \dfrac{\hat{\beta}_1 - 0}{s_{\hat{\beta}_1}} = \dfrac{.246}{\dfrac{1.292}{\sqrt{10.83333333}}} = .627$

e. To determine if x and y are linearly related, we test:

H_0: $\beta_1 = 0$
H_a: $\beta_1 \neq 0$

The test statistic is $t = .627$.

The rejection region requires $\alpha/2 = .01/2 = .005$ in each tail of the t distribution with df = $n - 2 = 6 - 2 = 4$. From Table VI, Appendix A, $t_{.005} = 4.604$. The rejection region is $t < -4.604$ or $t > 4.604$.

Since the observed value of the test statistic does not fall in the rejection region ($t = .627 \not> 4.604$), H_0 is not rejected. There is insufficient evidence to indicate that x and y are linearly related at $\alpha = .01$.

f. For confidence coefficient .99, $\alpha = 1 - .99 = .01$ and $\alpha/2 = .01/2 = .005$. From Table VI, Appendix A, with df = $n - 2 = 6 - 2 = 4$, $t_{.005} = 4.604$. The 99% confidence interval is:

$$\hat{\beta}_1 \pm t_{.005} s_{\hat{\beta}_1} \Rightarrow \hat{\beta}_1 \pm t_{.005} \frac{s}{\sqrt{SS_{xx}}} \Rightarrow .246 \pm 4.604 \frac{1.292}{\sqrt{10.8333333}}$$

$$\Rightarrow .246 \pm 1.807 \Rightarrow (-1.561, 2.053)$$

We are 99% confident that the true value of β_1 is between -1.561 and 2.053.

11.51 a. From Exercises 11.24 and 11.39, $SS_{xx} = 12{,}710.52318$, $\hat{\beta}_1 = -.305$, $s = 5.3647$,

To determine if math score and percentage of students below the poverty level are negatively linearly related, we test:

H_0: $\beta_1 = 0$
H_a: $\beta_1 < 0$

The test statistic is $t = \dfrac{\hat{\beta}_1 - 0}{s_{\hat{\beta}_1}} = \dfrac{-.305}{\dfrac{5.3647}{\sqrt{12{,}710.52318}}} = -6.410$

The rejection region requires $\alpha = .01$ in the lower tail of the t distribution with df = $n - 2$ = $22 - 2 = 20$. From Table VI, Appendix A, $t_{.01} = 2.582$. The rejection region is $t < -2.582$.

Since the observed value of the test statistic falls in the rejection region $(t = -6.410 < -2.582)$, H_0 is rejected. There is sufficient evidence to indicate the math score and percentage of students below the poverty level are negatively linearly related at $\alpha = .01$.

b. For confidence coefficient .99, $\alpha = 1 - .99 = .01$ and $\alpha/2 = .01/2 = .005$. From Table VI, Appendix A, with df $= n - 2 = 22 - 2 = 20$, $t_{.005} = 2.845$. The 99% confidence interval is:

$$\hat{\beta}_1 \pm t_{.005} s_{\hat{\beta}_1} \Rightarrow \hat{\beta}_1 \pm t_{.005} \frac{s}{\sqrt{SS_{xx}}} \Rightarrow -.305 \pm 2.845 \frac{5.3647}{\sqrt{12,710.52318}}$$

$$\Rightarrow -.305 \pm .135 \Rightarrow (-.440, \ -.170)$$

We are 99% confident that the change in the mean value of math scores for each unit change in percentage of students below the poverty level is between $-.440$ and $-.170$.

11.53 Some preliminary calculations are:

$$SS_{yy} = \sum y_i^2 - \frac{\left(\sum y_i\right)^2}{n} = 769.72 - \frac{(135.8)^2}{24} = 1.3183333$$

$$SSE = SS_{yy} - \hat{\beta}_1 SS_{xxy} = 1.3183333 - (-.002301769)(-129.94167) = 1.019237592$$

$$s^2 = \frac{SSE}{n-2} = \frac{1.019237592}{22} = .046329$$

$$s_{\hat{\beta}_1} = \sqrt{\frac{s^2}{SS_{xx}}} = \sqrt{\frac{.046329}{56452.958}} = .000906$$

For confidence level .90, $\alpha = .10$ and $\alpha/2 = .10/2 = .05$. From Table VI, Appendix A with df $= n - 2 = 24 - 2 = 22$, $t_{.05} = 1.717$.

The confidence interval is:

$$\hat{\beta}_1 \pm t_{.05} s_{\hat{\beta}_1} \Rightarrow -.0023 \pm 1.717(.000906)$$

$$\Rightarrow (-.0039, -.0007)$$

We are 90% confident that the change in the mean sweetness index for each one unit change in the pectin is between $-.0039$ and $-.0007$.

11.55 a. The model relating Anthropogenic Index, y, to Natural Origin Index, x, is:

$$y = \beta_0 + \beta_1 x + \varepsilon$$

b. Some preliminary calculations are:

$$\sum x_i = 1,047.22 \qquad \sum y_i = 1,283.46 \qquad \sum x_i y_i = 32,048.2$$

$$\sum x_i^2 = 24,607.5 \qquad \sum y_i^2 = 54,184.8$$

$$SS_{xy} = \sum x_i y_i - \frac{\sum x_i \sum y_i}{n} = 32,048.2 - \frac{1,047.22(1,283.46)}{54} = 7,158.10776$$

$$SS_{xx} = \sum x_i^2 - \frac{\left(\sum x_i\right)^2}{n} = 24,607.5 - \frac{1,047.22^2}{54} = 4,298.80133$$

$$\hat{\beta}_1 = \frac{SS_{xy}}{SS_{xx}} = \frac{7,158.10776}{4,298.80133} = 1.665140399$$

$$\hat{\beta}_0 = \bar{y} - \hat{\beta}_1 \bar{x} = \frac{1,283.46}{54} - (1.665140399)\left(\frac{1,047.22}{54}\right) = -8.524228315$$

The least squares prediction equation is $\hat{y} = -8.524 + 1.665x$

c. $\hat{\beta}_1 = 1.665$. For each unit increase in the Natural Origin Index, the mean Anthropogenic Index is estimated to increase by 1.665.

$\hat{\beta}_0 = 2.522$. Since $x = 0$ is not in the observed range of the Natural Origin Index, $\hat{\beta}_0$ has no interpretation other than the y-intercept.

d. Some preliminary calculations are:

$$SS_{yy} = \sum y_i^2 - \frac{\left(\sum y_i\right)^2}{n} = 54,184.8 - \frac{1,283.46^2}{54} = 23,679.80793$$

$$SSE = SS_{yy} - \hat{\beta}_1 SS_{xy} = 23,679.80793 - (1.665140399)(7,158.10776) = 11,760.55352$$

$$s^2 = \frac{SSE}{n-2} = \frac{11,760.55352}{54-2} = 226.1644908$$
$$s = \sqrt{s^2} = \sqrt{226.1644908} = 15.03876627$$

To determine if the natural origin index and anthropogenic index are positively linearly related, we test:

H_0: $\beta_1 = 0$
H_a: $\beta_1 > 0$

The test statistic is $t = \dfrac{\hat{\beta}_1 - 0}{s_{\hat{\beta}_1}} = \dfrac{1.665}{\dfrac{15.0688}{\sqrt{4,298.80133}}} = 7.245$

The rejection region requires $\alpha = .05$ in the upper tail of the t distribution with df $= n - 2$ $= 54 - 2 = 52$. From Table VI, Appendix A, $t_{.05} \approx 1.678$. The rejection region is $t > 1.678$.

Since the observed value of the test statistic falls in the rejection region ($t = 7.245 > 1.678$), H_0 is rejected. There is sufficient evidence to indicate the natural origin index and anthropogenic index are positively linearly related at $\alpha = .05$.

e. For confidence coefficient .95, $\alpha = 1 - .95 = .05$ and $\alpha/2 = .05/2 = .025$. From Table VI, Appendix A, with df $= n - 2 = 54 - 2 = 52$, $t_{.025} \approx 2.011$. The 95% confidence interval is:

$$\hat{\beta}_1 \pm t_{.025} s_{\hat{\beta}_1} \Rightarrow \hat{\beta}_1 \pm t_{.025} \frac{s}{\sqrt{SS_{xx}}} \Rightarrow 1.665 \pm 2.011 \frac{15.0688}{\sqrt{4,298.80133}}$$

$$\Rightarrow 1.665 \pm .462 \Rightarrow (1.203, \quad 2.127)$$

We are 95% confident that the change in the anthropogenic index for each unit increase in the natural origin index is between 1.203 and 2.127.

11.57 a. To determine if body plus head rotation and active head movement are positively linearly related, we test:

H_0: $\beta_1 = 0$
H_a: $\beta_1 > 0$

The test statistic is $t = \dfrac{\hat{\beta}_1 - 0}{s_{\hat{\beta}_1}} = \dfrac{.88 - 0}{.14} = 6.286$

The rejection region requires $\alpha = .05$ in each tail of the t distribution with df $= n - 2 = 39 - 2 = 37$. From Table VI, Appendix A, $t_{.05} \approx 1.687$. The rejection region is $t > 1.687$.

Since the observed value of the test statistic falls in the rejection region ($t = 6.286 > 1.687$), H_0 is rejected. There is sufficient evidence to indicate that the two variables are positively linearly related at $\alpha = .05$.

b. For confidence level .90, $\alpha = .10$ and $\alpha/2 = .10/2 = .05$. From Table VI, Appendix A, with df $= n - 2 = 39 - 2 = 37$, $t_{.05} \approx 1.687$. The confidence interval is:

$$\hat{\beta}_1 \pm t_{.05} s_{\hat{\beta}_1} \Rightarrow .88 \pm 1.687(.14)$$

$$\Rightarrow .88 \pm .23618$$
$$\Rightarrow (.6438, 1.1162)$$

We are 90% confident that the true value of β_1 is between .6438 and 1.1162.

c. Because the interval in part b contains the value 1, there is no evidence that the true slope of the line differs from 1.

11.59   Using the calculations from Exercise 11.28 and these calculations:

$$SS_{yy} = \sum y^2 - \frac{\left(\sum y\right)^2}{n} = 83.474 - \frac{103.07^2}{144} = 9.70021597$$

$$SSE = SS_{yy} - \hat{\beta}_1\left(SS_{xy}\right) = 9.70021597 - (.026421957)(19.975) = 9.172437366$$

$$s^2 = \frac{SSE}{n-2} = \frac{9.172437366}{144-2} = .064594629$$

$$s = \sqrt{s^2} = \sqrt{.064594629} = .254154735$$

To determine if there is a linear trend between the proportion of names recalled and position, we test:

H_0: $\beta_1 = 0$
H_a: $\beta_1 \neq 0$

The test statistic is $t = \dfrac{\hat{\beta}_1 - 0}{s_{\hat{\beta}}} = \dfrac{\hat{\beta}_1 - 0}{s / \sqrt{SS_{xx}}} = \dfrac{.02642 - 0}{.25415 / \sqrt{756}} = 2.858$

The rejection region requires $\alpha/2 = .01/2 = .005$ in each tail of the t distribution. From Table VI, Appendix A, with df = $n - 2 = 144 - 2 = 142$, $t_{.005} = 2.576$. The rejection region is $t < -2.576$ or $t > 2.576$.

Since the observed test statistic falls in the rejection region ($t = 2.858 > 2.576$), H_0 is rejected. There is sufficient evidence to indicate the proportion of names recalled is linearly related to position at $\alpha = .01$.

11.61   The coefficient of correlation, r, is a measure of the strength of the linear relationship between variables x and y. It can range from -1 (perfect negative linear relationship) to 1 (perfect positive linear relationship). A value of 0 indicates the variables are not related.

The coefficient of determination, r^2, is the proportion of the total sample variance around $\bar{y}$ that is explained by the linear relationship between x and y. Obviously, $0 \leq r^2 \leq 1$.

11.63   The statement "The correlation coefficient is a measure of the strength of the linear relationship between x and y." is a true statement.

11.65   a. $r = 1$ implies x and y are perfectly, positively related.

   b. $r = -1$ implies x and y are perfectly, negatively related.

   c. $r = 0$ implies x and y are not related.

   d. $r = .90$ implies x and y are positively related. Since r is close to 1, the strength of the relationship is very high.

e. $r = .10$ implies x and y are positively related. Since r is close to 0, the relationship is fairly weak.

f. $r = -.88$ implies x and y are negatively related. Since r is close to -1, the relationship is fairly strong.

11.67 From Exercises 11.17 and 11.35,

$$r^2 = 1 - \frac{SSE}{SS_{yy}} = 1 - \frac{5.13486841}{41.7142857} = .8769$$

87.69% of the total sample variability around $\bar{y}$ is explained by the linear relationship between y and x.

11.69 a. $r = .43$. Since the value is not particularly close to 1, there is a moderately weak positive linear relationship between time allotted to sports and audience ratings.

b. $r^2 = .43^2 = .1849$. 18.49% of the total sample variability around the sample mean audience rating is explained by the linear relationship between audience rating and total time allotted to sports.

11.71 a. $r = .84$. Since the value is fairly close to 1, there is a moderately strong positive linear relationship between the magnitude of a QSO and the redshift level.

b. The relationship between r and the estimated slope of the line is that they will both have the same sign. If r is positive, the slope of the line is positive. If r is negative, the slope of the line is negative.

c. $r^2 = .84^2 = .7056$. 70.56% of the total sample variability around the sample mean magnitude of a QSO is explained by the linear relationship between magnitude of a QSO and the redshift level.

11.73 a. $r = .70$. Since this value is moderately close to 1, there is a moderately strong positive linear relationship between self-knowledge skill level and goal-setting ability.

b. $p = .001$. Since the p-value is so small, we would reject H_0. There is sufficient evidence to indicate a linear relationship between self-knowledge skill level and goal-setting ability for any reasonable level of α.

c. $r^2 = .70^2 = .49$. 49% of the total sample variability around the sample mean goal-setting ability is explained by the linear relationship between goal-setting ability and self-knowledge skill level.

11.75 a. Piano: $r = .447$
Because this value if near .5, there is s slight positive linear relationship between recognition exposure time and goodness of view for piano.

Bench: $r = -.057$
Because this value is extremely close to 0, there is an extremely weak negative linear relationship between recognition exposure time and goodness of view for bench.

Motorbike: $r = .619$
Because this value is near .5, there is a moderate positive linear relationship between recognition exposure time and goodness of view for motorbike.

Armchair: $r = .294$
Because this value is fairly close to 0, there is a weak positive linear relationship between recognition exposure time and goodness of view for armchair.

Teapot: $r = .949$
Because this value is very close to 1, there is a strong positive linear relationship between recognition exposure time and goodness of view for teapot.

b. Piano: $r^2 = (.447)^2 = .1998$
19.98% of the total sample variability around the sample mean recognition exposure time is explained by the linear relationship between the recognition exposure time and the goodness of view for piano.

Bench: $r^2 = (-.057)^2 = .0032$
.32% of the total sample variability around the sample mean recognition exposure time is explained by the linear relationship between the recognition exposure time and the goodness of view for bench.

Motorbike: $r^2 = (.619)^2 = .3832$
38.32% of the total sample variability around the sample mean recognition exposure time is explained by the linear relationship between the recognition exposure time and the goodness of view for motorbike.

Armchair: $r^2 = (.294)^2 = .0864$
8.64% of the total sample variability around the sample mean recognition exposure time is explained by the linear relationship between the recognition exposure time and the goodness of view for armchair.

Teapot: $r^2 = (.949)^2 = .9006$
90.06% of the total sample variability around the sample mean recognition exposure time is explained by the linear relationship between the recognition exposure time and the goodness of view for teapot.

c. The test is:

H_0: $\beta_1 = 0$
H_a: $\beta_1 \neq 0$

Following are the values of α and $t_{\alpha/2}$ that correspond to df $= n - 2 = 25 - 2 = 23$.

α	.20	.10	.05	.02	.01	.002	.001
$t_{\alpha/2}$	1.319	1.714	2.069	2.500	2.807	3.485	3.767

Piano: $t = 2.40$
$2.069 < 2.40 < 2,500, p \approx .025$

For levels of significance greater than $\alpha = .025$, H_0 can be rejected. There is sufficient evidence to indicate that there is a linear relationship between goodness of view and recognition exposure time for piano for $\alpha > .025$.

Bench: $t = .27$
$.27 < 1.319, p > .2$
H_0 is not rejected. There is insufficient evidence to indicate that there is a linear relationship between goodness of view and recognition exposure time for bench for $\alpha \le .2$.

Motorbike: $t = 3.78$
$3.78 > 3.767, p < .001$
H_0 can be rejected for $\alpha \ge .001$. There is sufficient evidence to indicate that there is a linear relationship between goodness of view and recognition exposure time for motorbike for $\alpha \ge .001$.

Armchair: $t = 1.47$
$1.319 < 1.47 < 1.714, p \approx .15$
H_0 cannot be rejected for levels of significance $\alpha < .15$. There is insufficient evidence to indicate that there is a linear relationship between goodness of view and recognition exposure time for armchair for $\alpha < .15$.

Teapot: $t = 14.50$
$14.50 > 3.767, p < .001$
H_0 can be rejected for $\alpha \ge .001$. There is sufficient evidence to indicate that there is a linear relationship between goodness of view and recognition exposure time for teapot for $\alpha \ge .001$.

11.77 a. A straight line model is $y = \beta_0 + \beta_1 x + \varepsilon$.

b. The researcher hypothesized that therapists with more years of formal dance training will report a higher perceived success rate in cotherapy relationships. This indicates that $\beta_1 > 0$.

c. $r = -.26$. Because this value is fairly close to 0, there is a weak negative linear relationship between years of formal training and reported success rate.

d. To determine if there is a positive linear relationship between years of formal training and reported success rate, we test:

H_0: $\beta_1 = 0$
H_0: $\beta_1 > 0$

The test statistic is $t = \dfrac{r}{\sqrt{(1 - r^2)/(n - 2)}} = \dfrac{-.26}{\sqrt{(1 - (-.26^2))/(136 - 2)}} = -3.12$

The rejection region requires $\alpha = .05$ in the upper tail of the t distribution with df $= n - 2 = 136 - 2 = 134$. From Table VI, Appendix A, $t_{.05} \approx 1.645$. The rejection region is $t > 1.645$.

Since the observed value of the test statistic does not fall in the rejection region ($t = -8.66 \not> 1.645$), H_0 is not rejected. There is insufficient evidence to indicate that there is a positive linear relationship between years of formal training and perceived success rates at $\alpha = .05$.

11.79   Using the values computed in Exercise 11.56:

$$r = \frac{SS_{xy}}{\sqrt{SS_{xx}SS_{yy}}} = \frac{48.125}{\sqrt{379.9375(18.75)}} = .5702$$

Because r is moderately small, there is a rather weak positive linear relationship between blood lactate concentration and perceived recovery.

$r^2 = .5702^2 = .3251$.

32.51% of the sample variance of blood lactate concentration around the sample mean is explained by the linear relationship between blood lactate concentration and perceived recovery.

11.81   For a given x, y is the actual value of the dependent variable and $E(y)$ is the mean value of y at the given value of x.

11.83   The statement "The greater the deviation between x and $\bar{x}$, the wider the prediction interval for y will be." is true. The further x gets from $\bar{x}$, the less precise the interval will be.

11.85   a. $\hat{\beta}_1 = \frac{SS_{xy}}{SS_{xx}} = \frac{28}{32} = .875$

$\hat{\beta}_0 = \bar{y} - \hat{\beta}_1\bar{x} = 4 - .875(3) = 1.375$

The least squares line is $\hat{y} = 1.375 + .875x$.

b.   The least squares line is:

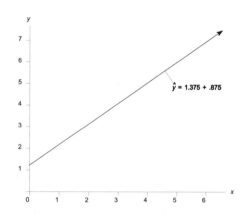

$\hat{y} = 1.375 + .875$

c. $SSE = SS_{yy} - \hat{\beta}_1 SS_{xy} = 26 - .875(28) = 1.5$

d. $s^2 = \dfrac{SSE}{n-2} = \dfrac{1.5}{10-2} = .1875$

e. $s = \sqrt{.1875} = .4330$

The form of the confidence interval is $\hat{y} \pm t_{\alpha/2}s\sqrt{\dfrac{1}{n} + \dfrac{(x_p - \bar{x})^2}{SS_{xx}}}$

For $x_p = 2.5$, $\hat{y} = 1.375 + .875(2.5) = 3.5625$

For confidence coefficient .95, $\alpha = .05$ and $\alpha/2 = .025$. From Table VI, Appendix A, with df $= n - 2 = 10 - 2 = 8$, $t_{.025} = 2.306$. The confidence interval is:

$$3.5625 \pm 2.306(.4330)\sqrt{\dfrac{1}{10} + \dfrac{(2.5 - 3)^2}{32}} \Rightarrow 3.5625 \pm .3279 \Rightarrow (3.2346, 3.8904)$$

f. The form of the prediction interval is $\hat{y} \pm t_{\alpha/2}s\sqrt{1 + \dfrac{1}{n} + \dfrac{(x_p - \bar{x})^2}{SS_{xx}}}$

For $x_p = 4$, $\hat{y} = 1.375 + .875(4) = 4.875$

For confidence coefficient .95, $\alpha = .05$ and $\alpha/2 = .025$. From Table VI, Appendix A, with df $= n - 2 = 10 - 2 = 8$, $t_{.025} = 2.306$. The prediction interval is:

$$4.875 \pm 2.306(.4330)\sqrt{1 + \dfrac{1}{10} + \dfrac{(4 - 3)^2}{32}} \Rightarrow 4.875 \pm 1.062 \Rightarrow (3.813, 5.937)$$

11.87   a, b. The scattergram is:

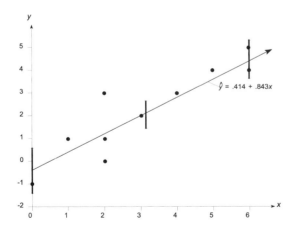

c.   SSE $= SS_{yy} - \hat{\beta}_1 SS_{xy} = 33.6 - .84318766(32.8) = 5.94344473$

$s^2 = \dfrac{SSE}{n-2} = \dfrac{5.94344473}{10-2} = .742930591$ $\qquad\qquad s = \sqrt{.742930591} = .8619$

$$\bar{x} = \frac{31}{10} = 3.1$$

The form of the confidence interval is $\hat{y} \pm t_{\alpha/2}\sqrt{\dfrac{1}{n} + \dfrac{(x_p - \bar{x})^2}{SS_{xx}}}$

For $x_p = 6$, $\hat{y} = -.414 + .843(6) = 4.644$

For confidence coefficient .95, $\alpha = .05$ and $\alpha/2 = .025$. From Table VI, Appendix A, with df $= n - 2 = 10 - 2 = 8$, $t_{.025} = 2.306$. The confidence interval is:

$$4.644 \pm 2.306(.8619)\sqrt{\frac{1}{10} + \frac{(6-3.1)^2}{38.9}} \Rightarrow 4.644 \pm 1.118 \Rightarrow (3.526, 5.762)$$

d.   For $x_p = 3.2$, $\hat{y} = -.414 + .843(3.2) = 2.284$

The confidence interval is:

$$2.284 \pm 2.306(.8619)\sqrt{\frac{1}{10} + \frac{(3.2-3.1)^2}{38.9}} \Rightarrow 2.284 \pm .629 \Rightarrow (1.655, 2.913)$$

For $x_p = 0$, $\hat{y} = -.414 + .843(0) = -.414$

The confidence interval is:

$$-.414 \pm 2.306(.8619)\sqrt{\frac{1}{10} + \frac{(0-3.1)^2}{38.9}} \Rightarrow -.414 \pm 1.717 \Rightarrow (-1.585, .757)$$

e.   The width of the confidence interval for the mean value of y depends on the distance x_p is from . The width of the interval for $x_p = 3.2$ is the smallest because 3.2 is the closest to $=$ 3.1. The width of the interval for $x_p = 0$ is the widest because 0 is the farthest from $= 3.1$.

11.89   a.   No. We know there is a significant linear relationship between sale price and appraised value. However, the actual sale prices maybe scattered quite far from the predicted line.

b.   From the printout, the 95% prediction interval for the actual sale price when the appraised value is \$300,000 is (275.86, 407.26) or (\$275,860, \$407,260). We are 95% confident that the actual sale price for a home appraised at \$300,000 is between \$275,860 and \$407,260.

c.   From the printout, the 95% confidence interval for the mean sale price when the appraised value is \$300,000 is (332.95, 350.17) or (\$332,950, \$350,170). We are 95% confident that the mean sale price for a home appraised at \$300,000 is between \$332,950 and \$350,170.

11.91   For observation 7, the 95% prediction interval for the actual annual rainfall when the maximum daily temperature is 11.4 is (92.298, 125.104). We are 95% confident that the actual rainfall in a site with a maximum daily temperature of 11.4 is between 92.298 and 125.104.

11.93   a.   The equation for the straight-line model relating duration to frequency is $y = \beta_0 + \beta_1 x + \varepsilon$.

b.   Some preliminary calculations are:

$$\bar{y} = \frac{\sum y}{n} = \frac{1,287}{11} = 117$$

$$\bar{x} = \frac{\sum x}{n} = \frac{394}{11} = 35.818$$

$$SS_{xy} = \sum xy - \frac{\sum x \sum y}{n} = 30,535 - \frac{394(1,287)}{11} = -15,563$$

$$SS_{xx} = \sum x^2 - \frac{\left(\sum x\right)^2}{n} = 28,438 - \frac{394^2}{11} = 14,325.63636$$

$$\hat{\beta}_1 = \frac{SS_{xy}}{SS_{xx}} = \frac{-15,563}{14,325.63636} = -1.086374079$$

$$\hat{\beta}_0 = \bar{y} - \hat{\beta}_1 \bar{x} = \frac{1,287}{11} - (-1.086374079)\left(\frac{394}{11}\right) = 155.9119443$$

The least squares prediction equation is $\hat{y} = 155.912 - 1.086x$.

c.   Some preliminary calculations are:

$$SS_{yy} = \sum y^2 - \frac{\left(\sum y\right)^2}{n} = 203,651 - \frac{1,287^2}{11} = 53,072$$

$$SSE = SS_{yy} - \hat{\beta}_1\left(SS_{xy}\right) = 53,072 - (-1.086374079)(-15,563) = 36,164.76021$$

$$s^2 = \frac{SSE}{n-2} = \frac{36,164.76021}{11-2} = 4,018.30669$$

$$s = \sqrt{s^2} = \sqrt{4,018.30669} = 63.39011508$$

To determine if there is a linear relationship between duration and frequency, we test:

$H_0: \beta_1 = 0$
$H_a: \beta_1 \neq 0$

The test statistic is $t = \dfrac{\hat{\beta}_1 - 0}{s_{\hat{\beta}}} = \dfrac{\hat{\beta}_1 - 0}{s / \sqrt{SS_{xx}}} = \dfrac{-1.086 - 0}{63.3901 / \sqrt{14,325.63636}} = -2.051$

The rejection region requires $\alpha/2 = .05/2 = .025$ in each tail of the t distribution. From Table VI, Appendix A, with df $= n - 2 = 11 - 2 = 9$, $t_{.025} = 2.262$. The rejection region is $t < -2.262$ or $t > 2.262$.

Since the observed test statistic does not fall in the rejection region ($t = -2.051 \nless -2.262$), H_0 is not rejected. There is insufficient evidence to indicate that duration and frequency are linearly related at $\alpha = .05$.

d. For $x = 25$, the predicted duration is $\hat{y} = 155.912 - 1.086 (25) = 128.762$.

For confidence coefficient .95, $\alpha = .05$ and $\alpha/2 = .05/2 = .025$. From Table VI, Appendix A, with df $= n - 2 = 11 - 2 = 9$, $t_{.025} = 2.262$. The 95% prediction interval is:

$$\hat{y} \pm t_{\alpha/2}s\sqrt{1 + \frac{1}{n} + \frac{(x_p - \bar{x})^2}{SS_{xx}}} \Rightarrow 128.762 \pm 2.262(63.3901)\sqrt{1 + \frac{1}{11} + \frac{(25 - 35.818)^2}{14,325.63636}}$$

$$\Rightarrow 128.762 \pm 150.324 \Rightarrow (-21.562, \ 279.086)$$

We are 95% confident that the actual duration of a person who participates 25 times a year is between -21.562 and 279.086 days. Since the duration cannot be negative, the actual duration will be between 0 and 279.086.

11.95   a. From Exercise 11.42, $SS_{xx} = 3000$ and $= 50$.

Also, for Brand A, $s = 1.211$; for Brand B, $s = .610$.

For Brand A, $\hat{y} = 6.62 - .0727(45) = 3.349$, while for Brand B, $\hat{y} = 9.31 - .1077(45) = 4.464$.

The degrees of freedom for both brands is $n - 2 = 15 - 2 = 13$. For confidence coefficient .90, (i.e., for all parts of this question), $\alpha = .10$ and $\alpha/2 = .05$. From Table VI, Appendix A, with df $= 13$, $t_{.05} = 1.771$.

The form of both confidence intervals is $\hat{y} \pm t_{\alpha/2}s\sqrt{\frac{1}{n} + \frac{(x_p - \bar{x})^2}{SS_{xx}}}$

For Brand A, we obtain:

$$3.349 \pm 1.771(1.211)\sqrt{\frac{1}{15} + \frac{(45 - 50)^2}{3000}} \Rightarrow 3.349 \pm .587 \Rightarrow (2.762, 3.936)$$

For Brand B, we obtain:

$$4.464 \pm 1.771(.610)\sqrt{\frac{1}{15} + \frac{(45 - 50)^2}{3000}} \Rightarrow 4.464 \pm .296 \Rightarrow (4.168, 4.760)$$

The first interval is wider, caused by the larger value of s.

b.   The form of both prediction intervals is $t_{\alpha/2}s\sqrt{1+\dfrac{1}{n}+\dfrac{(x_p-\bar{x})^2}{SS_{xx}}}$

For Brand A, we obtain:

$$3.349 \pm 1.771(1.211)\sqrt{1+\frac{1}{15}+\frac{(45-50)^2}{3000}} \Rightarrow 3.349 \pm 2.224 \Rightarrow (1.125, 5.573)$$

For Brand B, we obtain:

$$4.464 \pm 1.771(.610)\sqrt{1+\frac{1}{15}+\frac{(40+50)^2}{3000}} \Rightarrow 4.464 \pm 1.120 \Rightarrow (3.344, 5.584)$$

Again, the first interval is wider, caused by the larger value of s. Each of these intervals is wider than its counterpart from part **a**, since, for the same x, a prediction interval for an individual y is always wider than a confidence interval for the mean of y. This is due to an individual observation having a greater variance than the variance of the mean of a set of observations.

c.   To obtain a confidence interval for the life of a brand A cutting tool that is operated at 100 meters per minute, we use:

$$\hat{y} \pm t_{\alpha/1}s\sqrt{1+\frac{1}{n}+\frac{(x_p-\bar{x})}{SS_{xx}}}$$

For $x = 100$, $\hat{y} = 6.62 - .0727(100) = -.65$.

The degrees of freedom are $n - 2 = 15 - 2 = 13$. For confidence coefficient .95, $\alpha = .05$ and $\alpha/2 = .025$. From Table VI, Appendix A, with df = 13, $t_{.025} = 2.160$.

Here, we obtain:

$$-.65 \pm 2.160(1.211)\sqrt{1+\frac{1}{15}+\frac{(100-50)^2}{3000}} \Rightarrow -.65 \pm 3.606 \Rightarrow (-4.256, 2.956)$$

The additional assumption would be that the straight line model fits the data well for the x's actually observed all the way up to the value under consideration, 100. Clearly from the estimated value of $-.65$, this is not true (usually, negative "useful lives" are not found).

11.97   The general form of the straight-line model for $E(y)$ is $E(y) = \beta_0 + \beta_1 x$.

11.99   The statement "In simple linear regression, about 95% of the y-values in the sample will fall within $2s$ of their respective predicted values." is a true statement.

11.101 a.

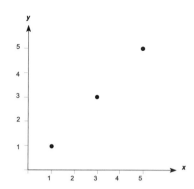

b. One possible line is $\hat{y} = x$.

x	y	$\hat{y}$	$y - \hat{y}$
1	1	1	0
3	3	3	0
5	5	5	0
			0

For this example $\sum(y - \hat{y}) = 0$

A second possible line is $\hat{y} = 3$.

x	y	$\hat{y}$	$y - \hat{y}$
1	1	3	−2
3	3	3	0
5	5	3	2
			0

For this example $\sum(y - \hat{y}) = 0$

c. Some preliminary calculations are:

$$\sum x_i = 9 \qquad \sum x_i^2 = 35 \qquad \sum x_i y_i = 35$$

$$\sum y_i = 9 \qquad \sum y_i^2 = 35$$

$$SS_{xy} = \sum x_i \sum y_i - \frac{\sum x_i \sum y_i}{n} = 35 - \frac{9(9)}{3} = 8$$

$$SS_{xx} = \sum x_i^2 - \frac{\left(\sum x_i\right)^2}{n} = 35 - \frac{9^2}{3} = 8$$

$$SS_{yy} = \sum y_i^2 - \frac{\left(\sum y_i\right)^2}{n} = 35 - \frac{9^2}{3} = 8$$

$$\hat{\beta}_1 = \frac{SS_{xy}}{SS_{xx}} = \frac{8}{8} = 1 \qquad\qquad \hat{\beta}_0 = \bar{y} - \hat{\beta}_1 \bar{x} = \frac{9}{3} - 1\left(\frac{9}{3}\right) = 0$$

The least squares line is $\hat{y} = 0 + 1x = x$.

d. For $\hat{y} = x$, SSE = $SS_{yy} - \hat{\beta_1} SS_{xy}$ = 8 – 1(8) = 0

   For $\hat{y} = 3$, SSE = $\sum (y_i - \hat{y}_i)^2$ = $(1-3)^2 + (3-3)^2 + (5-3)^2 = 8$

   The least squares line has the smallest SSE of all possible lines.

11.103 a. We would expect the slope of the line from modeling the relationship between the mean number of games won and the team's batting average to be positive. As the team's batting average increases, we would expect that the number of games won should also increase.

   b. Using MINITAB, a scattergram of the data is:

   The graph indicates that batting average and games won have a positive linear relationship. As batting average increases, the number of games won tends to increase.

   c. From the printout, $\hat{\beta_0} = -214.30$ and $\hat{\beta_1} = 1,118.4$. The least squares line is:
   $\hat{y} = -214 + 1,118.4x$

   d. The least squares line is plotted on the graph in part **a**. The data appear to fit the data fairly well.

   e. $\hat{\beta_0} = -214.30$. Since there is no team with a batting average of 0, this has no meaning other than the y-intercept.

   $\hat{\beta_1} = 1,118.4$. For each unit increase in batting average, the mean number of games won is estimated to increase by 1,118.4. This means very little since the batting average cannot increase by one unit. To make this interpretation more practical, we will look at only an increase of .01 in the batting average. For every .01 increase in batting average, the mean number of games won is estimated to increase by 11.184.

   f. To determine if the mean number of games won by a major league baseball team is positively linearly related to the team's batting average, we test:

H_0: $\beta_1 = 0$
H_a: $\beta_1 > 0$

The test statistic is $t = 4.32$ and the p-value is $p = 0.001$. Since we are running only a one-tailed test, we must divide the p-value by 2. Thus, the p-value of this test is $p = 0.001/2 = 0.0005$. Since the p-value is less than $\alpha = .05$ ($p = 0.0005 < .05$), H_0 is rejected. There is sufficient evidence to indicate the mean number of games won by a major league baseball team is positively linearly related to the team's batting average at $\alpha = .05$

g. From the printout, $r^2 = $ R-SQ $= 60.9\%$. 60.9% of the sample variability around the sample mean number of games won is explained by the linear relationship between the number of games won and the batting average of the team.

h. From the printout, the predicted number of games won by a team with a .275 batting average is 93.27.

i. From the printout, the 95% prediction interval for the number of games won by a team with a .275 batting average is (67.38 and 119.15). We are 95% confident that the actual number of games won by a team with a batting average of .275 is between 67.38 and 119.15 games.

11.105 a. The equation for the straight-line model is $y = \beta_0 + \beta_1 x + \varepsilon$.

b. Some preliminary calculations are:

$$\bar{y} = \frac{\sum y}{n} = \frac{398}{9} = 44.2222$$

$$\bar{x} = \frac{\sum x}{n} = \frac{1,444}{9} = 160.4444$$

$$SS_{xy} = \sum xy - \frac{\sum x \sum y}{n} = 60,428 - \frac{1,444(398)}{9} = -3,428.88889$$

$$SS_{xx} = \sum x^2 - \frac{\left(\sum x\right)^2}{n} = 235,866 - \frac{1,444^2}{9} = 4,184.2222$$

$$\hat{\beta}_1 = \frac{SS_{xy}}{SS_{xx}} = \frac{-3,428.88889}{4,184.2222} = -.819480593$$

$$\hat{\beta}_0 = \bar{y} - \hat{\beta}_1 \bar{x} = \frac{398}{9} - (-.819480593)\left(\frac{1,444}{9}\right) = 175.7033307$$

The fitted model is $\hat{y} = 175.7033 - .8195x$.

c. $\hat{\beta}_0 = 175.7033$. Since $x = 0$ (age of fish) is not in the observed range, $\hat{\beta}_0$ has no practical meaning.

d. $\hat{\beta}_1 = -.8195$. For each additional day of age, the mean number of strikes is estimated to decrease by .8195 strikes.

e.   Some additional calculations are:

$$\sum y_i = 398 \qquad \sum y_i^2 = 22,078$$

$$SS_{yy} = \sum y_i^2 - \frac{\left(\sum y_i\right)^2}{n} = 22,078 - \frac{398^2}{9} = 4,477.55556$$

$$SSE = SS_{yy} - \hat{\beta}_1 SS_{xy} = 4,477.55556 - (-.819480593)(-3,428.888889) = 1,667.647661$$

$$s^2 = \frac{SSE}{n-2} = \frac{1,667.647661}{9-2} = 238.2353801$$

$$s = \sqrt{s^2} = \sqrt{238.2353801} = 15.43487545$$

H_0: $\beta_1 = 0$
H_a: $\beta_1 < 0$

The test statistic is $t = \dfrac{\hat{\beta}_1 - 0}{s_{\hat{\beta}_1}} = \dfrac{-.8195 - 0}{15.4349 \Big/ \sqrt{4,184.2222}} = -3.434$

The rejection region requires $\alpha = .10$ in the lower tail of the t distribution with df $= n - 2 = 9 - 2 = 7$. From, Table VI, Appendix A, $t_{.10} = 1.415$. The rejection region is $t < -1.415$.

Since the observed value of the test statistic falls in the rejection region ($t = -3.434 < -1.415$), H_0 is rejected. There is sufficient evidence to indicate a negative linear relationship exists between the number of strikes and the age of the fish.

11.107 a.   To determine whether the number of leisure activities and GPA are linearly related, we test:

H_0: $\rho = 0$
H_a: $\rho \neq 0$

b.   The p-value $= .0512$. This implies that H_0 will not be rejected for $\alpha = .05$. There is insufficient evidence to indicate that the number of leisure activities and GPA are linearly related for $\alpha = .05$. For $\alpha > .0512$, H_0 will be rejected. There is sufficient evidence to indicate that the number of leisure activities and GPA are linearly related for $\alpha > .0512$.

Simple Linear Regression

11.109 Dependent Variable: VALUE

Analysis of Variance

Source	DF	Sum of Squares	Mean Square	F Value	Pr > F
Model	1	865746	865746	10.55	0.0021
Error	48	3939797	82079		
Corrected Total	49	4805543			

Root MSE	286.49451	R-Square	0.1802	
Dependent Mean	128.90000	Adj R-Sq	0.1631	
Coeff Var	222.26106			

Parameter Estimates

Variable	DF	Parameter Estimate	Standard Error	t Value	Pr > |t|
Intercept	1	-92.45768	79.29106	-1.17	0.2494
AGE	1	8.34682	2.57005	3.25	0.0021

Answers may vary. One possible answer may include:

The least squares line is $\hat{y} = -92.45768 + 8.34682x$. To determine if age can be used to predict market value, we test:

H_0: $\beta_1 = 0$
H_a: $\beta_1 \neq 0$

The test statistic is $t = 3.25$ with p-value = .0021. Reject the null hypothesis for levels of significance $\alpha > .0021$. There is sufficient evidence to indicate that age contributes information for the prediction of market value (y) at $\alpha > .0021$.

$r = .42$; Since this value is near .5, there is a moderate positive linear relationship between the value and age of the Beanie Baby.

11.111 a. Using MINITAB, the scattergram of the data is:

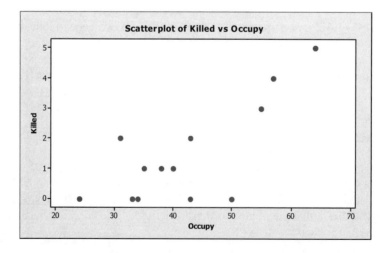

From the graph, it appears that as nest box tit occupancy increases, the number of flycatchers killed also increases.

b.   Some preliminary calculations are:

$$\sum x_i = 582 \qquad \sum y_i = 20 \qquad \sum x_i y_i = 1,009$$
$$\sum x_i^2 = 25,844 \qquad \sum y_i^2 = 62$$

$$SS_{xy} = \sum x_i y_i - \frac{\sum x_i \sum y_i}{n} = 1,009 - \frac{582(20)}{14} = 177.5714286$$

$$SS_{xx} = \sum x_i^2 - \frac{\left(\sum x_i\right)^2}{n} = 25,844 - \frac{582^2}{14} = 1,649.42857$$

$$\hat{\beta}_1 = \frac{SS_{xy}}{SS_{xx}} = \frac{177.5714286}{1,649.42857} = .107656331$$

For each unit increase in the nest box tit occupancy percent, the mean number of flycatchers killed is estimated to increase by .1077.

$$\hat{\beta}_0 = \bar{y} - \hat{\beta}_1 \bar{x} = \frac{20}{14} - (.107656331)\left(\frac{582}{14}\right) = -3.046856046$$

Since $x = 0$ is not in the observed range, $\hat{\beta}_0$ has no meaning other than the y-intercept.

c.   Some additional calculations are:

$$SS_{yy} = \sum y_i^2 - \frac{\left(\sum y_i\right)^2}{n} = 62 - \frac{20^2}{14} = 33.42857143$$

$$SSE = SS_{yy} - \hat{\beta}_1 SS_{xy} = 33.42857143 - (.107656331)(177.5714286) = 14.31188294$$

$$s^2 = \frac{SSE}{n-2} = \frac{14.31188294}{14-2} = 1.192656912 \qquad s = \sqrt{s^2} = \sqrt{1.192656912} = 1.0921$$

To determine if the model is useful in predicting the number of flycatchers killed, we test:

$H_0: \beta_1 = 0$
$H_a: \beta_1 \neq 0$

The test statistic is $t = \dfrac{\hat{\beta}_1 - 0}{s_{\hat{\beta}_1}} = \dfrac{.1077 - 0}{1.0921 / \sqrt{1,649.42857}} = 4.005$

The rejection region requires $\alpha/2 = .05/2 = .025$ in each tail of the t distribution. From Table VI, Appendix A, with df $= n - 2 = 14 - 2 = 12$, $t_{.025} = 2.179$. The rejection region is $t < -2.179$ or $t > 2.179$.

Since the observed value of the test statistic falls in the rejection region ($t = 4.005 > 2.179$), H_0 is rejected. There is sufficient evidence to indicate that the model is useful in predicting the number of flycatchers killed at $\alpha = .05$.

d. $$r = \frac{SS_{xy}}{\sqrt{SS_{xx}SS_{yy}}} = \frac{177.5714286}{\sqrt{1,649.42857(33.42857143)}} = .7562$$

The value of r is moderately close to 1. Thus, there is a moderately strong positive linear relationship between the number of flycatchers killed and the nest box tit occupancy.

$r^2 = .7562^2 = .572$. 57.2% of the sample variability around the sample mean number of flycatchers killed is explained by the linear relationship between the number of flycatchers killed and the nest box tit occupancy.

e. From part c, $s = 1.0921$. We would expect most of the observed number of flycatchers killed to fall within $2s$ or $2(1.0921) = 2.1842$ units of their predicted values.

f. Since there is a significant linear relationship between the number of flycatchers killed and the nest box tit occupancy, we would recommend using this model. In addition, the r^2 value is .572. Although this is not great, over half of the sample variation is explained by the model.

11.113 a. $\hat{\beta}_0 = -13.490347$ — has no meaning since $x = 0$ is not in the observed range. It is the y-intercept.

$\hat{\beta}_1 = -.052829$ — is the estimated change in the mean proportion of impurity passing through helium for each additional degree.

b. For confidence coefficient .95, $\alpha = .05$ and $\alpha/2 = .025$. From Table VI, Appendix A, with df $= n - 2 = 10 - 2 = 8$, $t_{.025} = 2.306$. The confidence interval is:

$$\hat{\beta}_1 \pm t_{\alpha/2} s_{\hat{\beta}_1} \Rightarrow -.0528 \pm 2.306(.00772828) \Rightarrow -.0528 \pm .0178 \Rightarrow (-.0706, -.0350)$$

We are 95% confident that the change in mean proportion of impurity passing through helium for each additional degree is between $-.0706$ and $-.0350$. Since 0 is not in the interval, there is evidence to indicate that temperature contributes information about the proportion of impurity passing through helium.

c. $r^2 = R$-square $= .8538$. 85.38% of the total sample variation around the mean proportion of impurity is explained by the linear relationship between proportion of impurity and temperature.

d. From the printout, the 95% prediction interval is $(.5987, 1.2653)$.

e. We cannot be sure that the relationship between the proportion of impurity passing through helium and temperature is the same outside the observed range.

11.115 a. The scattergram of the data is:

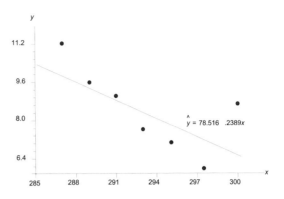

b. Some preliminary calculations are:

$$\sum x_i = 2,053 \qquad \sum y_i = 59.2 \qquad n = 7$$

$$\sum x_i^2 = 602,265.5 \qquad \sum y_i^2 = 517.22 \qquad \sum x_i y_i = 17,326.7$$

$$SS_{xy} = \sum x_i y_i - \frac{\left(\sum x_i\right)\left(\sum y_i\right)}{n} = 17,326.7 - \frac{2053(59.2)}{7} = -35.81429$$

$$SS_{xx} = \sum x_i^2 - \frac{\left(\sum x_i\right)^2}{n} = 602,265.5 - \frac{2053^2}{7} = 149.9286$$

$$SS_{yy} = \sum y_i^2 - \frac{\left(\sum y_i\right)^2}{n} = 517.22 - \frac{59.2^2}{7} = 16.5571429$$

$$\hat{\beta}_1 = \frac{SS_{xy}}{SS_{xx}} = \frac{-35.81429}{149.9286} = -.238875638 \approx -.2389$$

$$\hat{\beta}_0 = \bar{y} - \hat{\beta}_1 \bar{x} = \frac{59.2}{7} - (-.238875638)\frac{2053}{7} = 78.515955 \approx 78.516$$

The least squares line is $\hat{y} = 78.516 - .2389x$.

c. The least squares line is plotted on the graph in part **a**.

d. Some additional calculations:

$$SSE = SS_{yy} - \hat{\beta}_1 SS_{xy} = 16.5571429 - (-.238875638)(-35.81429) = 8.001980951$$

$$s^2 = \frac{SSE}{n-2} = \frac{8.001980951}{7-2} = 1.60039619 \quad s = \sqrt{1.60039619} = 1.2651$$

To determine if the model is adequate, we test:

$$H_0: \beta_1 = 0$$
$$H_a: \beta_1 \neq 0$$

The test statistic is $t = \dfrac{\hat{\beta}_1 - 0}{s_{\hat{\beta}_1}} = \dfrac{-.2389 - 0}{\dfrac{1.2651}{\sqrt{149.9286}}} = -2.31$

The rejection region requires $\alpha/2 = .01/2 = .005$ in each tail of the t distribution with df $= n - 2 = 7 - 2 = 5$. From Table VI, Appendix A, $t_{.005} = 4.032$. The rejection region is $t < -4.032$ or $t > 4.032$.

Since the observed value of the test statistic does not fall in the rejection region ($t = -2.31 \not< -4.032$), H_0 is not rejected. There is insufficient evidence to indicate that the model is adequate at $\alpha = .01$.

e. One point looks like a possible outlier: (301, 8.5).

f. We will redo the analysis after eliminating the above point:

(a) The scattergram of the data is:

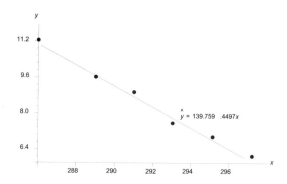

(b) Some preliminary calculations are:

$$\sum x_i = 1{,}752 \qquad \sum y_i = 50.7 \qquad n = 6$$

$$\sum x_i^2 = 511{,}664.5 \qquad \sum y_i^2 = 444.97 \qquad \sum x_i y_i = 14{,}768.2$$

$$SS_{xy} = \sum x_i y_i - \frac{\left(\sum x_i\right)\left(\sum y_i\right)}{n} = 14{,}768.2 - \frac{1752(50.7)}{6} = -36.2$$

$$SS_{xx} = \sum x_i^2 - \frac{\left(\sum x_i\right)^2}{n} = 511{,}664.5 - \frac{1752^2}{6} = 80.5$$

$$SS_{yy} = \sum y_i^2 - \frac{\left(\sum y_i\right)^2}{n} = 444.97 - \frac{50.7^2}{6} = 16.555$$

$$\hat{\beta}_1 = \frac{SS_{xy}}{SS_{xx}} = \frac{-36.2}{80.5} = -.449689441 \approx -.4497$$

$$\hat{\beta}_0 = \bar{y} - \hat{\beta}_1 \bar{x} = \frac{50.7}{6} - (-.449689441)\frac{1752}{6} = 139.7593168 \approx 139.759$$

The least squares line is $\hat{y} = 139.759 - .4497x$.

(c) The least squares line is plotted on the graph in part **f(a)**.

(d) Some additional calculations:

$$SSE = SS_{yy} - \hat{\beta}_1 SS_{xy} = 16.555 - (-.449689441)(-36.2) = .27624224$$

$$s^2 = \frac{SSE}{n-2} = \frac{.27624224}{6-2} = 0.06906056 \qquad\qquad s = \sqrt{0.06906056} = 0.2628$$

To determine if the model is adequate, we test:

H_0: $\beta_1 = 0$
H_a: $\beta_1 \neq 0$

The test statistic is $t = \dfrac{\hat{\beta}_1 - 0}{s_{\hat{\beta}_1}} = \dfrac{-.4497 - 0}{\dfrac{0.2628}{\sqrt{80.5}}} = -15.35$

The rejection region requires $\alpha/2 = .01/2 = .005$ in each tail of the t distribution with df $= n - 2 = 6 - 2 = 4$. From Table VI, Appendix A, $t_{.005} = 4.604$. The rejection region is $t < -4.604$ or $t > 4.604$.

Since the observed value of the test statistic falls in the rejection region ($t = -15.35 < -4.604$), H_0 is rejected. There is sufficient evidence to indicate that the model is adequate at $\alpha = .01$.

11.117 Some preliminary calculations are:

$$\sum x = 4305 \qquad\qquad \sum x^2 = 1{,}652{,}025 \qquad\qquad \sum xy = 76{,}652{,}695$$
$$\sum y = 201{,}558 \qquad\qquad \sum y^2 = 3{,}571{,}211{,}200$$

a. $\hat{\beta}_1 = \dfrac{\sum xy}{\sum x^2} = \dfrac{76{,}652{,}695}{1{,}652{,}025} = 46.39923427 \approx 46.3992$

The least squares line is $\hat{y} = 46.3992x$.

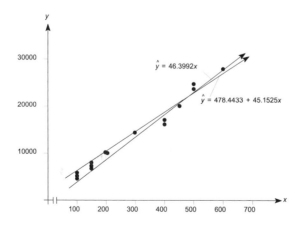

b. $SS_{xy} = \sum xy - \dfrac{\sum x \sum y}{n} = 76{,}652{,}695 = \dfrac{4305(201{,}558)}{15} = 18{,}805{,}549$

$SS_{xx} = \sum x^2 - \dfrac{\left(\sum x\right)^2}{n} = 1{,}652{,}025 - \dfrac{4305^2}{15} = 416{,}490$

$$\hat{\beta}_1 = \frac{SS_{xy}}{SS_{xx}} = \frac{18,805,549}{416,490} = 45.15246224 \approx 45.1525$$

$$\hat{\beta}_0 = \bar{y} - \hat{\beta}_1\bar{x} = \frac{201,558}{15} - 45.15246224\left(\frac{4305}{15}\right) = 478.4433$$

The least squares line is $\hat{y} = 478.4433 + 45.1525x$.

c. Because $x = 0$ is not in the observed range, we are trying to represent the data on the observed interval with the best fitting line. We are not concerned with whether the line goes through (0, 0) or not.

d. Some preliminary calculations are:

$$SS_{yy} = \sum y^2 - \frac{\left(\sum y\right)^2}{n} = 3,571,211,200 - \frac{201,558^2}{15} = 862,836,042$$

$$SSE = SS_{yy} - \hat{\beta}_1 SS_{xy} = 862,836,042 - 45.15246224(18,805,549) = 13,719,200.88$$

$$s^2 = \frac{SSE}{n-2} = \frac{13,719,200.88}{15-2} = 1,055,323.145 \quad s = 1027.2892$$

$H_0: \beta_0 = 0$
$H_a: \beta_0 \neq 0$

The test statistic is $t = \dfrac{\hat{\beta}_0 - 0}{s\sqrt{\dfrac{1}{n} + \dfrac{\bar{x}^2}{SS_{xx}}}} = \dfrac{478.443}{1027.2892\sqrt{\dfrac{1}{15} + \dfrac{287^2}{416,490}}} = .906$

The rejection region requires $\alpha/2 = .10/2 = .05$ in each tail of the t distribution with df $= n - 2 = 15 - 2 = 13$. From Table VI, Appendix A, $t_{.05} = 1.771$. The rejection region is $t < -1.771$ or $t > 1.771$.

Since the observed value of the test statistic does not fall in the rejection region ($t = .906 \not> 1.771$), H_0 is not rejected. There is insufficient evidence to indicate β_0 is different from 0 at $\alpha = .10$. Thus, β_0 should not be included in the model.

11.119 Answers may vary. Possible answer:

The scaffold-drop survey provides the most accurate estimate of spall rate in a given wall segment. However, the drop areas were not selected at random from the entire complex; rather, drops were made at areas with high spall concentrations. Therefore, if the photo spall rates could be shown to be related to drop spall rates, then the 83 photo spall rates could be used to predict what the drop spall rates would be.

a. Construct a scattergram for the data.

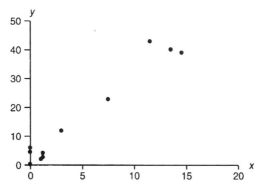

The scattergram shows a positive relationship between the photo spall rate (x) and the drop spall rate (y).

b. Find the prediction equation for drop spall rate. The MINITAB output shows the results of the analysis.

```
The regression equation is
drop = 2.55 + 2.76 photo

Predictor       Coef       StDev           T        P
Constant       2.548       1.637        1.56    0.154
photo         2.7599      0.2180       12.66    0.000

S = 4.164       R-Sq = 94.7%      R-Sq(adj) = 94.1%

Analysis of Variance

Source          DF          SS          MS          F        P
Regression       1      2777.5      2777.5     160.23    0.000
Residual Error   9       156.0        17.3
Total           10      2933.5

Unusual Observations
Obs       photo         drop         Fit   StDev Fit     Residual     St Resid
 11        11.8        43.00       35.11        1.97         7.89        2.15R

R denotes an observation with a large standardized residual
```

$\hat{y} = 2.55 + 2.76x$

c. Conduct a formal statistical hypthesis test to determine if the photo spall rates contribute information for the prediction of drop spall rates.

H_0: $\beta_1 = 0$
H_a: $\beta_1 \neq 0$

The test statistic is $t = 12.66$, with p-value $< .0001$.

Reject H_0 for any level of significance $\geq .0001$. There is sufficient evidence to indicate that photo spall rates contribute information for the prediction of drop spall rates at $\alpha \geq .0001$.

d. One could now use the 83 photos spall rates to predict values for 83 drop spall rates. Then use this information to estimate the true spall rate at a given wall segment and estimate to total spall damage.

Multiple Regression

12.1 a. $E(y) = \beta_0 + \beta_1 x_1 + \beta_2 x_2$

b. $E(y) = \beta_0 + \beta_1 x_1 + \beta_2 x_2 + \beta_3 x_3 + \beta_4 x_4$

c. $E(y) = \beta_0 + \beta_1 x_1 + \beta_2 x_2 + \beta_3 x_3 + \beta_4 x_4 + \beta_5 x_5$

12.3 The 6 steps in a multiple regression analysis are:

1. Hypothesize the deterministic component of the model. This model relates the mean, $E(y)$, to the independent variables $x_1, x_2, \ldots, x_k$. This involves the choice of the independent variables to be included in the model.

2. Use the sample data to estimate the unknown model parameters $\beta_0, \beta_1, \beta_2, \ldots, \beta_k$ in the model.

3. Specify the probability distribution of the random error term, ε, and estimate the standard deviation of the distribution, σ.

4. Check the assumptions on ε are satisfied, and make model modifications if necessary.

5. Statistically evaluate the usefulness of the model.

6. When satisfied that the model is useful, use it for prediction, estimation, and other purposes.

12.5 To test the overall adequacy of a multiple regression model, you would use a global test. The null hypothesis would be that all of the beta parameters are 0 and the alternative hypothesis would be that at least one beta parameter is not 0.

12.7 a. We are given $\hat{\beta}_2 = 2.7$, $s_{\hat{\beta}_2} = 1.86$, and $n = 30$.

$$H_0: \beta_2 = 0$$
$$H_a: \beta_2 \neq 0$$

The test statistic is $t = \dfrac{\hat{\beta}_2 - 0}{s_{\hat{\beta}_2}} = \dfrac{2.7}{1.86} = 1.45$

The rejection region requires $\alpha/2 = .05/2 = .025$ in each tail of the t distribution with df $= n - (k + 1) = 30 - (3 + 1) = 26$. From Table VI, Appendix A, $t_{.025} = 2.056$. The rejection region is $t < -2.056$ or $t > 2.056$.

Since the observed value of the test statistic does not fall in the rejection region ($t = 1.45 \not> 2.056$), H_0 is not rejected. There is insufficient evidence to indicate $\beta_2 \neq 0$ at $\alpha = .05$.

b.   We are given $\hat{\beta}_3 = .93$, $s_{\hat{\beta}_3} = .29$, and $n = 30$.

Test H_0: $\beta_3 = 0$
        H_a: $\beta_3 \neq 0$

The test statistic is $t = \dfrac{\hat{\beta}_3 - 0}{s_{\hat{\beta}_3}} = \dfrac{.93}{.29} = 3.21$

The rejection region is the same as part **a**, $t < -2.056$ or $t > 2.056$.

Since the observed value of the test statistic falls in the rejection region ($t = 3.21 > 2.056$), H_0 is rejected. There is sufficient evidence to indicate $\beta_3 \neq 0$ at $\alpha = .05$.

c. $\hat{\beta}_3$ has a smaller estimated standard error than $\hat{\beta}_2$. Therefore, the test statistic is larger for $\hat{\beta}_3$ even though $\hat{\beta}_3$ is smaller than $\hat{\beta}_2$.

12.9   The number of degrees of freedom available for estimating σ^2 is $n - (k + 1)$ where k is the number of variables in the regression model. Each additional independent variable placed in the model causes a corresponding decrease in the degrees of freedom.

12.11   a.   Yes. Since $R^2 = .92$ is close to 1, this indicates the model provides a good fit. Also, SSE $= .33$ is fairly small which indicates the model provides a good fit.

b. H_0: $\beta_1 = \beta_2 = \cdots = \beta_5 = 0$
      H_a: At least one of the parameters is not 0

The test statistic is $F = \dfrac{R^2 / k}{(1 - R^2)/[n - (k+1)]} = \dfrac{.92/5}{(1 - .92)/[30 - (5+1)]} = 55.2$

The rejection region requires $\alpha = .05$ in the upper tail of the F distribution with $v_1 = k = 5$ and $v_2 = n - (k + 1) = 30 - (5 + 1) = 24$. From Table IX, Appendix A, $F_{.05} = 2.62$. The rejection region is $F > 2.62$.

Since the observed value of the test statistic falls in the rejection region ($F = 55.2 > 2.62$), H_0 is rejected. There is sufficient evidence to indicate the model is useful in predicting y at $\alpha = .05$.

12.13   a.   From the output, the least squares prediction equation is
$\hat{y} = 3.70 + .34x_1 + .49x_2 + .72x_3 + 1.14x_4 + 1.51x_5 + .26x_6 - .14x_7 - .10x_8 - .10x_9$.

b. $\hat{\beta}_0 = 3.70$.   This value has no meaningful interpretation.

$\hat{\beta}_1 = .34$.   We estimate the mean number of runs scored by a team in a season to increase by .34 for each unit increase in the number of walks, when all the other independent variables are held fixed.

$\hat{\beta}_2 = .49.$ We estimate the mean number of runs scored by a team in a season to increase by .49 for each additional single, when all the other independent variables are held fixed.

$\hat{\beta}_3 = .72.$ We estimate the mean number of runs scored by a team in a season to increase by .72 for each additional double, when all the other independent variables are held fixed.

$\hat{\beta}_4 = 1.14.$ We estimate the mean number of runs scored by a team in a season to increase by 1.14 for each additional triple, when all the other independent variables are held fixed.

$\hat{\beta}_5 = 1.51.$ We estimate the mean number of runs scored by a team in a season to increase by 1.51 for each additional home run, when all the other independent variables are held fixed.

$\hat{\beta}_6 = .26.$ We estimate the mean number of runs scored by a team in a season to increase by .26 for each additional stolen base, when all the other independent variables are held fixed.

$\hat{\beta}_7 = -.14.$ We estimate the mean number of runs scored by a team in a season to decrease by .14 for each additional player caught stealing, when all the other independent variables are held fixed.

$\hat{\beta}_8 = -.10.$ We estimate the mean number of runs scored by a team in a season to decrease by .10 for each additional strikeout, when all the other independent variables are held fixed.

$\hat{\beta}_9 = -.10.$ We estimate the mean number of runs scored by a team in a season to decrease by .10 for each additional out, when all the other independent variables are held fixed.

c. $H_0: \beta_7 = 0$
      $H_a: \beta_7 < 0$

The test statistic is $t = \dfrac{\hat{\beta}_7 - 0}{s_{\hat{\beta}_7}} = \dfrac{-.14 - 0}{.14} = -1.00$

The rejection region requires $\alpha = .05$ in the lower tail of the t distribution. From Table VI, Appendix A, with df $= n - (k + 1) = 234 - (9 + 1) = 224$, $t_{.05} \approx 1.645$. The rejection region is $t < -1.645$.

Since the observed value of the test statistic does not fall in the rejection region ($t = -1.00 \not< -1.645$), H_0 is not rejected. There is insufficient evidence to indicate that there is a negative linear relationship between the number of runs scored and the number of times caught stealing at $\alpha = .05$.

d. For confidence coefficient .95, $\alpha = .05$ and $\alpha/2 = .05/2 = .025$. From Table VI, Appendix A, with df $= n - (k + 1) = 234 - (9 + 1) = 224$, $t_{.025} \approx 1.96$. The 95% confidence interval is:

$$\hat{\beta}_5 \pm t_{.025} s_{\hat{\beta}_5} \Rightarrow 1.51 \pm 1.96(.05) \Rightarrow 1.51 \pm .098 \Rightarrow (1.412, \ 1.608)$$

We are 95% confident that for each additional home run, the mean number of runs scored will increase by anywhere from 1.412 to 1.608, holding all the other variables constant.

12.15 a. The first order model is $y = \beta_0 + \beta_1 x_1 + \beta_2 x_2 + \beta_3 x_3 + \varepsilon$

b. $R^2 = .08$. 8% of the sample variation in the frequency of marijuana use in the past 6 months is explained by the model containing severity of inattention, severity of impulsivity-hyperactivity, and level of oppositional-defiant and conduct disorder.

c. The global F-test has the hypotheses:

H_0: $\beta_1 = \beta_2 = \beta_3 = 0$
H_a: At least one $\beta_i \neq 0$

The global F-test yielded a p-value less than .01. Since the p-value is so small, there is evidence to reject H_0 for $\alpha > .01$. There is sufficient evidence to indicate that at least one of the independent variables contributes to the prediction of the frequency of marijuana use in the past 6 months at $\alpha > .01$.

d. The test for β_1:

H_0: $\beta_1 = 0$
H_a: $\beta_1 \neq 0$

The p-value for the test is less than .01. Since the p-value is so small, there is evidence to reject H_o for $\alpha > .01$. There is sufficient evidence to indicate that severity of inattention contributes to the prediction of the frequency of marijuana use in the past 6 months, when holding severity of impulsivity-hyperactivity and level of oppositional-defiant and conduct disorder fixed at $\alpha > .01$.

e. The test for β_2:

H_0: $\beta_2 = 0$
H_a: $\beta_2 \neq 0$

The p-value for the test is greater than .05. Since the p-value is not small, there is no evidence to reject H_0 for $\alpha \leq .05$. There is insufficient evidence to indicate that severity of impulsivity-hyperactivity contributes to the prediction of the frequency of marijuana use in the past 6 months, when holding severity of inattention and level of oppositional-defiant and conduct disorder fixed at $\alpha \leq .05$.

f. The test for β_3:

$$H_0: \ \beta_3 = 0$$
$$H_a: \ \beta_3 \neq 0$$

The p-value for the test is greater than .05. Since the p-value is not small, there is no evidence to reject H_0 for $\alpha \leq .05$. There is insufficient evidence to indicate that level of oppositional-defiant and conduct disorder contributes to the prediction of the frequency of marijuana use in the past 6 months, when holding severity of inattention and severity of impulsivity-hyperactivity fixed at $\alpha \leq .05$.

12.17 a. The hypothesized equation is $y = \beta_0 + \beta_1 x_1 + \beta_2 x_2 + \beta_3 x_3 + \beta_4 x_4 + \varepsilon$

b. The p-value is $p = .005$. Since the p-value is less than α ($p = .005 < \alpha = .01$), H_0 is rejected. There is sufficient evidence to indicate that there is a negative linear relationship between the number of years played golf and the change from routine, when holding all the other independent variables fixed at $\alpha = .01$.

c. This statement would be correct if all the independent variables are independent of each other. However, if some of the independent variables are not independent of each other, then the interpretation of the individual beta parameters is questionable.

d. The null hypothesis for testing the overall adequacy of each first-order regression model is:

$$H_0: \ \beta_1 = \beta_2 = \beta_3 = \beta_4 = 0$$

e. The rejection region requires $\alpha = .01$ in the upper tail of the F distribution. From Table XI, Appendix A, with $v_1 = k = 4$ and $v_2 = n - (k + 1) = 393 - (4 + 1) = 388$, $F_{.01} \approx 3.32$. The rejection region is $F > 3.32$.

f. **For Thrill:**

$$H_0: \ \beta_1 = \beta_2 = \beta_3 = \beta_4 = 0$$
$$H_a: \ \text{At least one } \beta_i \neq 0$$

The test statistic is $F = 5.56$. Since the observed value of the test statistic falls in the rejection region ($F = 5.56 > 3.32$), H_0 is rejected. There is sufficient evidence to indicate that the model is adequate in predicting thrill at $\alpha = .01$.

For Change of Routine:

$$H_0: \ \beta_1 = \beta_2 = \beta_3 = \beta_4 = 0$$
$$H_a: \ \text{At least one } \beta_i \neq 0$$

The test statistic is $F = 3.02$. Since the observed value of the test statistic does not fall in the rejection region ($F = 3.02 \not> 3.32$), H_0 is not rejected. There is insufficient evidence to indicate that the model is adequate in predicting change of routine at $\alpha = .01$.

For Surprise:

H_0: $\beta_1 = \beta_2 = \beta_3 = \beta_4 = 0$
H_a: At least one $\beta_i \neq 0$

The test statistic is $F = 3.33$. Since the observed value of the test statistic falls in the rejection region ($F = 3.33 > 3.32$), H_0 is rejected. There is sufficient evidence to indicate that the model is adequate in predicting surprise at $\alpha = .01$.

g. For Thrill, the p-value is $p < .001$. Since the p-value is less than $\alpha = .01$, H_0 is rejected. This agrees with the solution in part f.

For Change of routine, the p-value is $p = .018$. Since the p-value is greater than $\alpha = .01$, H_0 is not rejected. This agrees with the solution in part f.

For Surprise, the p-value is $p = .011$. Since the p-value is greater than $\alpha = .01$, H_0 is not rejected. This does not agree with the solution in part f. However, we note that the critical F value found in the table was approximate since there was not a df for the denominator that corresponds with our problem in the table.

h. **For Thrill**: $R^2 = .055$. 5.5% of the total sample variation in the thrill scores is explained by the model containing number of rounds of golf, total number of golf vacations taken, number of years played golf, and average golf score.

For Change from routine: $R^2 = .030$. 3.0% of the total sample variation in the change from routine scores is explained by the model containing number of rounds of golf, total number of golf vacations taken, number of years played golf, and average golf score.

For Surprise: $R^2 = .023$. 2.3% of the total sample variation in the surprise scores is explained by the model containing number of rounds of golf, total number of golf vacations taken, number of years played golf, and average golf score.

12.19   a.   The first order model is $E(y) = \beta_0 + \beta_1 x_1 + \beta_2 x_2$.

b.   Using MINITAB, the results of fitting the model are:

Regression Analysis: Earnings versus Age, Worked

```
The regression equation is
Earnings = - 20 + 13.4 Age + 244 Worked

Predictor     Coef   SE Coef       T       P
Constant     -20.4     652.7   -0.03   0.976
Age         13.350     7.672    1.74   0.107
Worked      243.71     63.51    3.84   0.002

S = 547.737   R-Sq = 58.2%   R-Sq(adj) = 51.3%
```

```
Analysis of Variance
Source           DF      SS        MS       F      P
Regression        2   5018232   2509116   8.36   0.005
Residual Error   12   3600196    300016
Total            14   8618428


Source    DF    Seq SS
Age        1    600498
Worked     1   4417734
```

The least squares prediction equation is $\hat{y} = -20.4 + 13.350x_1 + 243.71x_2$.

c. $\hat{\beta}_0 = -20.4$. This has no meaning because $x_1 = 0$ and $x_2 = 0$ are not in the observed range.

$\hat{\beta}_1 = 13.350$. The mean annual earnings is estimated to increase by $13.350 for each additional year of age, holding hours worked per day constant.

$\hat{\beta}_2 = 243.71$. The mean annual earnings is estimated to increase by $243.71 for each additional hour worked per day, holding year of age constant.

d.   To determine if age is a predictor of annual earnings, we test:

H_0: $\beta_1 = 0$
H_a: $\beta_1 \neq 0$

From the printout, the test statistic is $t = 1.74$ and the p-value is $p = .107$. Since the p-value is greater than α ($p = .107 > .01$), H_0 is not rejected. There is insufficient evidence to indicate that age is a useful predictor of annual income, adjusting for hours worked per week, at $\alpha = .01$.

e.   For confidence coefficient .95, $\alpha = .05$ and $\alpha/2 = .05/2 = .025$. From Table VI, Appendix A, with df $= n - (k + 1) = 15 - (2 + 1) = 12$, $t_{.025} = 2.179$. The 95% confidence interval is:
$$\hat{\beta}_2 \pm t_{.025} s_{\hat{\beta}_2} \Rightarrow 243.71 \pm 2.179(63.51) \Rightarrow 243.71 \pm 138.388 \Rightarrow (105.322, \ 382.098)$$

We are 95% confident that for each additional hour worked per day, the mean annual salary will increase anywhere from $105.322 and $ 382.098, holding age constant.

f. $R^2 = \text{R-Sq} = 58.2\%$. 58.2% of the total sample variation of the annual earnings is explained by the model containing age and hours worked per day.

g. $R_a^2 = \text{R-Sq(adj)} = 51.3\%$. 51.3% of the total sample variation of the annual earnings is explained by the model containing age and hours worked per day, adjusted for the sample size and the number of independent variables in the model.

h. To determine if any of the independent variables are useful in the prediction of annual earnings, we test:

H_0: $\beta_1 = \beta_2 = 0$
H_a: At least one $\beta_i \neq 0$

The test statistic is $F = 8.36$ and the p-value is $p = .005$. Since the p-value is less than α ($p = .005 < \alpha = .01$), H_0 is rejected. There is sufficient evidence to indicate at least one of the two variables age and number of hours worked per week is useful in the prediction of annual earnings at $\alpha = .01$.

12.21 a. **Regression Analysis: WeightChg versus Digest, Fiber**

```
The regression equation is
WeightChg = 12.2 - 0.0265 Digest - 0.458 Fiber

Predictor        Coef      SE Coef          T        P
Constant       12.180        4.402       2.77    0.009
Digest       -0.02654      0.05349      -0.50    0.623
Fiber         -0.4578       0.1283      -3.57    0.001

S = 3.519        R-Sq = 52.9%      R-Sq(adj) = 50.5%

Analysis of Variance

Source            DF           SS          MS         F        P
Regression         2       542.03      271.02     21.88    0.000
Residual Error    39       483.08       12.39
Total             41      1025.12
```

$\hat{y} = 12.180 - .02654x_1 - .4578x_2$.

b. $\hat{\beta}_0$ = the estimate of the y-intercept

$\hat{\beta}_1 = -.0265$. We estimate that the mean weight change will decrease by .0265% for each additional increase of 1% in digestion efficiency, with acid-detergent fibre held constant.

$\hat{\beta}_2 = -.458$. We estimate that the mean weight change will decrease by .458% for each additional increase of 1% in acid-detergent fibre, with digestion efficiency held constant.

c. To determine if digestion efficiency is a useful predictor of weight change, we test:

H_0: $\beta_1 = 0$
H_a: $\beta_1 \neq 0$

The test statistic is $t = -.50$. The p-value is $p = .623$. Since the p-value is greater than α ($p = .623 > .01$), H_0 is not rejected. There is insufficient evidence to indicate that digestion efficiency is a useful linear predictor of weight change at $\alpha = .01$.

d. For confidence coefficient .99, $\alpha = 1 - .99 = .01$ and $\alpha/2 = .01/2 = .005$. From Table VI, Appendix A, with df $= n - (k + 1) = 42 - (2 + 1) = 39$, $t_{.005} \approx 2.704$. The 99% confidence interval is:

$$\hat{\beta}_2 \pm t_{.005} s_{\hat{\beta}} \Rightarrow -.4578 \pm 2.704 (.1283) \Rightarrow -.4578 \pm .3469 \Rightarrow (-.8047, -.1109)$$

We are 99% confident that the change in mean weight change for each unit change in acid-detergent fiber, holding digestion efficiency constant is between $-.8047$ and $-.1109$.

e. $R^2 = $ R-Sq $= 52.9\%$. 52.9% of the total sample variation in the weight change scores is explained by the model containing the independent variables digestion efficiency and acid-detergent fibre. $R_a^2 = $ R-Sq(adj) $= 50.5\%$. 50.5% of the total sample variation in the weight change scores is explained by the model containing the independent variables digestion efficiency and acid-detergent fibre, adjusting for the sample size and the number of independent variables in the model.

f. To determine if the overall model is useful in the prediction of weight change, we test:

H_0: $\beta_1 = \beta_2 = 0$
H_a: At least one $\beta_i \neq 0$, $i = 1, 2$

The test statistic is $F = 21.88$ and the p-value is $p = .000$. Since the p-value is less than α ($p = .000 < \alpha = .05$), H_0 is rejected. There is sufficient evidence to indicate at least one of the variables digestion efficiency and acid-detergent fibre is useful in the prediction weight change at $\alpha = .05$.

12.23 a. $E(y) = \beta_0 + \beta_1 x_1 + \beta_2 x_2 + \beta_3 x_3 + \beta_4 x_4 + \beta_5 x_5 + \beta_6 x_6 + \beta_7 x_7$

b. Using MINITAB, the output is:

```
The regression equation is y = 0.998 - 0.0224 x1 + 0.156x2 - 0.0172x3 - 0.00953x4
+ 0.421x5 + 0.417x6 - 0.155x7

Predictor        Coef        StDev           T            P
Constant       0.9981       0.2475        4.03        0.002
x1           -0.022429     0.005039       -4.45        0.001
x2            0.15571       0.07429        2.10        0.060
x3           -0.01719       0.01186       -1.45        0.175
x4           -0.009527      0.009619      -0.99        0.343
x5            0.4214        0.1008         4.18        0.002
x6            0.4171        0.4377         0.95        0.361
x7           -0.1552        0.1486        -1.04        0.319

S = 0.4365       R-Sq = 77.1%       R-Sq(adj) = 62.5%
```

```
Analysis of Variance

Source              DF          SS          MS          F          P
Regression           7      7.9578      1.1368       5.29      0.007
Residual            11      2.3632      0.2148
Error
Total               18     10.3210

Sourc      DF        Seq SS
e
x1          1        1.4016
x2          1        1.9263
x3          1        0.1171
x4          1        0.0446
x5          1        4.0771
x6          1        0.1565
x7          1        0.2345

Unusual Observations

Obs          x1          y       Fit  StDev Fit   Residual   St Resid
14         80.0      0.120     0.628      0.328      0.748      2.28R

R denotes an observation with a large standardized residual.
```

The least squares model is $= .9981 - .0224x_1 + .1557x_2 - .0172x_3 - .0095x_4 + .4214x_5 + .4171x_6 - .1552x_7$

c. $\hat{\beta}_0 = .9981 =$ the estimate of the y-intercept.

$\hat{\beta}_1 = -.0224$; We estimate that the mean voltage will decrease by .0224 kw/cm, for each additional increase of 1% of x_1, the disperse phase volume (with all other variables held constant).

$\hat{\beta}_2 = .1557$; We estimate that the mean voltage will increase by .1557 kw/cm for each additional increase of 1% of x_2, the salinity (with all other variables held constant).

$\hat{\beta}_3 = -.0172$; We estimate the the mean voltage will decrease by .0172 kw/cm for each additional increase of 1 degree of x_3, the temperature in Celcius (with all other variables held constant).

$\hat{\beta}_4 = -.0095$; We estimate that the mean voltage will decrease by .0095 kw/cm for each additional increase of 1 hour of x_4, the time delay (with all other variables held constant).

$\hat{\beta}_5 = .4214$; We estimate that the mean voltage will increase by .4124 kw/cm for each additional increase of 1% of x_5, sufficient concentration (with all other variables held constant).

$\hat{\beta}_6 = .4171$; We estimate that the mean voltage will increase by .4171 kw/cm for each additional increase of 1 unit of x_6, span: Triton (with all other variables held constant).

$\hat{\beta}_7 = -.1552$; We estimate that the mean voltage will decrease by .1552 kw/cm for each additional increase of 1% of x_7, the solid particles (with all other variables held constant).

12.25   a. $R^2 = .362$. 36.2% of the variability in the AC scores can be explained by the model containing the variables self-esteem score, optimism score, and group cohesion score.

b.   To test the utility of the model, we test:

H_0: $\beta_1 = \beta_2 = \beta_3 = 0$
H_a: At least one $\beta_i \neq 0$, $i = 1, 2, 3$

The test statistic is:

$$F = \frac{R^2/k}{(1-R^2)[n-(k+1)]} = \frac{.362/3}{(1-.362)/[31-(3+1)]} = 5.11$$

The rejection region requires $\alpha = .05$ in the upper tail of the F distribution with $v_1 = k = 3$ and $v_2 = n - (k+1) = 31 - (3+1) = 27$. From Table IX, Appendix A, $F_{.05} = 2.96$. The rejection region is $F > 2.96$.

Since the observed value of the test statistic falls in the rejection region ($F = 5.11 > 2.96$), H_0 is rejected. There is sufficient evidence that the model is useful in predicting AC score at $\alpha = .05$.

12.27   a.   **Model 1:**

H_0: $\beta_1 = 0$
H_a: $\beta_1 \neq 0$

The test statistic is $t = \dfrac{\hat{\beta}_1 - 0}{s_{\hat{\beta}_1}} = \dfrac{.0354}{.0137} = 2.58$.

Since no α was given, we will use $\alpha = .05$. The rejection region requires $\alpha/2 = .05/2 = .025$ in each tail of the t distribution. From Table VI, Appendix A, with df $= n - (k+1) = 12 - (1+1) = 10$, $t_{.025} = 2.228$. The rejection region is $t < -2.228$ or $t > 2.228$.

Since the observed value of the test statistic falls in the rejection region ($t = 2.58 > 2.228$), H_0 is rejected. There is sufficient evidence to indicate that there is a linear relationship between vintage and the logarithm of price.

Model 2:

H_0: $\beta_1 = 0$
H_a: $\beta_1 \neq 0$

The test statistic is $t = \dfrac{\hat{\beta}_1 - 0}{s_{\hat{\beta}_1}} = \dfrac{.0238}{.00717} = 3.32$

Since no α was given, we will use $\alpha = .05$. The rejection region requires $\alpha/2 = .05/2 = .025$ in each tail of the t distribution. From Table VI, Appendix A, with df $= n - (k + 1) = 12 - (4 + 1) = 7$, $t_{.025} = 2.365$. The rejection region is $t < -2.365$ or $t > 2.365$.

Since the observed value of the test statistic falls in the rejection region ($t = 3.32 > 2.365$), H_0 is rejected. There is sufficient evidence to indicate that there is a linear relationship between vintage and the logarithm of price, adjusting for all other variables.

H_0: $\beta_2 = 0$
H_a: $\beta_2 \neq 0$

The test statistic is $t = \dfrac{\hat{\beta}_2 - 0}{s_{\hat{\beta}_2}} = \dfrac{.616}{.0952} = 6.47$

The rejection region is $t < -2.365$ or $t > 2.365$.

Since the observed value of the test statistic falls in the rejection region ($t = 6.47 > 2.365$), H_0 is rejected. There is sufficient evidence to indicate that there is a linear relationship between average growing season temperature and the logarithm of price, adjusting for all other variables.

H_0: $\beta_3 = 0$
H_a: $\beta_3 \neq 0$

The test statistic is $t = \dfrac{\hat{\beta}_3 - 0}{s_{\hat{\beta}_3}} = \dfrac{-.00386}{.00081} = -4.77$

The rejection region is $t < -2.365$ or $t > 2.365$.

Since the observed value of the test statistic falls in the rejection region ($t = -4.77 < -2.365$), H_0 is rejected. There is sufficient evidence to indicate that there is a linear relationship between Sept./ Aug. rainfall and the logarithm of price, adjusting for all other variables.

H_0: $\beta_4 = 0$
H_a: $\beta_4 \neq 0$

The test statistic is $t = \dfrac{\hat{\beta}_4 - 0}{s_{\hat{\beta}_4}} = \dfrac{.0001173}{.000482} = 0.24.$

The rejection region is $t < -2.365$ or $t > 2.365$.

Since the observed value of the test statistic does not fall in the rejection region ($t = 0.24$ $\not> 2.365$), H_0 is not rejected. There is insufficient evidence to indicate that there is a linear relationship between rainfall in months preceding vintage and the logarithm of price, adjusting for all other variables.

Model 3:

H_0: $\beta_1 = 0$
H_a: $\beta_1 \neq 0$

The test statistic is $t = \dfrac{\hat{\beta}_1 - 0}{s_{\hat{\beta}_1}} = \dfrac{.0240}{.00747} = 3.21$

Since no α was given, we will use $\alpha = .05$. The rejection region requires $\alpha/2 = .05/2 = .025$ in each tail of the t distribution. From Table VI, Appendix A, with df $= n - (k + 1)$ $= 12 - (5 + 1) + 7$, $t_{.025} = 2.447$. The rejection region is $t < -2.447$ or $t > 2.447$.

Since the observed value of the test statistic falls in the rejection region ($t = 3.21 > 2.447$), H_0 is rejected. There is sufficient evidence to indicate that there is a linear relationship between vintage and the logarithm of price, adjusting for all other variables.

H_0: $\beta_2 = 0$
H_a: $\beta_2 \neq 0$

The test statistic is $t = \dfrac{\hat{\beta}_2 - 0}{s_{\hat{\beta}_2}} = \dfrac{.608}{.116} = 5.24.$

The rejection region is $t < -2.447$ or $t > 2.447$.

Since the observed value of the test statistic falls in the rejection region ($t = 5.24 > 2.447$), H_0 is rejected. There is sufficient evidence to indicate that there is a linear relationship between average growing season temperature and the logarithm of price, adjusting for all other variables.

H_0: $\beta_3 = 0$
H_a: $\beta_3 \neq 0$

The test statistic is $t = \dfrac{\hat{\beta}_3 - 0}{s_{\hat{\beta}_3}} = \dfrac{-.00380}{.00095} = -4.00$

The rejection region is $t < -2.447$ or $t > -2.447$.

Since the observed value of the test statistic falls in the rejection region ($t = -4.00 < -2.447$), H_0 is rejected. There is sufficient evidence to indicate that there is a linear relationship between Sept./Aug. rainfall and the logarithm of price, adjusting for all other variables.

H_0: $\beta_4 = 0$
H_a: $\beta_4 \neq 0$

The test statistic is $t = \dfrac{\hat{\beta}_4 - 0}{s_{\hat{\beta}_4}} = \dfrac{.00115}{.000505} = 2.28$

The rejection region is $t < -2.447$ or $t > 2.447$.

Since the observed value of the test statistic does not fall in the rejection region ($t = 2.28 \not> 2.365$), H_0 is not rejected. There is insufficient evidence to indicate that there is a linear relationship between rainfall in months preceding vintage and the logarithm of price, adjusting for all other variables.

H_0: $\beta_5 = 0$
H_a: $\beta_5 \neq 0$

The test statistic is $t = \dfrac{\hat{\beta}_5 - 0}{s_{\hat{\beta}_5}} = \dfrac{.00765}{.0565} = 0.14$.

The rejection region is $t < -2.447$ or $t > 2.447$.

Since the observed value of the test statistic does not fall in the rejection region ($t = 0.14 \not> 2.365$), H_0 is not rejected. There is insufficient evidence to indicate that there is a linear relationship between average September temperature and the logarithm of price, adjusting for all other variables.

b. **Model 1:**

$\hat{\beta}_1 = .0354$, $e^{.0354} - 1 = .036$

We estimate that the mean price will increase by 3.6% for each additional increase of unit of x_1, vintage year.

Model 2:

$\hat{\beta}_1 = .0238$, $e^{.0238} - 1 = .024$

We estimate that the mean price will increase by 2.4% for each additional increase of 1 unit of x_1, vintage year (with all other variables held constant).

$\hat{\beta}_2 = .616$, $e^{.616} - 1 = .852$

We estimate that the mean price will increase by 85.2% for each additional increase of 1 unit of x_2, average growing season temperature °C (with all other variables held constant).

$\hat{\beta}_3 = -.00386$, $e^{.00386} - 1 = -.004$

We estimate that the mean price will decrease by .4% for each additional increase of 1 unit of x_3, Sept./Aug. rainfall in cm (with all other variables held constant).

$\hat{\beta}_4 = .0001173$, $e^{.0001173} - 1 = .0001$

We estimate that the mean price will increase by .01% for each additional increase of 1 unit of x_4, rainfall in months prededing vintage in cm (with all other variables held constant).

Model 3:

$\hat{\beta}_1 = .0240$, $e^{.0240} - 1 = .024$

We estimate that the mean price will increase by 2.4% for each additional increase of 1 unit of x_1, vintage year (with all other variables held constant).

$\hat{\beta}_2 = .608$, $e^{.608} - 1 = .837$

We estimate that the mean price will increase by 83.7% for each additional increase of 1 unit of x_2, average growing season temperatures in °C (with all other variables held constant).

$\hat{\beta}_3 = -.00380$, $e^{.00380} - 1 = -.004$

We estimate that the mean price will decrease by .4% for each additional increase of 1 unit of x_3, Sept./Aug. rainfall in cm, (with all other variables held constant).

$\hat{\beta}_4 = .00115$, $e^{.00115} - 1 = .001$

We estimate that the average mean price will increase by .1% for each additional increase of 1 unit of x_4, rainfall in months preceding vintage in cm (with all other variables held constant).

$\hat{\beta}_5 = .00765$, $e^{.00765} - 1 = .008$

We estimate that the average mean price will increase by .8% for each additional increase of 1 unit of x_5, average Sept. temperature in °C (with all other variables held constant).

c. For model 1, $R^2 = .212$ and $s = .575$. For model 2, $R^2 = .828$ and $s = .287$. For Model 3, $R^2 = .828$ and $s = .293$.

Based on the R^2 and s values, the best model is model 2. Model 2 has the highest R^2 value and the lowest value of s.

12.29 The 95% confidence interval for E(y) will be narrower than the 95% prediction interval for y. When estimating the value of E(y) or mean value of y, there is some variance. However, when predicting the actual value of y, we must first find the mean (with some variance above). Once the mean is located, the actual values of y can vary around this mean.

12.31 a. For trial #1, the 95% confidence interval for E(y) is (−3.1722, 1.4365). We are 95% confident that the mean weight change for all goslings will be between −3.1722 and 1.4365 when the digestion efficiency is 0 and the acid-detergent fibre is 28.5.

       b. For trial #2, the 95% confidence interval for E(y) is (-2.7090, 1.7563). We are 95% confident that the mean weight change for all goslings will be between -2.7090 and 1.7563 when the digestion efficiency is 2.5 and the acid-detergent fibre is 27.5.

12.33 Using MINITAB, the results of the prediction are:

```
Predicted Values for New Observations

New
Obs    Fit   SE Fit       95% CI            95% PI
 1    11.75   16.66   (-21.19, 44.68)   (-183.76, 207.25)


Values of Predictors for New Observations

New
Obs   Miles  Length  Weight
 1     100    40.0     800
```

The 95% prediction interval is (−183.76, 207.25). We are 95% confident that the actual DDT level of a fish caught 100 miles upstream with a length of 40 centimeters and a weight of 800 grams will be between −186.76 and 207.25 parts per million. Since DDT levels cannot be negative, the actual interval would be 0 to 207.25.

12.35 The first order model is:

$$E(y) = \beta_0 + \beta_1 x_1 + \beta_2 x_2 + \beta_3 x_5$$

We want to find a 95% prediction interval for the actual voltage when the volume fraction of the disperse phase is at the high level ($x_1 = 80$), the salinity is at the low level ($x_2 = 1$), and the amount of surfactant is at the low level ($x_5 = 2$).

Using MINITAB, the output is:

```
The regression equation is
y = 0.993 - 0.243 x1 + 0.142 x2 + 0.385 x5

Predictor        Coef        StDev          T           P
Constant        0.9326      0.2482        3.76        0.002
x1            -0.024272     0.004900      -4.95        0.000
x2             0.14206      0.07573        1.88        0.080
x5             0.38457      0.09801        3.92        0.001

S = 0.4796      R-Sq = 66.6%      R-Sq(adj) = 59.9%

Analysis of Variance

Source           DF          SS          MS         F          P
Regression        3        6.8701      2.2900      9.95      0.001
Residual         15        3.4509      0.2301
Error
Total            18       10.3210
```

```
Source      DF      Seq SS
x1           1      1.4016
x2           1      1.9263
x5           1      3.5422

Unusual Observations
Obs       x1        y       Fit   StDev Fit   Residual   St Resid
  3      40.0    3.200     2.068     0.239      1.132       2.72R

R denotes an observation with a large standardized residual

Predicted Values for New Observations

New
Obs     Fit   SE Fit         95% CI             95% PI
  1   -0.098   0.232   (-0.592, 0.396)   (-1.233, 1.038)


Values of Predictors for New Observations

New
Obs     x1     x2     x5
  1   80.0   1.00   2.00
```

The 95% prediction interval is $(-1.233, 1.038)$. We are 95% confident that the actual voltage is between -1.233 and 1.038 when the volume fraction of the disperse phase is at the high level ($x_1 = 80$), the salinity is at the low level ($x_2 = 1$), and the amount of surfactant is at the low level ($x_5 = 2$).

12.37   a. $E(y) = \beta_0 + \beta_1 x_1 + \beta_2 x_2 + \beta_3 x_1 x_2$

   b. $E(y) = \beta_0 + \beta_1 x_1 + \beta_2 x_2 + \beta_3 x_3 + \beta_4 x_1 x_2 + \beta_5 x_1 x_3 + \beta_6 x_2 x_3$

12.39   a.   The response surface is a twisted surface in three-dimensional space.

   b.   For $x_1 = 0$, $E(y) = 3 + 0 + 2x_2 - 0x_2 = 3 + 2x_2$
        For $x_1 = 1$, $E(y) = 3 + 1 + 2x_2 - 1x_2 = 4 + x_2$
        For $x_1 = 2$, $E(y) = 3 + 2 + 2x_2 - 2x_2 = 5$

   The plot of the lines is:

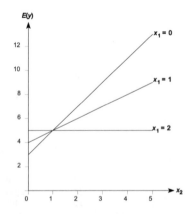

   c.   The lines are not parallel because interaction between x_1 and x_2 is present. Interaction between x_1 and x_2 means that the effect of x_2 on y depends on what level x_1 takes on.

d. For $x_1 = 0$, as x_2 increases from 0 to 5, $E(y)$ increases from 3 to 13.
For $x_1 = 1$, as x_2 increases from 0 to 5, $E(y)$ increases from 4 to 9.
For $x_1 = 2$, as x_2 increases from 0 to 5, $E(y) = 5$.

e. For $x_1 = 2$ and $x_2 = 4$, $E(y) = 5$
For $x_1 = 0$ and $x_2 = 5$, $E(y) = 13$

Thus, $E(y)$ changes from 5 to 13.

12.41   a.   The prediction equation is:

$$\hat{y} = -2.55 + 3.82x_1 + 2.63x_2 - 1.29x_1x_2$$

b. The response surface is a twisted plane, since the equation contains an interaction term.

c. For $x_2 = 1$, $= -2.55 + 3.82x_1 + 2.63(1) - 1.29x_1(1)$
      $= .08 + 2.53x_1$
For $x_2 = 3$, $= -2.55 + 3.82x_1 + 2.63(3) - 1.29x_1(3)$
      $= 5.34 - .05x_1$
For $x_2 = 5$, $= -2.55 + 3.82x_1 + 2.63(5) - 1.29x_1(5)$
      $= 10.6 - 2.63x_1$

d. If x_1 and x_2 interact, the effect of x_1 on y is different at different levels of x_2. When $x_2 = 1$, as x_1 increases, $\hat{y}$ also increases. When $x_2 = 5$, as x_1 increases, $\hat{y}$ decreases.

e. The hypotheses are:

H_0: $\beta_3 = 0$
H_a: $\beta_3 \neq 0$

f. The test statistic is $t = \dfrac{\hat{\beta}_3}{s_{\hat{\beta}_3}} = \dfrac{-1.285}{.159} = -8.06$

The rejection region requires $\alpha/2 = .01/2 = .005$ in each tail of the t distribution with df $= n - (k + 1) = 15 - (3 + 1) = 11$. From Table VI, Appendix A, $t_{.005} = 3.106$. The rejection region is $t < -3.106$ or $t > 3.106$.

Since the observed value of the test statistic falls in the rejection region ($t = -8.06 < -3.106$), H_0 is rejected. There is sufficient evidence to indicate that x_1 and x_2 interact at $\alpha = .01$.

12.43 a. The phrase "x_1 and x_2 interact" means that the effect of attitude toward drinking (x_1) on frequency of drinking alcoholic beverages (y) depends on the level of social support (x_2).

   b. To determine if attitude and social support interact, we test:

H_0: $\beta_3 = 0$
H_a: $\beta_3 \neq 0$

   c. Since the p-value is so small ($p < .001$), H_0 is rejected for any value of $\alpha > .001$. There is sufficient evidence to indicate that attitude toward drinking and social support interact to affect frequency of drinking.

12.45 a. $E(y) = \beta_0 + \beta_1 x_1 + \beta_2 x_2 + \beta_3 x_3 + \beta_4 x_4 + \beta_5 x_5$

   b. H_0: $\beta_4 = 0$

   c. $t = 4.408$, p-value $= .001$

Since the p-value is so small, there is strong evidence to reject H_0. There is sufficient evidence to indicate that the strength of client-therapist relationship contributes information for the prediction of a client's reaction for any $\alpha > .001$.

   d. Answers may vary.

   e. $R^2 = .2946$. 29.46% of the variability in the client's reaction scores can be explained by this model.

12.47 a. The phrase "client credibility and linguistic delivery style interact" means that the affect of client credibility on likelihood depends on the level of linguistic delivery style.

   b. To determine if the overall model is adequate for predicting likelihood, we test:

H_0: $\beta_1 = \beta_2 = \beta_3 = 0$
H_a: At least one $\beta_i \neq 0$, $i = 1, 2, 3$

   c. From the table, the test statistic is $F = 55.35$ and the p-value is $p < 0.0005$. Since the p value is so small, H_0 is rejected. There is sufficient evidence to indicate the model is adequate in predicting likelihood for any reasonable level of α.

   d. To determine if client credibility and linguistic delivery style interact, we test:

H_0: $\beta_3 = 0$
H_a: $\beta_3 \neq 0$

   e. From the table, $t = 4.008$ and the p-value is $p < .005$. Since the p-value is so small, H_0 is rejected. There is sufficient evidence to indicate the that client credibility and linguistic delivery style interact for any reasonable level of α.

f.   The least squares prediction equation is $\hat{y} = 15.865 + .037x_1 - .678x_2 + .036x_1x_2$.

When client credibility is 22, the least squares line is:

$$\hat{y} = 15.865 + .037(22) - .678x_2 + .036(22)x_2 = 16.679 + .114x_2$$

When client credibility is 22, for each unit increase in linguistic delivery score, the mean likelihood score is estimated to increase by .114.

g.   When client credibility is 46, the least squares line is:

$$\hat{y} = 15.865 + .037(46) - .678x_2 + .036(46)x_2 = 17.567 + .978x_2$$

When client credibility is 46, for each unit increase in linguistic delivery score, the mean likelihood score is estimated to increase by .978.

12.49 a. $E(y) = \beta_0 + \beta_1x_1 + \beta_2x_1^2$

       b. $E(y) = \beta_0 + \beta_1x_1 + \beta_2x_2 + \beta_3x_1^2 + \beta_4x_2^2 + \beta_5x_1x_2$

       c. $E(y) = \beta_0 + \beta_1x_1 + \beta_2x_2 + \beta_3x_3 + \beta_4x_1^2 + \beta_5x_2^2 + \beta_6x_3^2 + \beta_7x_1x_2 + \beta_8x_1x_3 + \beta_9x_2x_3$

12.51 a. H_0: $\beta_2 = 0$
             H_a: $\beta_2 \neq 0$

             The test statistic is $t = \dfrac{\hat{\beta}_2 - 0}{s_{\hat{\beta}_2}} - \dfrac{.47 - 0}{.15} = 3.133$

             The rejection region requires $\alpha/2 = .05/2 = .025$ in each tail of the t distribution with df $= n - (k + 1) = 25 - (2 + 1) = 22$. From Table VI, Appendix A, $t_{.025} = 2.074$. The rejection region is $t < -2.074$ or $t > 2.074$.

             Since the observed value of the test statistic falls in the rejection region ($t = 3.133 > 2.074$), H_0 is rejected. There is sufficient evidence to indicate the true relationship is given by the quadratic model at $\alpha = .05$.

       b. H_0: $\beta_2 = 0$
             H_a: $\beta_2 > 0$

             The test statistic is the same as in part **a**, $t = 3.133$.

             The rejection region requires $\alpha = .05$ in the upper tail of the t distribution with df $= 22$. From Table VI, Appendix A, $t_{.05} = 1.717$. The rejection region is $t > 1.717$.

             Since the observed value of the test statistic falls in the rejection region ($t = 3.133 > 1.717$), H_0 is rejected. There is sufficient evidence to indicate the quadratic curve opens upward at $\alpha = .05$.

12.53   a.

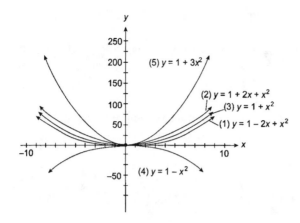

b.   It moves the graph to the right $(-2x)$ or to the left $(+2x)$ compared to the graph of $y = 1 + x^2$.

c.   It controls whether the graph opens up $(+x^2)$ or down $(-x^2)$. It also controls how steep the curvature is, i.e., the larger the absolute value of the coefficient of x^2, the narrower the curve is.

12.55   a.

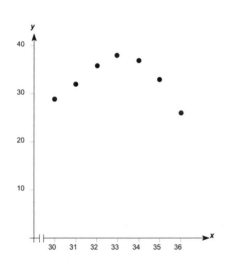

b.   If information was available only for $x = 30, 31, 32$, and 33, we would suggest a first-order model where $\beta_1 > 0$. If information was available only for $x = 33, 34, 35$, and 36, we would again suggest a first-order model where $\beta_1 < 0$. If all the information was available, we would suggest a second-order model.

12.57   a. $E(y) = \beta_0 + \beta_1 x_1 + \beta_2 x_2 + \beta_3 x_1 x_2 + \beta_4 x_1^2 + \beta_5 x_2^2$

b. $\beta_4 x_1^2$ and $\beta_5 x_2^2$

12.59   a.   Using MINITAB, a scattergram of the data is:

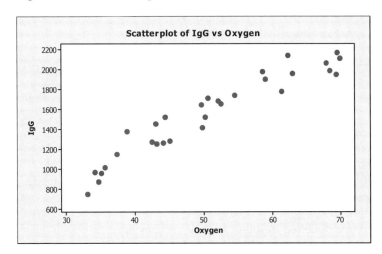

b.   From the plot, it looks like there is a linear relationship between IgG and maximal oxygen uptake. There could also be a slight downward curve to the data, requiring a quadratic model. The quadratic model is:

$$E(y) = \beta_0 + \beta_1 x + \beta_2 x^2$$

c.   Using MINITAB, the results are:

Regression Analysis: IgG versus Oxygen, Oxy-sq

```
The regression equation is
IgG = - 1464 + 88.3 Oxygen - 0.536 Oxy-sq


Predictor      Coef   SE Coef       T      P
Constant    -1464.4     411.4   -3.56  0.001
Oxygen        88.31     16.47    5.36  0.000
Oxy-sq      -0.5362    0.1582   -3.39  0.002


S = 106.427    R-Sq = 93.8%    R-Sq(adj) = 93.3%


Analysis of Variance

Source          DF        SS       MS       F      P
Regression       2   4602211  2301105  203.16  0.000
Residual Error  27    305818    11327
Total           29   4908029


Source    DF    Seq SS
Oxygen     1   4472047
Oxy-sq     1    130164
```

To determine if the model provides information for the prediction of IgG, we test:

H_0: $\beta_1 = \beta_2 = 0$
H_a: At least one $\beta_i \neq 0$, $i = 1, 2$

The test statistic is $F = 203.16$.

The rejection region requires $\alpha = .05$ in the upper tail of the F distribution with $v_1 = k = 2$ and $v_2 = n - (k + 1) = 30 - (2 + 1) = 27$. From Table IX, Appendix A, $F_{.05} \approx 3.35$. The rejection region is $F > 3.35$.

Since the observed value of the test statistic falls in the rejection region ($F = 203.16 > 3.35$), H_0 is rejected. There is sufficient evidence to indicate the model provides information for the prediction of IgG at $\alpha = .05$.

d.   To determine if the second-order term contributes information for the prediction of IgG, we test:

H_0: $\beta_2 = 0$
H_a: $\beta_2 \neq 0$

The test statistic is $t = -3.39$.

The rejection region requires $\alpha/2 = .05/2$ in each tail of the t distribution with df = $n - (k + 1) = 30 - (2 + 1) = 27$. From Table VI, Appendix A, $t_{.025} = 2.052$. The rejection region is $t > -2.052$ or $t > 2.052$.

Since the observed value of the test statistic falls in the rejection region ($t = -3.39 -2.052$), H_0 is rejected. There is sufficient evidence to indicate that the second-order terms provides information for the prediction of IgG at $\alpha = .05$.

12.61   a.   The quadratic model would be:

$$E(y) = \beta_0 + \beta_1 x + \beta_2 x^2$$

b.   From the plot, the β_2 would be positive because the points appear to form an upward curve.

c.   This value of r^2 applies to the linear model, not the quadratic model. The linear model is:

$$E(y) = \beta_0 + \beta_1 x$$

12.63   a.   The shape of the graph is not a straight line.

b.   The shape of the graph is not a parabola.

c.   The graph includes a reversal of curvature, so the cubic model would be the most appropriate.

12.65   The model is $E(y) = \beta_0 + \beta_1 x_1 + \beta_2 x_2$

where $x_1 = \begin{cases} 1 & \text{if the variable is at level 2} \\ 0 & \text{otherwise} \end{cases}$ $x_2 = \begin{cases} 1 & \text{if the variable is at level 3} \\ 0 & \text{otherwise} \end{cases}$

β_0 = mean value of y when qualitative variable is at level 1.
β_1 = difference in mean value of y between level 2 and level 1 of qualitative variable.
β_2 = difference in mean value of y between level 3 and level 1 of qualitative variable.

12.67   a.   The least squares prediction equation is:

$$\hat{y} = 80 + 16.8 x_1 + 40.4 x_2$$

b. β_1 is the difference in the mean value of the dependent variable between level 2 and level 1 of the independent variable.

β_2 is the difference in the mean value of the dependent variable between level 3 and level 1 of the independent variable.

c.   The hypothesis H_0: $\beta_1 = \beta_2 = 0$ is the same as H_0: $\mu_1 = \mu_2 = \mu_3$.

The hypothesis H_a: At least one of the parameters β_1 and β_2 differs from 0 is the same as H_a: At least one mean (μ_1, μ_2, or μ_3) is different.

d.   The test statistic is $F = \dfrac{\text{MSR}}{\text{MSE}} = \dfrac{2059.5}{83.3} = 24.72$

The rejection region requires $\alpha = .05$ in the upper tail of the test statistic with numerator df $= k = 2$ and denominator df $= n - (k + 1) = 15 - (2 + 1) = 12$. From Table IX, Appendix A, $F_{.05} = 3.89$. The rejection region is $F > 3.89$.

Since the observed value of the test statistic falls in the rejection region ($F = 24.72 > 3.89$), H_0 is rejected. There is sufficient evidence to indicate at least one of the means is different at $\alpha = .05$.

12.69   a.   The model is $E(y) = \beta_0 + \beta_1 x_1 + \beta_2 x_2$

where $x_1 = \begin{cases} 1 & \text{if political status is democratic} \\ 0 & \text{otherwise} \end{cases}$

$x_2 = \begin{cases} 1 & \text{is political status is dictatorship} \\ 0 & \text{otherwise} \end{cases}$

b. β_0 = mean value of level of assissination risk (y) for political status communist.

β_1 = difference in mean value of level of assissination risk (y) between political status democratic and political status communist.

β_2 = difference in mean value of level of assissination risk (y) between political status dictatorship and political status communist.

12.71   a.   Let y = mean body mass and $x_1 = \begin{cases} 1 & \text{if flightless} \\ 0 & \text{otherwise} \end{cases}$

The model is $y = \beta_0 + \beta_1 x_1 + \varepsilon$

b. Let y = mean body mass and

$x_1 = \begin{cases} 1 & \text{if vertebrates} \\ 0 & \text{otherwise} \end{cases}$ $x_2 = \begin{cases} 1 & \text{if vegetables} \\ 0 & \text{otherwise} \end{cases}$ $x_3 = \begin{cases} 1 & \text{if invertebrates} \\ 0 & \text{otherwise} \end{cases}$

The model is $y = \beta_o + \beta_1 x_1 + \beta_2 x_2 + \beta_3 x_3 + \varepsilon$

c. Let y = mean egg length and

$x_1 = \begin{cases} 1 & \text{if cavity within ground} \\ 0 & \text{otherwise} \end{cases}$ $x_2 = \begin{cases} 1 & \text{if tree} \\ 0 & \text{otherwise} \end{cases}$ $x_3 = \begin{cases} 1 & \text{if cavity above ground} \\ 0 & \text{otherwise} \end{cases}$

The model is $y = \beta_0 + \beta_1 x_1 + \beta_2 x_2 + \beta_3 x_3 + \varepsilon$

d. Using MINTAB, the results are:

Regression Analysis: Body Mass versus Flt

```
The regression equation is
Body Mass = 641 + 30647 Flt


Predictor    Coef   SE Coef     T       P
Constant      641      2665   0.24   0.810
Flt         30647      5331   5.75   0.000


S = 26521.3    R-Sq = 20.3%    R-Sq(adj) = 19.7%


Analysis of Variance

Source            DF            SS            MS       F       P
Regression         1   23246186220   23246186220   33.05   0.000
Residual Error   130   91439576421     703381357
Total            131   1.14686E+11
```

The fitted model is $\hat{y} = 641 + 30,647 x_1$

$\hat{\beta}_0 = 641$. The mean body mass for Volant birds is estimated to be 641.

$\hat{\beta}_1 = 30,647$. The difference in the mean body mass between Flightless birds and Volant birds is estimated to be 30,647.

e.   To determine if the model is useful in estimating body mass, we test:

H_0: $\beta_1 = 0$
H_a: $\beta_1 \neq 0$

The test statistic is $F = 33.05$ and the p-value is $p = .000$. Since the p-value is less than $\alpha (p = .000 < .01)$, H_0 is rejected. There is sufficient evidence to indicate a difference in mean body mass between the two types of flight capacity birds at $\alpha = .01$.

f.   Using MINITAB, the results are:

Regression Analysis: Body Mass versus DX1, DX2, DX3

```
The regression equation is
Body Mass = 903 + 2997 DX1 + 26206 DX2 - 660 DX3


Predictor    Coef   SE Coef      T       P
Constant      903      4171   0.22   0.829
DX1          2997     14298   0.21   0.834
DX2         26206      6090   4.30   0.000
DX3          -660      5772  -0.11   0.909


S = 27352.1   R-Sq = 16.5%   R-Sq(adj) = 14.5%


Analysis of Variance

Source            DF            SS           MS      F       P
Regression         3   18924196564   6308065521   8.43   0.000
Residual Error   128   95761566077    748137235
Total            131   1.14686E+11


Source   DF        Seq SS
X1        1      79962608
X2        1   18834456334
X3        1       9777622
```

The fitted model is $\hat{y} = 903 + 2{,}997 x_1 + 26{,}206 x_2 - 660 x_3$

$\hat{\beta}_0 = 903$. The mean body mass for birds on a fish diet is estimated to be 903.

$\hat{\beta}_1 = 2{,}997$. The difference in the mean body mass between birds on a vertebrate diet and birds on a fish diet is estimated to be 2,997.

$\hat{\beta}_2 = 26{,}206$. The difference in the mean body mass between birds on a vegetable diet and birds on a fish diet is estimated to be 26,206.

$\hat{\beta}_3 = -660$. The difference in the mean body mass between birds on an invertebrate diet and birds on a fish diet is estimated to be −660.

g. To determine if the model is useful in estimating body mass, we test:

H_0: $\beta_1 = \beta_2 = \beta_3 = 0$
H_a: At least one $\beta_i \neq 0$, $i = 1, 2, 3$

The test statistic is $F = 8.43$ and the p-value is $p = .000$. Since the p-value is less than α ($p = .000 < .01$), H_0 is rejected. There is sufficient evidence to indicate a difference in mean body mass among the four types of diets at $\alpha = .01$.

h. Using MINITAB, the results are:

Regression Analysis: Egg Length versus NX1, NX2, NX3

```
The regression equation is
Egg Length = 73.7 - 9.13 NX1 - 45.0 NX2 - 39.5 NX3


130 cases used, 2 cases contain missing values


Predictor      Coef  SE Coef       T       P
Constant     73.732    4.907   15.03   0.000
NX1          -9.132    9.515   -0.96   0.339
NX2          -45.01    14.45   -3.12   0.002
NX3         -39.510    9.253   -4.27   0.000


S = 40.7622   R-Sq = 16.1%   R-Sq(adj) = 14.1%


Analysis of Variance

Source             DF      SS      MS      F       P
Regression          3   40230   13410   8.07   0.000
Residual Error    126  209356    1662
Total             129  249586


Source  DF  Seq SS
NX1      1     482
NX2      1    9455
NX3      1   30293
```

The fitted model is $\hat{y} = 73.732 - 9.132x_1 - 45.01x_2 - 39.51x_3$

$\hat{\beta}_o = 73.732$. The mean egg length for nesting on the ground is estimated to be 73.732 mm.

$\hat{\beta}_1 = -9.132$. The difference in the mean egg length between birds nesting in a cavity within the ground and birds nesting on the ground is estimated to be -9.132.

$\hat{\beta}_2 = -45.01$. The difference in the mean egg length between birds nesting in a tree and birds nesting on the ground is estimated to be -45.01.

$\hat{\beta}_3 = -39.51$. The difference in the mean egg length between birds nesting in a cavity above ground and birds nesting on the ground is estimated to be -39.51.

i. To determine if the model is useful in estimating body mass, we test:

H_0: $\beta_1 = \beta_2 = \beta_3 = 0$
H_a: At least one $\beta_i \neq 0$, $i = 1, 2, 3$

The test statistic is $F = 8.07$ and the p-value is $p = .000$. Since the p-value is less than α ($p = .000 < .01$), H_0 is rejected. There is sufficient evidence to indicate a difference in mean egg length among the four types of nesting sites at $\alpha = .01$.

12.73 a.   Let $\begin{cases} 1 & \text{if pond is enriched} \\ 0 & \text{if otherwise} \end{cases}$

The model is $E(y) = \beta_0 + \beta_1 x_1$

b. β_0 = mean mosquito larvae in the natural pond
β_1 = difference in the mean mosquito larvae between the enriched pond and the natural pond

c. To determine if the mean larval density for the enriched pond exceeds the mean for the natural pond, we test:

H_0: $\beta_1 = 0$
H_a: $\beta_1 > 0$

d. The p-value for the global F test is $p = .004$. Thus, the p-value for this test is $p = .004/2 = .002$. Since the p-value is so small, there is evidence to reject H_0. There is sufficient evidence to indicate that the mean larval densities differ for the enriched pond and the natural pond at $\alpha > .002$.

12.75 a.   Let $x_1 = \begin{cases} 1 & \text{if adult female with offspring} \\ 0 & \text{if otherwise} \end{cases}$

$x_2 = \begin{cases} 1 & \text{if independent sub-adult female} \\ 0 & \text{if otherwise} \end{cases}$

$x_3 = \begin{cases} 1 & \text{if adult male} \\ 0 & \text{if otherwise} \end{cases}$

$x_4 = \begin{cases} 1 & \text{if independent sub-adult male} \\ 0 & \text{if otherwise} \end{cases}$

The model would be: $E(y) = \beta_0 + \beta_1 x_1 + \beta_2 x_2 + \beta_3 x_3 + \beta_4 x_4$

b. $\hat{\beta}_0 = \hat{\mu}_1 = 38$

$\hat{\beta}_1 = \hat{\mu}_2 - \hat{\mu}_1 = 16 - 38 = -22$

$\hat{\beta}_2 = \hat{\mu}_3 - \hat{\mu}_1 = 89 - 38 = 51$

$\hat{\beta}_3 = \hat{\mu}_4 - \hat{\mu}_1 = 43 - 38 = 5$

$\hat{\beta}_4 = \hat{\mu}_5 - \hat{\mu}_1 = 58 - 38 = 20$

c. To determine if the mean percent use of HTZ differs among the grizzly bear classes, we test:

$$H_0: \ \beta_1 = \beta_2 = \beta_3 = \beta_4 = 0$$
$$H_a: \ \text{At least one } \beta_i \neq 0, \ i = 1, 2, 3, 4$$

d. The p-value is .15. Since the p-value is not small, there is no evidence to indicate the mean percent use of HTZ differs among the grizzly bear classes for $\alpha < .15$.

12.77   a.   The first-order model is $E(y) = \beta_0 + \beta_1 x_1$

b. The new model is $E(y) = \beta_0 + \beta_1 x_1 + \beta_2 x_2 + \beta_3 x_3$

where $x_2 = \begin{cases} 1 & \text{if level 2} \\ 0 & \text{otherwise} \end{cases}$ $x_3 = \begin{cases} 1 & \text{if level 3} \\ 0 & \text{otherwise} \end{cases}$

c. To allow for interactions, the model is:

$$E(y) = \beta_0 + \beta_1 x_1 + \beta_2 x_2 + \beta_3 x_3 + \beta_4 x_1 x_2 + \beta_5 x_1 x_3$$

d. The response lines will be parallel if $\beta_4 = \beta_5 = 0$

e. There will be one response line if $\beta_2 = \beta_3 = \beta_4 = \beta_5 = 0$

12.79   The model is $E(y) = \beta_0 + \beta_1 x_1 + \beta_2 x_1^2 + \beta_3 x_2 + \beta_4 x_3 + \beta_5 x_4$
where x_1 is the quantitative variable and

$x_2 = \begin{cases} 1 & \text{if level 2 of qualitative variable} \\ 0 & \text{otherwise} \end{cases}$

$x_3 = \begin{cases} 1 & \text{if level 3 of qualitative variable} \\ 0 & \text{otherwise} \end{cases}$

$x_4 = \begin{cases} 1 & \text{if level 4 of qualitative variable} \\ 0 & \text{otherwise} \end{cases}$

12.81   a.   For $x_2 = 0$ and $x_3 = 0$,

$$\hat{y} = 48.8 - 3.4x_1 + .07x_1^2 - 2.4(0) - 7.5(0) + 3.7x_1(0) + 2.7x_1(0) - .02x_1^2(0) - .04x_1^2(0)$$

$$= 48.8 - 3.4x_1 + .07x_1^2$$

For $x_2 = 1$ and $x_3 = 0$,

$$\hat{y} = 48.8 - 3.4x_1 + .07x_1^2 - 2.4(1) - 7.5(0) + 3.7x_1(1) + 2.7x_1(0) - .02x_1^2(1) - .04x_1^2(0)$$
$$= 46.4 + .3\,x_1 + .05x_1^2$$

For $x_2 = 0$ and $x_3 = 1$,

$$\hat{y} = 48.8 - 3.4x_1 + .07x_1^2 - 2.4(0) - 7.5(1) + 3.7x_1(0) + 2.7\,x_1(1) - .02x_1^2(0) - .04x_1^2(1)$$

$$= 41.3 - .7x_1 + .03x_1^2$$

b.   The plots of the lines are:

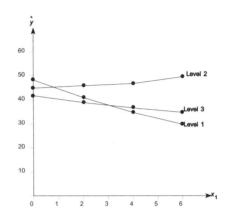

12.83   a.   Let x_1 = weight, $\quad x_2 = \begin{cases} 1 & \text{if Channel catfish} \\ 0 & \text{otherwise} \end{cases}$ and $\quad x_3 = \begin{cases} 1 & \text{if Largemouth bass} \\ 0 & \text{otherwise} \end{cases}$

b.   The model would be $y = \beta_0 + \beta_1 x_1 + \beta_2 x_2 + \beta_3 x_3 + \varepsilon$

c.   The new model would be $y = \beta_0 + \beta_1 x_1 + \beta_2 x_2 + \beta_3 x_3 + \beta_4 x_1 x_2 + \beta_5 x_1 x_3 + \varepsilon$

d.   Using MINITAB, the results are:

Regression Analysis: DDT versus X1, X2, X3

```
The regression equation is
DDT = 3.1 + 0.0037 X1 + 26.5 X2 - 4.1 X3


Predictor      Coef   SE Coef        T       P
Constant       3.13     38.89     0.08   0.936
X1          0.00371   0.02598     0.14   0.887
X2            26.51     21.52     1.23   0.220
X3            -4.09     37.91    -0.11   0.914
```

```
S = 98.5738    R-Sq = 1.7%    R-Sq(adj) = 0.0%


Analysis of Variance

Source              DF        SS      MS      F      P
Regression           3     23652    7884   0.81  0.490
Residual Error     140   1360351    9717
Total              143   1384003


Source  DF  Seq SS
X1       1     196
X2       1   23343
X3       1     113
```

The least squares prediction equation is $\hat{y} = 3.13 + .00371x_1 + 26.51x_2 - 4.09x_3$.

e. $\hat{\beta}_1 = .00371$. For each unit increase in weight, the mean DDT level is estimated to increase by .00371, holding species constant.

f. Using MINITAB, the results are:

Regression Analysis: DDT versus X1, X2, X3, X1X2, X1X3

```
The regression equation is
DDT = 3.5 + 0.0034 X1 + 25.6 X2 - 3.5 X3 + 0.0008 X1X2 - 0.0013 X1X3

Predictor       Coef   SE Coef       T      P
Constant        3.50     54.69    0.06  0.949
X1           0.00344   0.03843    0.09  0.929
X2             25.59     67.52    0.38  0.705
X3             -3.47     84.70   -0.04  0.967
X1X2         0.00082   0.05459    0.02  0.988
X1X3        -0.00129   0.09987   -0.01  0.990


S = 99.2853    R-Sq = 1.7%    R-Sq(adj) = 0.0%


Analysis of Variance

Source              DF        SS      MS      F      P
Regression           5     23657    4731   0.48  0.791
Residual Error     138   1360346    9858
Total              143   1384003


Source  DF  Seq SS
X1       1     196
X2       1   23343
X3       1     113
X1X2     1       4
X1X3     1       2
```

The least squares prediction equation is

$$\hat{y} = 3.5 + .00344x_1 + 25.59x_2 - 3.47x_3 + .00082x_1x_2 - .00129x_1x_3.$$

g. For Channel catfish, $x_2 = 1$ and $x_3 = 0$. Substituting these values into the fitted regression line, we get:

$$\hat{y} = 3.5 + .00344x_1 + 25.59(1) - 3.47(0) + .00082x_1(1) - .00129x_1(0)$$
$$= 29.09 + .00426x_1$$

The estimated slope of the new line is .00426.

12.85 a. The first-order model is $E(y) = \beta_0 + \beta_1x_1 + \beta_2x_2 + \beta_3x_1x_2$

where $x_2 = \begin{cases} 1 & \text{if plants} \\ 0 & \text{otherwise} \end{cases}$

b. Using MINITAB, the results are:

Regression Analysis: WeightChg versus X1, X2, X1X2

```
The regression equation is
WeightChg = 8.14 - 0.016 X1 - 10.4 X2 + 0.095 X1X2


Predictor      Coef   SE Coef       T      P
Constant      8.144     8.446    0.96  0.341
X1          -0.0165    0.1329   -0.12  0.902
X2          -10.354     8.538   -1.21  0.233
X1X2         0.0948    0.1418    0.67  0.508


S = 3.88175    R-Sq = 44.1%    R-Sq(adj) = 39.7%


Analysis of Variance

Source            DF       SS      MS      F      P
Regression         3   452.54  150.85  10.01  0.000
Residual Error    38   572.58   15.07
Total             41  1025.12


Source   DF   Seq SS
X1        1   384.24
X2        1    61.57
X1X2      1     6.73
```

The least squares prediction equation is $\hat{y} = 8.14 - .016x_1 - 10.4x_2 + .095x_1x_2$.

c. For diet = plants, $x_2 = 1$. The prediction equation is

$\hat{y} = 8.14 - .016x_1 - 10.4(1) + .095x_1(1) = -2.26 + .079x_1$. The slope of the line is .079.

For each unit increase is diet efficiency, the mean gosling weight change is estimated to increase by .079 for goslings fed plants.

d. For diet = duck chow, $x_2 = 0$. The prediction equation is

$\hat{y} = 8.14 - .016x_1 - 10.4(0) + .095x_1(0) = 8.14 - .016x_1$. The slope of the line is $-.016$.

For each unit increase is diet efficiency, the mean gosling weight change is estimated to decrease by .016 for goslings fed duck chow.

e. To determine if the slopes associated with the two diets are different, we test:

$H_0: \beta_3 = 0$
$H_a: \beta_3 \neq 0$

From the printout, the test statistic is $t = .67$ and the p-value is $p = .508$. Since the p-value is greater than α ($p = .508 > .05$), H_0 is not rejected. There is insufficient evidence to indicate the slopes associated with the two diets differ at $\alpha = .05$.

12.87 a. Let $x_2 = \begin{cases} 1 & \text{if intervention group} \\ 0 & \text{if otherwise} \end{cases}$

The first-order model would be:

$E(y) = \beta_0 + \beta_1x_1 + \beta_2x_2$

b. For the control group, $x_2 = 0$. The first-order model is:

$E(y) = \beta_0 + \beta_1x_1 + \beta_2(0) = \beta_0 + \beta_1x_1$

For the intervention group, $x_2 = 1$. The first-order model is:

$E(y) = \beta_0 + \beta_1x_1 + \beta_2(1) = \beta_0 + \beta_1x_1 + \beta_2 = (\beta_0 + \beta_2) + \beta_1x_1$

In both models, the slope of the line is β_1.

c. If pretest score and group interact, the first-order model would be:

$E(y) = \beta_0 + \beta_1x_1 + \beta_2x_2 + \beta_3x_1x_2$

d. For the control group, $x_2 = 0$. The first-order model including the interaction is:

$E(y) = \beta_0 + \beta_1x_1 + \beta_2(0) + \beta_3x_1(0) = \beta_0 + \beta_1x_1$

For the intervention group, $x_2 = 1$. The first-order model including the interaction is:

$E(y) = \beta_0 + \beta_1x_1 + \beta_2(1) + \beta_3x_1(1) = \beta_0 + \beta_1x_1 + \beta_2 + \beta_3x_1$
$= (\beta_0 + \beta_2) + (\beta_1 + \beta_3)x_1$

The slope of the model for the control group is β_1. The slope of the model for the intervention group is $\beta_1 + \beta_3$.

12.89   The models in parts **a** and **b** are nested:

The complete model is $E(y) = \beta_0 + \beta_1 x_1 + \beta_2 x_2$
The reduced model is $E(y) = \beta_0 + \beta_1 x_1$

The models in parts **a** and **d** are nested.

The complete model is $E(y) = \beta_0 + \beta_1 x_1 + \beta_2 x_2 + \beta_3 x_1 x_2$
The reduced model is $E(y) = \beta_0 + \beta_1 x_1 + \beta_2 x_2$
The models in parts **a** and **e** are nested.

The complete model is $E(y) = \beta_0 + \beta_1 x_1 + \beta_2 x_2 + \beta_3 x_1 x_2 + \beta_4 x_1^2 + \beta_5 x_2^2$
The reduced model is $E(y) = \beta_0 + \beta_1 x_1 + \beta_2 x_2$

The models in parts **b** and **c** are nested.

The complete model is $E(y) = \beta_0 + \beta_1 x_1 + \beta_2 x_1^2$
The reduced model is $E(y) = \beta_0 + \beta_1 x_1$

The models in parts **b** and **d** are nested.

The complete model is $E(y) = \beta_0 + \beta_1 x_1 + \beta_2 x_2 + \beta_3 x_1 x_2$
The reduced model is $E(y) = \beta_0 + \beta_1 x_1$

The models in parts **b** and **e** are nested.

The complete model is $E(y) = \beta_0 + \beta_1 x_1 + \beta_2 x_2 + \beta_3 x_1 x_2 + \beta_4 x_1^2 + \beta_5 x_2^2$
The reduced model is $E(y) = \beta_0 + \beta_1 x_1$

The models in parts **c** and **e** are nested.

The complete model is $E(y) = \beta_0 + \beta_1 x_1 + \beta_2 x_2 + \beta_3 x_1 x_2 + \beta_4 x_1^2 + \beta_5 x_2^2$
The reduced model is $E(y) = \beta_0 + \beta_1 x_1 + \beta_2 x_1^2$

The models in parts **d** and **e** are nested.

The complete model is $E(y) = \beta_0 + \beta_1 x_1 + \beta_2 x_2 + \beta_3 x_1 x_2 + \beta_4 x_1^2 + \beta_5 x_2^2$
The reduced model is $E(y) = \beta_0 + \beta_1 x_1 + \beta_2 x_2 + \beta_3 x_1 x_2$

12.91   A parsimonious model is a general linear model with a small number of β parameters. In situations where two competing models have essentially the same predictive power (as determined by an F-test), choose the model with the fewer number of βs.

12.93   a.   There are five β parameters in the complete model and three in the reduced model.

b.   The hypotheses are:

H_0: $\beta_3 = \beta_4 = 0$
H_a: At least one $\beta_i \neq 0$, $i = 3, 4$

c.   The test statistic is $F = \dfrac{(\text{SSE}_R - \text{SSE}_C)/(k - g)}{\text{SSE}_C/[n - (k+1)]}$

$$= \frac{(160.44 - 152.66)/(4 - 2)}{152.66/[20 - (4 + 1)]} = \frac{3.89}{10.1773} = .38$$

The rejection region requires $\alpha = .05$ in the upper tail of the F distribution with numerator df $= k - g = 4 - 2 = 2$ and denominator df $= n - (k + 1) = 20 - (4 + 1) = 15$. From Table IX, Appendix A, $F_{.05} = 3.68$. The rejection region is $F > 3.68$.

Since the observed value of the test statistic does not fall in the rejection region ($F = .38 \not> 3.68$), H_0 is not rejected. There is insufficient evidence to indicate the complete model is better than the reduced model at $\alpha = .05$.

12.95   a. $E(y) = \beta_0 + \beta_1 x_1 + \beta_2 x_2 + \beta_3 x_3 + \beta_4 x_4 + \beta_5 x_5 + \beta_6 x_6 + \beta_7 x_7 + \beta_8 x_8 + \beta_9 x_9$
$+ \beta_{10} x_{10} + \beta_{11} x_{11}$

b. $E(y) = \beta_0 + \beta_1 x_1 + \beta_2 x_2 + \beta_3 x_3 + \beta_4 x_4 + \beta_5 x_5 + \beta_6 x_6 + \beta_7 x_7$
$+ \beta_8 x_8 + \beta_9 x_9 + \beta_{10} x_{10} + \beta_{11} x_{11}$
$+ \beta_{12} x_1 x_9 + \beta_{13} x_1 x_{10} + \beta_{14} x_1 x_{11}$
$+ \beta_{15} x_2 x_9 + \beta_{16} x_2 x_{10} + \beta_{17} x_2 x_{11}$
$+ \beta_{18} x_3 x_9 + \beta_{19} x_3 x_{10} + \beta_{20} x_3 x_{11}$
$+ \beta_{21} x_4 x_9 + \beta_{22} x_4 x_{10} + \beta_{23} x_4 x_{11}$
$+ \beta_{24} x_5 x_9 + \beta_{25} x_5 x_{10} + \beta_{26} x_5 x_{11}$
$+ \beta_{27} x_6 x_9 + \beta_{28} x_6 x_{10} + \beta_{29} x_6 x_{11}$
$+ \beta_{30} x_7 x_9 + \beta_{31} x_7 x_{10} + \beta_{32} x_7 x_{11}$
$+ \beta_{33} x_8 x_9 + \beta_{34} x_8 x_{10} + \beta_{35} x_8 x_{11}$

c.   To test for interaction, we would use the hypothesis:

H_0: $\beta_{12} = \beta_{13} = \beta_{14} = \ldots = \beta_{35} = 0$
H_a: At least one $\beta_i \neq 0$, $i = 12, 13, 14, \ldots, 35$

We would compare the complete model in part **b** to the reduce model in part **a**.

12.97   a.   By including the interaction terms, it implies that the relationship between voltage and volume fraction of the disperse phase depend on the levels of salinity and surfactant concentration.

A possible sketch of the relationship is:

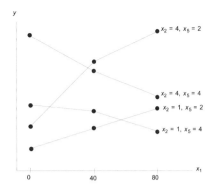

b. Using MINITAB, the results are:

Regression Analysis: y versus x1, x2, x5, x1x2, x1x5

```
The regression equation is
y = 0.906 - 0.0228 x1 + 0.305 x2 + 0.275 x5 - 0.00280 x1x2 + 0.00158 x1x5

Predictor        Coef    SE Coef       T       P
Constant       0.9057     0.2855    3.17   0.007
x1          -0.022753   0.008318   -2.74   0.017
x2             0.3047     0.2366    1.29   0.220
x5             0.2747     0.2270    1.21   0.248
x1x2        -0.002804   0.003790   -0.74   0.473
x1x5         0.001579   0.003947    0.40   0.696


S = 0.504650   R-Sq = 67.9%   R-Sq(adj) = 55.6%


Analysis of Variance

Source           DF        SS       MS      F      P
Regression        5    7.0103   1.4021   5.51  0.006
Residual Error   13    3.3107   0.2547
Total            18   10.3210


Source   DF   Seq SS
x1        1   1.4016
x2        1   1.9263
x5        1   3.5422
x1x2      1   0.0994
x1x5      1   0.0408
```

The fitted regression line is:

$$\hat{y} = .906 - .023x_1 + .305x_2 + .275x_5 - .003x_1x_2 + .002x_1x_5$$

To determine if the model is useful, we test:

H_0: $\beta_1 = \beta_2 = \beta_3 = \beta_4 = \beta_5 = 0$
H_a: At least one $\beta_i \neq 0$, for $i = 1, 2, ..., 5$

The test statistic is $F = 5.51$.

The rejection region requires $\alpha = .05$ in the upper tail of the F-distribution with $v_1 = k = 5$ and $v_2 = n - (k+1) = 19 - (5+1) = 13$. From Table VIII, Appendix B, $F_{.05} = 3.03$. The rejection region is $F > 3.03$.

Since the observed value of the test statistic falls in the rejection region ($F = 5.51 > 3.03$), H_0 is rejected. There is sufficient evidence to indicate the model is useful for predicting voltage at $\alpha = .05$.

$R^2 = 67.9\%$. Thus, 67.9% of the sample variation of voltage is explained by the model containing the three independent variables and two interaction terms.

The estimate of the standard deviation is $s = .505$.

Comparing this model to that fit in Exercise 12.23, the model in Exercise 12.23 appears to fit the data better. The model in Exercise 12.23 has a higher R^2 (77.1% vs 67.9%) and a smaller estimate of the standard deviation (.464 vs .505).

c. $\hat{\beta}_0 = .906$.   This is simply the estimate of the y-intercept.

$\hat{\beta}_1 = -.023$.   For each unit increase in disperse phase volume, we estimate that the mean voltage will decrease by .023 units, holding salinity and surfactant concentration at 0.

$\hat{\beta}_2 = .305$.   For each unit increase in salinity, we estimate that the mean voltage will increase by .305 units, holding disperse phase volume and surfactant concentration at 0.

$\hat{\beta}_3 = .275$.   For each unit increase in surfactant concentration, we estimate that the mean voltage will increase by .275 units, holding disperse phase volume and salinity at 0.

$\hat{\beta}_4 = -.003$.   This estimates the difference in the slope of the relationship between voltage and disperse phase volume for each unit increase in salinity, holding surfactant concentration constant.

$\hat{\beta}_5 = .002$.   This estimates the difference in the slope of the relationship between voltage and disperse phase volume for each unit increase in surfactant concentration, holding salinity constant.

d. Using MINITAB to fit the model without the interaction terms, the results are:

Regression Analysis: y versus x1, x2, x5
```
The regression equation is
y = 0.933 - 0.0243 x1 + 0.142 x2 + 0.385 x5


Predictor        Coef     SE Coef       T       P
Constant       0.9326      0.2482    3.76   0.002
x1          -0.024272    0.004900   -4.95   0.000
x2            0.14206     0.07573    1.88   0.080
x5            0.38457     0.09801    3.92   0.001
```

```
S = 0.479646   R-Sq = 66.6%   R-Sq(adj) = 59.9%


Analysis of Variance

Source              DF       SS       MS      F       P
Regression           3   6.8701   2.2900   9.95   0.001
Residual Error      15   3.4509   0.2301
Total               18  10.3210


Source  DF   Seq SS
x1       1   1.4016
x2       1   1.9263
x5       1   3.5422
```

To determine whether the interaction terms contribute significantly to the prediction of voltage, we test:

H_0: $\beta_4 = \beta_5 = 0$
H_a: At least one $\beta_i \neq 0$, $i = 4, 5$

The test statistic is $F = \dfrac{(SSE_R - SSE_C)/(k - g)}{SSE_C/[n-(k+1)]} = \dfrac{(3.4509 - 3.3017)/(5-3)}{3.3017/[19-(5+1)]} = .294$

The rejection region requires $\alpha = .05$ in the upper tail of the F distribution with $v_1 = k - g = 5 - 3 = 2$ and $v_2 = n - (k + 1) = 19 - (5 + 1) = 13$. From Table IX, Appendix A, $F_{.05} = 3.18$. The rejection region is $F > 3.18$.

Since the observed value of the test statistic does not fall in the rejection region ($F = .294 \not> 3.18$), H_0 is not rejected. There is insufficient evidence to indicate the interaction terms contribute to the prediction of voltage at $\alpha = .05$.

12.99   a.   The hypothesized alternative model is

$E(y) = \beta_0 + \beta_1 x_1 + \beta_2 x_2 + \beta_3 x_3 + \beta_4 x_4 + \beta_5 x_5 + \beta_6 x_6 + \beta_7 x_7 + \beta_8 x_8 + \beta_9 x_9 + \beta_{10} x_{10}$

b.   The null hypothesis would be H_0: $\beta_3 = \beta_4 = \beta_5 = \beta_6 = \beta_7 = \beta_8 = \beta_9 = \beta_{10} = 0$

c.   The test was statistically significant. Thus, H_o was rejected. There is sufficient evidence to indicate that at least one of the "control" variables contributes to the prediction of SAT-Math scores.

d. $R^2_{adj} = .79$. 79% of the sample variability of the SAT-Math scores around their means is explained by the proposed model relating SAT-Math scores to the 10 independent variables, adjusting for the sample size and the number of β parameters in the model.

e.   For confidence coefficient .95, $\alpha = .05$ and $\alpha/2 = .05/2 = .025$. From Table VI, Appendix A, with df $= n - (k + 1) = 3,492 - (10 + 1) = 3,481$, $t_{.025} = 1.96$. The 95% confidence interval is:

$\hat{\beta}_2 \pm t_{.025} s_{\hat{\beta}_2} \Rightarrow 14 \pm 1.96(3) \Rightarrow 14 \pm 5.88 \Rightarrow (8.12, 19.88)$

Multiple Regression

We are 95% confident that the difference in the mean SAT-Math scores between students who were coached and those who were not is between 8.12 and 19.88 points, holding all the other variables constant.

f.   Yes. From Exercise 12.68, the confidence interval for β_2 was (13.12, 24.88). In part e, the confidence interval for β_2 was (8.12, 19.88). Even though coaching is significant in both models, the change in the mean SAT-Math scores is not as great if the control variables are added to the model.

g.   The complete model would be:

$$E(y) = \beta_0 + \beta_1 x_1 + \beta_2 x_2 + \beta_3 x_3 + \beta_4 x_4 + \beta_5 x_5 + \beta_6 x_6 + \beta_7 x_7 + \beta_8 x_8 + \beta_9 x_9 + \beta_{10} x_{10} + \beta_{11} x_1 x_2$$
$$+ \beta_{12} x_3 x_2 + \beta_{13} x_4 x_2 + \beta_{14} x_5 x_2 + \beta_{15} x_6 x_2 + \beta_{16} x_7 x_2 + \beta_{17} x_8 x_2 + \beta_{18} x_9 x_2 + \beta_{19} x_{10} x_2$$

h.   The null hypothesis would be $H_0: \beta_{11} = \beta_{12} = \beta_{13} = \beta_{14} = \beta_{15} = \beta_{16} = \beta_{17} = \beta_{18} = \beta_{19} = 0$. To perform this test, you would fit the complete model specified in part **g**. You would also fit the reduced model specified in part **a**. Then, you would perform the test comparing the complete and reduced models.

12.101 a.   To determine whether the rate of increase of emotional distress with experience is different for the two groups, we test:

$H_0: \beta_4 = \beta_5 = 0$
$H_a:$ At least one $\beta_i \neq 0$, $i = 4, 5$

b.   To determine whether there are differences in mean emotional distress levels that are attributable to exposure group, we test:

$H_0: \beta_3 = \beta_4 = \beta_5 = 0$
$H_a:$ At least one $\beta_i \neq 0$, $i = 3, 4, 5$

12.103 Two caveats with using the stepwise regression results as the final model are:

1.   An extremely large number of t tests are performed, inflating the overall probability of a Type I error.

2.   The stepwise procedure does not include any higher order or interaction terms.

12.105 a.   In Step 1, all one-variable models are fit to the data. These models are of the form:

$$E(y) = \beta_0 + \beta_1 x_i$$

Since there are 7 independent variables, 7 models are fit. (Note: There are actually only 6 independent variables. One of the qualitative variables has three levels and thus two dummy variables. Some statistical packages will allow one to bunch these two variables together so that they are either both in or both out. In this answer, we are assuming that each x_i stands by itself.

b. In Step 2, all two-varirable models are fit to the data, where the variable selected in Step 1 is one of the variables. These models are of the form:

$$E(y) = \beta_0 + \beta_1 x_1 + \beta_2 x_i$$

Since there are 6 independent variables remaining, 6 models are fit.

c. In Step 3, all three-variable models are fit to the data, where the variables selected in Step 2 are two of the variables. These models are of the form:

$$E(y) = \beta_0 + \beta_1 x_1 + \beta_2 x_2 + \beta_3 x_i$$

Since there are 5 independent variables remaining, 5 models are fit.

d. The procedure stops adding independent variables when none of the remaining variables, when added to the model, have a p-value less than some predetermined value. This predetermined value is usually $\alpha = .05$.

e. Two major drawbacks to using the final stepwise model as the "best" model are:

(1) An extremely large number of single β parameter t-tests have been conducted. Thus, the probability is very high that one or more errors have been made in including or excluding variables.

(2) Often the variables selected to be included in a stepwise regression do not include the high-order terms. Consequently, we may have initially omitted several important terms from the model.

12.107 a. In the first step of stepwise regression, 11 models are fit. These would be all the one-variable models.

b. In step two, all two variable models that include the variable selected in step one are fit. There will be a total of 10 models fit in this step.

c. In step 11, there is one model fit – the model containing all the independent variables.

d. The equation for $E(y)$ is:

$$E(y) = \beta_0 + \beta_1 x_{11} + \beta_2 x_4 + \beta_3 x_2 + \beta_4 x_7 + \beta_5 x_{10} + \beta_6 x_1 + \beta_7 x_9 + \beta_8 x_3$$

e. $R^2 = .677$. 67.7% of the sample variation in the overall satisfaction with BRT scores is explained by the model containing the 8 independent variables.

f. In any stepwise regression, many t-tests are performed. This inflates the probability of committing a Type I error. In addition, there are certain combinations of variables that may never be reached because of the first few variables put in the model. Finally, you should consider including interaction and higher order terms in the model.

12.109 Two properties of the regression residuals from a model are:

1. The mean of the residuals is 0.

2. The standard deviation of the residuals is equal to the standard deviation of the fitted regression model, s.

12.111 Multicollinearity exists when two or more of the independent variables used in regression are correlated.

12.113 Extrapolation occurs when regression models are used to predict values of y for values of the independent variables that were outside the observed range.

12.115 Yes. x_2 and x_4 are highly correlated (.93), as well as x_4 and x_5 (.86). When highly correlated independent variables are present in a regression model, the results can be confusing. The researcher may want to include only one of the variables.

12.117 The independent variables that are highly correlated are x_4 (ln(GNP in 1980)) and x_5 (agricultural production in 1980). The correlation coefficient is $r = -.84$. Several other variables have moderate correlation: x_1 and x_3 with $r_{13} = .57$, x_4 and x_6 with $r_{46} = -.53$, and x_5 and x_7 with $r_{57} = -.50$. If these highly correlated variables are included in the model at the same time, signs of the estimates of the beta parameters may be different than what is expected. Also, the global test could indicate that at least one of the variables contributes to the prediction of y, but none of the individual variable tests are significant.

2.119 a. The residual for the last observation is $y - \hat{y} = 87 - 29.63 = 57.37$. The standard deviation is $s = 24.68$. The number of standard deviations $\hat{y}$ is from y is found by dividing the residual by the value of the standard deviation or $57.37 / 24.68 = 2.32$. This point is more than 2 standard deviations from 0 but less than 3. Thus, this point is a possible outlier.

b. Using MINITAB, the results are:

Regression Analysis: weight versus cigarettes

```
The regression equation is
weight = 41.2 - 0.262 cigarettes


Predictor        Coef   SE Coef       T       P
Constant       41.153     6.843    6.01   0.000
cigarettes    -0.2619     0.3702   -0.71   0.486


S = 24.6816    R-Sq = 2.1%    R-Sq(adj) = 0.0%


Analysis of Variance

Source           DF       SS       MS      F       P
Regression        1    304.9    304.9   0.50   0.486
Residual Error   23  14011.1    609.2
Total            24  14316.0
```

```
Unusual Observations

Obs   cigarettes   weight    Fit  SE Fit  Residual  St Resid
25          44.0    87.00  29.63   12.56     57.37     2.70RX

R denotes an observation with a large standardized residual.
 observation whose X value gives it large influence.
```

The residuals are:

resid	resid	resid
−35.15	−10.91	12.85
−31.22	−12.22	16.85
−28.68	−4.13	20.85
−27.13	−3.53	24.85
−24.91	1.85	30.87
−22.32	7.85	41.85
−16.37	8.85	57.37
−16.15	13.61	
−17.60	12.71	

They indeed sum to zero.

c. No other residual is more than 2 standard deviations (2(24.68) = 49.36) from the mean of 0. Thus, there are no other outliers.

2.121   Using MINITAB, the results of fitting the model are:

Regression Analysis: DDT versus Miles, Length, Weight

```
The regression equation is
DDT = - 108 + 0.0851 Miles + 3.77 Length - 0.0494 Weight


Predictor      Coef   SE Coef       T      P
Constant    -108.07     62.70   -1.72  0.087
Miles       0.08509   0.08221    1.03  0.302
Length        3.771     1.619    2.33  0.021
Weight     -0.04941   0.02926   -1.69  0.094


S = 97.4756   R-Sq = 3.9%   R-Sq(adj) = 1.8%


Analysis of Variance

Source           DF       SS     MS     F      P
Regression        3    53794  17931  1.89  0.135
Residual Error  140  1330210   9501
Total           143  1384003


Source    DF   Seq SS
Miles      1     1973
Length     1    24725
Weight     1    27095
```

```
Unusual Observations

Obs   Miles       DDT      Fit  SE Fit  Residual  St Resid
 33    280      3.00    -1.91   29.86      4.91      0.05 X
 80    305     22.00    92.76   32.78    -70.76     -0.77 X
105    320    360.00    43.80   12.74    316.20      3.27R
115    325   1100.00    50.40   14.29   1049.60     10.89R
143    345      0.35   -21.27   31.10     21.62      0.23 X

R denotes an observation with a large standardized residual.
X denotes an observation whose X value gives it large influence.
```

First, we will look at the plots of the residuals versus the 3 independent variables, miles captured upstream, length, and weight. The standardized residual are used in the plots. The standardized residuals have a mean of 0 and a standard deviation of 1. Using MINITAB, the plots are:

From this plot, there is no indication that the relationship between level of DDT and miles caught upstream is anything other than linear. There is no 'U' or 'upside-down U' shape to the plot.

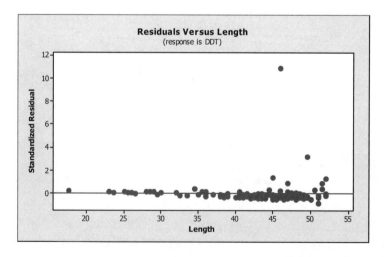

From this plot, there is no indication that the relationship between level of DDT and fish length is anything other than linear. There is no 'U' or 'upside-down U' shape to the plot.

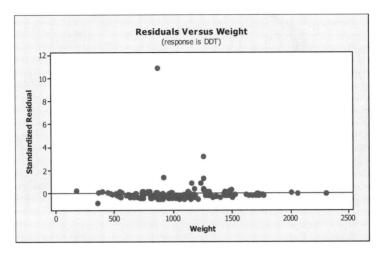

From this plot, there is no indication that the relationship between level of DDT and fish weight is anything other than linear. There is no 'U' or 'upside-down U' shape to the plot.

From the above plots, there is evidence that there are some outliers. Any standardized residual with values greater than 3 in absolute value are considered outliers. There are 2 observations with standardized residuals greater than 3 in absolute value. They are observation number 105 with a standardized residual of 3.2719 and observation # 115 with a standardized residual of 10.8855.

The histogram and normal probability plots of the standardized residuals are:

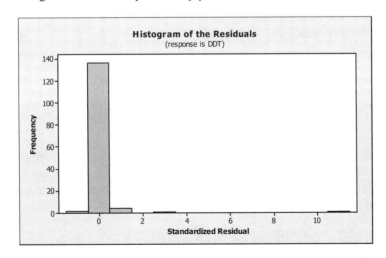

This histogram does not look very mound shaped. This indicates that the data may not be normal.

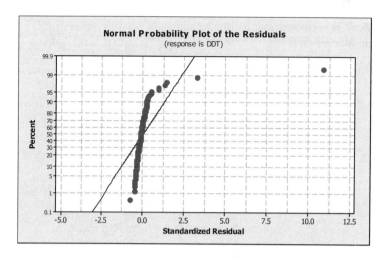

This normal probability plot does not look like a straight line. This indicates that the data are not normal.

To check for common variance, we look at the pot of the standardized residual versus the fitted values.

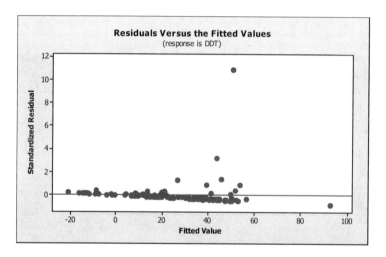

The data appear to be more spread out as the fitted values increase. Thus, our assumption of common variance does not appear to be valid.

12.123 a. Variables that are moderately or highly correlated have correlation coefficients of .5 or higher in absolute value. There are only two pairs of variables which are moderately or highly correlated. They are "year GRE taken" and "years in graduate program" ($r = -.602$), and "race" and "foreign status" ($r = -.515$).

b. When independent variables that are highly correlated with each other are included in a regression model, the results may be confusing. Highly correlated independent variables contribute overlapping information in the prediction of the dependent variable. The overall global test can indicate that the model is useful in predicting the dependent variable, while the individual t-tests on the independent variables can indicate that none of the independent variables are significant. This happens because the individual t-tests

tests for the significance of an independent variable after the other independent variables are taken into account. Usually, only one of the independent variables that are highly correlated with each other are included in the regression model.

12.125 $E(y) = \beta_0 + \beta_1 x_1 + \beta_2 x_2 + \beta_3 x_3$

where $x_1 = \begin{cases} 1, & \text{if level 2} \\ 0, & \text{otherwise} \end{cases}$ $x_2 = \begin{cases} 1, & \text{if level 3} \\ 0, & \text{otherwise} \end{cases}$ $x_3 = \begin{cases} 1, & \text{if level 4} \\ 0, & \text{otherwise} \end{cases}$

12.127 a. $E(y) = \beta_0 + \beta_1 x_1 + \beta_2 x_2 + \beta_3 x_3$

where $x_2 = \begin{cases} 1, & \text{if level 2} \\ 0, & \text{otherwise} \end{cases}$ $x_3 = \begin{cases} 1, & \text{if level 3} \\ 0, & \text{otherwise} \end{cases}$

   b. $E(y) = \beta_0 + \beta_1 x_1 + \beta_2 x_1^2 + \beta_3 x_2 + \beta_4 x_3 + \beta_5 x_1 x_2 + \beta_6 x_1 x_3 + \beta_7 x_1^2 x_2 + \beta_8 x_1^2 x_3$

   where x_1, x_2, and x_3 are as in part **a**.

12.129 a. To determine if at least one of the β parameters is not zero, we test:

H_0: $\beta_1 = \beta_2 = \beta_3 = \beta_4 = 0$
H_a: At least one $\beta_i \neq 0$

The test statistic is $F = \dfrac{R^2/k}{(1-R^2)/[n-(k+1)]} = \dfrac{.83/4}{(1-.83)/[25-(4+1)]} = 24.41$

The rejection region requires $\alpha = .05$ in the upper tail of the F distribution with numerator df $= k = 4$ and denominator df $= n - (k + 1) = 25 - (4 + 1) = 20$. From Table IX, Appendix A, $F_{.05} = 2.87$. The rejection region is $F > 2.87$.

Since the observed value of the test statistic falls in the rejection region ($F = 24.41 > 2.87$), H_0 is rejected. There is sufficient evidence to indicate at least one of the β parameters is nonzero at $\alpha = .05$.

   b. H_0: $\beta_1 = 0$
H_a: $\beta_1 < 0$

The test statistic is $t = \dfrac{\hat{\beta}_1 - 0}{s_{\hat{\beta}_1}} = \dfrac{-2.43 - 0}{1.21} = -2.01$

The rejection region requires $\alpha = .05$ in the lower tail of the t distribution with df $= n - (k + 1) = 25 - (4 + 1) = 20$. From Table VI, Appendix A, $t_{.05} = 1.725$. The rejection region is $t < -1.725$.

Since the observed value of the test statistic falls in the rejection region ($t = -2.01 < -1.725$), H_0 is rejected. There is sufficient evidence to indicate β_1 is less than 0 at $\alpha = .05$.

c. H_0: $\beta_2 = 0$
H_a: $\beta_2 > 0$

The test statistic is $t = \dfrac{\hat{\beta}_2 - 0}{s_{\hat{\beta}_2}} = \dfrac{.05 - 0}{.16} = .31$

The rejection region requires $\alpha = .05$ in the upper tail of the t distribution. From part **b** above, the rejection region is $t > 1.725$.

Since the observed value of the test statistic does not fall in the rejection region ($t = .31 \not> 1.725$), H_0 is not rejected. There is insufficient evidence to indicate β_2 is greater than 0 at $\alpha = .05$.

d. H_0: $\beta_3 = 0$
H_a: $\beta_3 \neq 0$

The test statistic is $t = \dfrac{\hat{\beta}_3 - 0}{s_{\hat{\beta}_3}} = \dfrac{.62 - 0}{.26} = 2.38$

The rejection region requires $\alpha/2 = .05/2 = .025$ in each tail of the t distribution with df = 20. From Table VI, Appendix A, $t_{.025} = 2.086$. The rejection region is $t < -2.086$ or $t > 2.086$.

Since the observed value of the test statistic falls in the rejection region ($t = 2.38 > 2.086$), H_0 is rejected. There is sufficient evidence to indicate β_3 is different from 0 at $\alpha = .05$.

12.131 The error of prediction is smallest when the values of x_1, x_2, and x_3 are equal to their sample means. The further x_1, x_2, and x_3 are from their means, the larger the error. When $x_1 = 60$, $x_2 = .4$, and $x_3 = 900$, the observed values are outside the observed ranges of the x values. When $x_1 = 30$, $x_2 = .6$, and $x_3 = 1300$, the observed values are within the observed ranges and consequently the x values are closer to their means. Thus, when $x_1 = 30$, $x_2 = .6$, and $x_3 = 1300$, the error of prediction is smaller.

12.133 Even though SSE = 0, we cannot estimate σ^2 because there are no degrees of freedom corresponding to error. With three data points, there are only two degrees of freedom available. The degrees of freedom corresponding to the model is $k = 2$ and the degrees of freedom corresponding to error is $n - (k + 1) = 3 - (2 + 1) = 0$. Without an estimate for σ^2, no inferences can be made.

12.135 a. To determine if the AD score is positively related to assertiveness level, once age and length of disability are accounted for, we test:

H_0: $\beta_1 = 0$
H_a: $\beta_1 > 0$

The test statistic is $t = 5.96$.

The p-value is $p = .0001/2 = .00005$. Since the p-value is less than α ($p = .00005 < .05$), H_0 is rejected. There is sufficient evidence to indicate that the AD score is positively related to assertiveness level, once age and length of disability are accounted for with $\alpha = .05$.

b. To determine if age is related to assertiveness level, once AD score and length of disability are accounted for, we test:

$H_0: \beta_2 = 0$
$H_a: \beta_2 \neq 0$

The test statistic is $t = 0.01$.

The p-value is $p = .9620$. Since the p-value is not less than $\alpha (p = .9620 \not< .05)$, H_0 is not rejected. There is insufficient evidence to indicate that Age score is related to assertiveness level, once AD score and length of disability are accounted for with $\alpha = .05$.

c. To determine if length of disability is positively related to assertiveness level, once AD score and age are accounted for, we test:

$H_0: \beta_3 = 0$
$H_a: \beta_3 > 0$

The test statistic is $t = 1.91$.

The p-value is $p = .0576/2 = .0288$. Since the p-value is less than $\alpha (p = .0288 < .05)$, H_0 is rejected. There is sufficient evidence to indicate that length of disability is positively related to assertiveness level, once the AD score and age are accounted for with $\alpha = .05$.

12.137 a. The first order model for $E(y)$ as a function of the first five independent variables is:

$$E(y) = \beta_0 + \beta_1 x_1 + \beta_2 x_2 + \beta_3 x_3 + \beta_4 x_4 + \beta_5 x_5$$

b. To test the utility of the model, we test:

$H_0: \beta_1 = \beta_2 = \beta_3 = \beta_4 = \beta_5 = 0$
$H_a:$ At least one $\beta_i \neq 0$, $i = 1, 2, 3, 4, 5$

The test statistic is $F = 34.47$.

The p-value is $p < .001$. Since the p-value is so small, there is sufficient evidence to indicate the model is useful for predicting GSI at $\alpha > .001$.

$R^2 = .469$. 46.9% of the variability in the GSI scores is explained by the model including the first five independent variables.

c. The first order model for $E(y)$ as a function of the first seven independent variables is:

$$E(y) = \beta_0 + \beta_1 x_1 + \beta_2 x_2 + \beta_3 x_3 + \beta_4 x_4 + \beta_5 x_5 + \beta_6 x_6 + \beta_7 x_7$$

d. $R^2 = .603$ 60.3% of the variability in the GSI scores is explained by the model including the first seven independent variables.

e. Since the *p*-values associated with the variables DES and PDEQ-SR are both less than .001, there is evidence that both variables contribute to the prediction of GSI, adjusted for all the other variables already in the model for $\alpha > .001$.

12.139 a. Because the estimated coefficient of the quadratic term is negative, the prediction equation will open downward something like the following:

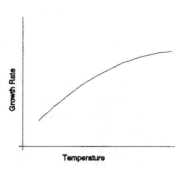

b. $R^2 = .67$. 67% of the variability in the daily growth rates is explained by the quadratic relationship between growth rate and temperature.

c. To test the utility of the model, we test:

H_0: $\beta_1 = \beta_2 = 0$
H_a: At least one $\beta_i \neq 0$, $i = 1, 2$

The test statistic is:

$$F = \frac{R^2/k}{(1-R^2)/[n-(k+1)]} = \frac{.67/2}{(1-.67)/[33-(2+1)]} = 30.45$$

The rejection region requires $\alpha = .05$ in the upper tail of the *F* distribution with $v_1 = k = 2$ and $v_2 = n - (k+1) = 33 - (2+1) = 30$. From Table IX, Appendix A, $F_{.05} = 3.32$. The rejection region is $F > 3.32$.
Since the observed value of the test statistic falls in the rejection region ($F = 30.45 > 3.32$), H_0 is rejected. There is sufficient evidence that the model is useful for predicting algae growth rate at $\alpha = .05$.

12.141 a. Diet is the independent variable.

b. $E(y) = \beta_0 + \beta_1 x_1 + \beta_2 x_2$

where $x_1 = \begin{cases} 1 & \text{if diet is high in carbohydrates} \\ 0 & \text{otherwise} \end{cases}$ $\begin{cases} 1 & \text{if diet is high in fruits} \\ 0 & \text{otherwise} \end{cases}$

12.143 a. The hypothesized model is:

$$E(y) = \beta_0 + \beta_1 x_1 + \beta_2 x_2 + \beta_3 x_3 + \beta_4 x_4 + \beta_5 x_5$$

$\beta_0 = y$-intercept. It has no interpretation in this model.

$\beta_1 =$ difference in the mean salaries between males and females, all other variables held constant.

β_2 = difference in the mean salaries between whites and nonwhites, all other variables held constant.

β_3 = change in the mean salary for each additional year of education, all other variables held constant.

β_4 = change in the mean salary for each additional year of tenure with firm, all other variables held constant.

β_5 = change in the mean salary for each additional hour worked per week, all other variables held constant.

b.   The least squares equation is:

$$\hat{y} = 15.491 + 12.774x_1 + .713x_2 + 1.519x_3 + .32x_4 + .205x_5$$

$\hat{\beta}_0$ = estimate of the y-intercept. It has no interpretation in this model.

$\hat{\beta}_1$: We estimate the difference in the mean salaries between males and females to be $12.774, all other variables held constant.

$\hat{\beta}_2$: We estimate the difference in the mean salaries between whites and nonwhites to be
$.713, all other variables held constant.

$\hat{\beta}_3$: We estimate the change in the mean salary for each additional year of education to be $1.519, all other variables held constant.

$\hat{\beta}_4$: We estimate the change in the mean salary for each additional year of tenure with firm to be $.320, all other variables held constant.

$\hat{\beta}_5$: We estimate the change in the mean salary for each additional hour worked per week to be $.205, all other variables held constant.

c. $R^2 = .240$. 24% of the total variability of salaries is explained by the model containing gender, race, educational level, tenure with firm, and number of hours worked per week.

To determine if the model is useful for predicting annual salary, we test:

H_0: $\beta_1 = \beta_2 = \beta_3 = \beta_4 = \beta_5 = 0$
H_a: At least one $\beta_i \neq 0$

The test statistic is $F = \dfrac{R^2/k}{(1-R^2)[n-(k+1)]} = \dfrac{.24/5}{(1-.24)/[191-(5+1)]} = 11.68$

The rejection region requires $\alpha = .05$ in the upper tail of the F distribution with numerator df $= k = 5$ and denominator df $= n - (k+1) = 191 - (5+1) = 185$. From Table IX, Appendix A, $F_{.05} \approx 2.21$. The rejection region is $F > 2.21$.

Since the observed value of the test statistic falls in the rejection region ($F = 11.68 > 2.21$), H_0 is rejected. There is sufficient evidence to indicate the model containing gender, race, educational level, tenure with firm, and number of hours worked per week is useful for predicting annual salary for $\alpha = .05$.

d. To determine if male managers are paid more than female managers, we test:

H_0: $\beta_1 = 0$
H_a: $\beta_1 > 0$

The p-value given for the test $p < .05/2 = .025$. Since the p-value is less than $\alpha = .05$, there is evidence to reject H_0. There is evidence to indicate male managers are paid more than female managers holding all other variables constant for $\alpha > .025$.

e. The salary paid an individual depends on many factors other than gender. Thus, in order to adjust for other factors influencing salary, we include them in the model.

12.145 a. Let x_1 = ASO scale, x_2 = Burns scale, and x_3 = Rotter scale. The first order model relating depression (Zung scale) to self-acceptance (ASO scale), perfectionism (Burns scale), and reinforcement (Rotter scale) is:

$$E(y) = \beta_0 + \beta_1 x_1 + \beta_2 x_2 + \beta_3 x_3$$

b. $R^2 = .70$.   70% of the variability in the depression scores is explained by the model including self-acceptance, perfectionism, and reinforcement.

c. To test if the model is useful for predicting depression, we test:

H_0: $\beta_1 = \beta_2 = \beta_3 = 0$
H_a: At least one $\beta_i \neq 0$, $i = 1, 2, 3$

The test statistic is $F = \dfrac{R^2/k}{(1-R^2)/[n-(k+1)]} = \dfrac{.70/3}{(1-.70)/[76-(3+1)]} = 56$

The rejection region requires $\alpha = .05$ in the upper tail of the F distribution with $v_1 = k = 3$ and $v_2 = n - (k+1) = 76 - (3+1) = 72$. From Table IX, Appendix A, $F_{.05} \approx 2.76$. The rejection region is $F > 2.76$.

Since the observed value of the test statistic falls in the rejection region ($F = 56 > 2.76$), H_0 is rejected. There is sufficient evidence that the model is useful in predicting depression at $\alpha = .05$.

d. The p-value for the perfectionism variable is .87. Since the p-value is so large, H_0 is not rejected. There is insufficient evidence to indicate perfectionism is useful for predicting depression, adjusting for self-acceptance and reinforcement already being in the model at $\alpha < .87$.

12.147 a. Since in the proposed model the funniness of the joke should increase and then decrease, the value of β_2 is expected to be negative.

b. To determine if the quadratic model relating pain to funniness rating is useful, we test:

H_0: $\beta_1 = \beta_2 = 0$
H_a: At least one $\beta_i \neq 0$, $i = 1, 2$

The test statistic is $F = 1.60$.

The rejection region requires $\alpha = .05$ in the upper tail of the F distribution with $v_1 = k = 2$ and $v_2 = n - (k + 1) = 32 - (2 + 1) = 29$. From Table IX, Appendix A, $F_{.05} = 3.33$. The rejection region is $F > 3.33$.

Since the observed value of the test statistic does not fall in the rejection region ($F = 1.60 \not> 3.33$), H_0 is not rejected. There is insufficient evidence to indicate that the quadratic model relating pain to funniness rating is useful at $\alpha = .05$.

c. To determine if the quadratic model relating aggression/hostility to funniness rating is useful, we test:

H_0: $\beta_1 = \beta_2 = 0$
H_a: At least one $\beta_i \neq 0$, $i = 1, 2$

The test statistic is $F = 1.61$.

The rejection region requires $\alpha = .05$ in the upper tail of the F distribution with $v_1 = k = 2$ and $v_2 = n - (k + 1) = 32 - (2 + 1) = 29$. From Table IX, Appendix A, $F_{.05} = 3.33$. The rejection region is $F > 3.33$.

Since the observed value of the test statistic does not fall in the rejection region ($F = 1.61 \not> 3.33$), H_0 is not rejected. There is insufficient evidence to indicate that the quadratic model relating aggression/hostility to funniness rating is useful at $\alpha = .05$.

12.149 a.

There is a curvilinear trend.

b. From MINITAB, the output is:

```
The regression equation is y = 42.2 - 0.0114x + 0.000001 xsq

Predictor          Coef         StDev             T           P
Constant         42.247         5.712          7.40       0.000
x              -0.011404      0.005053         -2.26       0.037
xsq           0.00000061    0.00000037          1.66       0.115

S = 21.81        R-Sq = 34.9%      R-Sq(adj) = 27.2%
```

```
Analysis of Variance
Source              DF          SS          MS          F          P
Regression           2       4325.4      2162.7       4.55      0.026
Residual Error      17       8085.5       475.6
Total               19      12410.9

Sourc       DF          Seq SS
e
x            1          3013.3
xsq          1          1312.1

Unusual Observations
Obs     x1          y          Fit    StDev Fit    Residual    St Resid
16     9150       4.60      -11.21       16.24       15.81        1.09 x
17    15022       2.20        8.09       21.40       -5.89       -1.41 x
```

X denotes an observation whose X value gives it large influence.

The fitted model is $\hat{y} = 42.2 - .0114x + .00000061x^2$

c. To determine if a curvilinear relationship exists, we test:

H_0: $\beta_2 = 0$
H_a: $\beta_2 \neq 0$

From MINITAB, the test statistic is $t = 1.66$ with p-value $= .115$. Since the p-value is greater than $\alpha = .05$, do not reject H_0. There is insufficient evidence to indicate that a curvilinear relationship exists between dissolved phosphorus percentage and soil loss at $\alpha = .05$.

12.151 a. $E(y) = \beta_0 + \beta_1 x_1 + \beta_2 x_6 + \beta_3 x_7$

where $x_7 = \begin{cases} 1 & \text{if condition is good} \\ 0 & \text{otherwise} \end{cases}$

$x_6 = \begin{cases} 1 & \text{if condition is fair} \\ 0 & \text{otherwise} \end{cases}$

b. The model specified in part **a** seems appropriate. The points for E, F, and G cluster around three parallel lines.

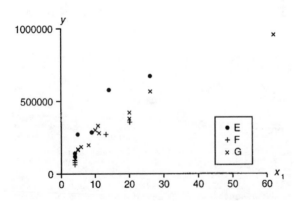

c. Using MINITAB, the output is

```
The regression equation is
y = 188875 + 15617 x1 - 103046 x6 - 152487 x7

Predictor       Coef        StDev          T          P
Constant      188875        28588       6.61      0.000
x1             15617         1066      14.66      0.000
x6           -103046        31784      -3.24      0.004
x7           -152487        39157      -3.89      0.001

S = 64624       R-Sq = 91.8%     R-Sq(adj) = 90.7%

Analysis of Variance

Source          DF           SS          MS         F          P
Regression       3    9.86170E+11   3.28723E+11    78.71      0.000
Residual Error  21    87700442851   4176211564
Total           24    1.07387E+12

Source     DF       SeqSS
x1          1   9.15776E+11
x6          1     7061463149
x7          1    63332198206

Unusual Observations
Obs    x1        y      Fit   StDev Fit   Residual   St Resid
 10  62.0   950000  1054078      53911    -104078    -2.92RX
 23  14.0   573200   407512      26670     165688     2.81R

R denotes an observation with a large standardized residual
X denotes an observation whose X value gives it large influence.
```

The fitted model is $\hat{y} = 188{,}875 + 15{,}617x_1 - 103{,}046x_6 - 152{,}487x_7$

For excellent condition, $\hat{y} = 188{,}875 + 15{,}617x_1$
For good condition, $\hat{y} = 85{,}829 + 15{,}617x_1$
For fair condition, $\hat{y} = 36{,}388 + 15{,}617x_1$

d.

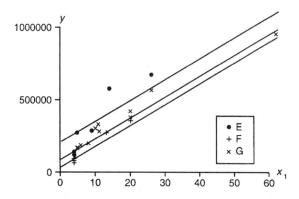

e. We must first fit a reduced model with just x_1, number of apartments. Using MINITAB, the output is:

```
The regression equation is
y = 101786 + 15525 x1

Predictor        Coef        StDev           T          P
Constant        101786       23291         4.37      0.000
x1               15525        1345        11.54      0.000

S = 82908        R-Sq = 85.3%     R-Sq(adj) = 84.6%

Analysis of Variance

Source           DF          SS            MS          F          P
Regression        1     9.15776E+11    9.15776E+11   133.23     0.000
Residual Error   23     1.58094E+11     6873656705
Total            24     1.07387E+12

Unusual Observations
Obs     x1        y         Fit     StDev Fit     Residual     St Resid
  4    26.0   676200      505433       24930       170757        2.16R
 10    62.0   950000     1064353       69058      -114353       -2.49RX
 23    14.0   573200      319140       16765       254060        3.13R

R denotes an observation with a large standardized residual
X denotes an observation whose X value gives it large influence.
```

To determine if the relationship between sale price and number of units differs depending on the physical condition of the apartments, we test:

H_0: $\beta_6 = \beta_7 = 0$
H_a: At least one $\beta_i \neq 0$, $i = 6, 7$

The test statistic is:

$$F = \frac{(\text{SSE}_R - \text{SSE}_C)/(k-g)}{\text{SSE}_C/[n-(k+1)]} = \frac{(1.58094 \times 10^{11} - 87700442851)/2}{4176211564} = 8.43$$

The rejection region requires $\alpha = .05$ in the upper tail of the F distribution with $v_1 = k - g = 3 - 1 = 2$ and $v_2 = n - (k+1) = 25 - (3+1) = 21$. From Table IX, Appendix A, $F_{.05} = 3.47$. The rejection region is $F > 3.47$.

Since the observed value of the test statistic falls in the rejection region ($F = 8.43 > 3.47$), H_0 is rejected. There is evidence to indicate that the relationship between sale price and number of units differs depending on the physical condition of the apartments at $\alpha = .05$.

f. We will look for high pairwise correlations

```
         x1       x2       x3       x4       x5       x6
x2    -0.014
x3     0.800   -0.188
x4     0.224   -0.363   0.166
x5     0.878    0.027   0.673  0.089
x6     0.175   -0.447   0.271  0.112    0.020
x7    -0.128    0.392  -0.118  0.050   -0.238  -0.564
```

When highly correlated independent variables are present in a regression model, the results are confusing. The researchers may only want to include one of the variables. This may be the case for the variables: x_1 and x_3, x_1 and x_5, x_3 and x_5

g. Use the following plots to check the assumptions on ε.

standardized residuals vs x_1
standardized residuals vs x_2
standardized residuals vs x_3
standardized residuals vs x_4
standardized residuals vs x_5
standardized resisduals vs predicted values
histogram of the standardized residuals
normal probability plot

From the plots of the residuals, there do not appear to be any outliers no standardized residuals are larger than 2.38 in magnitude. In all the plots of the residuals vs x_i, there is no trend that would indicate non-constant variance (no funnel shape). In addition, there is no U or upside-down U shape that would indicate that any of the variables should be squared.   In the histogram of the residuals, the plot is fairly mound-shaped, that would indicate the residuals are approximately normally distributed. The normal probability plot is a fairly straight line. This indicates that the assumption of normality is valid. All of the assumptions appear to be met.

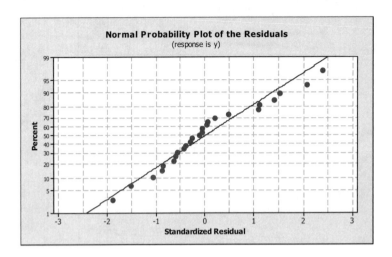

Normal Probability Plot of the Residuals
(response is y)

12.153 All of the independent variables are continuous except District. Four dummy variables were created for District before using the stepwise regression. Also, note that several observations had missing values. Thus, only 217 observations were used in the analysis. Since Ratio was computed from the ratio of Price and DOT estimate, it was not used as a predictor variable. Using SAS and $\alpha = .10$ for keeping variables in the model, the Stepwise regression results are:

```
                      The REG Procedure
                       Model: MODEL1
                  Dependent Variable: PRICE

                  Stepwise Selection: Step 1

    Variable DOTEST Entered: R-Square = 0.9763 and C(p) = 14.2985


                       Analysis of Variance

                             Sum of          Mean
    Source            DF     Squares        Square     F Value    Pr > F

    Model              1   687136244     687136244     8856.79    <.0001
    Error            215    16680334         77583
    Corrected Total  216   703816578


                 Parameter    Standard
    Variable     Estimate       Error    Type II SS  F Value  Pr > F

    Intercept    33.24768    22.19263       174129     2.24   0.1356
    DOTEST        0.90637     0.00963    687136244  8856.79   <.0001

               Bounds on condition number: 1, 1
```

Chapter 12

```
-----------------------------------------------------------------------------

                    Stepwise Selection: Step 2


          Variable STATUS Entered: R-Square = 0.9774 and C(p) = 5.9631


                           Analysis of Variance

                                   Sum of          Mean
      Source               DF      Squares        Square     F Value    Pr > F

      Model                 2     687894714     343947357    4622.87    <.0001
      Error               214      15921865         74401
      Corrected Total     216     703816578

                             The REG Procedure
                              Model: MODEL1
                         Dependent Variable: PRICE

                         Stepwise Selection: Step 2

                    Parameter      Standard
          Variable   Estimate        Error     Type II SS   F Value   Pr > F

          Intercept  -12.92808     26.10499         18247      0.25   0.6209
          DOTEST       0.91233      0.00961     669924194   9004.21   <.0001
          STATUS     132.16624     41.39440        758469     10.19   0.0016

               Bounds on condition number: 1.0392, 4.1569
-----------------------------------------------------------------------------

                    Stepwise Selection: Step 3


          Variable DAYS Entered: R-Square = 0.9779 and C(p) = 3.4115


                           Analysis of Variance

                                   Sum of          Mean
      Source               DF      Squares        Square     F Value    Pr > F

      Model                 3     688228730     229409577    3134.76    <.0001
      Error               213      15587848         73182
      Corrected Total     216     703816578


                    Parameter      Standard
          Variable   Estimate        Error     Type II SS   F Value   Pr > F

          Intercept  -59.79987     33.93608        227239      3.11   0.0795
          DOTEST       0.88616      0.01552     238455655   3258.37   <.0001
          STATUS     139.40952     41.19370        838166     11.45   0.0008
          DAYS         0.35761      0.16739        334016      4.56   0.0338

               Bounds on condition number: 2.7653, 19.698
-----------------------------------------------------------------------------
```

Multiple Regression   401

All variables left in the model are significant at the 0.1000 level.

The REG Procedure
Model: MODEL1
Dependent Variable: PRICE

Stepwise Selection: Step 3

No other variable met the 0.1500 significance level for entry into the model.

Summary of Stepwise Selection

Step	Variable Entered	Variable Removed	Number Vars In	Partial R-Square	Model R-Square	C(p)	F Value	Pr > F
1	DOTEST		1	0.9763	0.9763	14.2985	8856.79	<.0001
2	STATUS		2	0.0011	0.9774	5.9631	10.19	0.0016
3	DAYS		3	0.0005	0.9779	3.4115	4.56	0.0338

From the results, only three independent variables are selected to predict price using the stepwise regression and $\alpha = .05$. These variables are DOT estimate, Status, and Days.

A new model was fit with just the variables DOT estimate, Status, and Days using SAS. The results are:

The REG Procedure
Model: MODEL1
Dependent Variable: PRICE

Analysis of Variance

Source	DF	Sum of Squares	Mean Square	F Value	Pr > F
Model	3	688228730	229409577	3134.76	<.0001
Error	213	15587848	73182		
Corrected Total	216	703816578			

Root MSE	270.52243	R-Square	0.9779	
Dependent Mean	1126.66359	Adj R-Sq	0.9775	
Coeff Var	24.01093			

Parameter Estimates

Variable	DF	Parameter Estimate	Standard Error	t Value	Pr > |t|
Intercept	1	-59.79987	33.93608	-1.76	0.0795
DOTEST	1	0.88616	0.01552	57.08	<.0001
STATUS	1	139.40952	41.19370	3.38	0.0008
DAYS	1	0.35761	0.16739	2.14	0.0338

We see that this is a fairly good model. The R-square value is .9779. 97.79% of the variation in the PRICE values is explained by the model containing DODEST, STATUS, and DAYS.

We note that the parameter estimate for the parameter associated Bid Status is 139.40952. Since Bid Status is either 1 (fixed) or 0 (competitive), the PRICE for the fixed bid is estimated to be 139.40952 units higher than the competitive bid, all other variables held constant.

To check the model assumptions, we will look at the plots. The plots of the residuals versus the independent variables are:

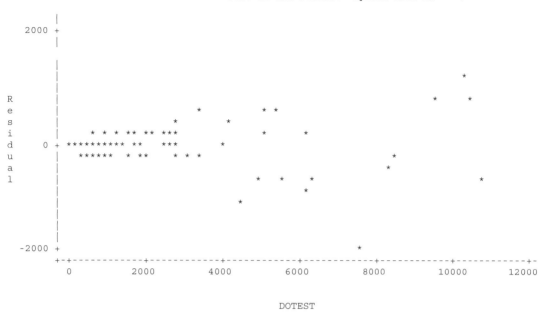

Plot of RES*DOTEST. Symbol used is '*'.

NOTE: 160 obs hidden.

There is no 'U' or 'upside-down U' shape to this plot

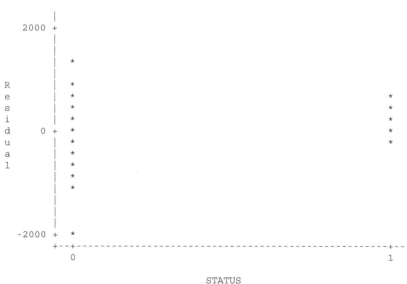

Plot of RES*STATUS. Symbol used is '*'.

NOTE: 200 obs hidden.

```
                    Plot of RES*DAYS.   Symbol used is '*'.

            |
     2000 + |
            |
            |
            |                                               *
            |
    R       |
    e       |                                    *                 *
    s       |                              *     *              *
    i       |                                    *       *          *
    d       |                    **     **      **  *  *   *       *
        0 + |  ******************  ***  **  *     **           *        *
    u       |      *  **   ******      *   *  *  **     *   *   *
    a       |                                    *
    l       |                         *            *   *       *
            |                                    *
            |                                                *
            |
            |
            |
            |
    -2000 + |                                  *
            +--+------------+------------+------------+------------+------------+--
              0           200          400          600          800         1000

                                       DAYS
```

NOTE: 146 obs hidden.

There are no 'U' or 'upside-down U' shapes to these plots. Thus, the relationship between PRICE and the independent variables appear to be linear. There are a total of 6 observations that are more than 3 standard deviations from the mean. These 6 points could be outliers.

A histogram of the data is:

```
                                 Histogram                        #
Boxplot
       1300+*                                     1                *
           .
           .*                                     1                *
           .**                                    4                *
           .*                                     3                0
           .***                                   8                0
           .*********************************   104            +--+--+
           .*************************            80            +-----+
           .***                                  9                0
           .
           .**                                    4                *
           .*                                     1                *
           .*                                     1                *
           .
           .
           .
           .
      -2100+*                                     1                *
           ----+----+----+----+----+----+----+
           * may represent up to 3 counts
```

This appears to be fairly mound shaped, so the assumption that the data are normal appears to be OK.

The plot of the residuals against the fitted values is:

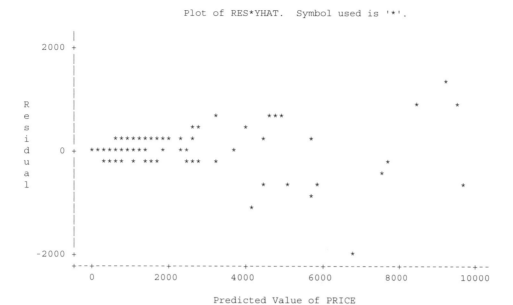

Plot of RES*YHAT. Symbol used is '*'.

NOTE: 158 obs hidden.

The spread of the data points appears to increase as the predicted value of y increases. This indicates that there is non-constant variance.

Thus, even though the fit of this model appears to be fairly good ($R^2 = .9779$), some of the model assumptions are not met. The data do appear to be normally distributed. However, there appears that there are several (6) outliers and that the variance is not constant.

Additional models could be tried. One could look at interactions of the 3 variables included so far. When this is tried, the interaction term of DOTEST*STATUS is significant. However, the R-square value does not increase and the problems with the assumptions still exist.

Categorical Data Analysis

13.1 The characteristics of the multinomial experiment are:

1. The experiment consists of n identical trials.
2. There are k possible outcomes to each trial.
3. The probabilities of the k outcomes, denoted $p_1, p_2, \ldots, p_k$, remain the same from trial to trial, where $p_1 + p_2 + \cdots + p_k = 1$.
4. The trials are independent.
5. The random variables of interest are the counts $n_1, n_2, \ldots, n_k$ in each of the k cells.

The characteristics of the binomial are the same as those for the multinomial with $k = 2$.

13.3 a. With df $= 10$, $\chi^2_{.05} = 18.3070$

b. With df $= 50$, $\chi^2_{.990} = 29.7067$

c. With df $= 16$, $\chi^2_{.10} = 23.5418$

d. With df $= 50$, $\chi^2_{.005} = 79.4900$

13.5 a. The rejection region requires $\alpha = .05$ in the upper tail of the χ^2 distribution with df $= k - 1 = 3 - 1 = 2$. From Table VII, Appendix A, $\chi^2_{.05} = 5.99147$. The rejection region is $\chi^2 > 5.99147$.

b. The rejection region requires $\alpha = .10$ in the upper tail of the χ^2 distribution with df $= k - 1 = 5 - 1 = 4$. From Table VII, Appendix A, $\chi^2_{.10} = 7.77944$. The rejection region is $\chi^2 > 7.77944$.

c. The rejection region requires $\alpha = .01$ in the upper tail of the χ^2 distribution with df $= k - 1 = 4 - 1 = 3$. From Table VII, Appendix A, $\chi^2_{.10} = 11.3449$. The rejection region is $\chi^2 > 11.3449$.

13.7 Some preliminary calculations are:

If the probabilities are the same, $p_{1,0} = p_{2,0} = p_{3,0} = p_{4,0} = .25$

$$E_1 = np_{1,0} = 205(.25) = 51.25$$
$$E_2 = E_3 = E_4 = 205(.25) = 51.25$$

a. To determine if the multinomial probabilities differ, we test:

H_0: $p_1 = p_2 = p_3 = p_4 = .25$
H_a: At least one of the probabilities differs from .25

The test statistic is $\chi^2 = \sum \dfrac{[n_i - E_i]^2}{E_i}$

$$= \frac{(43-51.25)^2}{51.25} + \frac{(56-51.25)^2}{51.25} + \frac{(59-51.25)^2}{51.25} + \frac{(47-51.25)^2}{51.25} = 3.293$$

The rejection region requires $\alpha = .05$ in the upper tail of the χ^2 distribution with df = k 1 = 4 − 1 = 3. From Table VII, Appendix A, $\chi^2_{.05} = 7.81473$. The rejection region is $\chi^2 > 7.81473$.

Since the observed value of the test statistic does not fall in the rejection region ($\chi^2 = 3.293 \not> 7.81473$), H_0 is not rejected. There is insufficient evidence to indicate the multinomial probabilities differ at $\alpha = .05$.

b.   The Type I error is concluding the multinomial probabilities differ when, in fact, they do not.

The Type II error is concluding the multinomial probabilities are equal, when, in fact, they are not.

c.   For confidence coefficient .95, $\alpha = .05$ and $\alpha/2 = .05/2 = .025$. From Table IV, Appendix A, $z_{.025} = 1.96$.

$\hat{p}_3 = 59/205 = .288$

The confidence interval is:

$$\hat{p} \pm z_{.025}\sqrt{\frac{\hat{p}\hat{q}}{n}} \Rightarrow .288 \pm 1.96\sqrt{\frac{.288(.712)}{205}} \Rightarrow .288 \pm .062 \Rightarrow (.226, .350)$$

13.9   a.   The qualitative variable of interest is nonfunctional jaw habits. It has 4 levels: bruxism, teeth clenching, both bruxism and clenching, and neither.

b.   A one-way table of the data is:

	\multicolumn{4}{c}{Cell}

	Bruxism	Clench	Bruxism & Clench	Neither
n_i	3	11	30	16

c.   To determine whether the percentages associated with the admitted habits differ, we test:

H_0: $p_1 = p_2 = p_3 = p_4 = .25$
H_a: At least one p_i differs from .25, $i = 1, 2, 3, 4$

d. $E_1 = E_2 = E_3 = E_4 = np_{i,0} = 60(.25) = 15$.

e. The test statistic is

$$\chi^2 = \sum \frac{[n_i - E_i]^2}{E_i} = \frac{[3-15]^2}{15} + \frac{[11-15]^2}{15} + \frac{[30-15]^2}{15} + \frac{[16-15]^2}{15} = 25.733$$

f. The rejection region requires $\alpha = .05$ in the upper tail of the χ^2 distribution with df = $k - 1 = 4 - 1 = 3$. From Table VII, Appendix A, $\chi^2_{.05} = 7.81473$. The rejection region is $\chi^2 > 7.81473$.

g. Since the observed value of the test statistic falls in the rejection region ($\chi^2 = 25.733 > 7.81473$), H_0 is rejected. There is sufficient evidence to indicate the percentages associated with the admitted habits differ at $\alpha = .05$.

h. $\hat{p}_3 = \frac{30}{60} = .5$

For confidence coefficient .95, $\alpha = .05$ and $\alpha/2 = .05/2 = .025$. From Table IV, Appendix A, $z_{.025} = 1.96$. The 95% confidence interval is:

$$\hat{p}_i \pm z_{.025}\sqrt{\frac{\hat{p}_i \hat{q}_i}{n}} \Rightarrow .5 \pm 1.96\sqrt{\frac{.5(.5)}{60}} \Rightarrow .5 \pm .127 \Rightarrow (.373, \ .627)$$

We are 95% confident that the true proportion of dental patients who admit to both habits is between .373 and .627.

13.11 a. The qualitative variable of interest in this problem is the type of pottery found. There are 4 levels of the variable: burnished, monochrome, painted, and other.

b. If all 4 types of pottery occur with equal probabilities, the values of p_1, p_2, p_3, and p_4 are all .25.

c. To determine if one type of pottery is more likely to occur at the site than any other, we test:

H_0: $p_1 = p_2 = p_3 = p_4 = .25$
H_a: At least one $p_i \ne .25$ for $i = 1, 2, 3, 4$

d. Some preliminary calculations are:

$E_1 = E_2 = E_3 = E_4 = np_{i,0} = 837(.25) = 209.25.$

$$\chi^2 = \sum \frac{[n_i - E_i]^2}{E_i} = \frac{[133 - 209.25]^2}{209.25} + \frac{[460 - 209.25]^2}{209.25} + \frac{[183 - 209.25]^2}{209.25} + \frac{[61 - 209.25]^2}{209.25}$$
$$= 436.591$$

e. The p-value is $p = P(\chi^2 \ge 436.591)$. Using Table VII, Appendix A, with df = $k - 1$ = $4 - 1 = 3$, $p = P(\chi^2 \ge 436.591) < .005$. Since the p-value is less than $\alpha = .10$, H_0 is rejected. There is sufficient evidence to indicate at least one type of pottery is more likely to occur at the site than another at $\alpha = .10$.

13.13   Some preliminary calculations are:

$$E_1 = E_2 = E_3 = E_4 = E_5 = np_{i,0} = 95(.20) = 19$$

To determine if the true percentages of ADEs in the 5 "cause" categories differ, we test:

H_0: $p_1 = p_2 = p_3 = p_4 = p_5 = .2$
H_a: At least one p_i differs from .2, $i = 1, 2, 3, 4, 5$

The test statistic is

$$\chi^2 = \sum \frac{[n_i - E_i]^2}{E_i} = \frac{[29-19]^2}{19} + \frac{[17-19]^2}{19} + \frac{[13-19]^2}{19} + \frac{[9-19]^2}{19} + \frac{[27-19]^2}{19} = 16$$

Since no α was given, we will use $\alpha = .05$. The rejection region requires $\alpha = .05$ in the upper tail of the χ^2 distribution with df $= k - 1 = 5 - 1 = 4$. From Table VII, Appendix A, $\chi^2_{.05} = 9.48773$. The rejection region is $\chi^2 > 9.48773$.

Since the observed value of the test statistic falls in the rejection region ($\chi^2 = 16 > 9.48773$), H_0 is rejected. There is sufficient evidence to indicate the true percentages of ADEs in the 5 "cause" categories differ at $\alpha = .05$.

13.15   a.   Some preliminary calculations are:

$$E_1 = np_{1,0} = 85(.26) = 22.1$$
$$E_2 = np_{2,0} = 85(.30) = 25.5$$
$$E_3 = np_{3,0} = 85(.11) = 9.35$$
$$E_4 = np_{4,0} = 85(.14) = 11.9$$
$$E_5 = np_{5,0} = 85(.19) = 16.15$$

To determine of probabilities differ from the hypothesized values, we test:

H_0: $p_1 = .26, p_2 = .30, p_3 = .11, p_4 = .14, p_5 = .19$
H_a: At least one of the probabilities differs from its hypothesized value.

The test statistic is $\chi^2 = \sum \dfrac{[n_i - E_i]^2}{E_i}$

$$= \frac{(32-22.1)^2}{22.1} + \frac{(26-25.5)^2}{25.5} + \frac{(15-9.35)^2}{9.35} + \frac{(6-11.9)^2}{11.9} + \frac{(6-16.15)^2}{16.15}$$

$$= 17.16$$

The rejection region requires $\alpha = .05$ in the upper tail of the χ^2 distribution with df $= k - 1 = 5 - 1 = 4$. From Table VII, Appendix A, $\chi^2_{.05} = 11.0705$. The rejection region is $\chi^2 > 11.0705$.

Since the observed value of the test statistic falls in the rejection region ($\chi^2 = 17.16 > 11.0705$), reject H_0. There is sufficient evidence to indicate the probabilities differ from their hypothesized values at $\alpha = .05$.

b. $\hat{p}_1 = \dfrac{32}{85} = .376$

For confidence coefficient .95, $\alpha = .05$ and $\alpha/2 = .05/2 = .025$. From Table IV, Appendix A, $z_{.025} = 1.96$. The 95% confidence interval is:

$$\hat{p}_i \pm z_{.025}\sqrt{\dfrac{\hat{p}_i\hat{q}_i}{n}} \Rightarrow .376 \pm 1.96\sqrt{\dfrac{.376(.624)}{85}} \Rightarrow .376 \pm .103 \Rightarrow (.273, \; .479)$$

We are 95% confident that the true proportion of Avonex MS patients who are exacerbation-free during a 2-year period is between .273 and .479.

c. From previous studies, it is known that 26% of the MS patients on a placebo experienced no exacerbations in a 2-year period. Since .26 does not fall in the 95% confidence interval, there is evidence that Avonex patients are more likely to have no exacerbations than the placebo patients at $\alpha = .05$.

13.17 a. Some preliminary calculations are:

$E_A = np_{A,0} = 700(.09) = 63$ $E_B = np_{B,0} = 700(.02) = 14$
$E_C = np_{C,0} = 700(.02) = 14$ $E_D = np_{D,0} = 700(.04) = 28$
$E_E = np_{E,0} = 700(.04) = 28$ $E_F = np_{F,0} = 700(.02) = 14$
$E_G = np_{G,0} = 700(.02) = 14$ $E_H = np_{H,0} = 700(.02) = 14$
$E_I = np_{I,0} = 700(.02) = 14$ $E_J = np_{J,0} = 700(.01) = 7$
$E_K = np_{K,0} = 700(.01) = 7$ $E_L = np_{L,0} = 700(.04) = 28$
$E_M = np_{M,0} = 700(.02) = 14$ $E_N = np_{N,0} = 700(.06) = 42$
$E_O = np_{O,0} = 700(.08) = 56$ $E_P = np_{P,0} = 700(.02) = 14$
$E_Q = np_{Q,0} = 700(.01) = 7$ $E_R = np_{R,0} = 700(.06) = 42$
$E_S = np_{S,0} = 700(.04) = 28$ $E_T = np_{T,0} = 700(.06) = 42$
$E_U = np_{U,0} = 700(.04) = 28$ $E_V = np_{V,0} = 700(.02) = 14$
$E_W = np_{W,0} = 700(.02) = 14$ $E_X = np_{X,0} = 700(.01) = 7$
$E_Y = np_{Y,0} = 700(.02) = 14$ $E_Z = np_{Z,0} = 700(.01) = 7$
$E_{BLANK} = np_{BL,0} = 700(.02) = 14$

To determine if the ScrabbleExpress™ presents the player with "unfair word selection opportunities" that are different from the Scrabble™ board game, we test:

H_0: $p_A = .09, p_B = .02, p_C = .02, p_D = .04, p_E = .12, p_F = .02, p_G = .03, p_H = .02, p_I = .09,$
$\quad p_J = .01, p_K = .01, p_L = .04, p_M = .02, p_N = .06, p_O = .08, p_P = .02, p_Q = .01, p_R = .06,$
$\quad p_S = .04, p_T = .06, p_U = .04, p_V = .02, p_W = .02, p_X = .01, p_Y = .02, p_Z = .01,$
$\quad p_{BLANK} = .02$
H_a: At least one p_i differs from its hypothesized value, i = A, B, …, BLANK

The test statistic is

$$\chi^2 = \sum \dfrac{[n_i - E_i]^2}{E_i} = \dfrac{[36-63]^2}{63} + \dfrac{[18-14]^2}{14} + \dfrac{[30-14]^2}{14} + \cdots + \dfrac{[34-14]^2}{14} = 360.48$$

The rejection region requires $\alpha = .05$ in the upper tail of the χ^2 distribution with df $= k - 1 = 27 - 1 = 26$. From Table VII, Appendix A, $\chi^2_{.05} = 38.8852$. The rejection region is $\chi^2 > 38.8852$.

Since the observed value of the test statistic falls in the rejection region ($\chi^2 = 360.48 > 38.8852$), H_0 is rejected. There is sufficient evidence to indicate the ScrabbleExpress™ presents the player with "unfair word selection opportunities" that are different from the Scrabble™ board game at $\alpha = .05$.

b. The true proportion of letters drawn from the board game is

$$p_A + p_E + p_I + p_O + p_U = .09 + .12 + .09 + .08 + .04 = .42$$

The number of vowels drawn by the electronic game is $39 + 31 + 25 + 20 + 21 = 136$. The proportion of vowels drawn is $136 / 700 = .194$.

For confidence coefficient .95, $\alpha = .05$ and $\alpha/2 = .05/2 = .025$. From Table IV, Appendix A, $z_{.025} = 1.96$. The 95% confidence interval is:

$$\hat{p}_i \pm z_{.025}\sqrt{\frac{\hat{p}_i\hat{q}_i}{n}} \Rightarrow .194 \pm 1.96\sqrt{\frac{.194(.806)}{700}} \Rightarrow .194 \pm .029 \Rightarrow (.165, \ .223)$$

We are 95% confident that the true proportion of vowels drawn by the electronic game is between .165 and .223. The actual proportion of vowels drawn in the board game is .42. Since this value is not contained in the 95% confidence interval, one can conclude that the ScrabbleExpress™ game produces too few vowels in the 7-letter draws.

13.19 The statement "One goal of a contingency table analysis is to determine if the two classifications are dependent" is true.

13.21 a. $df = (r - 1)(c - 1) = (5 - 1)(5 - 1) = 16$. From Table VII, Appendix A, $\chi^2_{.05} = 26.2962$. The rejection region is $\chi^2 > 26.2962$.

b. $df = (r - 1)(c - 1) = (3 - 1)(6 - 1) = 10$. From Table VII, Appendix A, $\chi^2_{.10} = 15.9871$. The rejection region is $\chi^2 > 15.9871$.

c. $df = (r - 1)(c - 1) = (2 - 1)(3 - 1) = 2$. From Table VII, Appendix A, $\chi^2_{.01} = 9.21034$. The rejection region is $\chi^2 > 9.21034$.

13.23 a. To convert the frequencies to percentages, divide the numbers in each column by the column total and multiply by 100. Also, divide the row totals by the overall total and multiply by 100. The column totals are 25, 64, and 78, while the row totals are 96 and 71. The overall sample size is 165. The table of percentages are:

	Column			
	1	**2**	**3**	
Row 1	$\frac{9}{25} \cdot 100 = 36\%$	$\frac{34}{64} \cdot 100 = 53.1\%$	$\frac{53}{78} \cdot 100 = 67.9\%$	$\frac{96}{167} \cdot 100 = 57.5\%$
2	$\frac{16}{25} \cdot 100 = 64\%$	$\frac{30}{64} \cdot 100 = 46.9\%$	$\frac{25}{78} \cdot 100 = 32.1\%$	$\frac{71}{167} \cdot 100 = 42.5\%$

b.

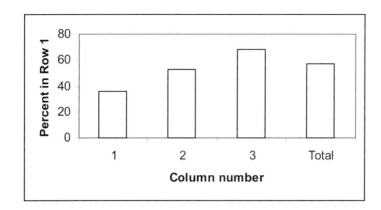

c.   If the rows and columns are independent, the row percentages in each column would be close to the row total percentages. This pattern is not evident in the plot, implying the rows and columns are not independent.

13.25   To convert the frequencies to percentages, divide the numbers in each column by the column total and multiply by 100. Also, divide the row totals by the overall total and multiply by 100.

	B_1	B_2	B_3	Totals
A_1	$\dfrac{40}{134} \cdot 100 = 29.9\%$	$\dfrac{72}{163} \cdot 100 = 44.2\%$	$\dfrac{42}{142} \cdot 100 = 29.6\%$	$\dfrac{154}{439} \cdot 100 = 35.1\%$
A_2	$\dfrac{63}{134} \cdot 100 = 47.0\%$	$\dfrac{53}{163} \cdot 100 = 32.5\%$	$\dfrac{70}{142} \cdot 100 = 49.3\%$	$\dfrac{186}{439} \cdot 100 = 42.4\%$
A_3	$\dfrac{31}{134} \cdot 100 = 23.1\%$	$\dfrac{38}{163} \cdot 100 = 23.3\%$	$\dfrac{30}{142} \cdot 100 = 21.1\%$	$\dfrac{99}{439} \cdot 100 = 22.6\%$

B is the column header spanning B_1, B_2, B_3, and **Row** labels the rows A_1, A_2, A_3.

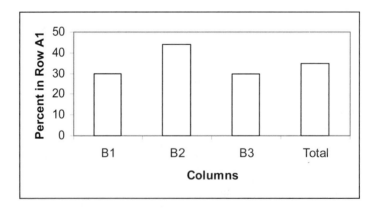

Since the columns are not the same height, there is evidence to indicate that the row and column classifications are dependent.

b.   The graph for row A2 is:

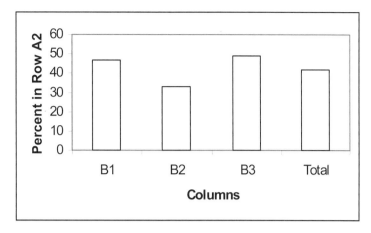

Since the columns are not the same height, there is evidence to indicate that the row and column classifications are dependent.

c.   The graph for row A3 is:

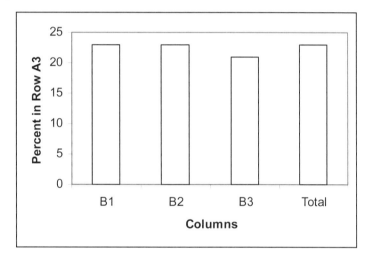

Since the columns are almost the same height, there is evidence to indicate that the row and column classifications are independent.

13.27   a.   The two qualitative variables were grade and reading ability. Grade had two levels: 4th grade and 5th grade. Reading ability had two levels: normal and reading disability.

b.	The contingency table would be:

Reading Ability

		Reading Disability	Normal	Totals
Grade	4th	32	55	87
	5th	34	40	74
	Totals	66	95	161

c.	The expected cell counts for the cells would be:

$$\hat{E}_{11} = \frac{r_1 c_1}{n} = \frac{87(66)}{161} = 35.66 \qquad \hat{E}_{12} = \frac{r_1 c_2}{n} = \frac{87(95)}{161} = 51.34$$

$$\hat{E}_{21} = \frac{r_2 c_1}{n} = \frac{74(66)}{161} = 30.34 \qquad \hat{E}_{22} = \frac{r_2 c_2}{n} = \frac{74(95)}{161} = 43.66$$

d.	The test statistic is

$$\chi^2 = \sum\sum \frac{[n_{ij} - \hat{E}_{ij}]^2}{\hat{E}_{ij}} = \frac{[32 - 35.66]^2}{35.66} + \frac{[55 - 51.34]^2}{51.34} + \frac{[34 - 30.34]^2}{30.34} + \frac{[40 - 43.66]^2}{43.66}$$

$$= 1.38$$

e.	The rejection region requires $\alpha = .10$ in the upper tail of the χ^2 distribution with df $= (r-1)(c-1) = (2-1)(2-1) = 1$. From Table VII, Appendix A, $\chi^2_{.10} = 2.70554$. The rejection region is $\chi^2 > 2.70554$.

f.	To determine if there is a link between reading disability and grade level, we test:

H_0: Reading Disability and Grade Level are independent
H_a: Reading Disability and Grade Level are dependent

The test statistic is $\chi^2 = 1.38$.

The rejection region is $\chi^2 > 2.70554$.
Since the observed value of the test statistic does not fall in the rejection region ($\chi^2 = 1.38 \not> 2.70554$), H_0 is not rejected. There is insufficient evidence of a link between reading disability and grade level at $\alpha = .10$.

13.29	a.	The two categorical variables are Risk of masculinity and type of event. Risk of masculinity has two levels: High and Low. Type of event has two levels: Violent event and Avoided-Violent event.

b.	The experimental units are 1,507 newly incarcerated men.

c. $\hat{E}_{11} = \dfrac{r_1 c_1}{n} = \dfrac{379(1,037)}{1,507} = 260.798$

d. $\hat{E}_{12} = \dfrac{r_1 c_2}{n} = \dfrac{379(470)}{1,507} = 118.202$ $\hat{E}_{21} = \dfrac{r_2 c_1}{n} = \dfrac{1,128(1,037)}{1,507} = 776.202$

$\hat{E}_{22} = \dfrac{r_2 c_2}{n} = \dfrac{1,128(470)}{1,507} = 351.798$

e. $\chi^2 = \sum\sum \dfrac{[n_{ij} - \hat{E}_{ij}]^2}{\hat{E}_{ij}} = \dfrac{[236 - 260.798]^2}{260.798} + \dfrac{[143 - 118.202]^2}{118.202}$

$+ \dfrac{[801 - 776.202]^2}{776.202} + \dfrac{[327 - 351.798]^2}{351.798} = 10.101$

f.   To determine whether event type depends on high/low risk masculinity, we test:

H_0: Event Type and High/Low Risk Masculinity are independent
H_a: Event Type and High/Low Risk Masculinity are dependent

The test statistic is $\chi^2 = 10.101$.

The rejection region requires $\alpha = .05$ in the upper tail of the χ^2 distribution with df $= (r - 1)(c - 1) = (2 - 1)(2 - 1) = 1$. From Table VII, Appendix A, $\chi^2_{.05} = 3.84146$. The rejection region is $\chi^2 > 3.84146$.

Since the observed value of the test statistic falls in the rejection region ($\chi^2 = 10.101 > 3.84146$), H_0 is rejected. There is sufficient evidence that event type depends on high/low risk masculinity at $\alpha = .05$.

13.31   Some preliminary calculations are:

$\hat{E}_{11} = \dfrac{r_1 c_1}{n} = \dfrac{62(106)}{275} = 23.90$ $\hat{E}_{12} = \dfrac{r_1 c_2}{n} = \dfrac{62(112)}{275} = 25.25$

$\hat{E}_{13} = \dfrac{r_1 c_3}{n} = \dfrac{62(57)}{275} = 12.85$ $\hat{E}_{21} = \dfrac{r_2 c_1}{n} = \dfrac{59(106)}{275} = 22.74$

$\hat{E}_{22} = \dfrac{r_2 c_2}{n} = \dfrac{59(112)}{275} = 24.03$ $\hat{E}_{23} = \dfrac{r_2 c_3}{n} = \dfrac{59(57)}{275} = 12.23$

$\hat{E}_{31} = \dfrac{r_3 c_1}{n} = \dfrac{59(106)}{275} = 22.74$ $\hat{E}_{32} = \dfrac{r_3 c_2}{n} = \dfrac{59(112)}{275} = 24.03$

$$\hat{E}_{33} = \frac{r_3 c_3}{n} = \frac{59(57)}{275} = 12.23 \qquad\qquad \hat{E}_{41} = \frac{r_4 c_1}{n} = \frac{95(106)}{275} = 36.62$$

$$\hat{E}_{42} = \frac{r_4 c_2}{n} = \frac{95(112)}{275} = 38.69 \qquad\qquad \hat{E}_{43} = \frac{r_4 c_3}{n} = \frac{95(57)}{275} = 19.69$$

To determine if political strategy of ethnic groups depends on world region, we test:

H_0: Political strategy and world region are independent
H_a: Political strategy and world region are dependent

The test statistic is $\chi^2 = \sum\sum \dfrac{[n_{ij} - \hat{E}_{ij}]^2}{\hat{E}_{ij}} = \dfrac{(24-23.90)^2}{23.90} + \dfrac{(31-25.25)^2}{25.25}$

$$+ \frac{(7-12.85)^2}{12.85} + \frac{(32-22.74)^2}{22.74} + \frac{(23-24.03)^2}{24.03} + \frac{(4-12.23)^2}{12.23} + \frac{(11-22.74)^2}{22.74}$$

$$+ \frac{(22-24.03)^2}{24.03} + \frac{(26-12.23)^2}{12.23} + \frac{(39-36.62)^2}{36.62} + \frac{(36-38.69)^2}{38.69} + \frac{(20-19.69)^2}{19.69}$$

$$= 35.409$$

The rejection region requires $\alpha = .10$ in the upper tail of the χ^2 distribution with df $=$ $(r-1)(c-1) = (4-1)(3-1) = 6$. From Table VIII, Appendix A, $\chi^2_{.10} = 10.6446$. The rejection region is $\chi^2 > 10.6446$.

Since the observed value of the test statistic falls in the rejection region ($\chi^2 = 35.409 >$ 10.6446), H_0 is rejected. There is sufficient evidence to indicate that the political strategy of the ethnic groups depends on world region at $\alpha = .10$.

To graph the data, we will first compute the percent of observations in each category of Political Strategy for each World Region. To do this, we divide each cell frequency by the row total and then multiply by 100%. Using SAS, a graph of the data is:

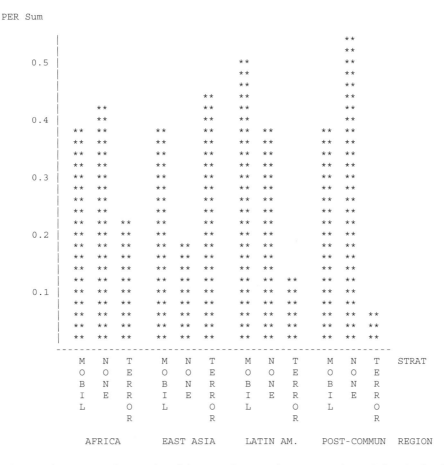

The graph supports the results of the test above. The percents in each level of Political Strategy differs for the different values of World Region.

13.33 First, the values of the variables will be defined.

1. The variable WAR has values 1, 2, and 9. 1 = Support, 2 = Oppose, and 9 = Don't know or refused to answer.
2. The variable INTERNET has values 1, 2, and 9. 1 = Yes, 2 = No, and 9 = Don't know or refused to answer.
3. The variable PARTY has values 1, 2, 3, 4, 5, and 9. 1 = Republican, 2 = Democrat, 3 = Independent, 4 = No preference, 5 = Other, and 9 = Don't know or refused to answer.
4. The variable VET has values 1, 2, 3, 4, and 9. 1 = Yes, I have, 2 = Yes, other household member, 3 = Yes, both, 4 = No, and 9 = Don't know or refused to answer.
5. The variable IDEO has values 1, 2, 3, 4, 5, and 9. 1 = Very conservative, 2 = Conservative, 3 = Moderate, 4 = Liberal, 5 = Very liberal, and 9 = Don't know or refused to answer.
6. The variable RACE has values 1, 2, 3, 4, 5, and 9. 1 = White, 2 = Black or African American, 3 = Asian or Pacific Islander, 4 = Mixed, 5 = Native American, 6 = Other and 9 = Don't know or refused to answer.

7. The variable INCRANGE has values 1, 2, 3, 4, 5, 6, 7, 8, and 9. 1 = <$10,000, 2 = $10,000-under $20,000, 3 = $20,000-under $30,000, 4 = $30,000-under $40,000, 5 = $40,000-under $50,000, 6 = $50,000-under $75,000, 7 = $75,000 to under $100,000, 8 = Over $100,000, and 9 = Don't know or refused to answer.
8. The variable CUMMUNIT has values 1, 2, 3, and 9. 1 = Urban, 2 = Suburban, 3 = Rural, and 9 = Don't know or refused to answer.

To do the analysis, all values of 9 were converted to missing values and are not included in the analysis. Alpha equal to .05 was used for all tests.

WAR versus INTERNET. Using MINITAB, the results of the analyses are:

Tabulated statistics: War, Internet

```
Rows: War   Columns: Internet

                 1         2  Missing      All

1              703       399        4     1102
             77.94     76.29        *    77.33

2              199       124        1      323
             22.06     23.71        *    22.67

Missing         27        38        0        *
                 *         *        *        *

All            902       523        *     1425
            100.00    100.00        *   100.00

Cell Contents:      Count
                    % of Column


Pearson Chi-Square = 0.512, DF = 1, P-Value = 0.474
Likelihood Ratio Chi-Square = 0.510, DF = 1, P-Value = 0.475
```

To determine if Support of Iraq War and access of internet are dependent, we test:

H_0: Support of the Iraq War and access of internet are independent
H_a: Support of the Iraq War and access of internet are dependent

The test statistic is $\chi^2 = .512$ and the p-value is $p = .474$. Since the p-value is not less than $\alpha = .05$, H_0 is not rejected. There is insufficient evidence to indicate that Support of Iraq war and access of internet are dependent at $\alpha = .05$.

WAR versus PARTY. Since only 3 respondents selected "Other" I combined the "Other" group with the "No preference" group" so that the expected counts in all cells are at least 5. Using MINITAB, the results of the analyses are:

Tabulated statistics: War, Party

```
Rows: War   Columns: Party

                1       2       3       4  Missing     All

1             451     262     315      53       25    1081
            95.55   60.23   73.77   80.30        *   77.21

2              21     173     112      13        5     319
             4.45   39.77   26.23   19.70        *   22.79

Missing         8      27      21       5        4       *
                *       *       *       *        *       *

All           472     435     427      66        *    1400
           100.00  100.00  100.00  100.00        *  100.00

Cell Contents:       Count
                     % of Column


Pearson Chi-Square = 164.761, DF = 3, P-Value = 0.000
Likelihood Ratio Chi-Square = 189.289, DF = 3, P-Value = 0.000
```

To determine if Support of Iraq War and Party are dependent, we test:

H_0: Support of the Iraq War and Party are independent
H_a: Support of the Iraq War and Party are dependent

The test statistic is $\chi^2 = 164.761$ and the p-value is $p = 0.000$. Since the p-value is less than $\alpha = .05$, H_0 is rejected. There is sufficient evidence to indicate that Support of Iraq war and Party are dependent at $\alpha = .05$.

If you look at the column percents in the above table, we see that 95.55% of the Republicans support the Iraq War, while only 60.23% of Democrats support the Iraq War. In addition, 73.33% of the Independents support the war and 80.3% of those with no preference or other support the war.

WAR versus VET. Using MINITAB, the results of the analyses are:

Tabulated statistics: War, vet

```
Rows: War    Columns: vet

                  1        2        3        4   Missing      All

1               209      237       27      631         2     1104
              84.27    76.45    77.14    75.66         *    77.37

2                39       73        8      203         1      323
              15.73    23.55    22.86    24.34         *    22.63

Missing           6       15        0       44         0        *
                  *        *        *        *         *        *

All             248      310       35      834         *     1427
             100.00   100.00   100.00   100.00         *   100.00

Cell Contents:        Count
                      % of Column


Pearson Chi-Square = 8.295, DF = 3, P-Value = 0.040
Likelihood Ratio Chi-Square = 8.858, DF = 3, P-Value = 0.031
```

To determine if Support of Iraq War and Veteran status are dependent, we test:

H_0: Support of the Iraq War and Veteran status are independent
H_a: Support of the Iraq War and Veteran status are dependent

The test statistic is $\chi^2 = 8.295$ and the p-value is $p = 0.040$. Since the p-value is less than $\alpha = .05$, H_0 is rejected. There is sufficient evidence to indicate that Support of Iraq War and Veteran status are dependent at $\alpha = .05$.

If you look at the column percents in the above table, we see that 84.27% of the veterans support the Iraq War, while 76.45% of those who have a family member who is a veteran support the Iraq War. In addition, 77.14% of those who are vets and have a family member who is a vet support the war and 75.66% of those who are not veterans support the war.

WAR versus IDEO. Using MINITAB, the results of the analyses are:

Tabulated statistics: War, ideo

```
Rows: War    Columns: ideo

                   1        2        3        4        5  Missing       All

1                 52      453      415      102       21       63      1043
               75.36    89.88    78.75    52.85    34.43        *     77.03

2                 17       51      112       91       40       13       311
               24.64    10.12    21.25    47.15    65.57        *     22.97

Missing            2       17       19       11        2       14         *
                   *        *        *        *        *        *         *

All               69      504      527      193       61        *      1354
              100.00   100.00   100.00   100.00   100.00        *    100.00

Cell Contents:       Count
                     % of Column


Pearson Chi-Square = 174.386, DF = 4, P-Value = 0.000
Likelihood Ratio Chi-Square = 161.296, DF = 4, P-Value = 0.000
```

To determine if Support of Iraq War and Political views are dependent, we test:

H_0: Support of the Iraq War and Political views are independent
H_a: Support of the Iraq War and Political views are dependent

The test statistic is $\chi^2 = 174.386$ and the p-value is $p = 0.000$. Since the p-value is less than $\alpha = .05$, H_0 is rejected. There is sufficient evidence to indicate that Support of Iraq War and Political views are dependent at $\alpha = .05$.

If you look at the column percents in the above table, we see that 75.36% of the Very Conservatives support the Iraq War, while 89.88% of the Conservatives support the Iraq War. In addition, 78.75% of Moderates support the war, 52.85% of Liberals support the war, and 34.43% of the Very Liberals support the war.

WAR versus RACE. Because there were less than 24 respondents for the race categories Asian/Pacific Islander, Mixed, Native American, and Other, these 4 categories were combined. Using MINITAB, the results of the analyses are:

Tabulated statistics: War, Race

```
Rows: War    Columns: Race

                 1        2        3  Missing      All

1              989       51       54       12     1094
             81.00    46.79    72.97        *    77.92

2              232       58       20       14      310
             19.00    53.21    27.03        *    22.08

Missing         50        9        4        2        *
                 *        *        *        *        *

All            1221      109       74        *     1404
            100.00   100.00   100.00        *   100.00

Cell Contents:       Count
                     % of Column


Pearson Chi-Square = 69.181, DF = 2, P-Value = 0.000
Likelihood Ratio Chi-Square = 57.984, DF = 2, P-Value = 0.000
```

To determine if Support of Iraq War and Race are dependent, we test:

H_0: Support of the Iraq War and Race are independent
H_a: Support of the Iraq War and Race are dependent

The test statistic is $\chi^2 = 69.181$ and the p-value is $p = 0.000$. Since the p-value is less than $\alpha = .05$, H_0 is rejected. There is sufficient evidence to indicate that Support of Iraq War and Race are dependent at $\alpha = .05$.

If you look at the column percents in the above table, we see that 81.00% of the Whites support the Iraq War, while 46.79% of the Blacks support the Iraq War. In addition, 72.96% of the Others support the war.

WAR versus INCRANGE Using MINITAB, the results of the analyses are:

Tabulated statistics: War, incrange

```
Rows: War   Columns: incrange

                 1        2        3        4        5        6        7        8

1               37       79      122      112      103      196      132      134
             61.67    73.15    77.71    77.78    83.06    82.35    77.19    74.03

2               23       29       35       32       21       42       39       47
             38.33    26.85    22.29    22.22    16.94    17.65    22.81    25.97

Missing         12       10        4        9        2        5        2        3
                 *        *        *        *        *        *        *        *

All             60      108      157      144      124      238      171      181
            100.00   100.00   100.00   100.00   100.00   100.00   100.00   100.00

           Missing      All

1              191      915
                 *    77.35

2               56      268
                 *    22.65

Missing         18        *
                 *        *

All              *     1183
                 *   100.00

Cell Contents:        Count
                      % of Column


Pearson Chi-Square = 16.387, DF = 7, P-Value = 0.022
Likelihood Ratio Chi-Square = 15.684, DF = 7, P-Value = 0.028
```

To determine if Support of Iraq War and Income range are dependent, we test:

H_0: Support of the Iraq War and Income range are independent
H_a: Support of the Iraq War and Income range are dependent

The test statistic is $\chi^2 = 16.387$ and the p-value is $p = 0.022$. Since the p-value is less than $\alpha = .05$, H_0 is rejected. There is sufficient evidence to indicate that Support of Iraq War and Income range are dependent at $\alpha = .05$.

If you look at the column percents in the above table, we see that those in the income ranges of $40,000 to under $50,000 and from $50,000 to under $75,000 support the Iraq War the most. Those in the lowest income range and the highest income range tend to not support the Iraq War as much as those in the middle income brackets.

WAR versus COMMUNIT Using MINITAB, the results of the analyses are:

Tabulated statistics: War, communit

```
Rows: War    Columns: communit

               1        2        3      All

1            235      605      266     1106
           69.73    78.27    83.13    77.34

2            102      168       54      324
           30.27    21.73    16.88    22.66

Missing       15       35       15        *
               *        *        *        *

All          337      773      320     1430
          100.00   100.00   100.00   100.00

Cell Contents:      Count
                    % of Column


Pearson Chi-Square = 17.618, DF = 2, P-Value = 0.000
Likelihood Ratio Chi-Square = 17.309, DF = 2, P-Value = 0.000
```

To determine if Support of Iraq War and Community are dependent, we test:

H_0: Support of the Iraq War and Community are independent
H_a: Support of the Iraq War and Community are dependent

The test statistic is $\chi^2 = 17.618$ and the p-value is $p = 0.000$. Since the p-value is less than $\alpha = .05$, H_0 is rejected. There is sufficient evidence to indicate that Support of Iraq War and Community are dependent at $\alpha = .05$.

If you look at the column percents in the above table, we see that 69.73% of those who live in the urban areas support the Iraq War, while 78.27% of those who live in suburban areas support the Iraq War. In addition, 83.13% of those who live in Rural areas support the war.

13.35 a. Using MINITAB, the results of the analyses are:

Tabulated statistics: SHSS, CAHS

```
Using frequencies in Fr

Rows: SHSS    Columns: CAHS

          H        L        M        V       All

H        19        6       14        3        42
      10.02    15.83    14.22     1.94     42.00

L         2       32       14        0        48
      11.45    18.09    16.25     2.22     48.00

M         6       11       14        0        31
       7.39    11.68    10.49     1.43     31.00

V         4        0        2        3         9
       2.15     3.39     3.05     0.42      9.00

All      31       49       44        6       130
      31.00    49.00    44.00     6.00    130.00

Cell Contents:       Count
                     Expected count


Pearson Chi-Square = 60.103, DF = 9
Likelihood Ratio Chi-Square = 59.638, DF = 9

* WARNING * 1 cells with expected counts less than 1
* WARNING * Chi-Square approximation probably invalid

* NOTE * 7 cells with expected counts less than 5
```

From the printout, 7 cells have expected counts less than 5. In order for the test to be valid, all of the cells should have expected counts greater than 5. Thus, we should not proceed with the analysis.

b. Combining the High and Very High categories, the new table is:

		CAHS LEVEL		
		Low	Medium	High/Very High
SHSS: C LEVEL	**Low**	32	14	2
	Medium	11	14	6
	High/Very High	6	16	29

c. The expected cell counts are:

$$\hat{E}_{11} = \frac{r_1 c_1}{n} = \frac{48(49)}{130} = 18.09 \qquad \hat{E}_{21} = \frac{r_2 c_1}{n} = \frac{31(49)}{130} = 11.68$$

$$\hat{E}_{12} = \frac{r_1 c_2}{n} = \frac{48(44)}{130} = 16.25 \qquad \hat{E}_{22} = \frac{r_2 c_2}{n} = \frac{31(44)}{130} = 10.49$$

Categorical Data Analysis

$$\hat{E}_{13} = \frac{r_1 c_3}{n} = \frac{48(37)}{130} = 13.66 \qquad \hat{E}_{23} = \frac{r_2 c_3}{n} = \frac{31(37)}{130} = 8.82$$

$$\hat{E}_{31} = \frac{r_3 c_1}{n} = \frac{51(49)}{130} = 19.22 \qquad \hat{E}_{32} = \frac{r_3 c_2}{n} = \frac{51(44)}{130} = 17.26$$

$$\hat{E}_{33} = \frac{r_3 c_3}{n} = \frac{51(37)}{130} = 14.52$$

Since all of the expected cell counts are now 5 or greater, the assumption is met.

d. To determine whether CAHS Levels and SHSS:C Levels are dependent, we test:

H_0: CAHS Levels and SHSS:C Levels are independent
H_a: CAHS Levels and SHSS:C Levels are dependent

The test statistic is $\chi^2 = \sum\sum \dfrac{[n_{ij} - \hat{E}_{ij}]^2}{\hat{E}_{ij}}$

$$= \frac{(32-18.09)^2}{18.09} + \frac{(14-16.25)^2}{16.25} + \frac{(2-13.66)^2}{13.66} + \frac{(11-11.68)^2}{11.68}$$

$$+ \frac{(14-10.49)^2}{10.49} + \frac{(6-8.82)^2}{8.82} + \frac{(6-19.22)^2}{19.22} + \frac{(16-17.26)^2}{17.26}$$

$$+ \frac{(29-14.52)^2}{14.52} = 46.70$$

The rejection region requires $\alpha = .05$ in the upper tail of the χ^2 distribution with df $= (r-1)(c-1) = (3-1)(3-1) = 4$. From Table VII, Appendix A, $\chi^2_{.05} = 9.48773$. The rejection region is $\chi^2 > 9.48773$.

Since the observed value of the test statistic falls in the rejection region ($\chi^2 = 46.70 > 9.48773$), H_0 is rejected. There is sufficient evidence to indicate that CAHS Levels and SHSS:C Levels are dependent at $\alpha = .05$.

13.37 a. Some preliminary calculations are:

$$\hat{E}_{11} = \frac{r_1 c_1}{n} = \frac{31(24)}{38} = 19.58 \qquad \hat{E}_{12} = \frac{r_1 c_2}{n} = \frac{31(14)}{38} = 11.42$$

$$\hat{E}_{21} = \frac{r_2 c_1}{n} = \frac{7(24)}{38} = 4.42 \qquad \hat{E}_{22} = \frac{r_2 c_2}{n} = \frac{7(14)}{38} = 2.58$$

To determine whether the vaccine is effective in treating the MN strain of HIV, we test:

H_0: Vaccine and MN strain are independent
H_a: Vaccine and MN strain are dependent

The test statistic is $\chi^2 = \sum\sum \frac{[n_{ij} - \hat{E}_{ij}]^2}{\hat{E}_{ij}} = \frac{(22 - 19.58)^2}{19.58} + \frac{(9 - 11.42)^2}{11.42}$

$$+ \frac{(2 - 4.42)^2}{4.42} + \frac{(5 - 2.58)^2}{2.58} = 4.407$$

The rejection region requires $\alpha = .05$ in the upper tail of the χ^2 distribution with df = $(r - 1)(c - 1) = (2 - 1)(2 - 1) = 1$. From Table VIII, Appendix A, $\chi^2_{.05} = 3.84146$. The rejection region is $\chi^2 > 3.84146$.

Since the observed value of the test statistic falls in the rejection region ($\chi^2 = 4.407 > 3.84146$), H_0 is rejected. There is sufficient evidence to indicate that the vaccine is effective in treating the MN strain of HIV at $\alpha = .05$.

b. The necessary assumptions are:

1. The n observed counts are a random sample from the population of interest.

2. The sample size, n, will be large enough so that, for every cell, the expected count, $E(n_{ij})$, will be equal to 5 or more.

For this example, the second assumption is violated. Two of the expected cell counts are less than 5. What we have computed for the test statistic may not have a χ^2 distribution.

c. For this contingency table:

$$p = \frac{\binom{7}{2}\binom{31}{22}}{\binom{38}{24}} = \frac{\frac{7!}{2!5!} \frac{31!}{22!9!}}{\frac{38!}{24!14!}} = .0438$$

d. If vaccine and MN strain are independent, then the proportion of positive results should be relatively the same for both patient groups. In the two tables presented, the proportion of positive results for the vaccinated group is smaller than the proportion for the original table.

For the first table,

$$p = \frac{\binom{7}{1}\binom{31}{23}}{\binom{38}{24}} = \frac{\frac{7!}{1!6!} \frac{31!}{23!8!}}{\frac{38!}{24!14!}} = .0057$$

For the second table:

$$p = \frac{\binom{7}{0}\binom{31}{24}}{\binom{38}{24}} = \frac{\frac{7!}{0!7!} \frac{31!}{24!7!}}{\frac{38!}{24!14!}} = .0003$$

e. The *p*-value for Fisher's exact test is $p = .0438 + .0057 + .0003 = .0498$. Since the *p*-value is small, there is evidence to reject H_0. There is sufficient evidence to indicate that the vaccine is effective in treating the MN strain of HIV at $\alpha > .0498$.

13.39 The statement "Rejecting the null hypothesis in a chi-square test for independence implies that a causal relationship between the two categorical variables exists." is false. If the variables are dependent (reject H_0), it simply implies that they are related. One cannot infer causal relationships from contingency table analysis.

13.41 a. Some preliminary calculations are:

If all the categories are equally likely,

$$p_{1,0} = p_{2,0} = p_{3,0} = p_{4,0} = p_{5,0} = .2$$

$$E_1 = E_2 = E_3 = E_4 = E_5 = np_{1,0} = 150(.2) = 30$$

To determine if the categories are not equally likely, we test:

H_0: $p_1 = p_2 = p_3 = p_4 = p_5 = .2$
H_a: At least one probability is different from .2

The test statistic is $\chi^2 = \sum \dfrac{[n_i - E_i]^2}{E_i}$

$$= \frac{(28-30)^2}{30} + \frac{(35-30)^2}{30} + \frac{(33-30)^2}{30} + \frac{(25-30)^2}{30} + \frac{(29-30)^2}{30} = 2.133$$

The rejection region requires $\alpha = .10$ in the upper tail of the χ^2 distribution with df $= k - 1 = 5 - 1 = 4$. From Table VII, Appendix A, $\chi^2_{.10} = 7.77944$. The rejection region is $\chi^2 > 7.77944$.

Since the observed value of the test statistic does not fall in the rejection region ($\chi^2 = 2.133 \not> 7.77944$), H_0 is not rejected. There is insufficient evidence to indicate the categories are not equally likely at $\alpha = .10$.

b. $\hat{p}_2 = \dfrac{35}{150} = .233$

For confidence coefficient .90, $\alpha = .10$ and $\alpha/2 = .05$. From Table IV, Appendix A, $z_{.05} = 1.645$. The confidence interval is:

$$\hat{p}_2 \pm z_{.05}\sqrt{\frac{\hat{p}_2\hat{q}_2}{n_2}} \Rightarrow .233 \pm 1.645\sqrt{\frac{.233(.767)}{150}} \Rightarrow .233 \pm .057 \Rightarrow (.176, .290)$$

13.43 a. The 2×2 contingency table is:

LLD

Genetic Trait	Yes	No	Total
Yes	21	15	36
No	150	306	456
Total	171	321	492

b. Some preliminary calculations are:

$$\hat{E}_{11} = \frac{r_1 c_1}{n} = \frac{36(171)}{492} = 12.51 \qquad\qquad \hat{E}_{12} = \frac{r_1 c_2}{n} = \frac{36(321)}{492} = 23.49$$

$$\hat{E}_{21} = \frac{r_2 c_1}{n} = \frac{456(171)}{492} = 158.49 \qquad\qquad \hat{E}_{22} = \frac{r_2 c_2}{n} = \frac{456(321)}{492} = 297.51$$

To determine if the genetic trait occurs at a higher rate in LDD patients than in the controls, we test:

H_0: Genetic trait and LDD group are independent
H_a: Genetic trait and LDD group are dependent

The test statistic is $\chi^2 = \sum\sum \dfrac{[n_{ij} - \hat{E}_{ij}]^2}{\hat{E}_{ij}} = \dfrac{(21 - 12.51)^2}{12.51} + \dfrac{(15 - 23.49)}{23.49}$

$$+ \dfrac{(150 - 158.49)^2}{158.49} + \dfrac{(306 - 297.51)^2}{297.51} = 9.52$$

The rejection region requires $\alpha = .01$ in the upper tail of the χ^2 distribution with df $= (r-1)(c-1) = (2-1)(2-1) = 1$. From Table VIII, Appendix A, $\chi^2_{.01} = 6.63490$. The rejection region is $\chi^2 > 6.63491$.

Since the observed value of the test statistic falls in the rejection region ($\chi^2 = 9.52 > 6.63491$), H_0 is rejected. There is sufficient evidence to indicate that the genetic trait occurs at a higher rate in LDD patients than in the controls at $\alpha = .01$.

c. To construct a bar graph, we will first compute the proportion of LDD/Control patients that have the genetic trait. Of the LLD patients, $21 / 171 = .123$ have the trait. For the Controls, $15 / 321 = .043$. The bar graph is:

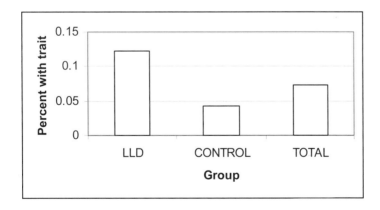

Because the bars are not close to being the same height, it indicates that the genetic trait appears at a higher rate among LLD patients than among the controls. This supports the conclusion of the test in part **b**.

13.45 **a.** No. In a multinomial experiment, each trial results in one of $k = 8$ possible outcomes. In this experiment, each trial cannot result in one of all of the eight possible outcomes. The people are assigned to a particular diet before the experiment. Once the people are assigned to a particular diet, there are only two possible outcomes, cancer tumors or no cancer tumors.

b. The expected cell counts are:

$$\hat{E}_{11} = \frac{r_1 c_1}{n} = \frac{80(30)}{120} = 20 \qquad \hat{E}_{21} = \frac{r_2 c_1}{n} = \frac{40(30)}{120} = 10$$

$$\hat{E}_{12} = \frac{r_1 c_2}{n} = \frac{80(30)}{120} = 20 \qquad \hat{E}_{22} = \frac{r_2 c_2}{n} = \frac{40(30)}{120} = 10$$

$$\hat{E}_{13} = \frac{r_1 c_3}{n} = \frac{80(30)}{120} = 20 \qquad \hat{E}_{23} = \frac{r_2 c_3}{n} = \frac{40(30)}{120} = 10$$

$$\hat{E}_{14} = \frac{r_1 c_4}{n} = \frac{80(30)}{120} = 20 \qquad \hat{E}_{24} = \frac{r_2 c_4}{n} = \frac{40(30)}{120} = 10$$

c. The test statistic is $\chi^2 = \sum\sum \dfrac{[n_{ij} - \hat{E}_{ij}]^2}{\hat{E}_{ij}}$

$$= \frac{(27-20)^2}{20} + \frac{(20-20)^2}{20} + \frac{(19-20)}{20} + \frac{(14-20)^2}{20} + \frac{(3-10)^2}{10} + \frac{(10-10)^2}{10}$$

$$+ \frac{(11-10)^2}{10} + \frac{(16-10)^2}{10} = 12.9$$

d. To determine if diet and presence/absence of cancer are independent, we test:

H_0: Diet and presence/absence of cancer are independent
H_a: Diet and presence/absence of cancer are dependent

The test statistic is $\chi^2 = 12.9$ (from part c).

The rejection region requires $\alpha = .05$ in the upper tail of the χ^2 distribution with df = $(r-1)(c-1) = (2-1)(4-1) = 3$. From Table VII, Appendix A, $\chi^2_{.05} = 7.81473$. The rejection region is $\chi^2 > 7.81473$.

Since the observed value of the test statistic falls in the rejection region ($\chi^2 = 12.9 > 7.81473$), H_0 is rejected. There is sufficient evidence to indicate that diet and presence/absence of cancer are dependent for $\alpha = .05$.

e. $\hat{p}_1 = 27/30 = .9$; $\hat{p}_2 = 20/30 = .667$

For confidence coefficient .95, $\alpha = .05$ and $\alpha/2 = .05/2 = .025$. From Table IV, Appendix A, $z_{.025} = 1.96$. The confidence interval is:

$$(\hat{p}_1 - \hat{p}_2) \pm z_{.025} \sqrt{\frac{\hat{p}_1 \hat{q}_1}{n_1} + \frac{\hat{p}_2 \hat{q}_2}{n_1}} \Rightarrow (.900 - .667) \pm 1.96 \sqrt{\frac{.900(.100)}{30} + \frac{.667(.333)}{30}}$$

$$\Rightarrow .233 \pm .200 \Rightarrow (.033, .433)$$

We are 95% confident that the difference in the percentage of rats on a high fat/no fiber diet with cancer and the percentage of rats on a high fat/fiber diet with cancer is between 3.3% and 43.3%.

13.47   a.   Some preliminary calculations:

$$E_1 = np_{1,0} = 28(.25) = 7$$
$$E_2 = np_{2,0} = 28(.25) = 7$$
$$E_3 = np_{3,0} = 28(.25) = 7$$
$$E_4 = np_{4,0} = 28(.25) = 7$$

To determine if the true proportions of intellectually disabled elderly patients in each of the hearing loss categories differ, we test:

H_0: $p_1 = p_2 = p_3 = p_4 = .25$
H_a: At least one p_i differs from .25, $i = 1, 2, 3, 4$

The test statistic is $\chi^2 = \sum \dfrac{[n_i - E_i]^2}{E_i} = \dfrac{(7-7)^2}{7} + \dfrac{(7-7)^2}{7} + \dfrac{(9-7)^2}{7} + \dfrac{(5-7)^2}{7}$
$$= 1.143$$

The rejection region requires $\alpha = .05$ in the upper tail of the χ^2 distribution with df $= k - 1 = 4 - 1 = 3$. From Table VII, Appendix A, $\chi^2_{.05} = 7.81473$. The rejection region is $\chi^2 > 7.81473$.

Since the observed value of the test statistic does not fall in the rejection region ($\chi^2 = 1.143 \not> 7.81473$), H_0 is not rejected. There is insufficient evidence to indicate that at least one of the true proportions of intellectually disabled elderly patients in each of the hearing loss categories differs at $\alpha = .05$.

   b. $\hat{p} = \dfrac{x}{n} = \dfrac{5}{28} = .179$

For confidence coefficient .90; $\alpha = .10$ and $\alpha/2 = .10/2 = .05$. From Table IV, Appendix A, $z_{.05} = 1.645$. The confidence interval is

$$\hat{p} \pm z_{.05} \sqrt{\dfrac{\hat{p}\hat{q}}{n}}$$
$$\Rightarrow .179 \pm 1.645 \sqrt{\dfrac{(.179)(1-.179)}{28}}$$
$$\Rightarrow .179 \pm .119$$
$$\Rightarrow (.060, .298)$$

We are 90% confident that the true proportion of disabled elderly patients with severe hearing loss is between .060 and .298.

Categorical Data Analysis

13.49   Using MINITAB, the contingency table analysis is:

Tabulated statistics: Ebert, Roeper

```
Rows: Ebert    Columns: Roeper

             DOWN       UP      All

DOWN           50       28       78
             64.10    35.90   100.00
             60.98    20.59    35.78

UP             32      108      140
             22.86    77.14   100.00
             39.02    79.41    64.22

All            82      136      218
             37.61    62.39   100.00
            100.00   100.00   100.00

Cell Contents:       Count
                     % of Row
                     % of Column


Pearson Chi-Square = 36.314, DF = 1, P-Value = 0.000
Likelihood Ratio Chi-Square = 36.343, DF = 1, P-Value = 0.000
```

To determine whether the movie reviews of the two critics are independent, we test:

H_0: The movie reviews of Ebert and Roeper are independent
H_a: The movie reviews of Ebert and Roeper are dependent

The test statistic is $\chi^2 = 36.314$ (from the printout)

The p-value is $p = 0.000$. Since the p-value is less than $\alpha = .05$, H_0 is rejected. There is sufficient evidence to indicate that the movie reviews of Ebert and Roeper are not independent at $\alpha = .05$.

13.51   Some preliminary calculations are:

If the strategies are equally preferred, $p_{1,0} = p_{2,0} = p_{3,0} = p_{4,0} = p_{5,0} = .2$

$E_1 = E_2 = E_3 = E_4 = E_5 = np = 100(.2) = 20$

To determine if there is a preference for one or more of the strategies, we test:

H_0: $p_1 = p_2 = p_3 = p_4 = p_5 = .2$
H_a: At least one probability differs from .2

The test statistic is $\chi^2 = \sum \dfrac{[n_i - E_i]^2}{E_i}$

$$= \frac{(17-20)^2}{20} + \frac{(27-20)^2}{20} + \frac{(22-20)^2}{20} + \frac{(15-20)^2}{20} + \frac{(19-20)^2}{20} = 4.4$$

The rejection region requires $\alpha = .05$ in the upper tail of the χ^2 distribution with df $= k - 1 = 5 - 1 = 4$. From Table VII, Appendix A, $\chi^2_{.05} = 9.48773$. The rejection region is $\chi^2 > 9.48773$.

Since the observed value of the test statistic does not fall in the rejection region ($\chi^2 = 4.4 \not> 9.48773$), H_0 is not rejected. There is insufficient evidence to indicate one of the strategies is preferred over any of the others at $\alpha = .05$.

13.53   Some preliminary calculations are:

$$\hat{E}_{11} = \frac{r_1 c_1}{n} = \frac{12(10)}{24} = 5 \qquad\qquad \hat{E}_{12} = \frac{r_1 c_2}{n} = \frac{12(14)}{24} = 7$$

$$\hat{E}_{21} = \frac{r_2 c_1}{n} = \frac{12(10)}{24} = 5 \qquad\qquad \hat{E}_{22} = \frac{r_2 c_2}{n} = \frac{12(14)}{24} = 7$$

To determine if a relationship exists between food choice and whether or not chickadees fed on gypsy moth eggs, we test:

H_0: Food choice and whether or not chickadees fed on gypsy moth eggs are independent
H_a: Food choice and whether or not chickadees fed on gypsy moth eggs are dependent

The test statistic is $\chi^2 = \displaystyle\sum\sum \frac{[n_{ij} - \hat{E}_{ij}]^2}{\hat{E}_{ij}}$

$$= \frac{(2-5)^2}{5} + \frac{(10-7)^2}{7} + \frac{(8-5)^2}{5} + \frac{(4-7)^2}{7} = 6.171$$

The rejection region requires $\alpha = .10$ in the upper tail of the χ^2 distribution with df $= (r-1)(c-1) = (2-1)(2-1) = 1$. From Table VII, Appendix A, $\chi^2_{.10} = 2.70554$. The rejection region is $\chi^2 > 2.70554$.

Since the observed value of the test statistic falls in the rejection region ($\chi^2 = 6.171 > 2.70554$), H_0 is rejected. There is sufficient evidence to indicate that a relationship exists between food choice and whether or not chickadees fed on gypsy moth eggs at $\alpha = .10$.

13.55 a. Calculate $\hat{E}_{ij} = \dfrac{r_i c_j}{n}$ for $i = 1, 2, 3, 4, 5$, and $j = 1, 2, 3, 4, 5$.

The expected values for each cell in the table is summarized below.

Observed and Estimated Expected (in Parentheses) Counts

| | | Wife's Lifestyle | | | | | |
		Pleasing	Outdoing	Avoiding	Control	Achieving	Totals
	Pleasing	9 (5.88)	6 (6.70)	6 (6.21)	3 (8.17)	9 (6.04)	33
	Outdoing	7 (8.20)	11 (9.34)	12 (8.65)	11 (11.39)	5 (8.43)	46
	Avoiding	8 (6.77)	8 (7.71)	6 (7.15)	11 (9.41)	5 (6.96)	38
Husband's Lifestyle	**Control**	8 (9.09)	10 (10.35)	7 (9.59)	15 (12.62)	11 (9.34)	51
	Achieving	4 (6.06)	6 (6.90)	7 (6.40)	10 (8.42)	7 (6.23)	34
	Totals	36	41	38	50	37	202

The test is: H_0: The wife's lifestyle types and the husband's lifestyle types are independent.
H_a: The wife's lifestyle types and the husband's lifestyle types are dependent.

The test statistic is $\chi^2 = \sum\sum \dfrac{[n_{ij} - \hat{E}_{ij}]^2}{\hat{E}_{ij}}$

$$= \dfrac{(9 - 5.88)^2}{5.88} + \dfrac{(6 - 6.70)^2}{6.70} + \cdots + \dfrac{(10 - 8.42)^2}{8.42} + \dfrac{(7 - 6.23)^2}{6.23}$$
$$= 13.715$$

Since no α is given we will use $\alpha = .05$. The rejection region requires $\alpha = .05$ in the upper tail of the χ^2 distribution with df $= (r - 1)(c - 1) = 4(4) = 16$. From Table VII, Appendix A, $\chi^2_{.05} = 26.2962$. The rejection region is $\chi^2 > 26.2962$.

Since the observed value of the test statistic does not fall in the rejection region ($\chi^2 = 13.715 \not> 26.2962$), H_0 is not rejected. There is insufficient evidence to indicate that the wife's lifestyle types and the husband's lifestyle types are dependent at $\alpha = .05$.

b. There are two tests:

Wife

To determine if there are differences in the proportions of wives who fall into the five personality profiles, we test:

H_0: $p_1 = p_2 = p_3 = p_4 = p_5 = .20$
H_a: At least one of the proportions differs from .20.

where
p_1 = proportion of all wives that are pleasing
p_2 = proportion of all wives that are outstanding
p_3 = proportion of all wives that are avoiding
p_4 = proportion of all wives that are controlling
p_5 = proportion of all wives that are achieving

$E_1 = E_2 = E_3 = E_4 = E_5 = 202(.2) = 40.4$

The test statistic is $\chi^2 = \sum \dfrac{[n_i - E_i]^2}{E_i}$

$$= \frac{(36-40.4)^2}{40.4} + \frac{(41-40.4)^2}{40.4} + \frac{(38-40.4)^2}{40.4} + \frac{(50-40.4)^2}{40.4} + \frac{(37-40.4)^2}{40.4}$$
$$= 3.198$$

Since no α is given, we will use $\alpha = .05$. The rejection region is $\chi^2 > 9.48773$ for df $= k - 1 = 5 - 1 = 4$. Since the observed value of the test statistic does not fall in the rejection region ($\chi^2 = 3.198 \not> 9.48773$), do not reject H_0. There is insufficient evidence to indicate that a difference exists in the proportions of wives who fall in the five personality profiles at $\alpha = .05$.

Husband

To determine if there are differences in the proportions of wives who fall into the five personality profiles, we test:

H_0: $p_1 = p_2 = p_3 = p_4 = p_5 = .20$
H_a: At least one of the proportions differs from .20.

where
p_1 = proportion of all husbands that are pleasing
p_2 = proportion of all husbands that are outdoing
p_3 = proportion of all husbands that are avoiding
p_4 = proportion of all husbands that are controlling
p_5 = proportion of all husbands that are achieving

$E_1 = E_2 = E_3 = E_4 = E_5 = 202(.2) = 40.4$

The test statistic is $\chi^2 = \sum \frac{[n_i - E_i]^2}{E_i}$

$$= \frac{(33 - 40.4)^2}{40.4} + \frac{(46 - 40.4)^2}{40.4} + \frac{(38 - 40.4)^2}{40.4} + \frac{(51 - 40.4)^2}{40.4} + \frac{(34 - 40.4)^2}{40.4}$$

$$= 6.069$$

Using $\alpha = .05$, in the rejection region is $\chi^2 > 9.48773$ for df $= k - 1 = 5 - 1 = 4$. Since the observed value of the test statistic does not fall in the rejection region ($\chi^2 = 6.069 \not> 9.48773$), do not reject H_0. There is insufficient evidence to indicate that a difference exists in the proportions of husbands who fall in the five personality profiles at $\alpha = .05$.

13.57   a. $\chi^2 = \sum \frac{[n_i - E_i]^2}{E_i}$

$$= \frac{(26 - 23)^2}{23} + \frac{(146 - 136)^2}{136} + \frac{(361 - 341)^2}{341} + \frac{(143 - 136)^2}{136} + \frac{(13 - 23)^2}{23}$$

$$= 9.647$$

b.   From Table VII, Appendix A, with df $= 5$, $\chi^2_{.05} = 11.0705$

c.   No. $\chi^2 = 9.647 \not> 11.0705$. Do not reject H_0. There is insufficient evidence to indicate the salary distribution is nonnormal for $\alpha = .05$.

d.   The p-value $= P(\chi^2 \geq 9.647)$.

Using Table VII, Appendix A, with df $= 5$,

$$.05 < P(\chi^2 \geq 9.647) < .10.$$

13.59   Using MINITAB, the results of the analyses are:

Tabulated statistics: Candidate, Time

```
Using frequencies in Fr


Rows: Candidate    Columns: Time

                 1        2        3        4        5        6      All

Coppin          55       51      109       98       88      104      505
             13.89    13.56    13.37    13.98    14.08    14.04    13.82
              54.7     52.0    112.6     96.9     86.4    102.4    505.0

Montes         133      117      255      211      186      227     1129
             33.59    31.12    31.29    30.10    29.76    30.63    30.90
             122.4    116.2    251.8    216.6    193.1    229.0   1129.0

Smith          208      208      451      392      351      410     2020
             52.53    55.32    55.34    55.92    56.16    55.33    55.28
             218.9    207.9    450.5    387.5    345.5    409.6   2020.0

All            396      376      815      701      625      741     3654
            100.00   100.00   100.00   100.00   100.00   100.00   100.00
             396.0    376.0    815.0    701.0    625.0    741.0   3654.0


Cell Contents:       Count
                     % of Column
                     Expected count

Pearson Chi-Square = 2.284, DF = 10, P-Value = 0.994
Likelihood Ratio Chi-Square = 2.272, DF = 10, P-Value = 0.994
```

To determine if time period and votes received by the candidates are independent, we test:

H_0: Votes received by candidates and time period are independent
H_a: Votes received by candidates and time period are dependent

The test statistic is $\chi^2 = 2.284$.   (from printout)

The p-value is $p = .994$. Since the p-value is so large, H_0 would not be rejected for any reasonable value of α. There is insufficient evidence to indicate that the votes received by the candidates are dependent on the time period. In other words, there is no evidence that the percentages of votes received by the candidates change over time. If one looks at the column percentages (the second number in each cell above), the values are very similar for each time period.

A graph of the column percents is:

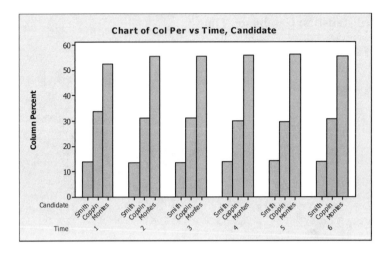

As one can see from the graph, the percent of votes received by the candidates are essentially the same for each time period.

All of the above indicates that the probability of a candidate receiving votes is independent of the time period. However, this does not necessarily imply a rigged election. If each time period is considered a random sample of voters, then the percentage of votes received by each candidate should be similar to the actual percentage of voters who favor each candidate.

Nonparametric Statistics

14.1   The sign test is preferred to the t-test when the population from which the sample is selected is not normal.

14.3   a. $P(x \geq 6) = 1 \leq P(x - 5) = 1 - .937 = .063$

b. $P(x \geq 5) = 1 \leq P(x - 4) = 1 - .500 = .500$

c. $P(x \geq 8) = 1 \leq P(x - 7) = 1 - .996 = .004$

d. $P(x \geq 10) = 1 \leq P(x - 9) = 1 - .849 = .151$

$\mu = np = 15(.5) = 7.5$ and $\sigma = \sqrt{npq} = \sqrt{15(.5)(.5)} = 1.9365$

$P(x \geq 10) \approx P\left(z \geq \dfrac{(10 - .5) - 7.5}{1.9365}\right) = P(z \geq 1.03) = .5 - .3485 = .1515$

e. $P(x \geq 15) = 1 \leq P(x \leq 14) = 1 - .788 = .212$

$\mu = np = 25(.5) = 12.5$ and $\sigma = \sqrt{npq} = \sqrt{25(.5)(.5)} = 2.5$

$P(x \geq 15) \approx P\left(z \geq \dfrac{(15 - .5) - 12.5}{2.5}\right) = P(z \geq .80) = .5 - .2881 = .2119$

14.5   To determine if the median is greater than 80, we test:

H_0: $\eta = 80$
H_a: $\eta > 80$

The test statistic is S = number of measurements greater than 80 = 16.

The p-value = $P(x \geq 16)$ where x is a binomial random variable with $n = 25$ and $p = .5$. From Table II,

p-value = $P(x \geq 16) = 1 - P(x \leq 15) = 1 - .885 = .115$

Since the p-value = $.115 > \alpha = .10$, H_0 is not rejected. There is insufficient evidence to indicate the median is greater than 80 at $\alpha = .10$.

We must assume the sample was randomly selected from a continuous probability distribution.

Note: Since $n \geq 10$, we could use the large-sample approximation.

14.7   To determine if the median cesium amount of lichen differs from .003, we test:

H_0: $\eta = .003$
H_a: $\eta \neq .003$

The test statistic is $S = \{$number of observations greater than .003$\} = 8$ (from printout). The p-value is $p = .0391$. Since the p-value is less than $\alpha = .10$, H_0 is rejected. There is sufficient evidence to indicate the median cesium amount of lichen differs from .003 at $\alpha = .10$.

This result agrees with the t-test in Exercise 8.65.

14.9   a.   To determine if the median daily ammonia concentration for all afternoon drive-time days exceeds 1.5 ppm, we test:

H_0: $\eta = 1.5$
H_a: $\eta > 1.5$

b.   The test statistic is $S = $ number of measurements greater than $1.5 = 3$.

c.   The p-value $= P(x \geq 3)$ where x is a binomial random variable with $n = 8$ and $p = .5$. From Table II, Appendix A,

$P(x \geq 3) = 1 - P(x \leq 2) = 1 - .145 = .855$.

d.   Sine the p-value is greater than α $(p = .855 > .05)$, H_0 is not rejected. There is insufficient evidence to indicate that the median daily ammonia concentration for all afternoon drive-time days exceeds 1.5 ppm at $\alpha = .05$.

14.11   a.   To determine whether the median biting rate is higher in bright, sunny weather, we test:

H_0: $\eta = 5$
H_a: $\eta > 5$

b.   The test statistic is $z = \dfrac{(S - .5) - .5n}{.5\sqrt{n}} = \dfrac{(95 - .5) - .5(122)}{.5\sqrt{122}} = 6.07$
(where $S = $ number of observations greater than 5)

The p-value is $p = P(z \geq 6.07)$. From Table IV, Appendix A, $p = P(z \geq 6.07) \approx 0.0000$.

c.   Since the observed p-value is less than α $(p = 0.0000 < .01)$, H_0 is rejected. There is sufficient evidence to indicate that the median biting rate in bright, sunny weather is greater than 5 at $\alpha = .01$.

14.13   a.   To determine whether the median is less than $2.25, we test:

H_0: $\eta = 2.25$
H_a: $\eta < 2.25$

The test statistic is $z = \dfrac{(S - .5) - .5n}{.5\sqrt{n}}$

$= \dfrac{(50 - .5) - .5(80)}{.5\sqrt{80}}$

$= 2.12$

(where S = number of observations less than 2.25)

The p-value is $p = P(z \geq 2.12)$. From Table IV, Appendix A, $p = P(z \geq 2.12) = .5 - .4830$ $= .0170$. Therefore, reject H_0 for $\alpha > .017$ and conclude that the median amount spent for hamburgers at lunch at McDonald's is less than \$2.25.

b. No; The sample was taken from only two restaurants in Boston.

c. The distribution of the prices is continuous. Nothing is assumed about the shape of the probability distribution.

14.15 The statement "If the rank sum for sample 1 is much larger than the rank sum for sample 2 when $n_1 = n_2$, then the distribution of population 1 is likely to be shifted to the right of the distribution of population 2." is true.

14.17 a. The test statistic is T_1, the rank sum of population A (because $n_1 < n_2$).

The rejection region is $T_1 \leq 41$ or $T_1 \geq 71$, from Table XII, Appendix A, with $n_1 = 7$, $n_2 = 8$, and $\alpha = .10$.

b. The test statistic is T_1, the rank sum of population A (because $n_1 = n_2$).

The rejection region is $T_1 \geq 50$, from Table XII, Appendix A, with $n_1 = 6$, $n_2 = 6$, and $\alpha = .05$.

c. The test statistic is T_1, the rank sum of population A (because $n_1 < n_2$).

The rejection region is $T_1 \leq 43$, from Table XII, Appendix A, with $n_1 = 7$, $n_2 = 10$, and $\alpha = .025$.

d. Since $n_1 = n_2 = 20$, the test statistic is $z = \dfrac{T_1 - \dfrac{n_1(n_1 + n_2 + 1)}{2}}{\sqrt{\dfrac{n_1 n_2 (n_1 + n_2 + 1)}{12}}}$

The rejection region is $z < -z_{\alpha/2}$ or $z > z_{\alpha/2}$. For $\alpha = .05$ and $\alpha/2 = .05/2 = .025$, $z_{.025} = 1.96$ from Table IV, Appendix A. The rejection region is $z < -1.96$ or $z > 1.96$.

14.19 H_0: The probability distributions of treatments A and B are identical
        H_a: The probability distribution of treatment A lies to the left of that for treatment B

The test statistic is

$$z = \frac{T_1 - \frac{n_2(n_1 + n_2 + 1)}{2}}{\sqrt{\frac{n_1 n_2(n_1 + n_2 + 1)}{12}}} = \frac{173 - \frac{15(15 + 15 + 1)}{2}}{\sqrt{\frac{15(15)(15 + 15 + 1)}{12}}} = \frac{-59.5}{24.1091} = -2.47$$

The rejection region requires $\alpha = .05$ in the lower tail of the z distribution. From Table IV, Appendix A, $z_{.05} = 1.645$. The rejection region is $z < -1.645$.

Since the observed value of the test statistic falls in the rejection region ($-2.47 < -1.645$), H_0 is rejected. There is sufficient evidence to conclude that distribution A is shifted to the left of distribution B for $\alpha = .05$.

14.21

Sample from Population 1 (A)	Rank	Sample from Population 2 (B)	Rank
15	13	5	2.5
10	8.5	12	10.5
12	10.5	9	6.5
16	14	9	6.5
13	12	8	4.5
8	4.5	4	1
	$T_1 = 62.5$	5	2.5
		10	8.5
			$T_2 = 42.5$

a. H_0: The two sampled populations have identical probability distributions
     H_a: The probability distribution for population A is shifted to the left or to the right of that for B

The test statistic is $T_1 = 62.5$ since sample A has the smallest number of measurements.

The null hypothesis will be rejected if $T_1 \leq T_L$ or $T_1 \geq T_U$ where T_L and T_U correspond to $\alpha = .05$ (two-tailed), $n_1 = 6$ and $n_2 = 8$. From Table XII, Appendix A, $T_L = 29$ and $T_U = 61$.

   Reject H_0 if $T_1 \leq 29$ or $T_1 \geq 61$.

Since $T_1 = 62.5 \geq 61$, we reject H_0 and conclude there is sufficient evidence to indicate population A is shifted to the left or right of population B at $\alpha = .05$.

b. H_0: The two sampled populations have identical probability distributions
     H_a: The probability distribution for population A is shifted to the right of population B

The test statistic remains $T_1 = 62.5$.

The null hypothesis will be rejected if $T_1 \geq T_U$ where T_U corresponds to $\alpha = .05$ (one-tailed), $n_1 = 6$ and $n_2 = 8$. From Table XII, Appendix A, $T_U = 58$.

Reject H_0 if $T_1 \geq 58$.

Since $T_1 = 62.5 \geq 58$, we reject H_0 and conclude there is sufficient evidence to indicate population A is shifted to the right of population B at $\alpha = .05$.

14.23   a.   To determine if the distribution of FNE scores for bulimic students is shifted above the corresponding distribution for female students with normal eating habits, we test:

H_0: The distribution of FNE scores for bulimic students is the same as the corresponding distribution for female students with normal eating habits

H_a: The distribution of FNE scores for bulimic students is shifted above the corresponding distribution for female students with normal eating habits

b.   The data ranked are:

Bulimic Students	Rank	Normal Students	Rank
21	21.5	13	8.5
13	8.5	6	1
10	4.5	16	13.5
20	19.5	13	8.5
25	25	8	3
19	17	19	17
16	13.5	23	23
21	21.5	18	15
24	24	11	6
13	8.5	19	17
14	11	7	2
		10	4.5
	$T_1 = 174.5$	15	12
		20	19.5
			$T_2 = 150.5$

c.   The sum of the ranks of the 11 FNE scores for bulimic students is $T_1 = 174.5$.

d.   The sum of the ranks of the 14 FNE scores for normal students is $T_2 = 150.5$.

The test statistic is $z = \dfrac{T_1 - \dfrac{n_1(n_1 + n_2 + 1)}{2}}{\sqrt{\dfrac{n_1 n_2 (n_1 + n_2 + 1)}{12}}} = \dfrac{174.5 - \dfrac{11(11 + 14 + 1)}{2}}{\sqrt{\dfrac{11(14)(11 + 14 + 1)}{12}}} = 1.72$

The rejection region requires $\alpha = .10$ in the upper tail of the z distribution. From Table IV, Appendix A, $z_{.10} = 1.28$. The rejection region is $z > 1.28$.

f. Since the observed value of the test statistic falls in the rejection region ($z = 1.72 > 1.28$), H_0 is rejected. There is sufficient evidence to indicate that the distribution of FNE scores for bulimic students is shifted above the corresponding distribution for female students with normal eating habits at $\alpha = .10$.

14.25 a.

Deaf Children	Rank	Hearing Children	Rank
2.75	18	1.15	1
3.14	19	1.65	6
3.23	20	1.43	4
2.30	15	1.83	8.5
2.64	17	1.75	7
1.95	10	1.23	2
2.17	13	2.03	12
2.45	16	1.64	5
1.83	8.5	1.96	11
2.23	14	1.37	3
	$T_1 = 150.5$		$T_2 = 59.5$

H_0: The probability distributions of eye movement rates are identical for deaf and hearing children

H_a: The probability distribution of eye movement rates for deaf children lies to the right of that for hearing children

The test statistic can be either T_1 or T_2 since the sample sizes are equal. Use $T_1 = 150.5$.

The null hypothesis will be rejected if $T_1 \geq T_U$ where $\alpha = .05$ (one-tailed), $n_1 = 10$ and $n_2 = 10$. From Table XII, Appendix A, $T_U = 127$.

Reject H_0 if $T_1 \geq 127$.

Since $T_1 = 150.5 \geq 127$, we reject H_0. There is sufficient evidence to indicate that deaf children have greater visual acuity than hearing children at $\alpha = .05$.

b. H_0: The probability distributions of eye movement rates are identical for deaf and hearing children

H_a: The probability distribution of eye movement rates for deaf children lies to the right of that for hearing children

The test statistic is $z = \dfrac{T_1 - \dfrac{n_1(n_1 + n_2 + 1)}{2}}{\sqrt{\dfrac{n_1 n_2 (n_1 + n_2 + 1)}{12}}} = \dfrac{150.5 - \dfrac{10(10 + 10 + 1)}{2}}{\sqrt{\dfrac{10(10)(10 + 10 + 1)}{12}}} = 3.44$

The rejection region requires $\alpha = .05$ in the upper tail of the z distribution. From Table IV, Appendix A, $z_{.05} = 1.645$. The rejection region is $z > 1.645$.

Since the observed value of the test statistic falls in the rejection region ($z = 3.44 > 1.645$), H_0 is rejected. There is sufficient evidence to support the psychologist's claim that deaf children have greater visual acuity than hearing children at $\alpha = .05$.

The results agree with those found in part a.

14.27 a. The Students' t procedure requires that the populations sampled from be normal. The distributions of the zinc measurements in the 3 locations may not be normal.

   b. The ranks of the observations and the sums for the two groups are:

Text-line	Rank	Intersection	Rank
.335	4	.393	7
.374	6	.353	5
.440	8	.285	1
		.295	2
		.319	3
	$T_1 = 18$		$T_2 = 18$

To determine if the distributions of zinc measurements for the text-line and the intersection have different centers of location, we test:

H_0: The distributions of zinc measurements for the text-line and the intersection are identical

H_a: The distribution of zinc measurements for the text-line is shifted to the right or left of that for the intersection

The test statistic is $T_1 = 18$.

The null hypothesis will be rejected if $T_1 \leq T_L$ or $T_1 \geq T_U$ where $\alpha = .05$ (two-tailed), $n_1 = 3$ and $n_2 = 5$. From Table XII, Appendix A, $T_L = 6$ and $T_U = 21$. The rejection region is $T_1 \leq 6$ or $T_1 \geq 21$.

Since the observed value of the test statistic does not fall in the rejection region ($T_1 \nleq 6$ and $T_1 \ngeq 21$), H_0 is not rejected. There is insufficient evidence to indicate the distributions of zinc measurements for the text-line and the intersection have different centers of location at $\alpha = .05$.

c.	The ranks of the observations and the sums for the two groups are:

Witness-line	Rank	Intersection	Rank
.210	2	.393	9
.262	3	.353	8
.188	1	.285	4
.329	7	.295	5
.439	11	.319	6
.397	10		
	$T_1 = 34$		$T_2 = 32$

To determine if the distributions of zinc measurements for the witness-line and the intersection have different centers of location, we test:

H_0: The distributions of zinc measurements for the witness-line and the intersection are identical

H_a: The distribution of zinc measurements for the witness-line is shifted to the right or left of that for the intersection

The test statistic is $T_2 = 32$.

The null hypothesis will be rejected if $T_2 \le T_L$ or $T_2 \ge T_U$ where $\alpha = .05$ (two-tailed), $n_1 = 6$ and $n_2 = 5$. From Table XII, Appendix A, $T_L = 19$ and $T_U = 41$. The rejection region is $T_2 \le 19$ or $T_2 \ge 41$.

Since the observed value of the test statistic does not fall in the rejection region ($T_2 \not\le 19$ and $T_2 \not\ge 41$), H_0 is not rejected. There is insufficient evidence to indicate the distributions of zinc measurements for the witness-line and the intersection have different centers of location at $\alpha = .05$.

d.	The median zinc score for the Text-line is .374. The median zinc score for the Witness-line is .296. The median zinc score for the Intersection is .319. We found no difference in the distributions of zinc scores between the Text-line and the Intersection. We also found no difference in the distributions of zinc scores between the Witness-line and the Intersection. However, we did not compare the Text-line and the Witness-line zinc scores. These two distributions appear to be the furthest apart.

14.29	a.	Since the data can take on a very limited number of values, the data are probably not from a normal distribution.

b.   Using SAS, the output for the Wilcoxon test is:

```
                        The NPAR1WAY Procedure

               Wilcoxon Scores (Rank Sums) for Variable GSHWS
                         Classified by Variable COND

                    Sum of      Expected      Std Dev          Mean
     COND      N    Scores      Under H0      Under H0         Score
     -------------------------------------------------------------------
     ATIPS    98     8039.0      11123.0     476.284142     82.030612
     TIPS    128    17612.0      14528.0     476.284142    137.593750

                  Average scores were used for ties.


                        Wilcoxon Two-Sample Test

                  Statistic              8039.0000

                  Normal Approximation
                  Z                        -6.4741
                  One-Sided Pr <   Z        <.0001
                  Two-Sided Pr >  |Z|       <.0001

                  t Approximation
                  One-Sided Pr <   Z        <.0001
                  Two-Sided Pr >  |Z|       <.0001

              Z includes a continuity correction of 0.5.


                        Kruskal-Wallis Test

                  Chi-Square              41.9273
                  DF                            1
                  Pr > Chi-Square          <.0001
```

To determine if there was a difference in the level of involvement in science homework assignments between TIPS and ATIPS students, we test:

H_0: The distributions of the involvement scores for science homework for the two groups have the same location

H_a: The distributions of the involvement scores for science homework for the TIPS students is shifted to the right or left of that for the ATIPS students

From the printout, the test statistic is $z = -6.4741$ and the p-value is $p < .0001$. Since the p-value is less than α ($p < .0001 < .05$), H_0 is rejected. There is sufficient evidence to indicate that there is a difference in the level of involvement in science homework assignments between TIPS and ATIPS students at $\alpha = .05$.

c.   Using SAS, the output for the Wilcoxon test is:

```
                    The NPAR1WAY Procedure

        Wilcoxon Scores (Rank Sums) for Variable MTHHWS
                  Classified by Variable COND

                    Sum of      Expected       Std Dev         Mean
   COND      N      Scores      Under H0       Under H0        Score
   --------------------------------------------------------------------
   ATIPS     98     10936.0     11123.0        472.485707      111.591837
   TIPS      128    14715.0     14528.0        472.485707      114.960938

              Average scores were used for ties.


                    Wilcoxon Two-Sample Test

              Statistic               10936.0000

              Normal Approximation
              Z                          -0.3947
              One-Sided Pr <  Z           0.3465
              Two-Sided Pr > |Z|          0.6930

              t Approximation
              One-Sided Pr <  Z           0.3467
              Two-Sided Pr > |Z|          0.6934

         Z includes a continuity correction of 0.5.


                    Kruskal-Wallis Test

              Chi-Square                  0.1566
              DF                               1
              Pr > Chi-Square             0.6923
```

To determine if there was a difference in the level of involvement in mathematics homework assignments between TIPS and ATIPS students, we test:

H_0: The distributions of the involvement scores for mathematics homework for the two groups have the same location
H_a: The distributions of the involvement scores for mathematics homework for the TIPS students is shifted to the right or left of that for the ATIPS students

From the printout, the test statistic is $z = -.3947$ and the p-value is $p = .6930$. Since the p-value is not less than α ($p = .6930 > .05$), H_0 is not rejected. There is insufficient evidence to indicate that there is a difference in the level of involvement in mathematics homework assignments between TIPS and ATIPS students at $\alpha = .05$.

d. Using SAS, the output for the Wilcoxon test is:

```
                    The NPAR1WAY Procedure

              Wilcoxon Scores (Rank Sums) for Variable LAHWS
                      Classified by Variable COND

                     Sum of      Expected       Std Dev        Mean
      COND      N    Scores      Under H0       Under H0       Score
      ---------------------------------------------------------------
      ATIPS    98   10496.0      11123.0      464.844149    107.102041
      TIPS    128   15155.0      14528.0      464.844149    118.398438

                 Average scores were used for ties.


                        Wilcoxon Two-Sample Test

                 Statistic              10496.0000

                 Normal Approximation
                 Z                         -1.3478
                 One-Sided Pr <  Z          0.0889
                 Two-Sided Pr > |Z|         0.1777

                 t Approximation
                 One-Sided Pr <  Z          0.0895
                 Two-Sided Pr > |Z|         0.1791

             Z includes a continuity correction of 0.5.


                         Kruskal-Wallis Test

                 Chi-Square                 1.8194
                 DF                              1
                 Pr > Chi-Square            0.1774
```

To determine if there was a difference in the level of involvement in language arts homework assignments between TIPS and ATIPS students, we test:

H_0: The distributions of the involvement scores for language arts homework for the two groups have the same location
H_a: The distributions of the involvement scores for language arts homework for the TIPS students is shifted to the right or left of that for the ATIPS students

From the printout, the test statistic is $z = -1.3478$ and the p-value is $p = .1777$. Since the p-value is not less than α ($p = .1777 > .05$), H_0 is not rejected. There is insufficient evidence to indicate that there is a difference in the level of involvement in language arts homework assignments between TIPS and ATIPS students at $\alpha = .05$.

14.31 We assume that the probability distribution of differences is continuous so that the absolute differences will have unique ranks. Although tied (absolute) differences can be assigned average ranks, the number of ties should be small relative to the number of observations to assure validity.

14.33 a. The hypotheses are:

H_0: The two sampled populations have identical probability distributions
H_a: The probability distributions for population A is shifted to the right of that for population B

Nonparametric Statistics   **449**

b. Some preliminary calculations are:

| Treatment | | Difference | Rank of Absolute |
A	B	A − B	Difference
54	45	9	5
60	45	15	10
98	87	11	7
43	31	12	9
82	71	11	7
77	75	2	2.5
74	63	11	7
29	30	−1	1
63	59	4	4
80	82	−2	2.5
			$T_- = 3.5$

The test statistic is $T_- = 3.5$

The rejection region is $T_- \le 8$, from Table XIII, Appendix A, with $n = 10$ and $\alpha = .025$.

Since the observed value of the test statistic falls in the rejection region ($T_- = 3.5 \le 8$), H_0 is rejected. There is sufficient evidence to indicate the responses for A tend to be larger than those for B at $\alpha = .025$.

14.35 a. H_0: The two sampled populations have identical probability distributions
       H_a: The probability distribution for population A is located to the right of that for population B

b. The test statistic is:

$$z = \frac{T_+ - \dfrac{n(n+1)}{4}}{\sqrt{\dfrac{n(n+1)(2n+1)}{24}}} = \frac{354 - \dfrac{30(30+1)}{4}}{\sqrt{\dfrac{30(30+1)(60+1)}{24}}} = \frac{121.5}{48.6184} = 2.499$$

The rejection region requires $\alpha = .05$ in the upper tail of the z distribution. From Table IV, Appendix A, $z = 1.645$. The rejection region is $z > 1.645$.

Since the observed value of the test statistic falls in the rejection region ($z = 2.499 > 1.645$), H_0 is rejected. There is sufficient evidence to indicate population A is located to the right of that for population B at $\alpha = .05$.

c. The p-value $= P(z \ge 2.499) = .5 - .4938 = .0062$ (using Table IV, Appendix A).

d. The necessary assumptions are:

1. The sample of differences is randomly selected from the population of differences.
2. The probability distribution from which the sample of paired differences is drawn is continuous.

14.37 a. The population of differences is probably not normal.

   b. To compare the male students' attitudes toward their father and their attitudes toward their mother, we test:

   H_0: The distributions of male students' attitudes toward their fathers has the same location as the distribution of male students' attitudes toward their mothers

   H_a: The distributions of male students' attitudes toward their fathers is shifted to the right or left of the distribution of male students' attitudes toward their mothers

   c.

Student	Attitude toward Father	Attitude toward Mother	Difference	Rank of Absolute Difference
1	2	3	-1	5.5
2	5	5	0	(eliminated)
3	4	3	1	5.5
4	4	5	-1	5.5
5	3	4	-1	5.5
6	5	4	1	5.5
7	4	5	-1	5.5
8	2	4	-2	11
9	4	5	-1	5.5
10	5	4	1	5.5
11	4	5	-1	5.5
12	5	4	1	5.5
13	3	3	0	(eliminated)

Positive rank sum $T_+ = 22$

   d. The sum of the ranks of the positive differences is $T_+ = 22$. The sum of the ranks of the negative differences is $T_- = 44$.

   e. The test statistic is $T =$ smaller of T_+ and T_- which is $T_+ = 22$.

   Reject H_0 if $T_+ \leq T_0$ where T_0 is based on $\alpha = .05$ and $n = 11$ (two-tailed).

   Reject H_0 if $T_+ \leq 11$ (From Table XIII, Appendix A.)

   f. Since the test statistic does not fall in the rejection region ($T_+ = 22 > 11$), H_0 is not rejected. There is insufficient evidence to indicate a difference in the male students' attitudes toward their father and their attitudes toward their mother at $\alpha = .05$.

14.39 a & b. The differences, ranks of absolute values of differences, and rank sums are:

Twin set	First Born	Second Born	Difference	Rank of Absolute difference
1	86	88	−2	3
2	71	77	−6	7
3	77	76	1	1.5
4	68	64	4	4
5	91	96	−5	5.5
6	72	72	0	eliminated
7	77	65	12	10
8	91	90	1	1.5
9	70	65	5	5.5
10	71	80	−9	9
11	88	81	7	8
12	87	72	15	11

Negative rank sum $T_- = 24.5$
Positive rank sum $T_+ = 41.5$

c. The signed rank statistic is $T =$ smaller of T_- and T_+ which is $T_- = 24.5$.

d. To determine if the data indicate the firstborn of a pair of twins is more aggressive than the other, we test:

H_0: The distribution of the firstborn twin's scores has the same location as the distribution of the secondborn twin's scores

H_a: The distribution of the firstborn twin's scores is shifted to the right of that for the secondborn twin's scores

The test statistics is $T = 24.5$.

Reject H_0 if $T_- \leq T_0$ where T_0 is based on $\alpha = .05$ and $n = 11$ (one-tailed).

Reject H_0 if $T_- \leq 14$ (From Table XIII, Appendix A)

Since the observed value of the test statistic does not fall in the rejection region ($T_- = 24.5 \nleq 14$), H_0 is not rejected. There is insufficient evidence to indicate firstborn of a pair of twins is more aggressive than the other at $\alpha = .05$.

14.41 Some preliminary calculations are:

Patient	Before Thickness	After Thickness	Difference	Rank of Absolute difference
1	11.0	11.5	−0.5	6
2	4.0	6.4	−2.4	20
3	6.3	6.1	0.2	3
4	12.0	10.0	2.0	15.5
5	18.2	14.7	3.5	24
6	9.2	7.3	1.9	14
7	7.5	6.1	1.4	12
8	7.1	6.4	0.7	8.5
9	7.2	5.7	1.5	13
10	6.7	6.5	0.2	3
11	14.2	13.2	1.0	10
12	7.3	7.5	−0.2	3
13	9.7	7.4	2.3	18.5
14	9.5	7.2	2.3	18.5
15	5.6	6.3	−0.7	8.5
16	8.7	6.0	2.7	21
17	6.7	7.3	−0.6	7
18	10.2	7.0	3.2	23
19	6.6	5.3	1.3	11
20	11.2	9.0	2.2	17
21	8.6	6.6	2.0	15.5
22	6.1	6.3	−0.2	3
23	10.3	7.2	3.1	22
24	7.0	7.2	−0.2	3
25	12.0	8.0	4.0	25

Negative rank sum $T_- = 50.5$
Positive rank sum $T_+ = 274.5$

To determine if the treatment for tendonitis tends to reduce the thickness of tendons, we test:

H_0: The distribution of the thickness before treatment has the same location as the distribution of the thickness after the treatment

H_a: The distribution of the thickness before the treatment is shifted to the right of that for the thickness after the treatment

The test statistics is T = smaller of T_- and T_+ which is $T_- = 50.5$.

Reject H_0 if $T_- \le T_0$ where T_0 is based on $\alpha = .10$ and $n = 25$ (one-tailed).

Reject H_0 if $T_- \le 101$ (From Table XIII, Appendix A)

(Note: There is no value for $\alpha = .10$ for a one-tailed test. However, if we reject H_0 for $\alpha = .05$, we would also reject H_0 for $\alpha = .10$.)

Since the observed value of the test statistic falls in the rejection region $(T_- = 50.5 \leq 101)$, H_0 is rejected. There is sufficient evidence to indicate the treatment for tendonitis tends to reduce the thickness of tendons at $\alpha = .10$.

14.43 Some preliminary calculations are:

Bowler	After 4 Strikes	After 4 Non-Strikes	Difference	Rank of Absolute difference
1	.683	.432	.251	3
2	.684	.400	.284	4
3	.632	.421	.211	2
4	.610	.529	.081	1
			Negative rank sum $T_- = 0$	
			Positive rank sum $T_+ = 10$	

a. To determine if the data support the "hot hand" theory in bowling, we test:

   H_0: The distribution of the proportion of strikes after rolling 4 strikes has the same location as the distribution of the proportion of strikes after rolling 4 non-strikes

   H_a: The distribution of the proportion of strikes after rolling 4 strikes is shifted to the right of the distribution of the proportion of strikes after rolling 4 non-strikes

   The test statistic is the smaller of T_- and T_+ which is $T_- = 0$.

   There are no table values in Table XII when $n = 4$. Even if all the observations support rejecting H_0, the p-value is greater than .05. Thus, we are unable to reject H_0. There is insufficient evidence to support the "hot hand" theory at $\alpha = .05$.

b. When all 43 bowlers are included, the p-value is $p = 0$. Since this p-value is so small, we would reject H_0 for any reasonable value of α. There is sufficient evidence to support the "hot hand" theory at any reasonable value of α.

14.45 The distribution of H is approximately a χ^2 if the null hypothesis is true and if the sample sizes, n_j, for each of the k distributions is more than 5.

14.47 a. A completely randomized design was used.

b. The hypotheses are:

   H_0: The three probability distributions are identical
   H_a: At least two of the three probability distributions differ in location

c. The rejection region requires $\alpha = .01$ in the upper tail of the χ^2 distribution with df $= k - 1 = 3 - 1 = 2$. From Table VII, Appendix A, $\chi^2_{.01} = 9.21034$. The rejection region is $H > 9.21034$.

d. Some preliminary calculations are:

I		II		III	
Observation	**Rank**	**Observation**	**Rank**	**Observation**	**Rank**
34	5.5	24	2	72	14
56	10	18	1	101	20
65	12	27	3	91	19
59	11	41	7	76	16
82	18	34	5.5	80	17
70	13	42	8	75	15
45	9	33	4		
	$R_A = 78.5$		$R_B = 30.5$		$R_C = 101$

The test statistic is $H = \dfrac{12}{n(n+1)} \sum \dfrac{R_j^2}{n_j} - 3(n+1)$

$$= \dfrac{12}{20(20+1)}\left[\dfrac{78.5^2}{7} + \dfrac{30.5^2}{7} + \dfrac{101^2}{6}\right] - 3(20+1) = 77.5252 - 63 = 14.5252$$

Since the observed value of the test statistic falls in the rejection region ($H = 14.5252 >$ 9.21034), H_0 is rejected. There is sufficient evidence to indicate at least two of the three probability distributions differ in location at $\alpha = .01$.

14.49   a – d. The ranks and sums of ranks appear in the table:

Scopolamine	Rank	Placebo	Rank	No Drug	Rank
5	2.5	8	13	8	13
8	13	10	20.5	9	17
8	13	12	26.5	11	23.5
6	6.5	10	20.5	12	26.5
6	6.5	9	17	11	23.5
6	6.5	7	10	10	20.5
6	6.5	9	17	12	26.5
8	13	10	20.5	12	26.5
6	6.5				
4	1				
5	2.5				
6	6.5				
	$R_1 = 84$		$R_2 = 145$		$R_3 = 177$

e. $H = \dfrac{12}{n(n+1)} \sum \dfrac{R_j^2}{n_j} - 3(n+1) = \dfrac{12}{28(28+1)}\left(\dfrac{84^2}{12} + \dfrac{145^2}{8} + \dfrac{177^2}{8}\right) - 3(28+1) = 18.40$

Nonparametric Statistics   455

f. To determine if the distributions of the number of word pairs recalled for the three groups have different locations, we test:

H_0: The three probability distributions are identical
H_a: At least two of the three probability distributions differ in location

The test statistic is $H = 18.40$.

The rejection region requires $\alpha = .05$ in the upper tail of the χ^2 distribution with df $= k - 1 = 3 - 1 = 2$. From Table VII, Appendix A, $\chi^2_{.05} = 5.99147$. The rejection region is $\chi^2 > 5.99147$.

Since the observed value of the test statistic falls in the rejection region ($H = 18.40 > 5.99147$), H_0 is rejected. There is sufficient evidence to indicate the distributions of the number of word pairs recalled for the three groups have different locations at $\alpha = .05$.

g. Re-ranking the data for only groups 1 and 2, we get:

Scopolamine	Rank	Placebo	Rank
5	2.5	8	12.5
8	12.5	10	18
8	12.5	12	20
6	6.5	10	18
6	6.5	9	15.5
6	6.5	7	10
6	6.5	9	15.5
8	12.5	10	18
6	6.5		
4	1		
5	2.5		
6	6.5		
	$T_1 = 82.5$		$T_2 = 127.5$

To determine if the distributions of the number of word pairs recalled for the Scopolamine group is shifted to the left of that for the Placebo group, we test:

H_0: The two probability distributions are identical
H_a: The probability distribution of the Scopolamine group is shifted to the left of that for the Placebo group

The test statistic is the T_2 because $n_2 < n_1$.

There is no table value for this problem since $n_1 = 12$ and the largest n in Table XII is 10. We will use the normal approximation even though both sample sizes are not greater than or equal to 10 ($n_2 = 8$).

The test statistic is $z = \dfrac{T_1 - \dfrac{n_1(n_1 + n_2 + 1)}{2}}{\sqrt{\dfrac{n_1 n_2 (n_1 + n_2 + 1)}{12}}} = \dfrac{82.5 - \dfrac{12(12 + 8 + 1)}{2}}{\sqrt{\dfrac{12(8)(12 + 8 + 1)}{12}}} = -3.36$

The rejection region requires $\alpha = .05$ in the lower tail of the z distribution. From Table IV, Appendix A, $z_{.05} = 1.645$. The rejection region is $z < -1.645$.

Since the observed value of the test statistic falls in the rejection region ($z = -3.36 < -1.645$), H_0 is rejected. There is sufficient evidence to indicate the distributions of the number of word pairs recalled for the Scopolamine group is shifted to the left of that for the Placebo group at $\alpha = .05$.

14.51   a.   To determine if the Group B subjects exercise for longer durations than the Group A subjects, we test:

H_0:   The two sampled populations have identical probability distributions
H_a: The group B probability distribution is shifted to the right of that of the probability distribution of Group A

b.   The test statistic is $H = 5.1429$.

The p-value is $p = .0233$. Since the p-value is so small, H_0 would be rejected for any $\alpha > .0233$. There is sufficient evidence to indicate that the Group B subjects exercise for longer durations than the Group A subjects for $\alpha > .0233$.

c.   For the Kruskal-Wallis H-test to be valid, the following assumptions must be met:

1.   The two samples are random and independent
2.   There are five or more measurements in each sample.
3.   The two probability distributions from which the samples are drawn are continuous.

For this problem, the second assumption is not met. One of the samples contained only four observations.

Since there are only two populations, the Wilcoxon Rank Sum test can be used. For this test, the only necessary assumptions are:

1.   The two samples are random and independent.
2.   The two probability distributions from which the samples are drawn are continuous.

14.53 a. Using MINITAB, the histograms of the three data sets are:

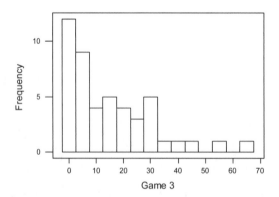

None of these three graphs look approximately normal. Thus, the assumption of normality necessary for ANOVA is likely violated.

b.   Using MINITAB, the results of the Kruskal-Wallis analysis are:

```
Kruskal-Wallis Test on Percent

Game        N     Median     Ave Rank          Z
1          50     32.000        83.1        2.88
2          42     26.000        73.0        0.59
3          47      9.000        53.3       -3.49
Overall   139                   70.0

H = 13.61  DF = 2  P = 0.001
H = 13.66  DF = 2  P = 0.001 (adjusted for ties)
```

To determine if the percentages of names recalled are different for the three retrieval methods, we test:

H_0: The distributions of the three retrieval methods are identical
H_a: At least two of the three retrieval methods have probability distributions that differ in location

From the printout, the test statistic is $H = 13.66$ and the p-value is $p = .001$. Since the p-value is less than α ($p = .001 < .05$), H_0 is rejected. There is sufficient evidence to indicate that the percentages of names recalled are different for the three retrieval methods at $\alpha = .05$.

14.55 To correctly rank the data in a randomized block design, we would use b - for each block, rank the data across the treatments from smallest to largest.

14.57 a.   The number of blocks, b, is 6.

b. H_0: The probability distributions for the four treatments are identical
H_a: At least two of the probability distributions differ in location

c.   The test statistic is $F_r = \dfrac{12}{bk(k+1)} \sum R_j^2 - 3b(k+1)$

$$= \dfrac{12}{6(4)(4+1)}[11^2 + 21^2 + 21^2 + 7^2] - 3(6)(4+1) = 105.2 - 90 = 15.2$$

The rejection region requires $\alpha = .10$ in the upper tail of the χ^2 distribution with df $= k - 1 = 4 - 1 = 3$. From Table VII, Appendix A, $\chi^2_{.10} = 6.25139$. The rejection region is $F_r > 6.25139$.

Since the observed value of the test statistic falls in the rejection region ($F_r = 15.2 > 6.25139$), reject H_0. There is sufficient evidence to indicate a difference in the location of at least two of the four treatments at $\alpha = .10$.

d.   The p-value $= P(F_r \geq 15.2) = P(\chi^2 \geq 15.2)$. With 3 degrees of freedom, $F_r = 15.2$ falls above $\chi^2_{.005}$; therefore, p-value $< .005$.

e. The means are:

$$\overline{R}_A = \frac{R_A}{b} = \frac{11}{6} = 1.833 \qquad\qquad \overline{R}_B = \frac{R_B}{b} = \frac{21}{6} = 3.5$$

$$\overline{R}_C = \frac{R_C}{b} = \frac{21}{6} = 3.5 \qquad\qquad \overline{R}_D = \frac{R_D}{b} = \frac{7}{6} = 1.167$$

$$\overline{R} = \frac{1}{2}(k+1) = \frac{1}{2}(4+1) = 2.5$$

$$F_r = \frac{12}{k(k+1)}\sum b(\overline{R}_j - \overline{R})^2$$

$$= \frac{12}{(4)(4+1)}[6(1.833-2.5)^2 + 6(3.5-2.5)^2 + 6(3.5-2.5)^2 + 6(1.167-2.5)^2]$$

$$= .6[25.3307] = 15.2$$

14.59 $R_1 = 16 \qquad R_2 = 7 \qquad R_3 = 23 \qquad R_4 = 14$

To determine if at least two of the treatment probability distributions differ in location, we test:

H_0: The probability distributions of the four treatments are identical
H_a: At least two of the probability distributions differ in location

The test statistic is $F_r = \dfrac{12}{bk(k+1)}\sum R_j^2 - 3b(k+1)$

$$= \frac{12}{6(4)(4+1)}[16^2 + 7^2 + 23^2 + 14^2] - 3(6)(4+1) = 103 - 90 = 13$$

The rejection region requires $\alpha = .05$ in the upper tail of the χ^2 distribution with df $= k - 1 = 4 - 1 = 3$. From Table VII, Appendix A, $\chi^2_{.05} = 7.84173$. The rejection region is $F_r > 7.81473$.

Since the observed value of the test statistic falls in the rejection region ($F_r = 13 > 7.81473$), reject H_0. There is sufficient evidence to indicate a difference in the location for at least two of the probability distributions at $\alpha = .05$.

14.61 a. From the printout, the rank sums are: $R_1 = 27.0$, $R_2 = 32.5$, $R_3 = 29.0$, and $R_4 = 31.5$.

b. $F_r = \dfrac{12}{bk(k+1)}\sum R_j^2 - 3b(k+1) = \dfrac{12}{12(4)(4+1)}(27^2 + 32.5^2 + 29^2 + 31.5^2) - 3(12)(4+1) = .925$

c. From the printout, $F_r = S = .93$ and the p-value is p $= .819$.

d. To determine if the atlas theme ranking distributions of the four groups differ, we test:

H_0: The probability distributions of the atlas theme rankings are the same for the four groups
H_a: The probability distributions of the atlas theme rankings differ in location

The test statistic is $F_r = .925$ and the p-value is $p = .819$. Since the p-value is so large, there is no evidence to reject H_0 for any reasonable value of α. There is insufficient evidence to indicate that the atlas theme ranking distributions of the four groups differ.

14.63 a. The rejection region requires $\alpha = .01$ in the upper tail of the χ^2 distribution with df = $k - 1 = 3 - 1 = 2$. From Table VII, Appendix A, $\chi^2_{.01} = 9.21034$. The rejection region is $\chi^2 > 9.21034$.

b. Since the observed value of the test statistic falls in the rejection region ($\chi^2 = 19.16 > 9.21034$), H_0 is rejected. There is sufficient evidence to indicate the distributions of proportions of eye fixations on the interior mirror differ in location among the 3 treatments at $\alpha = .01$.

c. Since the observed value of the test statistic does not fall in the rejection region ($\chi^2 = 7.80 \not> 9.21034$), H_0 is not rejected. There is insufficient evidence to indicate the distributions of proportions of eye fixations on the off-side mirror differ in location among the 3 treatments at $\alpha = .01$.

d. Since the observed value of the test statistic falls in the rejection region ($\chi^2 = 20.67 > 9.21034$), H_0 is rejected. There is sufficient evidence to indicate the distributions of proportions of eye fixations on the speedometer differ in location among the 3 treatments at $\alpha = .01$.

14.65 Some preliminary calculations are:

Student	Rank Live Plant	Rank Plant Photo	Rank No Plant
1	1	2	3
2	2	3	1
3	3	2	1
4	1	2	3
5	2	3	1
6	3	2	1
7	2	1	3
8	1	3	2
9	2	1	3
10	2	1	3
	$R_1 = 19$	$R_2 = 20$	$R_3 = 21$

To determine if the students' finger temperatures depend on the experimental conditions, we test:

H_0: The probability distributions of finger temperatures are the same for the three conditions

H_a: At least two probability distributions of finger temperatures differ in location

The test statistic is $F_r = \dfrac{12}{bk(k+1)} \sum R_j^2 - 3b(k+1)$

$$= \frac{12}{10(3)(3+1)}(19^2 + 20^2 + 21^2) - 3(10)(3+1) = 0.2$$

Since no α was given, we will use $\alpha = .05$. The rejection region requires $\alpha = .05$ in the upper tail of the χ^2 distribution with df $= k - 1 = 3 - 1 = 2$. From Table VII, Appendix A, $\chi^2_{.05} = 5.99147$. The rejection region is $F_r > 5.99147$.

Since the observed value of the test statistic does not fall in the rejection region ($F_r = 0.2 \not> 5.99147$), H_0 is not rejected. There is insufficient evidence to indicate that the students' finger temperatures depend on the experimental conditions at $\alpha = .05$.

Because the value of the test statistic is so small, H_0 would not be rejected for any reasonable value of α.

14.67   Some preliminary calculations are:

Location	Temephos	Rank	Malsathion	Rank	Fenitrothion	Rank	Fenthion	Rank	Chlorpyrifos	Rank
Anguilla	4.6	5	1.2	1	1.5	2.5	1.8	4	1.5	2.5
Antigua	9.2	5	2.9	3	2.0	1.5	7.0	4	2.0	1.5
Dominica	7.8	5	1.4	1	2.4	2	4.2	4	4.1	3
Guyana	1.7	2	1.9	4	2.2	5	1.5	1	1.8	3
Jamaica	3.4	3	3.7	4	2.0	2	1.5	1	7.1	5
St. Lucia	6.7	4	2.7	1.5	2.7	1.5	4.8	3	8.7	5
Suriname	1.4	1	1.9	3	2.0	4	2.1	5	1.7	2
	$R_1 = 13$		$R_2 = 15$		$R_3 = 18.5$		$R_4 = 22$		$R_5 = 22$	

To determine if the resistance ratio distributions of the 5 insecticides differ, we test:

H_0: The distributions of the 5 insecticide ratios are the same
H_a: At least two of the distributions of insecticide ratios differ

The test statistic is $F_r = \dfrac{12}{bk(k+1)} \sum R_j^2 - 3b(k+1)$

$$= \frac{12}{7(5)(5+1)}(25^2 + 17.5^2 + 18.5^2 + 22^2 + 22^2) - 3(7)(5+1) = 2.086$$

Since no α was given, we will use $\alpha = .05$. The rejection region requires $\alpha = .05$ in the upper tail of the χ^2 distribution with df $= k - 1 = 5 - 1 = 4$. From Table VII, Appendix A, $\chi^2_{.05} = 9.48773$. The rejection region is $F_r > 9.48773$.

Since the observed value of the test statistic does not fall in the rejection region ($F_r = 2.086 \not> 9.48773$), H_0 is not rejected. There is insufficient evidence to indicate that the resistance ratio distributions of the 5 insecticides differ at $\alpha = .05$.

14.69   The conditions required for a valid Spearman's test are:

1.   The sample of experimental units on which the two variables are measured is randomly selected.
2.   The probability distributions of the two variables are continuous.

14.71 a. From Table XIV with $n = 10$, $r_{s,\alpha/2} = r_{s,.025} = .648$. The rejection region is $r_s > .648$ or $r_s < -.648$.

b. From Table XIV with $n = 20$, $r_{s,\alpha} = r_{s,.025} = .450$. The rejection region is $r_s > .450$.

c. From Table XIV with $n = 30$, $r_{s,\alpha} = r_{s,.01} = .432$. The rejection region is $r_s < -.432$.

14.73 a. H_0: $\rho_s = 0$
H_a: $\rho_s \neq 0$

b. The test statistic is $r_s = \dfrac{SS_{uv}}{\sqrt{SS_{uu}SS_{vv}}}$

x	Rank, u	y	Rank, v	u^2	v^2	uv
0	3	0	1.5	9	2.25	45
3	5.5	2	5	30.25	25	27.5
0	3	2	5	9	25	15
−4	1	0	1.5	1	2.25	1.5
3	5.5	3	7	30.25	49	38.5
0	3	1	3	9	9	9
4	7	2	5	49	25	35
	$\sum u = 28$		$\sum v = 28$	$\sum u^2 = 137.5$	$\sum v^2 = 137.5$	$\sum uv = 131$

$$SS_{uv} = \sum uv - \frac{\left(\sum u\right)\left(\sum v\right)}{n} = 131 - \frac{28(28)}{7} = 19$$

$$SS_{uu} = \sum u^2 - \frac{\left(\sum u\right)^2}{n} = 137.5 - \frac{(28)^2}{7} = 25.5$$

$$SS_{vv} = \sum v^2 - \frac{\left(\sum v\right)^2}{n} = 137.5 - \frac{(28)^2}{7} = 25.5$$

$$r_s = \frac{19}{\sqrt{25.5(25.5)}} = .745$$

Reject H_0 if $r_s < -r_{s,\alpha/2}$ or $r_s > r_{s,\alpha/2}$ where $\alpha/2 = .025$ and $n = 7$:

Reject H_0 if $r_s < -.786$ or $r_s > .786$ (from Table XIV, Appendix A).

Since the observed value of the test statistic does not fall in the rejection region, ($r_s = .745 \not> .786$), do not reject H_0. There is insufficient evidence to indicate x and y are correlated at $\alpha = .05$.

c. The p-value is $P(r_s \geq .745) + P(r_s \leq -.745)$. For $n = 7$, $r_s = .745$ is above $r_{s,.025}$ where $\alpha/2 = .025$ and below $r_{s,.05}$ where $\alpha/2 = .05$. Therefore, $2(.025) = .05 < p\text{-value} < 2(.05) = .10$.

d. The assumptions of the test are that the samples are randomly selected and the probability distributions of the two variables are continuous.

14.75　a.　Some preliminary calculations are:

Blood Lactate Level	Rank u	Perceived Recovery	Rank v	u^2	v^2	uv
3.8	3	7	1.5	9	2.25	4.5
4.2	5.5	7	1.5	30.25	2.25	8.25
4.8	7	11	3	49	9	21
4.1	4	12	5	16	25	20
5.0	8	12	5	64	25	40
5.3	9.5	12	5	90.25	25	47.5
4.2	5.5	13	7	30.25	49	38.5
2.4	1	17	9	1	81	9
3.7	2	17	9	4	81	18
5.3	9.5	17	9	90.25	81	85.5
5.8	12	18	11.5	144	132.25	138
6.0	14	18	11.5	196	132.25	161
5.9	13	21	14.5	169	210.25	188.5
6.3	15	21	14.5	225	210.25	217.5
5.5	12	20	13	121	169	143
6.5	16	24	16	256	256	256
$\sum u = 136$		$\sum v = 136$		$\sum u^2 = 1495$	$\sum v^2 = 1490.5$	$\sum uv = 1396.25$

$$SS_{uv} = \sum uv - \frac{\left(\sum u\right)\left(\sum v\right)}{n} = 1396.25 - \frac{136(136)}{16} = 240.25$$

$$SS_{uu} = \sum u^2 - \frac{\left(\sum u\right)^2}{n} = 1495 - \frac{136^2}{16} = 339$$

$$SS_{vv} = \sum v^2 - \frac{\left(\sum v\right)^2}{n} = 1490.5 - \frac{136^2}{16} = 334.5$$

a.　The ranks of the blood lactate levels are stored in the "u" column above.

b.　The ranks of the perceived recovery values are stored in the "v" column above.

c.　$r_s = \dfrac{SS_{uv}}{\sqrt{SS_{uu}SS_{vv}}} = \dfrac{240.25}{\sqrt{339(334.5)}} = .713$

　　Since r_s is relatively close to 1, blood lactate level and perceived recovery are fairly strongly, positively, linearly rank related.

d.　Reject H_0 if $r_s < -r_{s,\alpha/2}$ or if $r_s > r_{s,\alpha/2}$ where $\alpha/2 = .05$ and $n = 16$;
　　Reject H_0 if $r_s < -.425$ or $r_s > .425$

e.　To determine if blood lactate level and perceived recovery are rank correlated, we test:

　　H_0: Blood lactate level and Perceived recovery are not rank correlated
　　H_a: Blood lactate level and Perceived recovery are rank correlated

The test statistic is $r_s = .713$.

Since the observed value of the test statistic falls in the rejection region, ($r_s = .713 >$ $.425$), H_0 is rejected. There is sufficient evidence to indicate that blood lactate level and perceived recovery are rank correlated at $\alpha = .10$.

14.77   a.   The correlation between a variable and itself will always be 1.00. Therefore, the Spearman's rank correlations on the diagonals are always 1.00.

       b.   The Spearman's rank correlation between EDSS and ARM is $-.439$. There is a moderately weak, negative relationship between the Expanded Disability Status Scale and the peak oxygen uptake during arm cranking exercise.

             The Spearman's rank correlation between EDSS and LEG/ARM is $-.655$. There is a moderately strong, negative relationship between the Expanded Disability Status Scale and the peak oxygen uptake during leg cycling and arm cranking exercise.

             The Spearman's rank correlation between EDSS and LEG is $-.512$. There is a moderate, negative relationship between the Expanded Disability Status Scale and the peak oxygen uptake during leg cycling exercise.

             The Spearman's rank correlation between ARM and LEG/ARM is $.634$. There is a moderately strong, positive relationship between the peak oxygen uptake during arm cranking exercise and the peak oxygen uptake during combined leg cycling and arm cranking exercise.

             The Spearman's rank correlation between ARM and LEG is $.722$. There is a moderately strong, positive relationship between the peak oxygen uptake during arm cranking exercise and the peak oxygen uptake during leg cycling exercise.

             The Spearman's rank correlation between LEG/ARM and LEG is $.890$. There is a strong, positive relationship between the peak oxygen uptake during combined leg cycling and arm cranking exercise and peak oxygen uptake during leg cycling exercise.

       c.   To determine if EDSS and peak oxygen uptake for arm cranking exercise are negatively correlated, we test:

H_0: $\rho_s = 0$
H_a: $\rho_s < 0$

The test statistic is $r_s = -.439$.

Reject H_0 is $r_s < -r_{s,\alpha}$ where $\alpha = .01$ and $n = 10$:

Reject H_0 if $r_s < -.745$ (using Table XIV, Appendix A)

Since the observed value of the test statistic does not fall in the rejection region ($r_s = -.439 \not< -.745$), H_0 is not rejected. There is insufficient evidence to indicate that there is a negative correlation between EDSS and peak oxygen uptake for arm cranking exercise at $\alpha = .01$.

To determine if EDSS and peak oxygen uptake for combined leg cycling and arm cranking exercise are negatively correlated, we test:

H_0: $\rho_s = 0$
H_a: $\rho_s < 0$

The test statistic is $r_s = -.655$.

Reject H_0 is $r_s < -r_{s,\alpha}$ where $\alpha = .01$ and $n = 10$:

Reject H_0 if $r_s < -.745$ (using Table XIV, Appendix A)

Since the observed value of the test statistic does not fall in the rejection region ($r_s = -.655 \not< -.745$), H_0 is not rejected. There is insufficient evidence to indicate that there is a negative correlation between EDSS and peak oxygen uptake for combined leg cycling and arm cranking exercise at $\alpha = .01$.

To determine if EDSS and peak oxygen uptake for leg cycling exercise are negatively correlated, we test:

H_0: $\rho_s = 0$
H_a: $\rho_s < 0$

The test statistic is $r_s = -.512$.

Reject H_0 is $r_s < -r_{s,\alpha}$ where $\alpha = .01$ and $n = 10$:

Reject H_0 if $r_s < -.745$ (using Table XIV, Appendix A)

Since the observed value of the test statistic does not fall in the rejection region ($r_s = -.512 \not< -.745$), H_0 is not rejected. There is insufficient evidence to indicate that there is a negative correlation between EDSS and peak oxygen uptake for leg cycling exercise at $\alpha = .01$.

14.79　a.　Some preliminary calculations are:

FCAT-Math	Rank, u	% Below Poverty	Rank, v	u^2	v^2	uv
166.4	7	91.7	22	49	484	154
159.6	4	90.2	21	16	441	84
159.1	3	86.0	20	9	400	60
155.5	1	83.9	19	1	361	19
164.3	5	80.4	18	25	324	90
169.8	9	76.5	17	81	289	153
155.7	2	76.0	16	4	256	32
165.2	6	75.8	15	36	225	90
175.4	13	75.6	14	169	196	182
178.1	16	75.0	13	256	169	208
167.1	8	74.7	12	64	144	96
177.0	15	63.2	11	225	121	165
174.2	11	52.9	10	121	100	110
175.6	14	48.5	9	196	81	126
170.8	10	39.1	8	100	64	80
175.1	12	38.4	7	144	49	84
182.8	20.5	34.3	6	420.25	36	123
180.3	18	30.3	4.5	324	20.25	81
178.8	17	30.3	4.5	289	20.25	76.5
181.4	19	29.6	3	361	9	57
182.8	20.5	26.5	2	420.25	4	41
186.1	22	13.8	1	484	1	22
	$\sum u = 253$		$\sum v = 253$	$\sum u^2 = 3794.5$	$\sum v^2 = 3794.5$	$\sum uv = 2133.5$

$$SS_{uv} = \sum uv - \frac{\sum u \sum v}{n} = 2133.5 - \frac{253(253)}{22} = -776$$

$$SS_{uu} = \sum u^2 - \frac{\left(\sum u\right)^2}{n} = 3794.5 - \frac{253^2}{22} = 885$$

$$SS_{vv} = \sum v^2 - \frac{\left(\sum v\right)^2}{n} = 3794.5 - \frac{253^2}{22} = 885$$

$$r_s = \frac{SS_{uv}}{\sqrt{SS_{uu}SS_{vv}}} = \frac{-776}{\sqrt{885(885)}} = -.877$$

Since r_s is very close to -1, there is a fairly strong, negative relationship between FCAT math scores and the percentage of students below the poverty level.

b.   Some preliminary calculations are:

FCAT-Read	Rank, u	% Below Poverty	Rank, v	u^2	v^2	uv
165.0	7.5	91.7	22	56.25	484	165
157.2	1	90.2	21	1	441	21
164.4	5	86.0	20	25	400	100
162.4	3	83.9	19	9	361	57
162.5	4	80.4	18	16	324	72
164.9	6	76.5	17	36	289	102
162.0	2	76.0	16	4	256	32
165.0	7.5	75.8	15	56.25	225	112.5
173.7	14	75.6	14	196	196	196
171.0	11	75.0	13	121	169	143
169.4	9	74.7	12	81	144	108
172.9	13	63.2	11	169	121	143
172.7	12	52.9	10	144	100	120
174.9	16	48.5	9	256	81	144
174.8	15	39.1	8	225	64	120
170.1	10	38.4	7	100	49	70
181.4	20	34.3	6	400	36	120
180.6	19	30.3	4.5	361	20.25	85.5
178.0	18	30.3	4.5	324	20.25	81
175.9	17	29.6	3	289	9	51
181.6	21	26.5	2	441	4	42
183.8	22	13.8	1	484	1	22
	$\sum u = 253$		$\sum v = 253$	$\sum u^2 = 3794.5$	$\sum v^2 = 3794.5$	$\sum uv = 2107$

$$SS_{uv} = \sum uv - \frac{\sum u \sum v}{n} = 2107 - \frac{253(253)}{22} = -802.5$$

$$SS_{uu} = \sum u^2 - \frac{\left(\sum u\right)^2}{n} = 3794.5 - \frac{253^2}{22} = 885$$

$$SS_{vv} = \sum v^2 - \frac{\left(\sum v\right)^2}{n} = 3794.5 - \frac{253^2}{22} = 885$$

$$r_s = \frac{SS_{uv}}{\sqrt{SS_{uu}SS_{vv}}} = \frac{-802.5}{\sqrt{885(885)}} = -.907$$

Since r_s is very close to -1, there is a fairly strong, negative relationship between FCAT reading scores and the percentage of students below the poverty level.

c. To determine whether the FCAT math scores and the percentage of students below the poverty level are negatively rank correlated, we test:

H_0: $\rho_s = 0$
H_a: $\rho_s < 0$

The test statistic is $r_s = -.877$.

Reject H_0 if $r_s < -r_{s, .01}$ with $n = 22$

Reject H_0 if $r_s < -.508$ (From Table XIV, Appendix A)

Since the observed value of the test statistic falls in the rejection region ($r_s = -.877 < -.508$), H_0 is rejected. There is sufficient evidence to indicate FCAT math scores and the percentage of students below the poverty level are negatively rank correlated at $\alpha = .01$.

d. To determine whether the FCAT reading scores and the percentage of students below the poverty level are negatively rank correlated, we test:

H_0: $\rho_s = 0$
H_a: $\rho_s < 0$

The test statistic is $r_s = -.907$.

Reject H_0 if $r_s < -r_{s, .01}$ with $n = 22$

Reject H_0 if $r_s < -.508$ (From Table XIV, Appendix A)

Since the observed value of the test statistic falls in the rejection region ($r_s = -.907 < -.508$), H_0 is rejected. There is sufficient evidence to indicate FCAT reading scores and the percentage of students below the poverty level are negatively rank correlated at $\alpha = .01$.

14.81   a.   Some preliminary calculations are:

Change KSADS-MRS	Rank, u	Improve CGI-BP	Rank, v	u^2	v^2	uv
80	18	6	18	324	324	324
65	17	5	17	289	289	289
20	15.5	4	15	240.25	225	232.5
−15	13	4	15	169	225	195
−50	9	4	15	81	225	135
20	15.5	3	12	240.25	144	186
−30	11	3	12	121	144	132
−70	5.5	3	12	30.25	144	66
−10	14	2	6	196	36	84
−25	12	2	6	144	36	72
−35	10	2	6	100	36	60
−65	7.5	2	6	56.25	36	45
−65	7.5	2	6	26.25	36	45
−70	5.5	2	6	30.25	36	33
−80	4	2	6	16	36	24
−90	2.5	2	6	6.25	36	15
−95	1	2	6	1	36	6
−90	2.5	1	1	6.25	1	2.5
	$\sum u = 171$		$\sum v = 171$	$\sum u^2 = 2107$	$\sum v^2 = 2045$	$\sum uv = 1946$

$$SS_{uv} = \sum uv - \frac{\sum u \sum v}{n} = 1946 - \frac{171(171)}{18} = 321.5$$

$$SS_{uu} = \sum u^2 - \frac{\left(\sum u\right)^2}{n} = 2107 - \frac{171^2}{18} = 482.5$$

$$SS_{vv} = \sum v^2 - \frac{\left(\sum v\right)^2}{n} = 2045 - \frac{171^2}{18} = 420.5$$

$$r_s = \frac{SS_{uv}}{\sqrt{SS_{uu}SS_{vv}}} = \frac{321.5}{\sqrt{482.5(420.5)}} = .714$$

b.   To determine if there is a positive rank correlation between the two test score changes in the population of all pediatric patients with manic symptoms, we test:

H_0: $\rho_s = 0$
H_a: $\rho_s > 0$

The test statistic is $r_s = .714$.

Reject H_0 if $r_s > r_{s, .05}$ with $n = 18$

Reject H_0 if $r_s > .399$ (From Table XIV, Appendix A)

Since the observed value of the test statistic falls in the rejection region ($r_s = .714 > .399$), H_0 is rejected. There is sufficient evidence to indicate there is a positive rank correlation between the two test score changes in the population of all pediatric patients with manic symptoms at $\alpha = .05$.

14.83   It is appropriate to use the t and F tests for comparing two or more population means when the populations sampled are normal and the population variances are equal.

14.85   a.   To compare two populations with independent samples, one would use the Wilcoxon Rank Sum test.

      b.   To make an inference about a population median, one would use the sign test.

      c.   To compare three or more populations with independent samples, one would use the Kruskal-Wallis H-test.

      d.   To make inferences about a rank correlation, one would use the Spearman's rank correlation coefficient test.

      e.   To compare two populations with matched pairs, one would use the Wilcoxon Signed Rank Test.

      f.   To compare three or more populations with a block design, one would use the Friedman's F_r-test.

14.87   a.   Some preliminary calculations are:

Pair	X	Rank u_i	Y	Rank v_i	u_i^2	v_i^2	$u_i v_i$
1	19	5	12	5	25	25	25
2	27	7	19	8	49	64	56
3	15	2	7	1	4	1	2
4	35	9	25	9	81	81	81
5	13	1	11	4	1	16	4
6	29	8	10	2.5	64	6.25	20
7	16	3.5	16	6	12.25	36	21
8	22	6	10	2.5	36	6.25	15
9	16	3.5	18	7	12.25	49	24.5
		$\sum u_i = 45$		$\sum v_i = 45$	$\sum u_i^2 = 284.5$	$\sum v_i^2 = 284.5$	$\sum u_i v_i = 248.5$

$$SS_{uv} = \sum u_i v_i - \frac{\sum u_i v_i}{n} = 248.5 - \frac{45(45)}{9} = 23.5$$

$$SS_{uu} = \sum u_i^2 - \frac{\left(\sum u_i\right)^2}{n} = 284.5 - \frac{45^2}{9} = 59.5$$

$$SS_{vv} = \sum v_i^2 - \frac{\left(\sum v_i\right)^2}{n} = 284.5 - \frac{45^2}{9} = 59.5$$

To determine if the Spearman rank correlation differs from 0, we test:

$H_0: \rho_s = 0$
$H_a: \rho_s \neq 0$

The test statistic is $r_s = \dfrac{SS_{uv}}{\sqrt{SS_{uu}SS_{vv}}} = \dfrac{23.5}{\sqrt{59.5(59.5)}} = .40$

Reject H_0 if $r_s < -r_{s,\alpha/2}$ or if $r_s > r_{s,\alpha/2}$ where $\alpha/2 = .025$ and $n = 9$:

Reject H_0 if $r_s < -.683$ or if $r_s > .683$ (from Table XIV, Appendix A)

Since the observed value of the test statistic does not fall in the rejection region ($r_s = .40$ $\not> .683$), H_0 is not rejected. There is insufficient evidence to indicate that Spearman's rank correlation between x and y is significantly different from 0 at $\alpha = .05$.

b. Use the Wilcoxon signed rank test. Some preliminary calculations are:

Pair	X	Y	Difference	Rank of Absolute Difference
1	19	12	7	3
2	27	19	8	4.5
3	15	7	8	4.5
4	35	25	10	6
5	13	11	2	1.5
6	29	10	19	8
7	16	16	0	(eliminated)
8	22	10	12	7
9	16	18	−2	1.5
				$T_- = 1.5$

To determine if the probability distribution of x is shifted to the right of that for y, we test:

H_0: The probability distributions are identical for the two variables
H_a: The probability distribution of x is shifted to the right of the probability distribution of y

The test statistic is $T = T_- = 1.5$

Reject H_0 if $T \leq T_0$ where T_0 is based on $\alpha = .05$ and $n = 8$ (one-tailed):

Reject H_0 if $T \leq 6$ (from Table XIII, Appendix A).

Since the observed value of the test statistic falls in the rejection region ($T = 1.5 \leq 6$), reject H_0 at $\alpha = .05$. There is sufficient evidence to conclude that the probability distribution of x is shifted to the right of that for y.

14.89   Some preliminary calculations are:

Block	1	Rank	2	Rank	3	Rank	4	Rank	5	Rank
1	75	4	65	1	74	3	80	5	69	2
2	77	3	69	1	78	4	80	5	72	2
3	70	4	63	1.5	69	3	75	5	63	1.5
4	80	3.5	69	1	80	3.5	86	5	77	2
		$R_1 = 14.5$		$R_2 = 4.5$		$R_3 = 13.5$		$R_4 = 20$		$R_5 = 7.5$

To determine whether at least two of the treatment probability distributions differ in location, use Friedman F_r test.

H_0:   The five treatments have identical probability distributions
H_a: At least two of the populations have probability distributions that differ in location

The test statistic is $F_r = \dfrac{12}{bk(k+1)}\sum R_j^2 - 3b(k+1)$

$$= \frac{12}{4(5)(6)}[(14.5)^2 + (4.5)^2 + (13.5)^2 + (20)^2 + (7.5)^2] - 3(4)(6) = 14.9$$

The rejection region requires $\alpha = .05$ in the upper tail of the χ^2 distribution with df $= k - 1$ $= 5 - 1 = 4$. From Table VII, Appendix A, $= 9.48773$. The rejection region is $F_r > 9.48773$.

Since the observed value of the test statistic falls in the rejection region ($F_r = 14.9 > 9.48773$), H_0 is rejected. There is sufficient evidence to indicate that at least two of the treatment means differ in location at $\alpha = .05$.

14.91

Test A	Rank	Test B	Rank
90	12	66	4
71	6	78	8
83	11	50	1
82	10	68	5
75	7	80	9
91	13	60	2
65	3		$T_2 = 29$
	$T_1 = 62$		

H_0: The probability distributions of scores for tests A and B are identical
H_a: There is a shift in the locations of the probability distributions of scores for tests A and B

The test statistic is $T_2 = 29$.

The null hypothesis will be rejected if $T_2 \le T_L$ or $T_2 \ge T_U$ where $\alpha = .05$ (two-tailed), $n_1 = 6$ and $n_2 = 7$. From Table XII, Appendix A, $T_L = 28$ and $T_U = 56$.

Reject H_0 if $T_2 \le 28$ or $T_2 \ge 56$.

Since $T_2 = 29 \not\le 28$ and $T_2 = 29 \not\ge 56$, do not reject H_0. There is insufficient evidence to indicate a shift in location for tests A and B at $\alpha = .05$.

Nonparametric Statistics

14.93   a.   Some preliminary calculations are:

Programmed	Rank	Standard	Rank	Open	Rank
.9	5.5	1.0	7.5	1.7	15
1.5	13	.8	4	.5	1.5
.7	3	.9	5.5	1.6	14
1.1	9	1.2	10	1.4	11.5
.5	1.5	1.4	11.5	1.0	7.5
	$R_1 = 32$		$R_2 = 38.5$		$R_3 = 49.5$

b.   The rank sums for the 3 methods are:

$R_1 = 32$, $R_2 = 38.5$, and $R_3 = 49.5$.

c.   The test statistic is $H = \dfrac{12}{n(n+1)} \sum \dfrac{R_j^2}{n_j} - 3(n+1)$

$$= \frac{12}{15(15+1)}\left[\frac{(32)^2}{5} + \frac{(38.5)^2}{5} + \frac{(49.5)^2}{5}\right] - 3(15+1) = 49.565 - 48 = 1.565$$

d.   To determine if the probability distributions of increases in reading level differ among the three methods, we test:

H_0: The probability distributions of the reading levels are the same for the three classes
H_a: At least two of the three reading levels differ in location

The rejection region requires $\alpha = .05$ in the upper tail of the χ^2 distribution with df $= k - 1 = 3 - 1 = 2$. From Table VII, Appendix A, $\chi^2_{.05} = 5.99147$. The rejection region is $H > 5.99147$.

Since the observed value of the test statistic does not fall in the rejection region, ($H = 1.565 \ngtr 5.99147$), do not reject H_0. There is insufficient evidence to indicate a difference in the reading levels among the three methods at $\alpha = .05$.

14.95   a.   Some preliminary calculations are:

Week	Number of Strikes	Rank u_i	Age of fish	Rank v_i	$d_i = u_i - v_i$	d_i^2
1	85	9	120	1	−8	64
2	63	8	136	2	−6	36
3	34	3	150	3	0	0
4	39	5	155	4	1	1
5	58	7	162	5	2	4
6	35	4	169	6	−2	4
7	57	6	178	7	−1	1
8	12	1	184	8	−7	49
9	15	2	190	9	−7	49
						$\sum d_i^2 = 208$

$$r_s = 1 - \frac{6 \sum d_i^2}{n(n^2 - 1)} = 1 - \frac{6(208)}{9(9^2 - 1)} = 1 - 1.733 = -.733$$

b. To determine whether the number of strikes and age are negatively correlated, we test:

H_0: $\rho_s = 0$
H_a: $\rho_s < 0$

The test statistic is $r_s = -.733$.

Reject H_0 if $r_s < -r_{s,\alpha}$ where $\alpha = .01$ and $n = 9$.

Reject H_0 if $r_s < -.783$ (From Table XIV, Appendix A)

Since the observed value of the test statistic does not fall in the rejection region ($r_s = -.733 \not< -.783$), H_0 is not rejected. There is insufficient evidence to indicate that the number of strikes and age are negatively correlated at $\alpha = .01$.

14.97 a.

Private Sector	Rank	Private Sector	Rank
2.58%	10	5.40%	15
5.05	13	2.55	9
.05	1	9.00	16
2.10	5	10.55	17
4.30	12	1.02	2
2.25	6	5.11	14
2.50	8	12.42	18
1.94	4	1.67	3
2.33	7	3.33	11
	$T_1 = 66$		$T_2 = 105$

To determine if the two populations have identical distributions, we test:

H_0: The two sampled sectors have identical probability distributions
H_a: The probability distribution for the public sector is shifted to the right of the private sector.

The test statistic is $T_2 = 105$.

The rejection region is $T_2 \geq 105$ from Table XII, Appendix A, with $n_1 = 9$, $n_2 = 9$ and $\alpha = .05$. Since the observed value of the test statistic falls in the rejection region ($T_2 = 105 \geq 105$), H_0 is rejected. We can conclude that the probability distribution for the public sector is shifted to the right of the private sector at $\alpha = .05$.

b. The p-value is approximately equal to .05 because the test statistic is equal to the critical value T_U.

c. 1. The two samples are random and independent.
    2. The two probability distributions from which the samples are drawn are continuous.

14.99 Some preliminary calculations are:

Metal	I	Rank	II	Rank	III	Rank
1	4.6	2	4.2	1	4.9	3
2	7.2	3	6.4	1	7.0	2
3	3.4	1.5	3.5	3	3.4	1.5
4	6.2	3	5.3	1	5.9	2
5	8.4	3	6.8	1	7.8	2
6	5.6	2	4.8	1	5.7	3
7	3.7	1.5	3.7	1.5	4.1	3
8	6.1	1	6.2	2	6.4	3
9	4.9	3	4.1	1	4.2	2
10	5.2	3	5.0	1	5.1	2
		$R_1 = 23$		$R_2 = 13.5$		$R_3 = 23.5$

To determine if there is a difference in the probability distributions of the amounts of corrosion among the three types of sealers, we test:

H_0: The probability distributions of corrosion amounts are identical for the three types of sealers

H_a: At least two of the probability distributions differ in location

The test statistic is $F_r = \dfrac{12}{bk(k+1)} \sum R_j^2 - 3b(k+1)$

$$= \frac{12}{10(3)(3+1)} [23^2 + 13.5^2 + 23.5^2] - 3(10)(3+1) = 126.35 - 120 = 6.35$$

The rejection region requires $\alpha = .05$ in the upper tail of the χ^2 distribution with df $= k - 1 = 3 - 1 = 2$. From Table VII, Appendix A, $\chi_{.05}^2 = 5.99147$. The rejection region is $F_r > 5.99147$.

Since the observed value of the test statistic falls in the rejection region ($F_r = 6.35 > 5.99147$), reject H_0. There is sufficient evidence to indicate a difference in the probability distributions among the three types of sealers at $\alpha = .05$.

14.101 Some preliminary calculations are:

List 1	Rank	List 2	Rank	List 3	Rank
48	19	41	14	18	2
43	16	36	10	42	15
39	12	29	5	28	4
57	20	40	13	38	11
21	3	35	9	15	1
47	18	45	17	33	8
58	21	32	7	31	6
	$R_1 = 109$		$R_2 = 75$		$R_3 = 47$

To determine if there is a difference between at least two of the probability distributions of the numbers of word associates that subjects can name for the three lists, we test:

H_0: The probability distributions of the numbers of word associates named are the same for the three lists
H_a: At least two of the three probability distributions differ in location

The test statistic is $H = \dfrac{12}{n(n+1)} \sum \dfrac{R_j^2}{n_j} - 3(n+1)$

$$= \dfrac{12}{21(21+1)} \left[\dfrac{(109)^2}{7} + \dfrac{(75)^2}{7} + \dfrac{(47)^2}{7} \right] - 3(21+1)$$

$$= 73.154 - 66 = 7.154$$

The rejection region requires $\alpha = .05$ in the upper tail of the χ^2 distribution with df $= k - 1 = 3 - 1 = 2$. From Table VII, Appendix A, $\chi_{.05}^2 = 5.99147$. The rejection region is $H > 5.99147$.

Since the observed value of the test statistic falls in the rejection region ($H = 7.154 > 5.99147$), reject H_0. There is sufficient evidence to indicate a difference in location for at least two of the probability distributions of the numbers of word associates at $\alpha = .05$.

14.103 a. Some preliminary calculations are:

Difference Highway 1 – Highway 2	Rank of Absolute Differences
−25	5
4	1
−23	4
−16	2.5
−16	2.5
	$T_+ = 1$

To determine if the heavily patrolled highway tends to have fewer speeders per 100 cars than the occasionally patrolled highway, we test:

H_0: The two sampled populations have identical probability distributions
H_a: The probability distribution for highway 1 is shifted to the left of that for highway 2

The test statistic is $T_+ = 1$.

The rejection region is $T_+ \leq 1$ from Table XIII, Appendix A, with $n = 5$ and $\alpha = .05$.

Since the observed value of the test statistic falls in the rejection region ($T_+ = 1 \leq 1$), H_0 is rejected. There is sufficient evidence to indicate the probability distribution for highway 1 is shifted to the left of that for highway 2 at $\alpha = .05$.

b.   Some preliminary calculations are:

Day	Difference Highway 1 – Highway 2
1	25
2	4
3	−23
4	−16
5	−16

$$\bar{x}_D = \frac{\sum x_D}{n} = \frac{-76}{5} = -15.2$$

$$s_D^2 = \frac{\sum x_D^2 - \frac{\left(\sum x_D\right)^2}{n}}{n-1} = \frac{1682 - \frac{(-76)^2}{5}}{5-1} = 131.7$$

$$s_D = \sqrt{131.7} = 11.4761$$

To determine if the mean number of speeders per 100 cars differ for the two highways, we test:

$H_0: \mu_1 = \mu_2$
$H_a: \mu_1 \neq \mu_2$

The test statistic is $t = \dfrac{\bar{x}_D - 0}{s_D/\sqrt{n}} = \dfrac{-15.2}{\dfrac{11.4761}{\sqrt{5}}} = -2.96$

The rejection region requires $\alpha/2 = .05/2 = .025$ in each tail of the t distribution with df $= n - 1 = 5 - 1 = 4$. From Table VI, Appendix A, $t_{.025} = 2.776$. The rejection region is $t > 2.776$ and $t < -2.776$.

Since the observed value of the test statistic falls in the rejection region ($t = -2.96$ < -2.776), H_0 is rejected. There is sufficient evidence to indicate the mean number of speeders per 100 cars differ for the two highways at $\alpha = .05$.

We must assume that the population of differences is normally distributed and that a random sample of differences was selected.

14.105 Some preliminary calculations are:

Hours	Rank	Fraction Defective	Rank	d_i	d_i^2
1	1	.02	1	0	0
2	2	.05	3	−1	1
3	3	.03	2	1	1
4	4	.08	5	−1	1
5	5	.06	4	1	1
6	6	.09	6	0	0
7	7	.11	8	−1	1
8	8	.10	7	1	1
					$\sum d_i^2 = 6$

To determine if the fraction defective increases as the day progresses, we test:

H_0: $\rho_s = 0$
H_a: $\rho_s > 0$

The test statistic is $r_s = 1 - \dfrac{6 \sum d_i^2}{n(n^2 - 1)} = 1 - \dfrac{6(6)}{8(8^2 - 1)} = 1 - .071 = .929$

Reject H_0 if $r_s > r_{s,\alpha}$ where $\alpha = .05$ and $n = 8$:

Reject H_0 if $r_s > .643$ (from Table XIV, Appendix A).

Since $r_s = .929 > .643$, reject H_0. There is sufficient evidence to indicate that the fraction defective increases as the day progresses at $\alpha = .05$.

14.107 a. Some preliminary calculations are:

Ear	Rank Spray A	Rank Spray B	Rank Spray C
1	2	3	1
2	2	3	1
3	1	3	2
4	3	2	1
5	2	1	3
6	1	3	2
7	2.5	2.5	1
8	2	3	1
9	2	3	1
10	2	3	1
	$R_1 = 19.5$	$R_2 = 26.5$	$R_3 = 14$

To determine whether the distributions of the levels of aflatoxins in corn differ for at least two of the three sprays, we test:

H_0: The three populations have probability distributions that are identical
H_a: At least two of the populations have probability distributions that differ in location

The test statistic is $F_r = \dfrac{12}{bk(k+1)} \sum R_j^2 - 3b(k+1)$

$$= \dfrac{12}{10(3)(4)} \left[(19.5)^2 + (26.5)^2 + (14)^2 \right] - 3(10)(4) = 127.85 - 120 = 7.85$$

The rejection region requires $\alpha = .05$ in the upper tail of the χ^2 distribution with df = $k - 1 = 3 - 1 = 2$. From Table VII, Appendix A, $\chi_{.05}^2 = 5.99147$. The rejection region is $F_r > 5.99147$.

Since the observed value of the test statistic falls in the rejection region ($F_r = 7.85 > 5.99147$), H_0 is rejected. There is sufficient evidence to indicate that the distributions of the levels of aflatoxin in corn differ for at least 2 of the 3 sprays at $\alpha = .05$.